Organic Reactions

VOLUME 10

NEW YORK

JOHN WILEY & SONS, INC.

London · CHAPMAN & HALL, Limited

Library of Congress Catalog Card Number: 42–20265

PRINTED IN THE UNITED STATES OF AMERICA

PREFACE TO THE SERIES

In the course of nearly every program of research in organic chemistry the investigator finds it necessary to use several of the better-known synthetic reactions. To discover the optimum conditions for the application of even the most familiar one to a compound not previously subjected to the reaction often requires an extensive search of the literature; even then a series of experiments may be necessary. When the results of the investigation are published, the synthesis, which may have required months of work, is usually described without comment. The background of knowledge and experience gained in the literature search and experimentation is thus lost to those who subsequently have occasion to apply the general method. The student of preparative organic chemistry faces similar difficulties. The textbooks and laboratory manuals furnish numerous examples of the application of various syntheses, but only rarely do they convey an accurate conception of the scope and usefulness of the processes.

For many years American organic chemists have discussed these problems. The plan of compiling critical discussions of the more important reactions thus was evolved. The volumes of *Organic Reactions* are collections of chapters each devoted to a single reaction, or a definite phase of a reaction, of wide applicability. The authors have had experience with the processes surveyed. The subjects are presented from the preparative viewpoint, and particular attention is given to limitations, interfering influences, effects of structure, and the selection of experimental techniques. Each chapter includes several detailed procedures illustrating the significant modifications of the method. Most of these procedures have been found satisfactory by the author or one of the editors, but unlike those in *Organic Syntheses* they have not been subjected to careful testing in two or more laboratories. When all known examples of the reaction are not mentioned in the text, tables are given to list compounds which have been prepared by or subjected to the reaction. Every effort has been made to include in the tables all such compounds and references; however, because of the very nature of the reactions discussed and their frequent use as one of the several steps of syntheses in which not all of the intermediates have been isolated, some instances may well have been missed. Nevertheless, the investigator will be able to use the tables and their accompanying bibliographies in place of most or all of the literature search so often required.

Because of the systematic arrangement of the material in the chapters and the entries in the tables, users of the books will be able to find information desired by reference to the table of contents of the appropriate chapter. In the interest of economy the entries in the indices have been kept to a minimum, and, in particular, the compounds listed in the tables are not repeated in the indices.

The success of this publication, which will appear periodically, depends upon the cooperation of organic chemists and their willingness to devote time and effort to the preparation of the chapters. They have manifested their interest already by the almost unanimous acceptance of invitations to contribute to the work. The editors will welcome their continued interest and their suggestions for improvements in *Organic Reactions*.

CONTENTS

CHAPTER 1

THE COUPLING OF DIAZONIUM SALTS WITH ALIPHATIC CARBON ATOMS

STANLEY M. PARMERTER
Wheaton College

CONTENTS

INTRODUCTION

A diazonium salt will couple with an aliphatic compound containing an activated carbon-hydrogen bond. This discussion is limited to those reactions in which both nitrogen atoms of the diazonium salt are retained in the resulting molecule. The discussion is further limited by the exclusion of coupling reactions which occur with the elimination of a group from an activated methinyl compound, the Japp-Klingemann reaction, as these reactions are discussed in Chapter 2.

Victor Meyer was the first to report the coupling of a diazonium salt with an activated aliphatic carbon atom.[1] He found that benzenediazonium sulfate reacts with the sodium salt of nitroethane to give a colored product which was assigned the azo structure I.

$$C_6H_5N{=}NCH(CH_3)NO_2$$

I

Coupling with other nitroparaffins[2–5] as well as with ethyl acetoacetate[6,7] was soon reported. A question regarding the structure of the reaction products arose when it was discovered that benzenediazonium chloride coupled with diethyl malonate to give a product identical with the phenylhydrazone of diethyl mesoxalate (II).[8a]

$$C_6H_5N_2Cl + CH_2(CO_2C_2H_5)_2 \searrow$$
$$C_6H_5NHN{=}C(CO_2C_2H_5)_2$$
$$C_6H_5NHNH_2 + CO(CO_2C_2H_5)_2 \nearrow$$

II

Much of the early work with the coupling reaction was prompted by the desire to determine whether the products were of the azo or hydrazone

[1] Meyer and Ambühl, *Ber.*, **8**, 751 (1875).
[2] Meyer and Ambühl, *Ber.*, **8**, 1073 (1875).
[3] Friese, *Ber.*, **8**, 1078 (1875).
[4] Meyer, *Ber.*, **9**, 384 (1876).
[5] Züblin, *Ber.*, **10**, 2087 (1877).
[6] Meyer, *Ber.*, **10**, 2075 (1877).
[7] Züblin, *Ber.*, **11**, 1417 (1878).
[8a] Meyer, *Ber.*, **21**, 118 (1888).

structure. It is difficult to establish with certainty the structures in such cases where two tautomeric forms are possible. However, it is generally assumed that the hydrazone is the stable form whenever coupling occurs at a methyl or methylene carbon. Recently, Wiley and Jarboe have presented ultraviolet and infrared absorption data which corroborate this view.[8b] In the limited number of compounds where coupling occurs on a methinyl carbon without the elimination of a group only the azo structure is possible.

MECHANISMS OF THE REACTIONS

Various mechanisms for the coupling reaction have been proposed. Dimroth observed that reaction occurred only with the enol forms of various ketones.[9] He proposed that the first product was an enol ether which rearranged to give the final product. The isolation of intermediate

$$C_6H_5N{=}NOH + {-}CH{=}\underset{\displaystyle OH}{\underset{|}{C}}{-} \rightarrow {-}CH{=}\underset{\displaystyle ON{=}NC_6H_5}{\underset{|}{C}}{-} \rightarrow {-}\underset{\displaystyle N{=}NC_6H_5}{\underset{|}{C}}{=}\overset{\displaystyle OH}{\overset{|}{C}}{-}$$

O-azo compounds in certain instances gave further support to his proposal.[10–12] However, these intermediates were isolated only from highly substituted aliphatic reactants such as tribenzoylmethane. It is probable that this mechanism is applicable in special cases.

When certain α,α-diarylethylenes react with diazonium salts, a crystalline intermediate can be isolated.[13,14] This is considered to be the carbonium salt III. The salt readily loses hydrogen halide to give an

$$Ar_2C{=}CH_2 + Ar'N_2X \rightarrow \underset{\text{III}}{(Ar_2CCH_2N_2Ar')^+X^-} \rightarrow Ar_2C{=}CHN{=}NAr' + HX$$

azo compound. Since these intermediates have been isolated only with rather complex molecules, it may be unwise to propose their formation as part of a general mechanism for coupling with all unsaturated hydrocarbons and enols.

Busch has studied the mechanism of the reaction of diazonium salts

[8b] Wiley and Jarboe, *J. Am. Chem. Soc.*, **77**, 403 (1955).
[9] Dimroth, *Ber.*, **40**, 2404 (1907).
[10] Dimroth and Hartmann, *Ber.*, **41**, 4012 (1908).
[11] Dimroth, Leichtlin, and Friedemann, *Ber.*, **50**, 1534 (1917).
[12] Auwers, *Ann.*, **378**, 243 (1910).
[13] Dilthey and Blankenburg, *J. prakt. Chem.*, [2], **142**, 177 (1935).
[14] Wizinger and Cyriax, *Helv. Chim. Acta*, **28**, 1018 (1945).

with hydrazones.[15–18] From the observation that primary hydrazones (IV) couple readily with diazonium salts, whereas secondary hydrazones (V) do not react,[19] he proposed that the first product was an N-azo compound (VI) which rearranged to give the formazan derivative VII.* A crystalline intermediate, assumed to be the N-azo compound, was isolated from the reaction of benzenediazonium chloride with benzaldehyde

$$\underset{\text{IV}}{\text{RNHN}{=}\text{CHR}} + \text{ArN}_2\text{X} \rightarrow \underset{\text{VI}}{\text{RNN}(\text{N}{=}\text{NAr}){=}\text{CHR}} \rightarrow \underset{\text{VII}}{\text{RNHN}{=}\text{CR}(\text{N}{=}\text{NAr})}$$

$$\underset{\text{V}}{\text{R}_2\text{NN}{=}\text{CHR}} + \text{ArN}_2\text{X} \rightarrow \text{No reaction}$$

phenylhydrazone in alcoholic sodium acetate.[18] Evaporation of an ether solution of this compound produced a formazan.

More recent study of the reaction between benzaldehyde phenylhydrazone and benzenediazonium chloride has shown that the product was dependent on the *p*H of the reaction medium.[19a,19b] In a solution of *p*H 3, benzaldehyde *p*-phenylazophenylhydrazone was isolated. Reaction at *p*H values of 4 to 8 produced up to 66% yields of 4-benzylidene-1,3-diphenyl-1-tetrazene, whereas at a *p*H greater than 9 the product was N,N′,C-triphenylformazan. The tetrazene changed to the formazan within a few hours at room temperature or rapidly when heated to 90°. Rearrangement also occurred in pyridine or ethanolic potassium hydroxide. The fact that no 1-phenylazo-2-naphthol was formed when the rearrangement was carried out in ethanolic potassium hydroxide containing β-naphthol indicated that the reaction was intramolecular.

$$C_6H_5CH{=}NNHC_6H_5 + C_6H_5N_2Cl \xrightarrow{pH\ 3} C_6H_5CH{=}NNHC_6H_4(N{=}NC_6H_5)\text{-}p$$

$$C_6H_5CH{=}NNHC_6H_5 + C_6H_5N_2Cl \xrightarrow{pH\ 4\text{–}8} C_6H_5CH{=}NN(N{=}NC_6H_5)C_6H_5$$

$$C_6H_5CH{=}NNHC_6H_5 + C_6H_5N_2Cl \xrightarrow{pH > 9} C_6H_5C(N{=}NC_6H_5){=}NNHC_6H_5$$

[15] Busch and Pfeiffer, *Ber.*, **59,** 1162 (1926).

[16] Busch and Schmidt, *Ber.*, **63,** 1950 (1930).

[17] Busch and Schmidt, *J. prakt. Chem.*, [2], **129,** 151 (1931).

[18] Busch and Schmidt, *J. prakt. Chem.*, [2], **131,** 182 (1931).

[19] von Pechmann, *Ber.*, **27,** 1679 (1894).

* These compounds are named as derivatives of the hypothetical formazan, $H_2NN{=}CHN{=}NH$.

[19a] Hauptmann and Périsse, *Experientia*, **10,** 60 (1954) [*C. A.* **49,** 4554 (1955)].

[19b] Hauptmann and Périsse, *Chem. Ber.*, **89,** 1081 (1956).

However, when the tetrazene was dissolved in a cold solution of hydrogen chloride in ethanol, benzaldehyde phenylhydrazone and benzenediazonium chloride were regenerated.

Most of the current theories formulate the reaction as the direct attack of the diazonium cation on a carbanion or a carbon atom with high electron density.[19c,19d] Tarbell has proposed such a mechanism for the reaction of a diazonium salt with nitromethane.[20] The reaction of the

$$ArN_2^+ + (CH_2NO_2)^- \rightarrow ArN{=}NCH_2NO_2 \rightleftharpoons ArNHN{=}CHNO_2$$

product with a second molecule of diazonium salt also was postulated as being ionic in nature.

$$ArN_2^+ + (ArN{=}NCHNO_2)^- \rightarrow ArN{=}\underset{\displaystyle NO_2}{\underset{|}{C}}{=}NNHAr$$

Although the second reaction seems to be at variance with the experiments of Busch mentioned above, it should be noted that the facts given by Busch do not exclude the possibility of an ionic mechanism for the reaction. Since the reactions in the system appear to be reversible, the isolation of N-azo compounds and the fact that they can generate the final product do not prove that they are intermediates. An alternative explanation for the observation that secondary hydrazones, such as V above, do not react may be that the coupling reaction requires the resonance-stabilized carbanion VIII*a* ↔ VIII*b*.[21]

$$RNHN{=}CHR \xrightarrow{\text{Base}} \underset{\text{VIII}a}{RN{=}N\bar{C}HR} \longleftrightarrow \underset{\text{VIII}b}{R\bar{N}N{=}CHR}$$

The diazonium salts prepared from *o*-aminophenylacetylenes undergo intramolecular coupling to yield 4-hydroxycinnolines. Schofield and his co-workers believe that the first step in this reaction is the coordination of the diazonium cation with one carbon atom of the acetylene, followed by the addition of hydroxyl ion to the other carbon atom.[22,23]

$$o\text{-}(C{\equiv}CH)C_6H_4N_2^+ \longrightarrow \text{(cyclic } C^+{=}CH\text{–}N{=}N\text{ cation)} \xrightarrow{OH^-} \text{4-hydroxycinnoline (OH)}$$

[19c] Hünig and Boes, *Ann.*, **579**, 28 (1953).

[19d] Scott, O'Sullivan, and Reilly, *J. Am. Chem. Soc.*, **75**, 5309 (1953).

[20] Tarbell, Todd, Paulson, Lindstrom, and Wystrach, *J. Am. Chem. Soc.*, **70**, 1381 (1948).

[21] D. S. Tarbell, private communication.

[22] Schofield and Simpson, *J. Chem. Soc.*, **1945**, 520.

[23] Schofield and Swain, *J. Chem. Soc.*, **1949**, 2393.

Diazotized *o*-aminoacetophenones also couple intramolecularly with the formation of 4-hydroxycinnolines. This reaction, which is favored by a strongly acidic reaction medium, is believed to proceed through an acid-catalyzed enolization of the carbonyl group.[24]

$$o\text{-}C_6H_4(COCH_3)(N_2^+) \xrightarrow{H^+} o\text{-}C_6H_4(C(=OH^+)CH_3)(N_2^+) \xrightarrow{-H^+} o\text{-}C_6H_4(C(OH)=CH_2)(N_2^+) \longrightarrow \text{cyclic } C(=\overset{+}{O}H)CH_2N{=}N \xrightarrow{-H^+} \text{4-hydroxycinnoline}$$

SCOPE AND LIMITATIONS

Since the principal factor that influences this reaction is the nature of the aliphatic reactant rather than that of the diazonium salt, the following discussion is based upon the types of compounds that undergo coupling.

Ketones

Few examples of the reaction of a simple ketone with a diazonium salt have been reported. Acetone reacts with benzenediazonium chloride in alkaline solution to give a product[25] that was later identified as methyl formazyl ketone (IX).[26] The methyl group in pyruvic acid likewise reacts with two molecules of diazonium salt.[27] When one of the hydrogen atoms of acetone is replaced by an activating group, the

$$CH_3COCH_3 + 2C_6H_5N_2Cl \rightarrow C_6H_5N{=}NC(COCH_3){=}NNHC_6H_5 \quad \text{(IX)}$$

[24] Schofield and Simpson, *J. Chem. Soc.*, **1948,** 1170.
[25] Bamberger and Wulz, *Ber.*, **24,** 2793 (1891).
[26] von Pechmann, *Ber.*, **25,** 3190 (1892).
[27] Bamberger and Müller, *Ber.*, **27,** 147 (1894).

methylene carbon is the one attacked. Compounds of this type that have been investigated include chloroacetone,[28] 2,4-dinitrophenyiacetone,[29] acetonylpyridinium bromide,[30] and a variety of 3-acetonyl-1,2,4-oxadiazoles.[31,32] The product from acetonylpyridinium bromide had the betaine structure X.

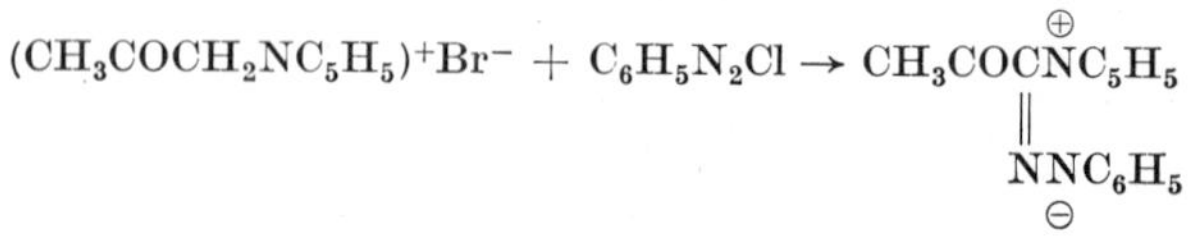

$$(CH_3COCH_2NC_5H_5)^+Br^- + C_6H_5N_2Cl \rightarrow CH_3CO\underset{\underset{\ominus}{NNC_6H_5}}{\overset{\oplus}{C}}NC_5H_5$$

X

Dieckmann reported that cyclopentane-1,2-dione reacts with benzenediazonium chloride to give the 1-phenylhydrazone of cyclopentane-1,2,3-trione.[33] The only instance of the coupling of 2 moles of a diazonium salt with a cyclic ketone was the reaction used by Willstätter to show the presence of two active methylene groups in tropinone (XI).[34]

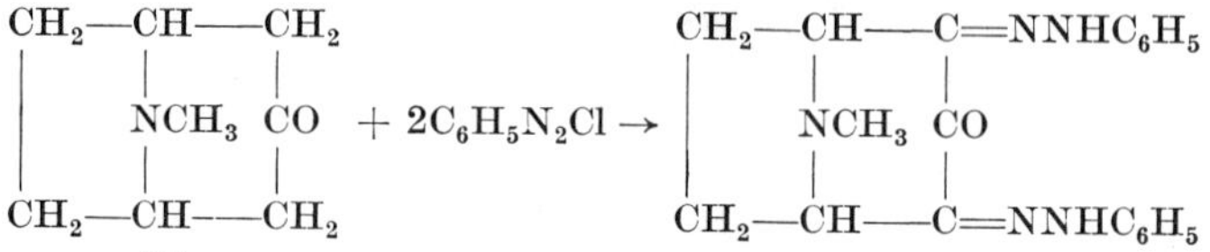

$$\begin{array}{l} CH_2—CH—CH_2 \\ \quad\quad NCH_3 \;\; CO \\ CH_2—CH—CH_2 \end{array} + 2C_6H_5N_2Cl \rightarrow \begin{array}{l} CH_2—CH—C{=}NNHC_6H_5 \\ \quad\quad NCH_3 \;\; CO \\ CH_2—CH—C{=}NNHC_6H_5 \end{array}$$

XI

The reaction of a diazonium salt with 1-ethoxalylindene (XII) produces the 1-arylazocompound.[35] This contrasts with the observation that the

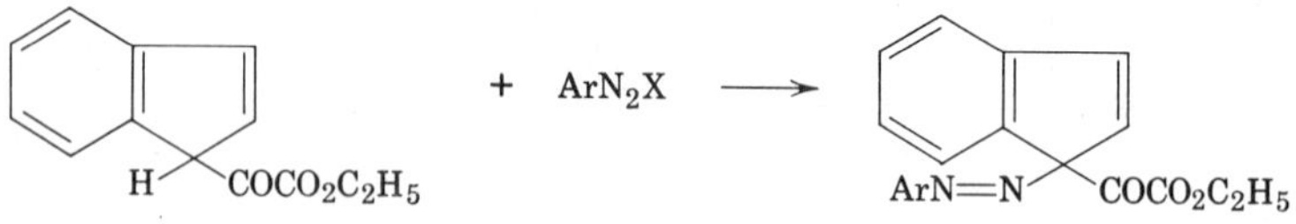

XII (H, $COCO_2C_2H_5$) + ArN_2X → (ArN=N, $COCO_2C_2H_5$)

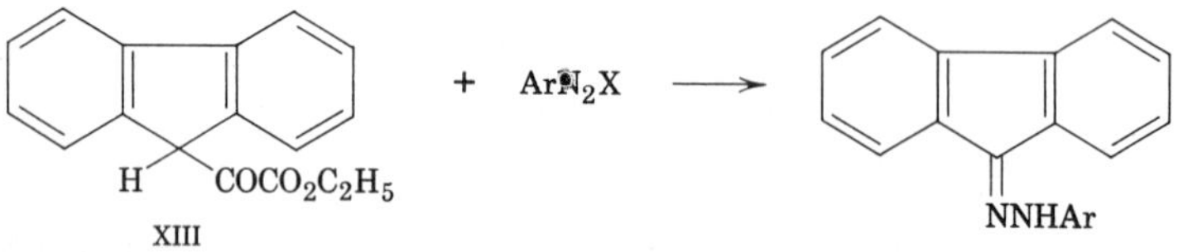

XIII (H, $COCO_2C_2H_5$) + ArN_2X → (NNHAr)

[28] Favrel, *Bull. soc. chim. France*, [4], **41**, 1494 (1927).
[29] Borsche, *Ber.*, **42**, 601 (1909).
[30] Krollpfeiffer and Braun, *Ber.*, **70**, 89 (1937).
[31] Merckx, *Chimie & industrie*, **63**, No. 3 bis, 453 (1950).
[32] Merckx, *Bull. soc. chim. belges*, **58**, 183 (1949).
[33] Dieckmann, *Ber.*, **35**, 3201 (1902).
[34] Willstätter, *Ber.*, **30**, 2679 (1897).
[35] Wislicenus and Hentrich, *Ann.*, **436**, 9 (1924).

ethoxalyl group was eliminated when 9-ethoxalylfluorene (XIII) was treated with a diazonium salt.[36] The reaction of heterocyclic esters with 2 moles of a diazonium salt is a convenient preparation of C-heterocyclic formazans.[36a] Ethyl 2-quinolylpyruvate, for example, reacts with *p*-bromobenzenediazonium chloride to give a 79% yield of the formazan.

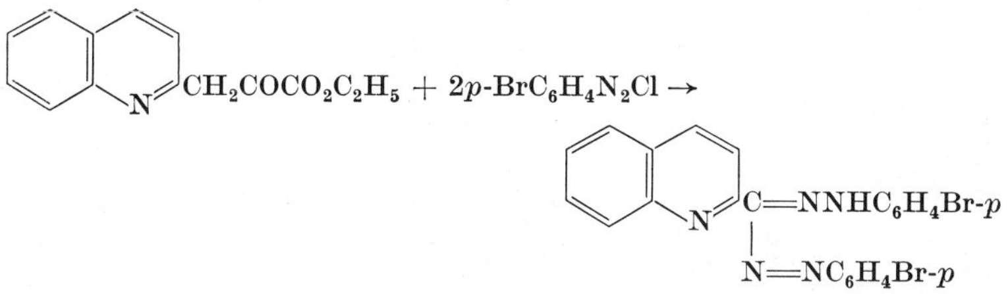

$$\text{(2-quinolyl)}CH_2COCO_2C_2H_5 + 2p\text{-}BrC_6H_4N_2Cl \rightarrow \text{(2-quinolyl)}C(=NNHC_6H_4Br\text{-}p)N{=}NC_6H_4Br\text{-}p$$

The only acetophenones that have been shown to undergo coupling are the *o*-aminoacetophenones. When these amines are diazotized, reaction occurs intramolecularly to give 4-hydroxycinnolines. Although this reaction is favored by the presence of electronegative groups ortho or para to the amino group, a 70–75% yield of 4-hydroxycinnoline (XIV)

$$o\text{-}NH_2C_6H_4COCH_3 \xrightarrow{NaNO_2 + HCl} \text{4-hydroxycinnoline (XIV)}$$

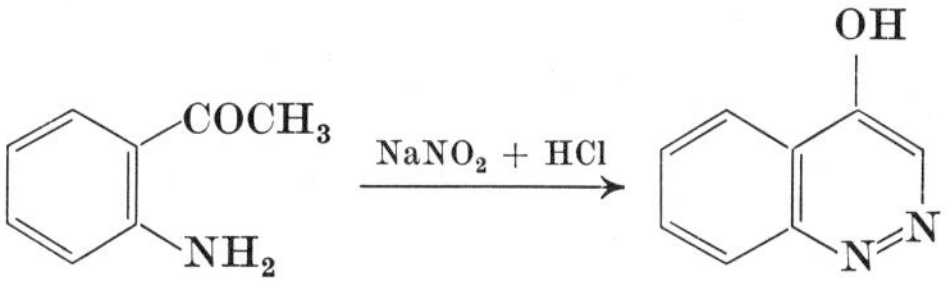

XIV

could be obtained by warming a solution of diazotized *o*-aminoacetophenone in hydrochloric acid.[37] This transformation proceeds smoothly with a variety of substituted *o*-aminoacetophenones. It has been extended to include *o*-aminophenacyl halides which give 3-halogenated 4-hydroxycinnolines.[24,38] Higher homologs of *o*-aminoacetophenone produce the corresponding 3-alkyl-4-hydroxycinnolines.[39–41]

The methylene group in *β*-diketones reacts readily with diazonium salts. The product may be formulated as the monohydrazone of a triketone. Benzoylacetone, for example, has been converted into the monophenylhydrazone XV in 90% yield.[42] A variety of *β*-diketones has been employed in the same general reaction. Cyclic *β*-diketones, such as

[36] Kuhn and Levy, *Ber.*, **61,** 2240 (1928).
[36a] Ried and Hoffschmidt, *Ann.*, **581,** 23 (1953).
[37] Keneford and Simpson, *J. Chem. Soc.*, **1947,** 917.
[38] Schofield, Swain, and Theobald, *J. Chem. Soc.*, **1949,** 2399.
[39] Leonard and Boyd, *J. Org. Chem.*, **11,** 419 (1946).
[40] Keneford and Simpson, *J. Chem. Soc.*, **1948,** 354.
[41] Keneford and Simpson, *J. Chem. Soc.*, **1948,** 2318.
[42] Chattaway and Lye, *J. Chem. Soc.*, **1933,** 480.

cyclohexane-1,3-dione,[43] methone,[44–46] and indan-1,3-dione[47,48] react as readily as the acyclic analogs.

$$C_6H_5COCH_2COCH_3 + C_6H_5N_2Cl \rightarrow \underset{\textstyle \text{XV}}{C_6H_5CO\underset{\textstyle NNHC_6H_5}{\underset{\|}{C}}COCH_3}$$

A limited number of β-keto aldehydes has been investigated.[49–51] In these compounds, the methylene group reacts in the same manner as in β-diketones.

β-Keto Acids, Esters, and Amides

When a β-keto carboxylic acid is treated with a diazonium salt, carbon dioxide is eliminated. The product from the reaction of benzenediazonium chloride with acetoacetic acid is the 1-phenylhydrazone of pyruvaldehyde (XVI). If 2 moles of diazonium salt are employed, methyl formazyl ketone (XVII) is the product.[52] In carrying out this reaction, the general practice is to saponify a β-keto ester and then to add the diazonium salt solution directly to the hydrolysis mixture without isolation of the unstable β-keto acid.[53–55]

$$CH_3COCH_2CO_2H + C_6H_5N_2Cl \rightarrow \underset{\text{XVI}}{CH_3COCH{=}NNHC_6H_5}$$

$$CH_3COCH{=}NNHC_6H_5 + C_6H_5N_2Cl \rightarrow \underset{\textstyle \text{XVII}}{C_6H_5N{=}N\underset{\textstyle COCH_3}{\underset{|}{C}}{=}NNHC_6H_5}$$

Acetonedicarboxylic acid reacts with 2 moles of diazonium salt with the elimination of both carboxyl groups.[56,57] The resulting product is a mesoxaldehyde diarylhydrazone (XVIII).

$$CO(CH_2CO_2H)_2 + 2ArN_2Cl \rightarrow \underset{\text{XVIII}}{CO(CH{=}NNHAr)_2}$$

[43] Vorländer, *Ann.*, **294,** 253 (1897).
[44] Lifschitz, *Ber.*, **47,** 1401 (1914).
[45] Iyer and Chakravarti, *J. Indian Inst. Sci.*, **17A,** 41 (1934) [*C. A.*, **28,** 4390 (1934)].
[46] Iyer, *J. Indian Inst. Sci.*, **21A,** Pt. 6, 65 (1938) [*C. A.*, **33,** 148 (1939)].
[47] Wislicenus and Reitzenstein, *Ann.*, **277,** 362 (1893).
[48] Das and Ghosh, *J. Am. Chem. Soc.*, **43,** 1739 (1921).
[49] Beyer and Claisen, *Ber.*, **21,** 1697 (1888).
[50] Benary, Meyer, and Charisius, *Ber.*, **59,** 108 (1926).
[51] Benary, *Ber.*, **60,** 914 (1927).
[52] Bamberger and Lorenzen, *Ber.*, **25,** 3539 (1892).
[53] Japp and Klingemann, *J. Chem. Soc.*, **53,** 519 (1888).
[54] Japp and Klingemann, *Ann.*, **247,** 190 (1888).
[55] Reynolds and Van Allan, *Org. Syntheses*, **32,** 84 (1952).
[56] von Pechmann and Jenisch, *Ber.*, **24,** 3255 (1891).
[57] von Pechmann and Vanino, *Ber.*, **27,** 219 (1894).

A β-keto sulfonic acid retains the acid group when it couples with a diazonium salt.[58,59] For example, the phenylhydrazone XIX has been prepared in 60% yield from 2-oxo-2-phenylethane-1-sulfonic acid.

$$C_6H_5COCH_2SO_3H + C_6H_5N_2Cl \rightarrow \underset{\text{XIX}}{C_6H_5C(=NNHC_6H_5)SO_3H}$$

The reactions of β-keto esters with diazonium salts have been studied extensively. Products from ethyl acetoacetate and over fifty different diazonium salts have been reported. Good yields of the α-hydrazones of α,β-diketo esters are obtained if 1 mole of the diazonium salt is employed. However, the use of 2 moles of benzenediazonium chloride causes the elimination of the acetyl group to give an 80% yield of C-carbethoxy-N,N′-diphenylformazan (XX).[60]

$$CH_3COCH_2CO_2C_2H_5 + C_6H_5N_2Cl \rightarrow CH_3COC(=NNHC_6H_5)CO_2C_2H_5$$

$$CH_3COC(=NNHC_6H_5)CO_2C_2H_5 + C_6H_5N_2Cl \rightarrow \underset{\text{XX}}{C_6H_5N{=}NC(=NNHC_6H_5)CO_2C_2H_5}$$

Diethyl oxaloacetate likewise can react with 1 or 2 moles of benzenediazonium chloride.[61–63] If 1 mole of the salt is used, the product is diethyl dioxosuccinate phenylhydrazone (XXI). The addition of 2 moles of diazonium salt in strongly alkaline solution causes the replacement of the ethoxalyl group.

$$C_2H_5O_2CCH_2COCO_2C_2H_5 + C_6H_5N_2Cl \rightarrow \underset{\text{XXI}}{C_2H_5O_2CC(=NNHC_6H_5)COCO_2C_2H_5}$$

$$C_2H_5O_2CC(=NNHC_6H_5)COCO_2C_2H_5 + C_6H_5N_2Cl \rightarrow C_2H_5O_2CC(=NNHC_6H_5)N{=}NC_6H_5$$

There are no reports of the elimination of groups other than acetyl and ethoxalyl when 2 moles of a diazonium salt react with a β-keto ester

[58] Parkes and Fisher, *J. Chem. Soc.*, **1936,** 83.

[59] Parkes and Tinsley, *J. Chem. Soc.*, **1934,** 1861.

[60] Bamberger and Wheelwright, *J. prakt. Chem.*, [2], **65,** 125 (1902).

[61] Wislicenus and Jensen, *Ber.*, **25,** 3448 (1892).

[62] Rabischong, *Bull. soc. chim. France*, [3], **31,** 76 (1904).

[63] Rabischong, *Bull. soc. chim. France*, [3], **31,** 83 (1904).

containing a methylene group. However, by analogy with the Japp-Klingemann reaction (p. 143), it would be expected that other acyl groups could be eliminated as well.

Diethyl acetonedicarboxylate (XXII) reacts smoothly with 1 mole of diazonium salt.[64,65] There have been no reports of further reaction with the second methylene group present in the molecule.

$$\underset{\text{XXII}}{C_2H_5O_2CCH_2COCH_2CO_2C_2H_5} + C_6H_5N_2Cl \rightarrow C_2H_5O_2C\underset{\substack{\| \\ NNHC_6H_5}}{C}COCH_2CO_2C_2H_5$$

Diethyl oxalocrotonate (XXIII) may be regarded as a vinylog of diethyl oxaloacetate. Its behavior with diazonium salts depends upon the *p*H of the reaction mixture.[66] When the ester is treated with excess *p*-bromobenzenediazonium chloride in ethanolic hydrochloric acid, the only product is the monophenylhydrazone XXIV. This product is converted into the azo derivative XXV if sodium acetate is added. The original ester reacts with 2 moles of diazonium salt in dilute ammonia with the loss of the ethoxalyl group.

$$\underset{\text{XXIII}}{\begin{array}{c} COCO_2C_2H_5 \\ | \\ CH_2 \\ | \\ CH \\ \| \\ CH \\ | \\ CO_2C_2H_5 \end{array}} \xrightarrow[(HCl)]{ArN_2X} \underset{\text{XXIV}}{\begin{array}{l} COCO_2C_2H_5 \\ | \\ C{=}NNHAr \\ | \\ CH \\ \| \\ CH \\ | \\ CO_2C_2H_5 \end{array}} \xrightarrow[(CH_3CO_2Na)]{ArN_2X} \underset{\text{XXV}}{\begin{array}{l} COCO_2C_2H_5 \\ | \\ C{=}NNHAr \\ | \\ CH \\ \| \\ C{-}N{=}NAr \\ | \\ CO_2C_2H_5 \end{array}}$$

$$\text{XXIII} \xrightarrow[(NH_4OH)]{ArN_2X} \begin{array}{c} ArN{=}NC{=}NNHAr \\ | \\ CH \\ \| \\ CH \\ | \\ CO_2C_2H_5 \end{array}$$

The coupling of diazonium salts with β-keto anilides has been studied extensively, because the products have found use as yellow dyes and

[64] Bülow and Höpfner, *Ber.*, **34,** 71 (1901).
[65] Bülow and Göller, *Ber.*, **44,** 2835 (1911).
[66] Prager, *Ann.*, **338,** 360 (1905).

pigments. The Hansa Yellows are obtained from the reactions of acetoacetanilides with various diazonium salts.[67–69] Many variations in the anilide as well as in the diazonium salt have been studied in attempts to improve the color, stability, and solubility of the resulting dyes. Limitations of space preclude a survey of the extensive patent literature on this subject. However, those β-keto amides whose coupling has been reported in the general literature are included in Table II*C*. The dyes may be formulated as existing in both hydrazone (XXVI) and azo (XXVII*a* and *b*) tautomeric forms.

$$\underset{\text{XXVI}}{\mathrm{RCOC(=NNHAr)CONHAr}} \rightleftharpoons \underset{\text{XXVII}a}{\mathrm{RC(OH){=}C(N{=}NAr)CONHAr}} \rightleftharpoons \underset{\text{XXVII}b}{\mathrm{RCOCH(N{=}NAr)CONHAr}}$$

Malonic Acids, Esters, and Amides

Malonic acid can react with 1, 2, or 3 moles of a diazonium salt. It appears that the reaction proceeds through the following steps, with decarboxylation occurring in the first and second stages.[70] Even when

$$CH_2(CO_2H)_2 + ArN_2X \rightarrow ArNHN{=}CHCO_2H$$

$$ArNHN{=}CHCO_2H + ArN_2X \rightarrow ArNHN{=}CHN{=}NAr$$

$$ArNHN{=}CHN{=}NAr + ArN_2X \rightarrow ArNHN{=}C(N{=}NAr)_2$$

equimolecular amounts of acid and salt are used, the reaction usually gives a mixture of the first two products. The relative amounts of these substances formed depend upon the nature of the diazonium salt employed. Busch and Wolbring were able to isolate the phenylhydrazone XXVIII in 50% yield from the reaction of malonic acid with *o*-nitrobenzenediazonium chloride, but under similar conditions *p*-bromobenzenediazonium chloride gave mainly N,N′-di-(*p*-bromophenyl)formazan

$$\underset{\text{XXVIII}}{o\text{-}O_2NC_6H_4NHN{=}CHCO_2H} \qquad \underset{\text{XXIX}}{p\mathrm{BrC_6H_4NHN{=}CHN{=}NC_6H_4Br}\text{-}p}$$

(XXIX).[71] A formazan derivative is the main product with either 1 or 2 moles of most diazonium salts.

[67] Fierz-David and Ziegler, *Helv. Chim. Acta*, **11**, 776 (1928).

[68] Burr and Rowe, *J. Soc. Dyers Colourists*, **44**, 205 (1928) [*C. A.*, **22**, 3400 (1928)].

[69] Rowe, Burr, and Corbishley, *J. Soc. Dyers Colourists*, **42**, 80 (1926) [*C. A.*, **20**, 1718 1926)].

[70] von Pechmann, *Ber.*, **25**, 3175 (1892).

[71] Busch and Wolbring, *J. prakt. Chem.*, [2], **71**, 366 (1905).

If an acidic solution of a diazonium salt is added to a solution of potassium malonate and sodium nitrite, both nitrosation and coupling take place to yield the azo derivative of formaldoxime.[71]

$$ArN_2X + CH_2(CO_2K)_2 \xrightarrow[CH_3CO_2H]{NaNO_2} ArN{=}NCH{=}NOH$$

Formazyl chloride (XXX) is obtained from the reaction of 2 moles of benzenediazonium chloride with chloromalonic acid.[72] Alkylmalonic acids are converted into formazyl alkanes (XXXI) in a similar reaction.[73]

$$\underset{\text{XXX}}{C_6H_5NHN{=}\underset{\underset{Cl}{|}}{C}N{=}NC_6H_5} \qquad \underset{\text{XXXI}}{C_6H_5NHN{=}\underset{\underset{R}{|}}{C}N{=}NC_6H_5}$$

When malonic acid monoethyl ester reacts with a diazonium salt, carbon dioxide is eliminated with the formation of an arylhydrazone of ethyl glyoxalate (XXXII).[74a] This hydrazone can react with a second mole of diazonium salt to give the formazan XXXII*a*. It appears that the formazan is the only product isolated unless there is an *o*-substituent in the diazonium salt.[19c,74b] Diethyl malonate, on the other hand, gives the arylhydrazone of diethyl mesoxalate (XXXIII).[74c] Similarly,

$$HO_2CCH_2CO_2C_2H_5 + ArN_2X \rightarrow \underset{\text{XXXII}}{ArNHN{=}CHCO_2C_2H_5} \rightarrow$$

$$\underset{\text{XXXII}a}{ArNHN{=}C(CO_2C_2H_5)N{=}NAr}$$

$$CH_2(CO_2C_2H_5)_2 + ArN_2X \rightarrow \underset{\text{XXXIII}}{ArNHN{=}C(CO_2C_2H_5)_2}$$

malonamide and its N-substituted derivatives are converted into the hydrazones of the corresponding mesoxalamides.[75]

Diethyl glutaconate (XXXIV) may be regarded as a vinylog of diethyl malonate. Henrich has studied its reactions with both 1 and 2 equivalents of diazonium salt.[76] The use of 1 equivalent of salt gives diethyl oxoglutaconate phenylhydrazone (XXXV). A second equivalent couples at the other α-carbon atom.

[72] Fusco and Romani, *Gazz. chim. ital.*, **76**, 419 (1946).
[73] Walker, *J. Chem. Soc.*, **123**, 2775 (1923).
[74a] Leonard, Boyd, and Herbrandson, *J. Org. Chem.*, **12**, 47 (1947).
[74b] S. Parmerter and E. J. Hodges, unpublished observations.
[74c] Hantzsch and Thompson, *Ber.*, **38**, 2266 (1905).
[75] Whiteley and Yapp, *J. Chem. Soc.*, **1927**, 521.
[76] Henrich et al., *Ann.*, **376**, 121 (1910).

$$C_2H_5O_2CCH_2CH{=}CHCO_2C_2H_5 + C_6H_5N_2Cl \rightarrow \underset{\textstyle \| \atop \textstyle NNHC_6H_5}{C_2H_5O_2CCCH{=}CHCO_2C_2H_5}$$

XXXIV XXXV

$$\underset{\textstyle | \atop \textstyle N{=}NC_6H_5}{C_2H_5O_2CC}{=}\overset{\textstyle NNHC_6H_5 \atop \textstyle \|}{CHCCO_2C_2H_5} \xleftarrow{C_6H_5N_2Cl} \underset{\textstyle | \atop \textstyle N{=}NC_6H_5}{C_2H_5O_2CC}{=}CHCH_2CO_2C_2H_5$$

Arylacetic Acids and Esters

The only arylacetic acid that has been observed to couple with diazonium salts is 2,4-dinitrophenylacetic acid.[77] Decarboxylation occurs as two molecules of the salt attack the α-carbon atom to yield the formazan derivative XXXVI.

$$2,4\text{-}(O_2N)_2C_6H_3CH_2CO_2H + 2ArN_2X \rightarrow 2,4\text{-}(O_2N)_2C_6H_3{-}C(N{=}NAr){=}NNHAr$$

XXXVI

Reactions of a variety of diazonium salts with methyl 2,4-dinitrophenylacetate have given good yields of the hydrazones of methyl 2,4-dinitrophenylglyoxalate (XXXVII).[78,79] These hydrazones undergo ring closure in the presence of alkali with the formation of 1-arylindazoles (XXXVIII).[78–80]

$$2,4\text{-}(O_2N)_2C_6H_3CH_2CO_2CH_3 \xrightarrow{ArN_2X} 2,4\text{-}(O_2N)_2C_6H_3{-}C({=}NNHAr)CO_2CH_3 \xrightarrow{NaOH}$$

XXXVII

$$\text{6-nitro-1-aryl-indazole-3-}CO_2Na + NaNO_2$$

XXXVIII

Although diethyl homophthalate does not react with benzenediazonium chloride, homophthalic anhydride in ethanol-chloroform solution is

[77] Parkes and Aldis, *J. Chem. Soc.*, **1938,** 1841.
[78] Borsche and Bütschli, *Ann.*, **522,** 285 (1936).
[79] Borsche and Diacont, *Ann.*, **510,** 287 (1934).
[80] Meyer, *Ber.*, **22,** 319 (1889).

converted into the α-phenylhydrazono compound.[81] Dimethyl 5-nitrohomophthalate (XXXIX) also couples, and a simultaneous ring closure produces the substituted dihydrophthalazone XL.[79]

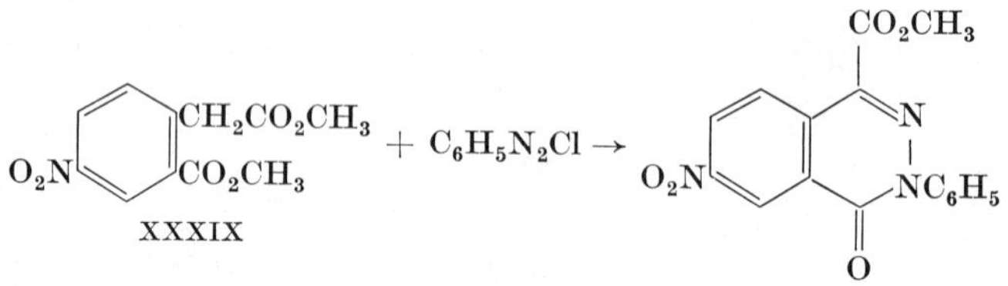

$$O_2N\text{-}C_6H_3(CH_2CO_2CH_3)(CO_2CH_3) \text{ (XXXIX)} + C_6H_5N_2Cl \rightarrow \text{XL}$$

XXXIX

XL

Nitriles

A nearly quantitative yield of ethyl cyanoglyoxalate phenylhydrazone (XLI) is obtained from ethyl cyanoacetate and benzenediazonium

$$C_6H_5N_2Cl + \underset{\displaystyle CN}{CH_2CO_2C_2H_5} \rightarrow C_6H_5NHN{=}\underset{\displaystyle CN}{CCO_2C_2H_5}$$

XLI

chloride in the presence of sodium acetate or sodium carbonate.[82] A variety of diazonium salts has been used in similar reactions with esters of cyanoacetic acid. Other nitriles that undergo the same type of coupling contain a methylene group between the cyano group and some other activating group. Examples are malononitrile,[83,84] cyanoacetaldehyde,[85,86] cyanoacetanilide,[74a] ethyl cyanopyruvate,[86,87] nitroacetonitrile,[88,89] β-iminonitriles,[90,91] and β-sulfonitriles.[92,93] The coupling products from β-ketonitriles form chromium complexes that are dyes.[94] Cyanoacetic acid combines with 2 equivalents of benzenediazonium chloride to produce formazyl cyanide.[95a]

[81] Dieckmann and Meiser, *Ber.*, **41,** 3253 (1908).
[82] Krückeberg, *J. prakt. Chem.*, [2], **49,** 321 (1894).
[83] Schmidtmann, *Ber.*, **29,** 1168 (1896).
[84] Lythgoe, Todd, and Topham, *J. Chem. Soc.*, **1944,** 315.
[85] Claisen, *Ber.*, **36,** 3664 (1903).
[86] Borsche and Manteuffel, *Ann.*, **512,** 97 (1934).
[87] Fleischhauer, *J. prakt. Chem.*, [2], **47,** 375 (1893).
[88] Steinkopf and Bohrmann, *Ber.*, **41,** 1044 (1908).
[89] Steinkopf, *J. prakt. Chem.*, [2], **81,** 193 (1910).
[90] von Meyer, *J. prakt. Chem.*, [2], **52,** 81 (1895).
[91] von Meyer, *J. prakt. Chem.*, [2], **78,** 497 (1908).
[92] Tröger and Berndt, *J. prakt. Chem.*, [2], **102,** 1 (1921).
[93] Tröger and Wunderlich, *J. prakt. Chem.*, [2], **101,** 157 (1921).
[94] Long, *J. Am. Chem. Soc.*, **69,** 990 (1947).
[95a] Wedekind, *Ber.*, **30,** 2993 (1897).

Ring closure to give a 71% yield of 3-cyanoindazole (XLII) takes place when *o*-aminophenylacetonitrile is diazotized.[95b] It appears that this cyclization has not been investigated with nuclear-substituted *o*-aminophenylacetonitriles.

$$o\text{-}C_6H_4(CH_2CN)(NH_2) \xrightarrow{NaNO_2 + HCl} \text{3-cyanoindazole}$$

XLII

Nitriles in which the cyano group is adjacent to a methinyl carbon vary in their reactions with diazonium salts. Benzylmalononitrile (XLIII),[96] α-cyano-γ-hydroxybutyric acid lactone (XLIV),[97] 1,2,3,4-

$C_6H_5CH_2CH(CN)_2$

XLIII

XLIV

XLV

$ArSO_2CH(CH_3)CN$

XLVI

tetrahydroacridine-4-carbonitrile (XLV),[98] and α-arylsulfonylpropionitriles (XLVI)[93] form the azo compounds. Ethyl α-cyanobutyrate is reported to undergo two different reactions. With this ester Favrel isolated the hydrazone XLVII formed by migration of the ethyl group,

$$C_2H_5CH(CN)CO_2C_2H_5 + C_6H_5N_2Cl \rightarrow$$

$$C_6H_5N(C_2H_5)N{=}C(CN)CO_2C_2H_5 + C_6H_5N{=}NC(C_2H_5)(CN)CO_2C_2H_5$$

XLVII XLVIII

[95b] Pschorr and Hoppe, *Ber.*, **43**, 2543 (1910).

[96] Curtin and Russell, *J. Am. Chem. Soc.*, **73**, 4975 (1951).

[97] Feofilaktov and Onishchenko, *J. Gen. Chem. U.S.S.R.*, **9**, 325 (1939) [*C. A.*, **34**, 379 (1940)].

[98] Borsche and Manteuffel, *Ann.*, **534**, 56 (1938).

as well as the expected azo compound XLVIII.[99] When an acetyl group is attached at the methinyl carbon, as in ethyl α-cyanoacetoacetate, the Japp-Klingemann reaction occurs with loss of the acetyl group.[100]

One example of the loss of the cyano group during a coupling reaction has been reported.[36a] The products isolated from the reaction of 3-methylquinoxaline-2-acetonitrile and *p*-chlorobenzenediazonium chloride in dilute ammonium hydroxide were the formazan (XLVIII*a*) and urea.

$$\text{3-CH}_3\text{-quinoxaline-2-CH}_2\text{CN} + 2p\text{-ClC}_6\text{H}_4\text{N}_2\text{Cl} \xrightarrow{\text{NH}_4\text{OH}} \text{3-CH}_3\text{-quinoxalin-2-yl-C}(=\text{NNHC}_6\text{H}_4\text{Cl-}p)\text{-N}=\text{NC}_6\text{H}_4\text{Cl-}p$$

XLVIII*a*

Sulfones

A methylene group adjacent to two sulfonyl groups is attacked by a diazonium salt. The normal product is the monophenylhydrazone XLIX*a* even when an excess of the salt is used.[101] However, in the reaction of *p*-nitrobenzenediazonium fluoroborate with various sulfones two other products, the arylazosulfone XLIX*b* and the tetrazolium betaine XLIX*c*, were isolated also.[19c]

$$\text{ArN}_2^{\oplus} + (\text{RSO}_2)_2\text{CH}_2 \rightarrow \underset{\text{XLIX}a}{(\text{RSO}_2)_2\text{C}=\text{NNHAr}} + \underset{\text{XLIX}b}{\text{ArN}=\text{NSO}_2\text{R}} + \underset{\text{XLIX}c}{\text{Ar}\overset{\oplus}{\text{N}}(=\text{N}-\text{N(Ar)}-)\text{-N}=\text{C}-\text{CO}^{\ominus}}$$

Other sulfones that couple with diazonium salts have a methylene group between a sulfonyl and some other activating group such as nitro,[19c,102] cyano,[19c,92,93] carboxyl,[19c,92] carbethoxy,[19c,92] or carboxamide.[19c,92] Claass prepared a series of dyes from the cyclic amide of

[99] Favrel, *Bull. soc. chim. France*, [4], **47**, 1290 (1930).

[100] Favrel, *Bull. soc. chim. France*, [3], **27**, 200 (1902).

[101] Backer, *Rec. trav. chim.*, **70**, 733 (1951).

[102] Tröger and Nolte, *J. prakt. chem.*, [2], **101**, 136 (1921).

o-aminophenylsulfonylacetic acid (sulfazone) (XLIX*d*) and various diazonium salts.[103]

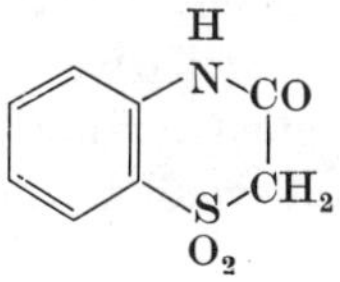

$$\text{(benzene ring fused with } -NH-CO-CH_2-SO_2- \text{ ring)}$$

XLIX*d*

Nitro Compounds

A nitroparaffin that has one or more hydrogen atoms on the α-carbon atom can couple with a diazonium salt. A mixture of products is obtained from the interaction of nitromethane and benzenediazonium chloride.[104] Nitroformaldehyde phenylhydrazone (L) is obtained when the reaction is carried out in dilute hydrochloric acid.[105] However, N,N'-diphenyl-C-nitroformazan (LI) is the principal product in weakly alkaline solution or even at *p*H 4.5.[20] In alkaline solution, a third molecule of diazonium salt causes replacement of the nitro group by a phenyl group.

$$CH_3NO_2 \xrightarrow{C_6H_5N_2Cl} \underset{\text{L}}{C_6H_5NHN{=}CHNO_2} \xrightarrow{C_6H_5N_2Cl}$$

$$\underset{\text{LI}}{C_6H_5NHN{=}\underset{\displaystyle C_6H_5N{=}N}{\underset{|}{C}}NO_2} \xrightarrow{C_6H_5N_2Cl} C_6H_5NHN{=}\underset{\displaystyle C_6H_5N{=}N}{\underset{|}{C}}C_6H_5$$

The product isolated from the reaction of nitromethane with other diazonium salts usually has been the nitroformazan derivative.[20,106]

Other primary nitroparaffins couple only once to give hydrazones of 1-nitroaldehydes, and secondary nitroparaffins yield azo compounds.

$$RCH_2NO_2 + ArN_2X \rightarrow R\underset{\displaystyle NNHAr}{\underset{\|}{C}}NO_2$$

$$R_2CHNO_2 + ArN_2X \rightarrow R_2\underset{\displaystyle N{=}NAr}{\underset{|}{C}}NO_2$$

[103] Claass, *Ber.*, **45**, 747 (1912).
[104] Bamberger, Schmidt, and Levinstein, *Ber.*, **33**, 2043 (1900).
[105] Bamberger, *Ber.*, **27**, 155 (1894).
[106] Hubbard and Scott, *J. Am. Chem. Soc.*, **65**, 2390 (1943).

Degradation of the molecule sometimes occurs when a nitroalcohol reacts with a diazonium salt. For example, 2-nitropropanol and benzenediazonium chloride give formaldehyde and a 78% yield of 1-nitroacetaldehyde phenylhydrazone.[107] Similarly, 2-nitro-1-butanol is converted into 1-nitropropionaldehyde phenylhydrazone. If the reaction mixture from 2-nitro-1-butanol and a diazonium salt is acidified immediately, the

$$CH_3CH_2CH(NO_2)CH_2OH + ArN_2X \rightarrow \underset{\text{LII}}{CH_3CH_2C(N{=}NAr)(NO_2)CH_2OH} \rightarrow CH_3CH_2C(NO_2){=}NNHAr + CH_2O$$

2-arylazo-2-nitro-1-butanol (LII) can be isolated.[108] 2-Hydroxy-1-nitroparaffins couple normally to give the phenylhydrazones of 2-hydroxy-1-nitroaldehydes. However, the addition of a second mole of diazonium salt causes the elimination of aldehyde from these products.[107]

$$RCH(OH)CH_2NO_2 \xrightarrow{C_6H_5N_2X} RCH(HO)C(NO_2){=}NNHC_6H_5 \xrightarrow{C_6H_5N_2X} C_6H_5N{=}NC(NO_2){=}NNHC_6H_5 + RCHO$$

Migration of the nitro group is observed when the α-carbon atom holds two other electron-attracting substituents, one of which is a phenyl group. In these instances the nitro group migrates to the position para to the hydrazone group. (If the para position is blocked, the nitro group enters the ortho position.) Examples that have been reported include phenyldinitromethane (LIII),[109–111] diphenylnitromethane,[112,113] and α-nitrophenylacetonitrile.[114]

$$\underset{\text{LIII}}{C_6H_5CH(NO_2)_2} + C_6H_5N_2Cl \rightarrow C_6H_5C(NO_2){=}NNH\text{-}C_6H_4\text{-}NO_2$$

[107] Jones and Kenner, *J. Chem. Soc.*, **1930**, 919.

[108] Gochenour and Degering, *Proc. Indiana Acad. Sci.*, **57**, 88 (1948) [*C. A.*, **43**, 4646 (1949)].

[109] Ponzio, *Gazz. chim. ital.*, **39**, II, 535 (1909).

[110] Ponzio and Macciotta, *Gazz. chim. ital.*, **44**, I, 269 (1914).

[111] Ponzio and Macciotta, *Gazz. chim. ital.*, **44**, II, 63 (1914).

[112] Ponzio, *Gazz. chim. ital.*, **42**, I, 525 (1912).

[113] Busch and Schäffner, *Ber.*, **56**, 1612 (1923).

[114] Ponzio and Giovetti, *Gazz. chim. ital.*, **39**, II, 546 (1909).

Hydrocarbons

In this section are included aliphatic hydrocarbons and compounds containing a reactive hydrocarbon radical bonded to an aromatic ring.

A number of aliphatic hydrocarbons with conjugated double bonds form monoazo derivatives with diazonium salts.[115,116] The yields are usually low, even with the reactive diazonium salts prepared from *p*-nitroaniline or 2,4-dinitroaniline. Coupling occurs at the carbon atom having the highest electron density. In 1,3-butadiene this is carbon 1, whereas in 1,3-pentadiene it is carbon 4.

$$p\text{-}O_2NC_6H_4N_2X + CH_2{=}CHCH{=}CH_2 \rightarrow p\text{-}O_2NC_6H_4N{=}NCH{=}CHCH{=}CH_2$$

$$p\text{-}O_2NC_6H_4N_2X + CH_3CH{=}CHCH{=}CH_2 \rightarrow p\text{-}O_2NC_6H_4N{=}NC(CH_3){=}CHCH{=}CH_2$$

The only two monoölefins that couple are 2-methylpropene and 2-methyl-2-butene.[116] The cyclic hydrocarbons cyclopentadiene[117,118] and indene[118] also give monoazo derivatives.

The coupling of α,α-diarylethylenes with diazonium salts was discussed above (p. 4). A similar reaction, which occurs intramolecularly when *o*-aminophenylethylenes are diazotized, is the Widman-Stoermer synthesis of cinnolines.[119–121] The scope of this reaction has been studied by

$$o\text{-}H_2NC_6H_4C(R'){=}CHR \xrightarrow{NaNO_2 + HCl} \text{4-R'-3-R-cinnoline}$$

Simpson and Stephenson,[122] and by Schofield,[123] who have found that good yields of the cinnoline are obtained when R′ is methyl or aryl and R is hydrogen. Cinnoline formation also occurs when both R and R′ are aromatic. However, if R′ is hydrogen or carboxyl and R is aromatic,

[115] Meyer, *Ber.*, **52,** 1468 (1919).

[116] Terent'ev and Demidova, *J. Gen. Chem. U.S.S.R.*, **7,** 2464 (1937) [*C. A.*, **32,** 2094 (1938)].

[117] Eibner and Laue, *Ber.*, **39,** 2022 (1906).

[118] Terent'ev and Gomberg, *J. Gen. Chem. U.S.S.R.*, **8,** 662 (1938) [*C. A.*, **33,** 1285 (1939)].

[119] Widman, *Ber.*, **17,** 722 (1884).

[120] Stoermer and Fincke, *Ber.*, **42,** 3115 (1909).

[121] Stoermer and Gaus, *Ber.*, **45,** 3104 (1912).

[122] Simpson and Stephenson, *J. Chem. Soc.*, **1942,** 353.

[123] Schofield, *J. Chem. Soc.*, **1949,** 2408.

the diazotized amine undergoes the Pschorr reaction to yield a phenanthrene derivative.

When *p*-methoxyphenylacetylene couples with 2,4-dinitrobenzenediazonium sulfate, a 69% yield of α-*p*-anisylglyoxal β-2,4-dinitrophenylhydrazone (LIV) is formed.[124] This reaction is similar to the synthesis

$$CH_3O\text{-}C_6H_4\text{-}C{\equiv}CH + HO_4SN_2\text{-}C_6H_3(NO_2)_2 \rightarrow CH_3O\text{-}C_6H_4\text{-}COCH{=}NNH\text{-}C_6H_3(NO_2)_2$$

LIV

of 4-hydroxycinnoline (LV) from diazotized *o*-aminophenylacetylene.[125] In each case the elements of a hydroxyl group, derived from the aqueous reaction medium, appear in the product. This ring closure was used first

$$o\text{-}C_6H_4(C{\equiv}CH)(NH_2) \xrightarrow{NaNO_2 + HCl} \text{4-hydroxycinnoline (OH, N=N)}$$

LV

by von Richter to make 4-hydroxycinnoline-3-carboxylic acid from *o*-aminophenylpropiolic acid.[126] Recent examples of the reaction have employed nuclear substituted *o*-aminophenylacetylenes, *o*-aminophenylpropiolic acids, and *o*-aminodiphenylacetylene.[23,125]

Although styrene does not react with 2,4-dinitrobenzenediazonium sulfate, *p*-methoxystyrene (LVI) is converted to the 2,4-dinitrophenylhydrazone of anisaldehyde by this reagent.[124] The same product is obtained when the dry diazonium salt is added to an alcoholic solution of anethole (LVII).[127] Acetaldehyde is eliminated in the second reaction. Other compounds that show a similar coupling with the loss of acetaldehyde are isoeugenol,[128] isosafrole,[127] isoapiole,[127] and *p*-propenyldimethylaniline.[129] It is even possible to obtain a 60% yield of *p*-hydroxybenzaldehyde *p*-nitrophenylhydrazone from the action of dry

[124] Ainley and Robinson, *J. Chem. Soc.*, **1937**, 369.

[125] Schofield and Simpson, *J. Chem. Soc.*, **1945**, 512.

[126] von Richter, *Ber.*, **16**, 677 (1883).

[127] Quilico and Freri, *Gazz. chim. ital.*, **58**, 380 (1928).

[128] Quilico and Fleischner, *Gazz. chim. ital.*, **59**, 39 (1929).

[129] Quilico and Freri, *Gazz. chim. ital.*, **60**, 606 (1930).

$$CH_3O\text{-}C_6H_4\text{-}CH{=}CH_2 \text{ (LVI)} \xrightarrow{(O_2N)_2C_6H_3N_2SO_4H} CH_3O\text{-}C_6H_4\text{-}CH{=}NNH\text{-}C_6H_3(NO_2)_2$$

$$CH_3O\text{-}C_6H_4\text{-}CH{=}CHCH_3 \text{ (LVII)} \xrightarrow{(O_2N)_2C_6H_3N_2SO_4H} CH_3O\text{-}C_6H_4\text{-}CH{=}NNH\text{-}C_6H_3(NO_2)_2$$

p-nitrobenzenediazonium sulfate on an alcoholic solution of *p*-propenylphenol.[130]

The reaction of an α,β-unsaturated tertiary amine with a diazonium salt resembles that of an unsaturated hydrocarbon. Coupling occurs at the β-carbon atom, and the amino group is eliminated. If there is a hydrogen substituent on the β-carbon, the β-arylhydrazone of a glyoxal is obtained. However, if there is no hydrogen attached to the β-carbon, the enamine is cleaved to give the hydrazone of a ketone.[130a]

$$RCH{=}CHNR_2' + ArN_2X \rightarrow RC({=}NNHAr)CHO + R_2'NH$$

$$R_2C{=}CHNR_2' + ArN_2X \rightarrow R_2C{=}NNHAr + R_2'NCHO$$

Methyl groups in the α or γ positions of some heterocyclic compounds combine with diazonium salts. For example, 9-methylacridine (LVIII)

$$\text{9-}CH_3\text{-acridine (LVIII)} + ArN_2X \longrightarrow \text{9-}(CH{=}NNHAr)\text{-acridine}$$

has been coupled with a number of salts to give the arylhydrazones of acridine 9-carboxaldehyde.[131] If the hetero atom is converted into the onium salt, the activity of the methyl group is increased.[132] 2,3,3-Trimethylindolenine is an exception, for the base is more reactive than

[130] Quilico and Freri, *Gazz. chim. ital.*, **59,** 600 (1929).

[130a] Crary, Quayle, and Lester, *J. Am. Chem. Soc.*, **78,** 5584 (1956).

[131] Poraĭ-Koshits and Kharkharov, *Bull. acad. sci. U.R.S.S. classe sci. chim.*, **1944,** 143 [*C. A.*, **39,** 1631 (1945)].

[132] Kharkharov, *J. Gen. Chem. U.S.S.R.*, **23,** 1175–1181 (1953) [*C. A.*, **47,** 12390 (1953)].

its salts.[132a] Heterocyclic compounds that have been studied include α-picoline,[132] 9-methylxanthylium perchlorate,[14] 9-methylthioxanthylium perchlorate,[14] 2,3-dimethylbenzothiazolium salts,[132a–g] quinaldinium salts,[132g,133,134] and 2,3,3-trimethylindolenium salts.[132a,133,135] The methyl group of 2,4,6-trinitrotoluene also reacts with *p*-nitrobenzenediazonium chloride in pyridine solution.[132] In addition, the ethylidene group in 1-phenyl-3-methyl-4-ethylidene-5-pyrazolones shows a reactivity toward diazonium salts.[135a]

A ring closure which involves a methyl group is the indazole synthesis via intramolecular coupling of diazotized *o*-toluidines. Although *o*-toluidine gives only a small yield of indazole,[136] many substituted *o*-toluidines give excellent yields of substituted indazoles.[137] The preparation of 5-nitroindazole (LIX) is typical.[138]

$$O_2N\text{-}C_6H_3(CH_3)(NH_2) \xrightarrow[CH_3CO_2H]{NaNO_2} \text{LIX (5-nitroindazole, } O_2N, \text{N-H)}$$

LIX

Hydrazones

Arylhydrazones of many aliphatic and aromatic aldehydes have been coupled with diazonium salts to yield formazan derivatives. An example is the production of N,N′-diphenyl-C-methylformazan (LX) in 88% yield from acetaldehyde phenylhydrazone.[139] The fact that the reaction does

$$CH_3CH{=}NNHC_6H_5 + C_6H_5N_2Cl \rightarrow CH_3C(N{=}NC_6H_5){=}NNHC_6H_5$$

LX

[132a] Gault and Wahl, *Compt. rend.*, **240,** 983 (1955).
[132b] Wahl and Le Bris, *Bull. soc. chim. France*, **1954,** 587.
[132c] Wahl and Le Bris, *Compt. rend.*, **234,** 631 (1952).
[132d] Le Bris and Wahl, *Bull. soc. chim. France*, **1954,** 248.
[132e] Wahl, *Bull. soc. chim. France*, **1954,** 251.
[132f] Poraĭ-Koshits and Muravich, *J. Gen. Chem. U.S.S.R.*, **23,** 1583–1593 (1953) [*C. A.*, **48** 11399 (1954)].
[132g] Wizinger and Atakan, *Helv. Chim. Acta*, **39,** 1330 (1956).
[133] König, *Ber.*, **57,** 891 (1921).
[134] König, *Ber.*, **56,** 1543 (1923).
[135] König and Muller, *Ber.*, **57,** 144 (1924).
[135a] Poraĭ-Koshits and Dinaburg, *J. Gen. Chem. U.S.S.R.*, **24,** 2208 (1954) [*C. A.*, **50,** 310 (1956)].
[136] Bamberger, *Ann.*, **305,** 289 (1899).
[137] Nölting, *Ber.*, **37,** 2556 (1904).
[138] Porter and Peterson, *Org. Syntheses*, Coll. Vol. III, 660 (1955).
[139] Bamberger and Billeter, *Helv. Chim. Acta*, **14,** 219 (1931).

not take place with secondary hydrazones was mentioned on p. 5.[19] The reaction of the phenylhydrazones of 2-hydroxy-1-nitroaldehydes with degradation of the molecule to give an aldehyde and nitroformazan was mentioned under the discussion of nitro compounds. The formazans obtained from phenylhydrazones of aldoses have proved to be useful derivatives of these sugars.[139a–f]

The hydrazones of only two kinds of ketones have been converted into formazans. These are the arylhydrazones of α-keto acids (LXI)[19,140–145] and the α-arylhydrazones of α,β-diketobutyric esters (LXII).[19,60,142,146] With the first type coupling causes decarboxylation, and with the second type an acetyl group is replaced. These eliminations are very similar to the Japp-Klingemann reaction.

$$\underset{\text{LXI}}{\underset{\|}{RC}(=NNHC_6H_5)CO_2H} + C_6H_5N_2X \rightarrow RC(=NNHC_6H_5)N{=}NC_6H_5 + CO_2$$

$$\underset{\text{LXII}}{CH_3COC(=NNHC_6H_5)CO_2R} + C_6H_5N_2X \rightarrow C_6H_5N{=}NC(=NNHC_6H_5)CO_2R + CH_3CO_2H$$

Reports of the isolation of two isomeric forms of unsymmetrical formazans[18,147] have been shown to be erroneous.[148–150] The unsymmetrical formazans obtained by both possible routes (A and B) are identical. The isolation of the same compound from both of these reactions has been rationalized by the assumption that the product has the structure of the resonance hybrid of the chelated forms LXIII.[148,149]

[139a] Mester, *J. Am. Chem. Soc.*, **77**, 4301 (1955).
[139b] Mester and Major, *J. Am. Chem. Soc.*, **78**, 1403 (1956).
[139c] Zemplén and Mester, *Acta Chim. Acad. Sci. Hung.*, **2**, 9 (1952) [*C. A.*, **48**, 1966 (1954)].
[139d] Mester and Major, *J. Am. Chem. Soc.*, **77**, 4305 (1955).
[139e] Mester and Major, *J. Am. Chem. Soc.*, **77**, 4297 (1955).
[139f] Zemplén, Mester, Messmer, and Eckhart, *Acta Chim. Acad. Sci. Hung.*, **2**, 25 (1952) [*C. A.*, **48**, 1966 (1954)].
[140] Bamberger, *Ber.*, **25**, 3547 (1892).
[141] Wedekind and Stauwe, *Ber.*, **31**, 1746 (1898).
[142] Bamberger and de Gruyter, *J. prakt. Chem.*, [2], **64**, 222 (1901).
[143] Busch and von Beust, *Ber.*, **58**, 442 (1925).
[144] Ragno and Bruno, *Gazz. chim. ital.*, **76**, 485 (1946).
[145] Fusco and Romani, *Gazz. chim. ital.*, **78**, 342 (1948).
[146] Lapworth, *J. Chem. Soc.*, **83**, 1114 (1903).
[147] Fichter and Schiess, *Ber.*, **33**, 747 (1900).
[148] Kuhn and Jerchel, *Ber.*, **74**, 941 (1941).
[149] Hunter and Roberts, *J. Chem. Soc.*, **1941**, 820.
[150] Hausser, Jerchel, and Kuhn, *Chem. Ber.*, **84**, 651 (1951).

Path A: RCH═NNHAr + Ar′N₂Cl ⟶ (ring structure: RC with N—N(Ar), N═N(Ar′), H)

↕

Path B: RCH═NNHAr′ + ArN₂Cl ⟶ (ring structure: RC with N—N(Ar′), N═N(Ar), H)

LXIII

A formazan in which the carbon is joined to a carboxyl,[19,70,140,151,152] acetyl,[52,142] or oxalyl group[153] loses that group when it couples with another molecule of diazonium salt.

$$\mathrm{RNHN{=}C(X)N{=}NR + ArN_2Cl \rightarrow RNHN{=}C(N{=}NAr)N{=}NR}$$

$$(\mathrm{X = -CO_2H, -COCH_3, -COCO_2H})$$

Heterocyclic Compounds

In this section are included those heterocyclic compounds that have a methylene group with a carbonyl group adjacent to it in the ring. These reactants can exist in the tautomeric enolic form as well.

Of the compounds in this group, the 5-pyrazolones have been investigated most extensively because of the successful use of their azo derivatives as dyes. No attempt has been made to include here all of the pyrazolones that appear in the patent literature. The early patents in this field have been reviewed by Roux and Martinet,[154] and some of the more recent ones have been discussed by Venkataraman.[155] The 1-aryl-3-methyl-5-pyrazolones (LXIV) have been used most frequently in the preparation of dyes. Pyrazolones with a methyl group in the

151 Bamberger and Wheelwright, *Ber.*, **25,** 3201 (1892).

152 Chattaway and Lye, *Proc. Roy. Soc. London,* **A137,** 489 (1932) [*C. A.*, **26,** 5555 (1932)].

153 Bamberger and Müller, *J. prakt. Chem.*, [2], **64,** 199 (1901).

154 Roux and Martinet, *Rev. gén. mat. color.*, **27,** 115–120, 134–139, 152–155 (1923), **28,** 13–14, 74–77 (1924).

155 Venkataraman, *The Chemistry of Synthetic Dyes*, Chapter XVIII, Academic Press, New York, 1952.

4-position fail to react with diazonium salts.[156] On the other hand, pyrazolones with an ethylene, isopropylidene, or benzal group in the 4-position couple with the loss of that substituent.[157,158]

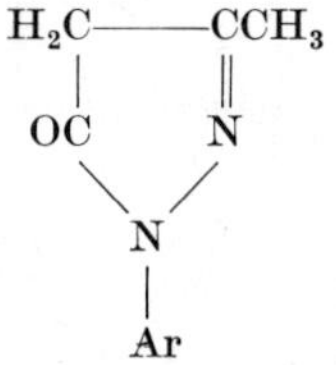

LXIV 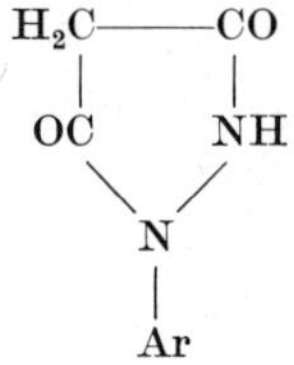 LXV 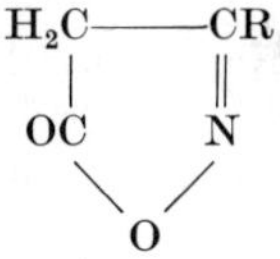 LXVI 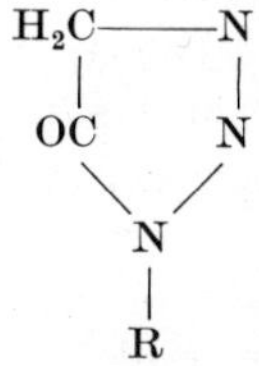 LXVII

Other heterocycles that contain a methylene group active toward diazonium salts include 3,5-pyrazolidinediones (LXV), 5-isoxazolones (LXVI), 1,2,3-triazole-5-ones (LXVII), 2(3)-thianaphthenone (LXVIII), 3(2)-thianaphthenone (LXIX), 1-phenyloxindole (LXX), indoxyl (LXXI), barbituric acid, and homophthalimide.

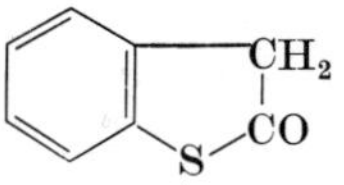

LXVIII 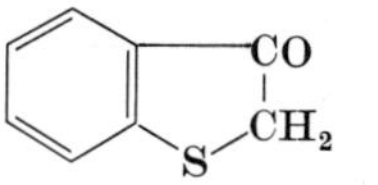 LXIX

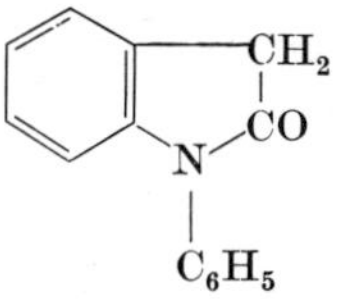

LXX 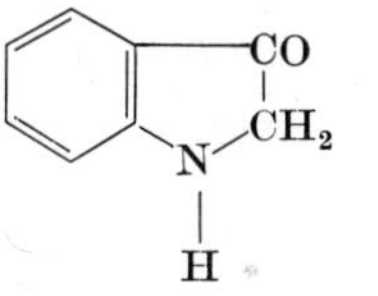 LXXI

SYNTHETIC APPLICATIONS

The reactions of diazonium salts with many aliphatic compounds have been used only to prepare derivatives for purposes of characterization. The adaptability of the reaction to large-scale syntheses is evident from the quantities of dyes that have been produced from β-ketoamides and 5-pyrazolones. The Pschorr synthesis and related diazonium ring closure reactions are discussed in Chapter 7 of *Organic Reactions*, Volume 9.

Cinnolines

All of the general methods for the preparation of cinnolines employ the intramolecular coupling of a diazonium salt with some aliphatic substituent

[156] Verkade and Dhont, *Rec. trav. chim.*, **64,** 165 (1945).

[157] Stolz, *Ber.*, **28,** 623 (1895).

[158] Sawdey, Ruoff, and Vittum, *J. Am. Chem. Soc.*, **72,** 4947 (1950).

in the ortho position. The Borsche synthesis[159] from *o*-aminophenyl ketones (LXXII) has been used to prepare a variety of 3-, 5-, 6-, 7-, and 8-substituted 4-hydroxycinnolines.[22,24,37–41,159–167a,b] The method of von Richter[126] based upon *o*-aminophenylacetylenes (LXXIII) produces 3-carboxy- or 3-phenyl-4-hydroxycinnolines.[23,125] Cinnolines with alkyl or aryl substituents in the 4 position are obtained by the Widman–Stoermer synthesis from *o*-aminoarylethylenes (LXXIV).[119–121,167c]

$COCH_2R$, NH_2 (LXXII) $\xrightarrow{NaNO_2 + HX}$ OH, R, N=N

LXXII

$C{\equiv}CR$, NH_2 (LXXIII) $\xrightarrow{NaNO_2 + HX + H_2O}$ OH, R, N=N

LXXIII

R, $C{=}CHR'$, NH_2 (LXXIV) $\xrightarrow{NaNO_2 + HX}$ R, R, N=N

LXXIV

3-Nitrocinnolines have been synthesized by coupling diazotized *o*-aminobenzaldehyde or *o*-aminoacetophenone with nitromethane and cyclizing the resulting arylhydrazone of nitroformaldehyde.[167d]

$$o\text{-}RCOC_6H_4N_2X + CH_3NO_2 \rightarrow$$

$$o\text{-}RCOC_6H_4NHN{=}CHNO_2 \rightarrow$$ R, NO_2, N=N

$(R = H \text{ or } CH_3)$

[159] Borsche and Herbert, *Ann.*, **546**, 293 (1941).
[160] Koelsch, *J. Org. Chem.*, **8**, 295 (1943).
[161] Atkinson and Simpson, *J. Chem. Soc.*, **1947**, 232.
[162] Keneford and Simpson, *J. Chem. Soc.*, **1947**, 227.
[163] Simpson, *J. Chem. Soc.*, **1947**, 237.
[164] Keneford, Morley, and Simpson, *J. Chem. Soc.*, **1948**, 1702.
[165] Schofield and Theobald, *J. Chem. Soc.*, **1949**, 2404.
[166] McIntyre and Simpson, *J. Chem. Soc.*, **1952**, 2606.
[167a] Alford, Irving, Marsh, and Schofield, *J. Chem. Soc.*, **1952**, 3009.
[167b] Castle and Kruse, *J. Org. Chem.*, **17**, 1571 (1952).
[167c] Albert and Hampton, *J. Chem. Soc.*, **1952**, 4985.
[167d] Baumgarten and DeBrunner, *J. Am. Chem. Soc.*, **76**, 3489 (1954).

Indazoles

Intramolecular coupling of diazotized *o*-toluidines has been used to prepare a number of substituted indazoles. This method is best for the synthesis of nitroindazoles (LIX). A good yield of indazole-3-carboxylic acid is obtained via the nitrile XLII from *o*-aminophenylacetonitrile.[95b,168] A method for the preparation of 1-aryl-6-nitroindazoles (XXXVIII) employs the reaction of a diazonium salt with methyl 2,4-dinitrophenylacetate. When the resulting hydrazone is treated with alkali, it undergoes ring closure with the loss of one nitro group.[78–80]

Tetrazolium Salts

When a formazan is oxidized with lead tetraacetate, a tetrazolium salt (LXXV) is produced. The formazans in turn are synthesized by coupling a diazonium salt with an arylhydrazone. This general route appears to be the only good one for the preparation of tetrazolium salts. The preparations and uses of formazans and tetrazolium salts have been reviewed by Ried[169] and by Nineham.[169]

$$\mathrm{RCH{=}NNHAr} + \mathrm{Ar'N_2X} \rightarrow$$

$$\begin{array}{l} \mathrm{RC{=}NNHAr} \\ \quad | \\ \mathrm{N{=}NAr'} \end{array} \xrightarrow[\text{then HX}]{\mathrm{Pb(OCOCH_3)_4},} \left[\begin{array}{l} \quad\ \mathrm{N{-}NAr} \\ \ \ /\!\!/ \qquad | \\ \mathrm{RC} \qquad\ \ | \\ \ \ \backslash \qquad\ \ | \\ \quad\ \mathrm{N{=}NAr'} \end{array} \right]^{+} X^{-}$$

LXXV

Thiocarbazones

The first step in the synthesis of thiocarbazones utilizes the reaction of nitromethane with two equivalents of diazonium salt.[20,106,170] The resulting nitroformazan is reduced by ammonium sulfide to the thiocarbazide LXXVI which is oxidized readily to the thiocarbazone.

$$2\mathrm{ArN_2X} + \mathrm{CH_3NO_2} \rightarrow \mathrm{ArNHN{=}\overset{\overset{\displaystyle NO_2}{|}}{C}N{=}NAr} \xrightarrow{\mathrm{(NH_4)_2S}}$$

$$\underset{\text{LXXVI}}{\mathrm{(ArNHNH)_2CS}} \xrightarrow{\mathrm{(O)}} \mathrm{ArNHNH\overset{\overset{\displaystyle S}{\|}}{C}N{=}NAr}$$

[168] Rousseau and Lindwall, *J. Am. Chem. Soc.*, **72,** 3047 (1950).

[169] Ried, *Angew. Chem.*, **64,** 391 (1952); Nineham, *Chem. Revs.*, **55,** 355 (1955).

[170] Oesper and Klingenberg, *J. Org. Chem.*, **13,** 309 (1948).

A related synthesis starts with chloromalonic acid.[170a] In this method the chloroformazan is converted directly to the thiocarbazone by sodium hydrogen sulfide.

$$2ArN_2X + ClCH(CO_2H)_2 \rightarrow ArNHN{=}\underset{}{\overset{Cl}{\overset{|}{C}}}N{=}NAr \xrightarrow{NaSH} ArNHNH\overset{S}{\overset{\|}{C}}N{=}NAr$$

Amidrazones*

The catalytic reduction of arylhydrazones of α-nitrobenzaldehyde (LXXVII) offers a convenient synthesis of amidrazones.[171] Coupling of a diazonium salt with phenylnitromethane furnishes the required hydrazone. Ponzio obtained the amidrazones from the reaction of the α-nitrobenzaldehyde arylhydrazone with ammonia.[172]

$$ArN_2X + C_6H_5CH_2NO_2 \rightarrow \underset{\text{LXXVII}}{C_6H_5\underset{NO_2}{\underset{|}{C}}{=}NNHAr} \xrightarrow{H_2\,(Ni)} C_6H_5\underset{NH_2}{\underset{|}{C}}{=}NNHAr$$

Amines

The only report of the use of the coupling reaction to introduce the amino group into active methylene compounds appears in the patent literature.[173] In this method the phenylhydrazones obtained from ethyl acetoacetate, ethyl cyanoacetate, or acetylacetone and benzenediazonium chloride were reduced with zinc and acetic acid to give the α-acetamido compounds.

EXPERIMENTAL CONDITIONS

Diazonium salts react with so many different types of aliphatic compounds that it is difficult to make generalizations about experimental conditions. However, the following summary may serve as a useful guide.

Diazonium Salts

For the diazotization of most arylamines a solution of sodium nitrite is added to a cold solution of the arylamine in aqueous mineral acid.

[170a] Irving and Bell, *J. Chem. Soc.*, **1953,** 3538.

* Amidrazones may be represented by the general formula $RC(NH_2){=}NNHR'$. They are indexed in *Chemical Abstracts* as the hydrazones of amides.

[171] Jerchel and Fischer, *Ann.*, **574,** 85 (1951).

[172] Ponzio, *Gazz. chim. ital.*, **40,** I, 312 (1910).

[173] Pfister and Tishler, U.S. pat. 2,489,927 [*C. A.*, **44,** 2552 (1950)].

For weakly basic amines or amino acids it is necessary to employ special techniques. These methods have been reviewed by Saunders.[174]

Solvents

These reactions have been conducted most frequently in cold dilute aqueous solutions buffered with sodium acetate. Alcohol or occasionally pyridine or acetic acid is added if the reactants are too insoluble in water. Special reactions that have been carried out under anhydrous conditions were discussed under Scope and Limitations, pp. 22–23.

*p*H

Reaction can occur between a diazonium salt and many active methylene compounds over a wide *p*H range. Coupling in dilute hydrochloric acid[66,82] or in dilute sodium hydroxide[175] is usually less satisfactory than coupling in the presence of sodium carbonate or sodium acetate buffers.[82] The general practice is to use a large excess of sodium acetate.

Hünig and Boes made an extensive study of the relative reactivity of various methylene compounds, XCH_2Y, toward *p*-nitrobenzenediazonium fluoroborate over a *p*H range from 2 to 10.[19c] The lowest *p*H at which a compound would couple was taken as an indication of its reactivity. The substituents X and Y arranged in the order of their decreasing ability to activate were: NO_2, CHO, $COCH_3$, CN, $CO_2C_2H_5$, $CONH_2$, CO_2CH_3, $SO_2C_2H_5$, $SOCH_3$, C_6H_5. Only the most active compounds coupled in acidic solution, and the least active failed to couple even in alkaline solution.

In the intramolecular coupling reactions used to prepare cinnolines or indazoles a strongly acidic solution is employed. This promotes the coupling reaction and decreases the competing decomposition of the diazonium salt to the phenol. Acidic solutions are used in the reactions of diazonium salts with hydrocarbons for similar reasons.

The optimum reaction conditions for nitro compounds vary considerably. It has been customary to employ an aqueous solution of the sodium salt of the *aci*-nitro compound. The coupling of nitromethane, on the other hand, proceeds well at a *p*H of 4.5.[20] With nitro alcohols a fairly high *p*H is required. The reaction of 2-nitro-1-butanol with *p*-chlorobenzenediazonium chloride does not occur below *p*H 10.8, and best yields are obtained at *p*H 13.9.[108] It has been reported that solutions

[174] Saunders, *The Aromatic Diazo-Compounds*, Edward Arnold & Co., London, 1949.

[175] von Rothenburg, *Ber.*, **27**, 685 (1894).

of 1-N-morpholino-2-nitropropane between *p*H 7 and 10 *explode with great violence during the coupling process.*[176a]

Reactant Ratios

Equivalent amounts of reactant and diazonium salt are most commonly employed. Excess diazonium salt should be avoided since the product is frequently a hydrazone which can couple with another molecule of the salt to produce a formazan derivative. The latter reaction is favored by a strongly alkaline solution.

Time of the Reaction

Since most of the coupling reactions are rapid, the product can be isolated soon after the diazonium salt has been added. However, the reactions that involve intramolecular coupling require more time for completion. In the preparation of indazoles, the diazotized *o*-toluidine derivative may be left for several days to effect the ring closure.[137,138] Likewise, the formation of cinnolines is often slow.[23,38,39,164–167a–d] For certain cinnolines this cyclization is accelerated by the use of a warm, strongly acidic reaction medium.[37,40]

EXPERIMENTAL PROCEDURES

The preparation of pyruvaldehyde 1-phenylhydrazone from acetoacetic acid and benzenediazonium chloride in 73–82% yield is described in *Organic Syntheses.*[55]

Directions for the preparation of 5-nitroindazole in yields of 72–80% by the intramolecular coupling of diazotized 2-methyl-4-nitroaniline are given in *Organic Syntheses.*[138]

Ethyl α,β-Dioxobutyrate α-Phenylhydrazone.[235] A solution of 73 g. (1.06 moles) of sodium nitrite in 250 ml. of water is added slowly below the surface of a cold, well-stirred solution of 93 g. (1.0 mole) of aniline in 500 ml. of 5 *N* hydrochloric acid. The temperature of the solution is kept at 0–5° during the addition. After ten minutes the solution is made alkaline to Congo red by the addition of saturated sodium acetate solution. The diazonium solution is added slowly with stirring to a cold slurry of 130 g. (1.0 mole) of ethyl acetoacetate, 120 g. (1.46 moles) of sodium acetate, and 200 ml. of water in 750 ml. of ethanol. The temperature is held below 10° during the addition. The mixture is stirred for a further thirty minutes at 5–10° and for ninety minutes at

[176a] Van Biema and Degering, *J. Am. Chem. Soc.*, **66**, 1514 (1944).

room temperature. One liter of water is added before the yellow solid is collected. The yield is 229 g. (98%) of product that melts at about 70°, but whose melting point varies markedly with the rate of heating.

Ethyl Cyanoglyoxalate *m*-Chlorophenylhydrazone.[74a] A solution of 38 g. (0.30 mole) of *m*-chloroaniline in 85 ml. of concentrated hydrochloric acid and 300 ml. of water is cooled to 5° with stirring. Diazotization is effected by the slow addition of a solution of 23 g. (0.33 mole) of sodium nitrite in 50 ml. of water while the temperature is held below 5°. The solution is stirred with activated carbon for an additional ten minutes (temperature below 10°) and filtered. The filtrate is added dropwise during one hour to a well-stirred mixture of 33.9 g. (0.30 mole) of ethyl cyanoacetate in 300 ml. of water at 5–10°. Sodium carbonate (100 g.) is added in small portions to keep the mixture alkaline to litmus. The mixture is extracted with ether until the extracts are no longer colored. The combined ether extracts are dried over magnesium sulfate and concentrated. The residue is crystallized from ethanol to give 73 g. (97%) of pale-orange crystals, m.p. 89–90°.

By the same procedure, diethyl malonate is converted into diethyl mesoxalate *m*-chlorophenylhydrazone in 78% yield. Likewise, ethyl acetoacetate is converted into ethyl α,β-dioxobutyrate α-*m*-chlorophenylhydrazone in 78% yield.

1-Nitro-1-*p*-chlorophenylhydrazonoethane.[176b] To a cold solution of 8.4 g. (0.066 mole) of *p*-chloroaniline in 17 ml. of concentrated hydrochloric acid and 200 ml. of water is added slowly with stirring a solution of 4.7 g. (0.068 mole) of sodium nitrite in 50 ml. of water. The temperature is held at 0–5° during the addition. After ten minutes, the solution is diluted with 1.7 l. of cold water, and 30 g. of sodium acetate trihydrate is added. Meanwhile, 5 g. (0.066 mole) of nitroethane is dissolved in an ice-cold solution of 2.6 g. of sodium hydroxide in 20 ml. of water. The nitroethane solution is added dropwise during ten minutes to a well-stirred solution of the diazonium salt. The temperature of the mixture is held at 5–10° during the addition. After thirty minutes the orange solid is collected. The yield of product melting at 116–118° is 14 g. (100%). Recrystallization from ethanol gives orange-yellow crystals which decompose at 126–127° when placed in a bath preheated to 120°.

1-(*p*-Nitrophenylazo)-2,3-dimethyl-1,3-butadiene.[115] A warm solution of 13.8 g. (0.10 mole) of *p*-nitroaniline in 25 ml. of concentrated hydrochloric acid and 25 ml. of water is poured onto 100 g. of ice. The mixture is stirred with a solution of 7 g. (0.10 mole) of sodium nitrite in 50 ml. of water until the solid dissolves. The solution is diluted with 100 ml. of water and shaken for two hours with 9 g. (0.11 mole) of

[176b] Bamberger and Grob, *Ber.*, **35**, 67 (1902).

2,3-dimethyl-1,3-butadiene.[176c] The solid is collected and dried to give 12 g. (47%) of product. After recrystallization from acetic acid containing some charcoal, the product melts at 177°.

N,N'-Diphenyl-C-methylformazan.[139] Aqueous benzenediazonium chloride is prepared by the addition of a solution of 7 g. (0.1 mole) of sodium nitrite in 15 ml. of water to 9.3 g. (0.1 mole) of aniline dissolved in 25 ml. of concentrated hydrochloric acid and 25 ml. of water. A warm solution of 13.4 g. (0.1 mole) of acetaldehyde phenylhydrazone (α or β form) in 100 ml. of ethanol is mixed with a warm solution of 30 g. of sodium acetate trihydrate in 150 ml. of ethanol. The mixture is cooled to 5° with vigorous stirring before the diazonium salt solution is added dropwise. The product separates as an oil which soon solidifies. The solid is collected and washed with a little cold ethanol to give 21 g. (88%) of N,N'-diphenyl-C-methylformazan, which melts at 123°. Recrystallization from ethanol raises the melting point to 125°.

4-Hydroxy-3-methylcinnoline.[40] To a cold solution of 45.5 g. (0.31 mole) of *o*-aminopropiophenone in 1.2 l. of concentrated hydrochloric acid is added slowly with stirring 23 g. (0.33 mole) of sodium nitrite in 30 ml. of water. The temperature is kept at 5–10° during the addition. The solution is filtered, and 4 l. of concentrated hydrochloric acid is added to the filtrate. The reaction mixture is warmed at 60° for four hours before it is evaporated to a small volume under reduced pressure. An excess of saturated sodium acetate solution is added to precipitate the product, which is collected and dried to give 40.7 g. (83%) of almost pure 4-hydroxy-3-methylcinnoline. Recrystallization from 50% aqueous ethanol gives slender, silvery needles, m.p. 241–242°.

TABULAR SURVEY OF THE COUPLING OF DIAZONIUM SALTS WITH ALIPHATIC CARBON ATOMS

The tables include those reactions recorded prior to the January, 1956, issue of *Chemical Abstracts*. Some more recent examples are also given. The reactants within a table are in general listed in order of increasing size and complexity.

Where more than one reference is given for a single entry, the yield reported is taken from the first reference. Since yields are but infrequently reported, the omission of parenthesized figures in the product column indicates that no yield was reported.

[176c] Allen and Bell, *Org. Syntheses Coll. Vol.* **3**, 312 (1955).

TABLE I

COUPLING OF DIAZONIUM SALTS WITH KETONES

A. Monoketones

Ketone	Substituent(s) in Aniline*	Product (Yield, %)	References
Acetone	—	$C_6H_5NHN{=}C(COCH_3)N{=}NC_6H_5$	25
Chloroacetone	—	$CH_3COC(Cl){=}NNHC_6H_5$ (30)	28
	2-Methyl	$CH_3COC(Cl){=}NNHC_6H_4CH_3$-*o* (25)	28
	4-Methyl	$CH_3COC(Cl){=}NNHC_6H_4CH_3$-*p* (15)	28
α,α′-Dichloroacetone	—	$ClCH_2COC(Cl){=}NNHC_6H_5$	177
	2-Methyl	$ClCH_2COC(Cl){=}NNHC_6H_4CH_3$-*o*	177
	4-Methyl	$ClCH_2COC(Cl){=}NNHC_6H_4CH_3$-*p*	177
α,α-Dichloroacetone	—	$(C_6H_5N{=}N)_2CCl_2$	177
	4-Methyl	$(p\text{-}CH_3C_6H_4N{=}N)_2CCl_2$	177
sym-Tetrachloroacetone	—	$(C_6H_5N{=}N)_2CCl_2$	177
	4-Methyl	$(p\text{-}CH_3C_6H_4N{=}N)_2CCl_2$	177
Nitroacetone	4-Nitro	$CH_3COC(NO_2){=}NNHC_6H_4NO_2$-*p* (59)	19*c*
Methylsulfonylacetone	4-Nitro	$CH_3SO_2C(COCH_3){=}NNHC_6H_4NO_2$-*p* (70)	19*c*
4-Imino-2-pentanone	—	$CH_3COC(N{=}NC_6H_5){=}C(NH_2)CH_3$	178
Pyruvic acid	—	$C_6H_5NHN{=}C(N{=}NC_6H_5)COCO_2H$ (57)	153, 227
Levulinic acid	—	Diformazyl† (88)	179, 153, 180
γ-Oxopimelic acid	—	Diformazyl†‡ (13–17)	153, 180
Cyclopentane-1,2-dione	—	Cyclopentane-1,2,3-trione 1-phenylhydrazone	33
α-Hydroxy-α-methyl-γ-oxoglutaric acid lactone	—	α-Hydroxy-α-methyl-β,γ-dioxoglutaric acid lactone β-phenylhydrazone	181
Ethyl 3-hydroxy-2,5-dioxo-3-cyclopentene-1-carboxylic acid	—	Ethyl 3-hydroxy-2,5-dioxo-4-phenylazo-3-cyclopentene-1-carboxylic acid	182
2,4-Dinitrophenylacetone	—	1-(2,4-Dinitrophenyl)propane-1,2-dione 1-phenylhydrazone	29
2-Nitro-4-carbomethoxyphenylacetone	—	1-(2-Nitro-4-carbomethoxyphenyl)propane-1,2-dione 1-phenylhydrazone	183

Note: References 177–480 are on pp. 136–142.

* The full name is given when it is awkward to name the arylamine as a derivative of aniline.

† The formula of the formazyl radical is $C_6H_5NHN{=}CN{=}NC_6H_5$.

‡ Succinic acid was eliminated.

TABLE I—*Continued*

A. *Monoketones—Continued*

Substituent R in CH_3COCH_2C (oxadiazole ring: N—CR, =N, O)	Substituent(s) in Aniline	Substituents in Product, $CH_3COC(=NNHR')$ (oxadiazole ring: N—CR, =N, O): R′	R	Yield, %	References
Phenyl	—	Phenyl	Phenyl	40	31, 32
p-Tolyl	—	Phenyl	*p*-Tolyl	35	31, 32
	2-Methyl	*o*-Tolyl	*p*-Tolyl	55	31, 32
	4-Methyl	*p*-Tolyl	*p*-Tolyl	40	31, 32
	2,4-Dimethyl	2,4-Dimethylphenyl	*p*-Tolyl	40	31, 32
	2,5-Dimethyl	2,5-Dimethylphenyl	*p*-Tolyl	—	32
	2-Methoxy	*o*-Anisyl	*p*-Tolyl	35	31, 32
	3-Methoxy	*m*-Anisyl	*p*-Tolyl	35	31, 32
	3-Chloro	*m*-Chlorophenyl	*p*-Tolyl	55	31, 32
	4-Chloro	*p*-Chlorophenyl	*p*-Tolyl	30	31, 32
	2-Nitro	*o*-Nitrophenyl	*p*-Tolyl	45	31, 32
	3-Nitro	*m*-Nitrophenyl	*p*-Tolyl	20	31, 32
	4-Nitro	*p*-Nitrophenyl	*p*-Tolyl	20	31, 32
	4-Dimethylamino	*p*-Dimethylaminophenyl	*p*-Tolyl	25	31, 32
	2-Carboxy	*o*-Carboxyphenyl	*p*-Tolyl	50	31, 32
	4-Carboxy	*p*-Carboxyphenyl	*p*-Tolyl	45	31, 32
	α-Naphthylamine	α-Naphthyl	*p*-Tolyl	40	31, 32
	β-Naphthylamine	β-Naphthyl	*p*-Tolyl	35	31, 32
	4-Phenyl	*p*-Biphenylyl	*p*-Tolyl	40	31, 32
	4-Benzyl	*p*-Benzylphenyl	*p*-Tolyl	45	31, 32
	3,3-Dimethoxybenzidine	3,3-Dimethoxybiphenylene	*p*-Tolyl	20	32
m-Nitrophenyl	—	Phenyl	*m*-Nitrophenyl	80	31, 32
	2-Methoxy	*o*-Anisyl	*m*-Nitrophenyl	50	31, 32

Ketone	Substituent(s) in Aniline	Product (Yield, %)	References
Acetonylpyridinium bromide	—	$CH_3COC(\overset{+}{N}C_5H_5)=N\overset{-}{N}C_6H_5$ (84)	30
Phenacyl chloride	—	$C_6H_5COC(Cl)=NNHC_6H_5$	177
4-Carbomethoxy-3-methyl-5-phenyl-3-cyclohexenone	—	4-Carbomethoxy-3-methyl-5-phenyl-3-cyclohexene-1,2-dione 2-phenylhydrazone	276
4-Carbethoxy-3-methyl-5-phenyl-3-cyclohexenone	—	4-Carbethoxy-3-methyl-5-phenyl-3-cyclohexene-1,2-dione 2-phenylhydrazone	276
4-Carbethoxy-3,5-diphenyl-1,3-cyclohexadien-1-ol	—	4-Carbethoxy-3,5-diphenyl-3-cyclohexene-1, 2-dione 2-phenylhydrazone	277
Phenyl 2,4-dinitrobenzyl ketone	—	$2,4\text{-}(NO_2)_2C_6H_3COC(C_6H_5)=NNHC_6H_5$ (quant.)	78
Phenacylpyridinium bromide	—	$C_6H_5COC(\overset{+}{N}C_5H_5)=N\overset{-}{N}C_6H_5$ (89)	30
	2-Nitro	$C_6H_5COC(\overset{+}{N}C_5H_5)=N\overset{-}{N}C_6H_4NO_2\text{-}o$	30
	3-Nitro	$C_6H_5COC(\overset{+}{N}C_5H_5)=N\overset{-}{N}C_6H_4NO_2\text{-}m$	30
	4-Nitro	$C_6H_5COC(\overset{+}{N}C_5H_5)=N\overset{-}{N}C_6H_4NO_2\text{-}p$	30
p-Bromophenacylpyridinium bromide	—	$p\text{-}BrC_6H_4COC(\overset{+}{N}C_5H_5)=N\overset{-}{N}C_6H_5$ (74)	184
5-*p*-Nitrophenacyl-3-*p*-tolyl-1,2,4-oxadiazole	—	1-(3-*p*-Tolyl-1,2,4-oxadiazol-5-yl)-3-*p*-nitrophenylethane-1,2-dione 1-phenylhydrazone (65)	32
	2-Methoxy	1-(3-*p*-Tolyl-1,2,4-oxadiazol-5-yl)-3-*p*-nitrophenylethane-1,2-dione 1-*o*-methoxyphenylhydrazone (20)	32
	4-Nitro	1-(3-*p*-Tolyl-1,2,4-oxadiazol-5-yl)-3-*p*-nitrophenylethane-1,2-dione 1-*p*-nitrophenylhydrazone (20)	32
Tropinone	—	2,4-Dioxotropinone diphenylhydrazone (80)	34
1-Ethoxalylindene	—	1-Phenylazo-1-ethoxalylindene	35
	3-Nitro	1-*m*-Nitrophenylazo-1-ethoxalylindene	35
	4-Nitro	1-*p*-Nitrophenylazo-1-ethoxalylindene	35

Note: References 177–480 are on pp. 136–142.

TABLE I—*Continued*

A. Monoketones—Continued

Ketone	Substituent(s) in Aniline	Product (Yield, %)	References
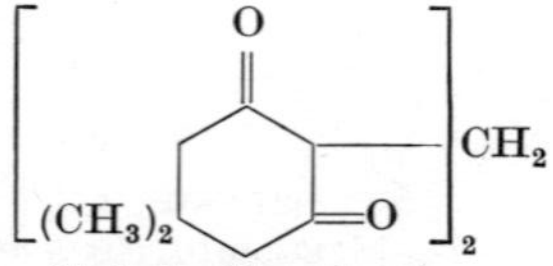 $[(CH_3)_2C_6H_5O_2]_2CH_2$ (Methylenebismethone)	—	2,2′-Methylenebis-(3-hydroxy-5,5-dimethyl-6-phenylazo-2-cyclohexen-1-one) (quant.)	186, 185
	2-Methyl	2,2′-Methylenebis-(3-hydroxy-5,5-dimethyl-6-*o*-tolylazo-2-cyclohexen-1-one)	185, 186
	2,3-Dimethyl	2,2′-Methylenebis-[3-hydroxy-5,5-dimethyl-6-(2,3-xylylazo)-2-cyclohexen-1-one]	185, 186
	2,5-Dimethyl	2,2′-Methylenebis-(3-hydroxy-5,5-dimethyl-6-*p*-xylylazo-2-cyclohexen-1-one)	185
	4-Bromo	2,2′-Methylenebis-(3-hydroxy-5,5-dimethyl-6-*p*-bromophenylazo-2-cyclohexen-1-one)	185, 186
	α-Naphthylamine	2,2′-Methylenebis-(3-hydroxy-5,5-dimethyl-6-α-naphthylazo-2-cyclohexen-1-one)	185, 186
	β-Naphthylamine	2,2′-Methylenebis-(3-hydroxy-5,5-dimethyl-6-β-naphthylazo-2-cyclohexen-1-one)	185, 186
	Benzidine	?	186
Ethyl 2-quinolylpyruvate	4-Bromo	N,N′-Di-(*p*-bromophenyl)-C-2-quinolylformazan (79)§	36*a*
Ethyl 2-quinoxalylpyruvate	4-Bromo	N,N′-Di-(*p*-bromophenyl)-C-2-quinoxalylformazan (78)	36*a*
Ethyl 2-quinazolylpyruvate	4-Bromo	N,N′-Di-(*p*-bromophenyl)-C-2-quinazolylformazan	36*a*
Ethyl 2-benzoxazolylpyruvate	4-Bromo	N.N′-Di-(*p*-bromophenyl)-C-2-benzoxazolylformazan (76)	36*a*

Ethyl 2-benzothiazolylpyruvate	4-Bromo	N,N′-Di-(*p*-bromophenyl)-C-2-benzothiazolylformazan (62)	36*a*
Ethyl 2-oxo-5-(2-benzoxazolyl)-4-pentenoate	4-Bromo	N,N′-Di-(*p*-bromophenyl)-C-[2-(2-benzoxazolyl)vinyl] formazan	36*a*
Ethyl 2-oxo-5-(2-benzothiazolyl)-4-pentenoate	4-Bromo	N,N′-Di-(*p*-bromophenyl)-C-[2-(2-benzothiazolyl)-vinyl]formazan (46)	36*a*

B. *β-Ketoaldehydes*

β-Ketoaldehyde	Substituent(s) in Aniline	Product (Yield, %)	References
β-Oxobutyraldehyde	—	$CH_3COC(CHO){=}NNHC_6H_5$	49
	4-Nitro	$CH_3COC(CHO){=}NNHC_6H_4NO_2$-*p* (17)	19*c*
β-Oxovaleraldehyde	—	$C_2H_5COC(CHO){=}NNHC_6H_5$	50
5-Methyl-3-oxo-4-hexenal	—	$(CH_3)_2C{=}CHCOC(CHO){=}NNHC_6H_5$	51
β-Oxo-β-phenylpropionaldehyde	—	$C_6H_5COC(CHO){=}NNHC_6H_5$	49
β-Oxo-β-*p*-tolylpropionaldehyde	—	*p*-$CH_3C_6H_4COC(CHO){=}NNHC_6H_5$	50
β-Oxo-β-*p*-anisylpropionaldehyde	—	*p*-$CH_3OC_6H_4COC(CHO){=}NNHC_6H_5$	50

C. *β-Diketones*

β-Diketone	Substituent(s) in Aniline*	Product (Yield, %)	References
Pentane-2,4-dione	—	$CH_3COC(COCH_3){=}NNHC_6H_5$	12, 187, 188
	4-Methyl	$CH_3COC(COCH_3){=}NNHC_6H_4CH_3$-*p* (92)	189
	4-Bromo	$CH_3COC(COCH_3){=}NNHC_6H_4Br$-*p*	190
	2,4-Dibromo	$CH_3COC(COCH_3){=}NNHC_6H_3Br_2$-2,4	190
	2,4,6-Tribromo	$CH_3COC(COCH_3){=}NNHC_6H_2Br_3$-2,4,6	190
	2-Nitro	$CH_3COC(COCH_3){=}NNHC_6H_4NO_2$-*o*	188, 190

Note: References 177–480 are on pp. 136–142.

* The full name is given when it is awkward to name the arylamine as a derivative of aniline.

§ These compounds are named as derivatives of the hypothetical formazan, $H_2NN{=}CHN{=}NH$.

TABLE I—*Continued*

C. β-Diketones—Continued

β-Diketone	Substituent(s) in Aniline*	Product (Yield, %)	References
Pentane-2,4-dione (*Cont.*)	3-Nitro	$CH_3COC(COCH_3){=}NNHC_6H_4NO_2$-*m*	188
	4-Nitro	$CH_3COC(COCH_3){=}NNHC_6H_4NO_2$-*p*	188, 190
	4-Methyl-3-nitro	$CH_3COC(COCH_3){=}NNHC_6H_3CH_3$-4-$NO_2$-3	189
	4-Bromo-2-nitro	$CH_3COC(COCH_3){=}NNHC_6H_3Br$-4-$NO_2$-2	190
	2,4-Dibromo-6-nitro	$CH_3COC(COCH_3){=}NNHC_6H_2Br_2$-2,4-$NO_2$-6	190
	Benzidine	3,3′-(4,4′-Biphenylenedihydrazono)bis(pentane-2,3,4-trione)	191, 192
	3,3′-Dimethylbenzidine	3,3′-(3,3′-Dimethyl-4,4′-biphenylenedihydrazono) bis(pentane-2,3,4-trione)	191, 192
	3,3′-Dimethoxybenzidine	3,3′-(3,3′-Dimethoxy-4,4′-biphenylenedihydrazono) bis(pentane-2,3,4-trione)	191, 192
	4-(3-Methyl-5-phenylpyrazol-1-yl)	Pentane-2,3,4-trione 3-arylhydrazone	193
	1-Phenyl-2,3-dimethyl-4-amino-5-isopyrazolone	Pentane-2,3,4-trione 3-arylhydrazone	194
	1-Phenyl-3,5-dimethyl-4-aminopyrazole	Pentane-2,3,4-trione 3-arylhydrazone	195
	3,5-Dimethyl-4-aminopyrazole	Pentane-2,3,4-trione 3-arylhydrazone	196
	5-Amino-3-isopropyl-1,2,4-triazole	Pentane-2,3,4-trione 3-arylhydrazone	197
Pentane-2,4-dione enol ethyl ether	4-Nitro	$CH_3COC(COCH_3){=}NNHC_6H_4NO_2$-*p*	198
1,5-Dichloropentane-2,4-dione	4-Nitro	$ClCH_2COC(COCH_2Cl){=}NNHC_6H_4NO_2$-*p*	199
Hexane-2,4-dione	4-Nitro	$CH_3COC(COC_2H_5){=}NNHC_6H_4NO_2$-*p*	199
Heptane-2,4-dione	—	$CH_3COC(COCH_2C_2H_5){=}NNHC_6H_5$	200

6-Methylheptane-2,4-dione	4-Nitro	$(CH_3)_2CHCH_2COC(COCH_3){=}NNHC_6H_4NO_2$-*p*	199
Heptane-3,5-dione	4-Chloro	$C_2H_5COC(COC_2H_5){=}NNHC_6H_4Cl$-*p*	199
Heptane-2,4,6-trione	—	$(C_6H_5NHN{=}CHCOCHN{=}NC_6H_5)_2CO$	201
	—	2,6-Dimethyl-3,5-diphenylazopyrone	202
Nonane-4,6-dione	4-Chloro	*n*-$C_3H_7COC(COC_3H_7$-*n*$){=}NNHC_6H_4Cl$-*p*	199
	4-Nitro	*n*-$C_3H_7COC(COC_3H_7$-*n*$){=}NNHC_6H_4NO_2$-*p*	199
1-Phenylbutane-1,3-dione	—	$C_6H_5COC(COCH_3){=}NNHC_6H_5$ (90)	42, 187
	—	$C_6H_5N{=}NC(COC_6H_5){=}NNHC_6H_5$‖ (25)	203, 204
	2-Nitro	$C_6H_5COC(COCH_3){=}NNHC_6H_4NO_2$-*o*	205
	4-Nitro	$C_6H_5COC(COCH_3){=}NNHC_6H_4NO_2$-*p* (quant.)	205, 206
	4-Acetamido	$C_6H_5COC(COCH_3){=}NNHC_6H_4NHCOCH_3$-*p*	207
	2,4-Dibromo	$C_6H_5COC(COCH_3){=}NNHC_6H_3Br_2$-2,4	42
	2,4,6-Tribromo	$C_6H_5COC(COCH_3){=}NNHC_6H_2Br_3$-2,4,6	42
	3,5-Dimethyl-4-aminopyrazole	1-Phenylbutane-1,2,3-trione 2-(3,5-dimethyl-4-pyrazolyl)hydrazone	196
1-*o*-Anisylbutane-1,3-dione	4-Nitro	*o*-$CH_3OC_6H_4COC(COCH_3){=}NNHC_6H_4NO_2$-*p*	208
1-(2,4-Dimethoxyphenyl)butane-1,3-dione	4-Nitro	2,4-$(CH_3O)_2C_6H_3COC(COCH_3){=}NNHC_6H_4NO_2$-*p*	208
1-(2,4-Diethoxyphenyl)butane-1,3-dione	—	2,4-$(C_2H_5O)_2C_6H_3COC(COCH_3){=}NNHC_6H_5$ (good)	210, 209
1-Phenylpentane-2,4-dione	4-Nitro	$C_6H_5CH_2COC(COCH_3){=}NNHC_6H_4NO_2$-*p*	199
2,8-Dimethylnonane-4,6-dione	4-Nitro	$[(CH_3)_2CHCH_2CO]_2C{=}NNHC_6H_4NO_2$-*p*	199
1-Phenylhexane-3,5-dione	4-Nitro	$C_6H_5CH_2CH_2COC(COCH_3){=}NNHC_6H_4NO_2$-*p* (70)	211
1,3-Diphenylpropane-1,3-dione	—	$(C_6H_5CO)_2C{=}NNHC_6H_5$	187
	4-Nitro	$(C_6H_5CO)_2C{=}NNHC_6H_4NO_2$-*p*	199
	4-Sulfo	$(C_6H_5CO)_2C{=}NNHC_6H_4SO_3H$-*p*	187
1,3-Di-*p*-nitrophenylpropane-1,3-dione	4-Nitro	(*p*-$O_2NC_6H_4CO)_2C{=}NNHC_6H_4NO_2$-*p*	199

Note: References 177–480 are on pp. 136–142.

* The full name is given when it is awkward to name the arylamine as a derivative of aniline.

‖ This product was obtained by the use of excess diazonium salt.

TABLE I—*Continued*

C. *β-Diketones—Continued*

β-Diketone	Substituent(s) in Aniline*	Product (Yield, %)	References
1-(3,5-Dimethoxyphenyl)-3-phenylpropane-1,3-dione	—	3,5-$(CH_3O)_2C_6H_3COC(COC_6H_5)$=$NNHC_6H_5$	212
1-(2,4,6-Trimethoxyphenyl)-3-phenylpropane-1,3-dione	—	2,4,6-$(CH_3O)_3C_6H_2COC(COC_6H_5)$=$NNHC_6H_5$	209
1-(2,4,6-Trimethoxyphenyl)-3-*p*-anisylpropane-1,3-dione	—	2,4,6-$(CH_3O)_3C_6H_2COC(COC_6H_4OCH_3$-*p*)=$NNHC_6H_5$	209
1-(2,4,6-Trimethoxyphenyl)-3-(2-ethoxyphenyl)propane-1,3-dione	—	2,4,6-$(CH_3O)_3C_6H_2COC(COC_6H_4OC_2H_5$-*p*)=$NNHC_6H_5$	209
1-(2,4,6-Trimethoxyphenyl)-3-(3-methoxy-4-ethoxyphenyl)-propane-1,3-dione	—	2,4,6-$(CH_3O)_3C_6H_2COC(COC_6H_3OCH_3$-3-$OC_2H_5$-4)=$NNHC_6H_5$	209
1,4-Diphenylbutane-1,3-dione	—	$C_6H_5CH_2COC(COC_6H_5)$=$NNHC_6H_5$ (quant.)	213
1,5-Diphenylpentane-2,4-dione	4-Nitro	$(C_6H_5CH_2CO)_2C$=$NNHC_6H_4NO_2$-*p*	199
1-(2-Hydroxy-1-naphthyl)-3-phenylpropane-1,3-dione	—	1-(2-Hydroxy-1-naphthyl)-3-phenylpropane-1,2,3-trione 2-phenylhydrazone (79)	214
α,γ-Dioxovaleric acid	—	$CH_3COC(COCO_2H)$=$NNHC_6H_5$	215
Ethyl α,γ-dioxovalerate	—	$CH_3COC(COCO_2C_2H_5)$=$NNHC_6H_5$ (96)	216, 187
	2-Methyl	$CH_3COC(COCO_2C_2H_5)$=$NNHC_6H_4CH_3$-*o* (78)	216
	4-Methyl	$CH_3COC(COCO_2C_2H_5)$=$NNHC_6H_4CH_3$-*p* (98)	216
	3-Chloro	$CH_3COC(COCO_2C_2H_5)$=$NNHC_6H_4Cl$-*m* (99)	216
	3-Bromo	$CH_3COC(COCO_2C_2H_5)$=$NNHC_6H_4Br$-*m* (99)	216
	2-Nitro	$CH_3COC(COCO_2C_2H_5)$=$NNHC_6H_4NO_2$-*o* (73)	216
	3-Nitro	$CH_3COC(COCO_2C_2H_5)$=$NNHC_6H_4NO_2$-*m* (90)	216
	4-Nitro	$CH_3COC(COCO_2C_2H_5)$=$NNHC_6H_4NO_2$-*p* (76)	216

Diethyl xanthochelidonate	—	Diethyl β,δ-diphenylazoxanthochelidonate¶	202
α,γ-Dioxo-γ-phenylbutyric acid	—	$C_6H_5COC(COCO_2H){=}NNHC_6H_5$	217
Ethyl α,γ-dioxo-γ-phenylbutyrate	—	$C_6H_5COC(COCO_2C_2H_5){=}NNHC_6H_5$	187, 217
	2-Carboxy	$C_6H_5COC(COCO_2C_2H_5){=}NNHC_6H_4CO_2H$-*o*	217
	Benzidine	β,β′-(4,4′-Biphenylenedihydrazono)bis(ethyl α,β,γ-trioxo-γ-phenylbutyrate)	217
Ethyl α,γ-dioxo-γ-(*p*-acetamidophenyl)butyrate	—	Ethyl α,β,γ-trioxo-γ-(*p*-acetamidophenyl)butyrate β-phenylhydrazone	218
Ethyl 2,4-dioxo-6-methyl-5-heptenoate	4-Nitro	Ethyl 2,3,4-trioxo-6-methyl-5-heptenoate 3-*p*-nitrophenylhydrazone	9
Ethyl α,γ-dioxo-γ-[*p*-(3,4-dicarbethoxy-2,5-dimethylpyrazol-1-yl)phenyl]butyrate	—	Ethyl α,β,γ-trioxo-γ-[*p*-(3,4-dicarbethoxy-2,5-dimethylpyrazol-1-yl)phenyl]butyrate β-phenylhydrazone	219
		D. Cyclic β-Diketones	
Cyclohexane-1,3-dione	4-Methyl	Cyclohexane-1,2,3-trione 2-*p*-tolylhydrazone	43
5,5-Dimethylcyclohexane-1,3-dione (methone)	—	5,5-Dimethylcyclohexane-1,2,3-trione 2-phenylhydrazone	44, 45
	2-Methyl	5,5-Dimethylcyclohexane-1,2,3-trione 2-*o*-tolylhydrazone	45
	3-Methyl	5,5-Dimethylcyclohexane-1,2,3-trione 2-*m*-tolylhydrazone	45
	4-Methyl	5,5-Dimethylcyclohexane-1,2,3-trione 2-*p*-tolylhydrazone	45
	4-Nitro	5,5-Dimethylcyclohexane-1,2,3-trione 2-*p*-nitrophenylhydrazone	46

Note: References 177–480 are on pp. 136–142.

* The full name is given when it is awkward to name the arylamine as a derivative of aniline.

¶ Other products were also isolated from the reaction mixture.

TABLE I—*Continued*

D. Cyclic β-Diketones—Continued

β-Diketone	Substituent(s) in Aniline*	Product (Yield, %)	References
5,5-Dimethylcyclohexane-1,3-dione (methone) (*Cont.*)	2-Arsono	5,5-Dimethylcyclohexane-1,2,3-trione 2-*o*-arsonophenylhydrazone	220
	3-Arsono	5,5-Dimethylcyclohexane-1,2,3-trione 2-*m*-arsonophenylhydrazone	220
	4-Arsono	5,5-Dimethylcyclohexane-1,2,3-trione 2-*p*-arsonophenylhydrazone	220
	α-Naphthylamine	5,5-Dimethylcyclohexane-1,2,3-trione 2-α-naphthylhydrazone	45
	β-Naphthylamine	5,5-Dimethylcyclohexane-1,2,3-trione 2-β-naphthylhydrazone	45
	Benzidine	2,2′-(4,4′-Biphenylenedihydrazono)bis-[5,5-dimethylcyclohexane-1,2,3-trione]	46
	3,3′-Dimethylbenzidine	2,2′-(3,3′-Dimethyl-4,4′-biphenylenedihydrazono)bis-[5,5-dimethylcyclohexane-1,2,3-trione]	46
	3,3′-Dimethoxybenzidine	2,2′-(3,3′-Dimethoxy-4,4′-biphenylenedihydrazono)bis-[5,5-dimethylcyclohexane-1,2,3-trione]	46
5-Phenylcyclohexane-1,3-dione	—	5-Phenylcyclohexane-1,2,3-trione 2-phenylhydrazone (quant.)	221

4-Cyano-5-phenylcyclohexane-1,3-dione	—	4-Cyano-5-phenylcyclohexane-1,2,3-trione 2-phenylhydrazone	43
4-Carbethoxy-5-phenylcyclohexane-1,3-dione	—	4-Carbethoxy-5-phenylcyclohexane-1,2,3-trione 2-phenylhydrazone	43
5-(2-Furyl)cyclohexane-1,3-dione	—	5-(2-Furyl)cyclohexane-1,2,3-trione 2-phenylhydrazone	221
Filicinic acid	—	6,6-Dimethylcyclohexane-1,2,3,4,5-pentaone 2,4-diphenylhydrazone	222
2-Butyryl-6,6-dimethylcyclohexane-1,3,5-trione	—	2-Butyryl-6,6-dimethylcyclohexane-1,3,4,5-tetraone 4-phenylhydrazone	222
2,2′-Methylenebis-(6,6-dimethylcyclohexane-1,3,5-trione)	—	2,2′-Methylenebis-(6,6-dimethylcyclohexane-1,3,4,5-tetraone 4-phenylhydrazone)	223
Indan-1,3-dione	—	Indan-1,2,3-trione 2-phenylhydrazone (35)	47
	4-Methyl	Indan-1,2,3-trione 2-*p*-tolylhydrazone	48
	4-Nitro	Indan-1,2,3-trione 2-*p*-nitrophenylhydrazone	48
	β-Naphthylamine	Indan-1,2,3-trione 2-β-naphthylhydrazone	48
	Benzidine	2,2′-(4,4′-Biphenylenedihydrazono)bis(indan-1,2,3-trione)	48
2,4-Dioxo-1,2,3,4,4*a*,9,10,10*a*-octahydrophenanthrene	—	2,3,4-Trioxo-1,2,3,4,4*a*,9,10,10*a*-octahydrophenanthrene 3-phenylhydrazone	224

Note: References 177–480 are on pp. 136–142.

* The full name is given when it is awkward to name the arylamine as a derivative of aniline.

TABLE I—*Continued*

E. 4-Hydroxycinnolines from o-Aminoketones

Reactant	Substituent(s) in 4-Hydroxycinnoline (Yield, %) 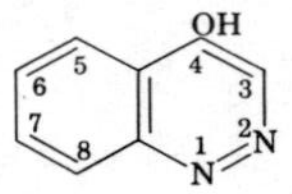	References
Acetophenone		
2-Amino	— (70–75)	37, 22, 39
2-Amino-4-methyl	7-Methyl (58)	164
2-Amino-3-methyl	8-Methyl (78)	164
2-Amino-6-methoxy	5-Methoxy (55)	224*a*
2-Amino-5-methoxy	6-Methoxy (53)	224*a*
2-Amino-4-methoxy	7-Methoxy (63)	224*a*
2-Amino-3-methoxy	8-Methoxy (92)	167*a*
2-Amino-5-chloro	6-Chloro (74)	22, 39
2-Amino-4-chloro	7-Chloro (90–95)	37, 39, 161
2-Amino-3-chloro	8-Chloro (69)	22
2-Amino-5-bromo	6-Bromo (95)	39, 22
2-Amino-3-bromo	8-Bromo (57)	22
2-Amino-5-iodo	6-Iodo	39
2-Amino-6-nitro	5-Nitro (70)	165
2-Amino-5-nitro	6-Nitro (87)	39, 22, 159
2-Amino-4-nitro	7-Nitro (76)	165, 166
2-Amino-3-nitro	8-Nitro (70)	163, 164
	8-Chloro** (45)	164
2-Amino-5-cyano	6-Cyano (70–90)	22
2-Amino-4-acetyl	7-Acetyl (47)	165
2-Amino-5-acetamido	6-Acetamido (33)	39
2-Amino-phenylazo	6-Phenylazo (60)	166
2-Amino-5-(3-acetylphenylazo)	6-(3-Acetylphenylazo) (50)	166

2-Amino-4,5-dimethyl	6,7-Dimethyl (91)	38
2-Amino-4,5-dimethoxy	6,7-Dimethoxy (67)	167*b*
2-Amino-4,5-dichloro	6,7-Dichloro (91)	162
2-Amino-3,4-dichloro	7,8-Dichloro (59)	162
2-Amino-3,5-dibromo	6,8-Dibromo (65)	39
2-Amino-5-chloro-4-methyl	6-Chloro-7-methyl (90)	162, 24
2-Amino-3-chloro-4-methyl	8-Chloro-7-methyl (75)	162
2-Amino-5-bromo-4-methyl	6-Bromo-7-methyl (37)	162
2-Amino-4-methyl-5-nitro	7-Methyl-6-nitro (76)	164
2-Amino-4-chloro-5-nitro	7-Chloro-6-nitro (57)	161
2-Amino-4-chloro-3-nitro	7-Chloro-8-nitro (57)	161
Phenacyl Chloride		
2-Amino	3-Chloro (85)	24
2-Amino-5-methyl	3-Chloro-6-methyl (87)	38
2-Amino-5-chloro	3,6-Dichloro (73)	24
2-Amino-4,5-dimethyl	3-Chloro-6,7-dimethyl (80)	38
Phenacyl Bromide		
2-Amino	3-Bromo (73)	24
2-Amino-5-chloro	3-Bromo-6-chloro (77)	24
2-Amino-5-bromo	3,6-Dibromo (76)	24
Propiophenone		
2-Amino	3-Methyl (83)	40, 39
2-Amino-5-chloro	6-Chloro-3-methyl (94)	40
2-Amino-5-bromo	6-Bromo-3-methyl (76)	39, 40
2-Amino-5-nitro	3-Methyl-6-nitro (65)	39, 40
2-Amino-3-nitro	3-Methyl-8-nitro (96)	40

Note: References 177–480 are on pp. 136–142.
** The 8-chloro compound is obtained if the diazotization is run in hydrochloric acid.

TABLE I—*Continued*

E. 4-Hydroxycinnolines from o-Aminoketones—Continued

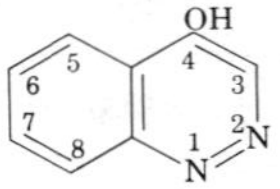

Reactant	Substituent in 4-Hydroxycinnoline (Yield, %)	References
Miscellaneous o-Aminoketones		
2-Aminobutyrophenone	3-Ethyl (68)	41
γ-(2-Aminobenzoyl)butyric acid	3-Carboxyethyl (53)	41
β-(2-Amino-4,5-dimethoxybenzoyl)propionic acid	3-Carboxymethyl-6,7-dimethoxy (71)	22
Ethyl β-(2-amino-4-carbethoxybenzoyl)propionate	3-Carbethoxymethyl-7-carbethoxy (13)	160
3,3′-Diacetyl-4,4′-diaminoazobenzene	4,4′-Dihydroxy-6,6′-azocinnoline (69)	166
5-Amino-6-acetylindane	6,7-Cyclopenteno (60)	38
4-Amino-5-acetylindane	7,8-Cyclopenteno	38
5-Amino-6-chloroacetylindane	3-Chloro-6,7-cyclopenteno (57)	38
1,2,3,4-Tetrahydro-6-amino-7-acetylnaphthalene	6,7-Cyclohexeno (70)	38
1,2,3,4-Tetrahydro-5-amino-6-acetylnaphthalene	7,8-Cyclohexeno	38
1,2,3,4-Tetrahydro-6-amino-7-chloroacetylnaphthalene	3-Chloro-6,7-cyclohexeno (67)	38

Note: References 177–480 are on pp. 136–142.

TABLE II

COUPLING OF DIAZONIUM SALTS WITH β-KETO ACIDS, ESTERS, AND AMIDES

A. β-Keto Acids

β-Keto Acid	Substituent(s) in Aniline*	Product (Yield, %)	References
Acetoacetic acid	—	$CH_3COCH{=}NNHC_6H_5$ (73–82)	55, 53, 54, 225
		$CH_3COC(N{=}NC_6H_5){=}NNHC_6H_5$† (41)	52, 226
		$C_6H_5C(N{=}NC_6H_5){=}NNHC_6H_5$‡	140
	4-Methyl	$CH_3COC(N{=}NC_6H_4CH_3\text{-}p){=}NNHC_6H_4CH_3\text{-}p$†	52
	2-Methoxy	$CH_3COCH{=}NNHC_6H_4OCH_3\text{-}o$	227
	2-Nitro	$CH_3COCH{=}NNHC_6H_4NO_2\text{-}o$	228, 229
	3-Nitro	$CH_3COCH{=}NNHC_6H_4NO_2\text{-}m$	228
	4-Nitro	$CH_3COCH{=}NNHC_6H_4NO_2\text{-}p$	228
	2,4-Dibromo	$CH_3COCH{=}NNHC_6H_3Br_2\text{-}2,4$	152
	2-Bromo-4-nitro	$CH_3COCH{=}NNHC_6H_3Br\text{-}2\text{-}NO_2\text{-}4$	228
	2,4,6-Trichloro	$CH_3COCH{=}NNHC_6H_2Cl_3\text{-}2,4,6$	230
	2,4,6-Tribromo	$CH_3COCH{=}NNHC_6H_2Br_3\text{-}2,4,6$	230
	2,6-Dibromo-4-nitro	$CH_3COCH{=}NNHC_6H_2Br_2\text{-}2,6\text{-}NO_2\text{-}4$	228
	α-Naphthylamine	$CH_3COCH{=}NNHC_{10}H_7\text{-}\alpha$	225
		$CH_3COC(N{=}NC_{10}H_7\text{-}\alpha){=}NNHC_{10}H_7\text{-}\alpha$†	52
Propionylacetic acid	4-Nitro	$C_2H_5COCH{=}NNHC_6H_4NO_2\text{-}p$	130*a*
α-Acetopropionic acid	—	$CH_3C(N{=}NC_6H_5){=}NNHC_6H_5$†	153
Tetronic acid	—	γ-Hydroxy-α,β-dioxobutyric acid lactone β-phenylhydrazone	231
Benzoylacetic acid	—	$C_6H_5COCH{=}NNHC_6H_5$	232
		$C_6H_5COC(N{=}NC_6H_5){=}NNHC_6H_5$† (39)	204, 203

Note: References 177–480 are on pp. 136–142.

* The full name is given when it is awkward to name the arylamine as a derivative of aniline.

† This product was obtained when 2 equivalents of the diazonium salt were used.

‡ This product was obtained when 3 equivalents of the diazonium salt were used.

TABLE II—*Continued*

A. *β-Keto Acids—Continued*

β-Keto Acid	Substituent(s) in Aniline*	Product (Yield, %)	References
Benzoylacetic acid (*Cont.*)	4-Methoxy	$C_6H_5COCH{=}NNHC_6H_4OCH_3$-*p*	130*a*
	4-Chloro	$C_6H_5COCH{=}NNHC_6H_4Cl$-*p*	130*a*
	2-Nitro	$C_6H_5COCH{=}NNHC_6H_4NO_2$-*o*	232
	3-Nitro	$C_6H_5COCH{=}NNHC_6H_4NO_2$-*m*	232
	4-Nitro	$C_6H_5COCH{=}NNHC_6H_4NO_2$-*p*	232, 130*a*
	4-Carboxy	$C_6H_5COCH{=}NNHC_6H_4CO_2H$-*p*	130*a*
o-Carboxybenzoylacetic acid	2-Hydroxy-5-chloro	*o*-$HO_2CC_6H_4COC(N{=}NC_6H_3OH$-2-Cl-5)$=NNHC_6H_3OH$-2-Cl-5	232*a*
Acetonedicarboxylic acid	—	$CO(CH{=}NNHC_6H_5)_2$ (39)	56
	4-Methyl	$CO(CH{=}NNHC_6H_4CH_3$-*p*$)_2$ (80)	57
	4-Chloro	$CO(CH{=}NNHC_6H_4Cl$-*p*$)_2$ (70)	57
2-Oxo-1-propanesulfonic acid	—	$CH_3COC(SO_3H){=}NNHC_6H_5$	58
	4-Chloro	$CH_3COC(SO_3H){=}NNHC_6H_4Cl$-*p*	58
	4-Bromo	$CH_3COC(SO_3H){=}NNHC_6H_4Br$-*p*	58
	2-Nitro	$CH_3COC(SO_3H){=}NNHC_6H_4NO_2$-*o*	58
	3-Nitro	$CH_3COC(SO_3H){=}NNHC_6H_4NO_2$-*m*	58
	4-Nitro	$CH_3COC(SO_3H){=}NNHC_6H_4NO_2$-*p*	58
	2,4-Dichloro	$CH_3COC(SO_3H){=}NNHC_6H_3Cl_2$-2,4	58
	2,4-Dibromo	$CH_3COC(SO_3H){=}NNHC_6H_3Br_2$-2,4	58
2-Oxo-2-phenyl-1-ethane-sulfonic acid	—	$C_6H_5COC(SO_3H){=}NNHC_6H_5$ (60)	59
	4-Chloro	$C_6H_5COC(SO_3H){=}NNHC_6H_4Cl$-*p*	59
	4-Bromo	$C_6H_5COC(SO_3H){=}NNHC_6H_4Br$-*p*	59
	2-Nitro	$C_6H_5COC(SO_3H){=}NNHC_6H_4NO_2$-*o*	59
	4-Nitro	$C_6H_5COC(SO_3H){=}NNHC_6H_4NO_2$-*p*	59
	2,4-Dichloro	$C_6H_5COC(SO_3H){=}NNHC_6H_3Cl_2$-2,4	59
	2,4-Dibromo	$C_6H_5COC(SO_3H){=}NNHC_6H_3Br_2$-2,4	59
	2,4,6-Trichloro	$C_6H_5COC(SO_3H){=}NNHC_6H_2Cl_3$-2,4,6	59

	2,4,6-Tribromo	$C_6H_5COC(SO_3H){=}NNHC_6H_2Br_3$-2,4,6	59
	4-Bromo-2-nitro	$C_6H_5COC(SO_3H){=}NNHC_6H_3Br$-4-$NO_2$-2	59

B. β-Keto Esters

β-Keto Ester	Substituent(s) in Aniline*	Product (Yield, %)	References
Ethyl formylacetate	—	$HCOC(CO_2C_2H_5){=}NNHC_6H_5$	233
Ethyl acetoacetate	—	$CH_3COC(CO_2C_2H_5){=}NNHC_6H_5$ (94–98)	236, 6, 7, 234, 235
		$C_6H_5N{=}NC(CO_2C_2H_5){=}NNHC_6H_5$† (80)	60, 140
	2-Methyl	$CH_3COC(CO_2C_2H_5){=}NNHC_6H_4CH_3$-*o* (80–90)	237, 238
	4-Methyl	$CH_3COC(CO_2C_2H_5){=}NNHC_6H_4CH_3$-*p* (95)	238, 7, 234, 237
	2-Chloro	$CH_3COC(CO_2C_2H_5){=}NNHC_6H_4Cl$-*o*	239
	3-Chloro	$CH_3COC(CO_2C_2H_5){=}NNHC_6H_4Cl$-*m* (78)	74*a*, 239
	4-Chloro	$CH_3COC(CO_2C_2H_5){=}NNHC_6H_4Cl$-*p*	239
	4-Chloro	*p*-$ClC_6H_4N{=}NC(CO_2C_2H_5){=}NNHC_6H_4Cl$-*p*†	239*a*
	2-Bromo	$CH_3COC(CO_2C_2H_5){=}NNHC_6H_4Br$-*o*	239
	2-Nitro	$CH_3COC(CO_2C_2H_5){=}NNHC_6H_4NO_2$-*o*	228, 229, 239
	3-Nitro	$CH_3COC(CO_2C_2H_5){=}NNHC_6H_4NO_2$-*m*	228
		m-$O_2NC_6H_4N{=}NC(CO_2C_2H_5){=}NNHC_6H_4NO_2$-*m*†	240
	4-Nitro	$CH_3COC(CO_2C_2H_5){=}NNHC_6H_4NO_2$-*p* (quant.)	241, 228, 239
	4-Ethoxy	*p*-$C_2H_5OC_6H_4N{=}NC(CO_2C_2H_5){=}NNHC_6H_4OC_2H_5$-*p* (57)†	240
	2-Carboxy	$CH_3COC(CO_2C_2H_5){=}NNHC_6H_4CO_2H$-*o* (90)	237
	3-Carboxy	$CH_3COC(CO_2C_2H_5){=}NNHC_6H_4CO_2H$-*m*	242
	4-Acetamido	$CH_3COC(CO_2C_2H_5){=}NNHC_6H_4NHCOCH_3$-*p*	243

Note: References 177–480 are on pp. 136–142.

* The full name is given when it is awkward to name the arylamine as a derivative of aniline.

† This product was obtained when 2 equivalents of the diazonium salt were used.

TABLE II—*Continued*

B. β-Keto Esters—Continued

β-Keto Ester	Substituent(s) in Aniline*	Product (Yield, %)	References
Ethyl acetoacetate (*Cont.*)	4-Sulfamyl	$CH_3COC(CO_2C_2H_5){=}NNHC_6H_4SO_2NH_2$-*p*	244
	2,4-Dimethyl	$CH_3COC(CO_2C_2H_5){=}NNHC_6H_3(CH_3)_2$-2,4 (75)	237
	2,4-Dichloro	$CH_3COC(CO_2C_2H_5){=}NNHC_6H_3Cl_2$-2,4 (85)	235
	3,5-Dichloro	$CH_3COC(CO_2C_2H_5){=}NNHC_6H_3Cl_2$-3,5	245
	3,5-Dibromo	$CH_3COC(CO_2C_2H_5){=}NNHC_6H_3Br_2$-3,5	245
	2,4,6-Trichloro	$CH_3COC(CO_2C_2H_5){=}NNHC_6H_2Cl_3$-2,4,6 (quant.)	230, 246
	2,4,6-Tribromo	$CH_3COC(CO_2C_2H_5){=}NNHC_6H_2Br_3$-2,4,6 (quant.)	230, 239
	3,4,5-Tribromo	$CH_3COC(CO_2C_2H_5){=}NNHC_6H_2Br_3$-3,4,5	245
	2-Methyl-4-nitro	$CH_3COC(CO_2C_2H_5){=}NNHC_6H_3CH_3$-2-$NO_2$-4	247
	2-Methyl-5-nitro	$CH_3COC(CO_2C_2H_5){=}NNHC_6H_3CH_3$-2-$NO_2$-5	247
	2-Methyl-6-nitro	$CH_3COC(CO_2C_2H_5){=}NNHC_6H_3CH_3$-2-$NO_2$-6	247
	4-Methyl-2-nitro	$CH_3COC(CO_2C_2H_5){=}NNHC_6H_3CH_3$-4-$NO_2$-2 (90)	247, 229
	4-Methyl-3-nitro	$CH_3COC(CO_2C_2H_5){=}NNHC_6H_3CH_3$-4-$NO_2$-3	247
	2-Chloro-4-nitro	$CH_3COC(CO_2C_2H_5){=}NNHC_6H_3Cl$-2-$NO_2$-4	248
	4-Chloro-2-nitro	$CH_3COC(CO_2C_2H_5){=}NNHC_6H_3Cl$-4-$NO_2$-2	248
	2-Bromo-4-nitro	$CH_3COC(CO_2C_2H_5){=}NNHC_6H_3Br$-2-$NO_2$-4	228
	3,5-Dichloro-4-bromo	Ethyl α,β-dioxobutyrate α-(3,5-dichloro-4-bromophenylhydrazone)	245
	2,6-Dichloro-4-nitro	Ethyl α,β-dioxobutyrate α-(2,6-dichloro-4-nitrophenylhydrazone)	248
	2,6-Dibromo-4-nitro	Ethyl α,β-dioxobutyrate α-(2,6-dibromo-4-nitrophenylhydrazone)	228
	2-Bromo-4-methyl-5-nitro	Ethyl α,β-dioxobutyrate α-(2-bromo-4-methyl-5-nitrophenylhydrazone)	247
	2-Bromo-4-methyl-6-nitro	Ethyl α,β-dioxobutyrate α-(2-bromo-4-methyl-6-nitrophenylhydrazone)	247

2-Bromo-6-methyl-4-nitro	Ethyl α,β-dioxobutyrate α-(2-bromo-6-methyl-4-nitrophenylhydrazone)	247
4-Bromo-2-methyl-6-nitro	Ethyl α,β-dioxobutyrate α-(4-bromo-2-methyl-6-nitrophenylhydrazone)	247
2,6-Dibromo-3-nitro-4-methyl	Ethyl α,β-dioxobutyrate α-(2,6-dibromo-3-nitro-4-methylphenylhydrazone)	247
4,6-Dibromo-2-methyl-5-nitro	Ethyl α,β-dioxobutyrate α-(4,6-dibromo-2-methyl-5-nitrophenylhydrazone)	247
α-Naphthylamine	Ethyl α,β-dioxobutyrate α-(α-naphthylhydrazone) (quant.)	249, 237
β-Naphthylamine	Ethyl α,β-dioxobutyrate α-(β-naphthylhydrazone)	237, 249
2-Aminoanthraquinone	Ethyl α,β-dioxobutyrate α-(2-anthraquinonylhydrazone) (quant.)	250
3-Aminocarbazole	Ethyl α,β-dioxobutyrate α-(3-carbazolylhydrazone)	251
N-Ethyl-3-aminocarbazole	Ethyl α,β-dioxobutyrate α-(N-ethyl-3-carbazolylhydrazone)	251
p-(3-Carboxy-4-hydroxyphenylazo)	Ethyl α,β-dioxobutyrate α-arylhydrazone	252
p-(*p*-Dimethylsulfamylphenylsulfamyl)	Ethyl α,β-dioxobutyrate α-[*p*-(*p*-dimethylsulfamylphenylsulfamyl)phenylhydrazone]	244
3,5-Dimethyl-4-aminopyrazole	Ethyl α,β-dioxobutyrate α-(3,5-dimethyl-4-pyrazolylhydrazone)	196
1-Phenyl-3,5-dimethyl-4-aminopyrazole	Ethyl α,β-dioxobutyrate α-(1-phenyl-3,5-dimethyl-4-pyrazolylhydrazone)	195
p-(3,4-Dicarbomethoxy-5-methyl-1-pyrazolyl)	Ethyl α,β-dioxobutyrate α-arylhydrazone	253

Note: References 177–480 are on pp. 136–142.

* The full name is given when it is awkward to name the arylamine as a derivative of aniline.

TABLE II—*Continued*

B. *β-Keto Esters—Continued*

β-Keto Ester	Substituent(s) in Aniline*	Product (Yield, %)	References
Ethyl acetoacetate (*Cont.*)	3-Amino-5-isopropyl-1,2,4-triazole	Ethyl α,β-dioxobutyrate α-(5-isopropyl-1,2,4-triazol-3-yl-) hydrazone	197
	Benzidine	α,α′-(4,4′-Biphenylenedihydrazono)bis(ethyl α,β-dioxobutyrate) (98)	254, 255
	3,3′-Dicarboxybenzidine	α,α′-(3,3′-Dicarboxy-4,4′-biphenylenedihydrazono)bis(ethyl α,β-dioxobutyrate)	256
l-Menthyl acetoacetate	—	$CH_3COC(CO_2C_{10}H_{19}\text{-}l){=}NNHC_6H_5$	146
	4-Methyl	$CH_3COC(CO_2C_{10}H_{19}\text{-}l){=}NNHC_6H_4CH_3\text{-}p$	146
		$p\text{-}CH_3C_6H_4N{=}NC(CO_2C_{10}H_{19}\text{-}l){=}NNHC_6H_4CH_3\text{-}p$†	146
	4-Chloro	$CH_3COC(CO_2C_{10}H_{19}\text{-}l){=}NNHC_6H_4Cl\text{-}p$	146
	4-Bromo	$CH_3COC(CO_2C_{10}H_{19}\text{-}l){=}NNHC_6H_4Br\text{-}p$	146
Methyl γ-chloroacetoacetate	—	$ClCH_2COC(CO_2CH_3){=}NNHC_6H_5$	257
	2-Methyl	$ClCH_2COC(CO_2CH_3){=}NNHC_6H_4CH_3\text{-}o$	257
	4-Methyl	$ClCH_2COC(CO_2CH_3){=}NNHC_6H_4CH_3\text{-}p$	257
Ethyl γ-chloroacetoacetate	—	$ClCH_2COC(CO_2C_2H_5){=}NNHC_6H_5$	152, 257
	2-Methyl	$ClCH_2COC(CO_2C_2H_5){=}NNHC_6H_4CH_3\text{-}o$	257
	4-Methyl	$ClCH_2COC(CO_2C_2H_5){=}NNHC_6H_4CH_3\text{-}p$	257
	4-Chloro	$ClCH_2COC(CO_2C_2H_5){=}NNHC_6H_4Cl\text{-}p$	152
	4-Nitro	$ClCH_2COC(CO_2C_2H_5){=}NNHC_6H_4NO_2\text{-}p$	248
	2,4-Dichloro	$ClCH_2COC(CO_2C_2H_5){=}NNHC_6H_3Cl_2\text{-}2,4$	152
	2,4,6-Trichloro	$ClCH_2COC(CO_2C_2H_5){=}NNHC_6H_2Cl_3\text{-}2,4,6$	230
	2,4,6-Tribromo	$ClCH_2COC(CO_2C_2H_5){=}NNHC_6H_2Br_3\text{-}2,4,6$	230
	2-Chloro-4-nitro	$ClCH_2COC(CO_2C_2H_5){=}NNHC_6H_3Cl\text{-}2\text{-}NO_2\text{-}4$	248
	2,6-Dichloro-4-nitro	$ClCH_2COC(CO_2C_2H_5){=}NNHC_6H_2Cl_2\text{-}2,6\text{-}NO_2\text{-}4$	248

Methyl γ-bromoacetoacetate	—	$BrCH_2COC(CO_2CH_3){=}NNHC_6H_5$	258
	2-Methyl	$BrCH_2COC(CO_2CH_3){=}NNHC_6H_4CH_3\text{-}o$	258
	4-Methyl	$BrCH_2COC(CO_2CH_3){=}NNHC_6H_4CH_3\text{-}p$	258
Ethyl γ-bromoacetoacetate	—	$BrCH_2COC(CO_2C_2H_5){=}NNHC_6H_5$ (good)	259, 230, 258
	2-Methyl	$BrCH_2COC(CO_2C_2H_5){=}NNHC_6H_4CH_3\text{-}o$	258
	4-Methyl	$BrCH_2COC(CO_2C_2H_5){=}NNHC_6H_4CH_3\text{-}p$	258
	4-Bromo	$BrCH_2COC(CO_2C_2H_5){=}NNHC_6H_4Br\text{-}p$	152
	2-Nitro	$BrCH_2COC(CO_2C_2H_5){=}NNHC_6H_4NO_2\text{-}o$	228
	3-Nitro	$BrCH_2COC(CO_2C_2H_5){=}NNHC_6H_4NO_2\text{-}m$	228
	4-Nitro	$BrCH_2COC(CO_2C_2H_5){=}NNHC_6H_4NO_2\text{-}p$	228
	2,4-Dibromo	$BrCH_2COC(CO_2C_2H_5){=}NNHC_6H_3Br_2\text{-}2,4$	152
	2,4,6-Trichloro	$BrCH_2COC(CO_2C_2H_5){=}NNHC_6H_2Cl_3\text{-}2,4,6$	230
	2,4,6-Tribromo	$BrCH_2COC(CO_2C_2H_5){=}NNHC_6H_2Br_3\text{-}2,4,6$ (80)	230
	2-Bromo-4-nitro	$BrCH_2COC(CO_2C_2H_5){=}NNHC_6H_3Br\text{-}2\text{-}NO_2\text{-}4$	228
	2,6-Dibromo-4-nitro	$BrCH_2COC(CO_2C_2H_5){=}NNHC_6H_2Br_2\text{-}2,6\text{-}NO_2\text{-}4$	228
Ethyl 3-oxohexanoate	—	$n\text{-}C_3H_7COC(CO_2C_2H_5){=}NNHC_6H_5$	260
	4-Nitro	$n\text{-}C_3H_7COC(CO_2C_2H_5){=}NNHC_6H_4NO_2\text{-}p$	260
Ethyl 3-oxononanoate	—	$n\text{-}C_6C_{13}COC(CO_2C_2H_5){=}NNHC_6H_5$	260
Methyl benzoylacetate	—	$C_6H_5COC(CO_2CH_3){=}NNHC_6H_5$	261, 262
	4-Nitro	$C_6H_5COC(CO_2CH_3){=}NNHC_6H_4NO_2\text{-}p$	261, 262
Ethyl benzoylacetate	—	$C_6H_5COC(CO_2C_2H_5){=}NNHC_6H_5$ (70)	265, 140, 263, 264
	4-Methyl	$C_6H_5COC(CO_2C_2H_5){=}NNHC_6H_4CH_3\text{-}p$	264
	2-Nitro	$C_6H_5COC(CO_2C_2H_5){=}NNHC_6H_4NO_2\text{-}o$	263, 266
	3-Nitro	$C_6H_5COC(CO_2C_2H_5){=}NNHC_6H_4NO_2\text{-}m$	266
	4-Nitro	$C_6H_5COC(CO_2C_2H_5){=}NNHC_6H_4NO_2\text{-}p$	264
	4-Acetamido	$C_6H_5COC(CO_2C_2H_5){=}NNHC_6H_4NHCOCH_3\text{-}p$	267
	4-Methyl-2-nitro	$C_6H_5COC(CO_2C_2H_5){=}NNHC_6H_3CH_3\text{-}4\text{-}NO_2\text{-}2$	263

Note: References 177–480 are on pp. 136–142.

* The full name is given when it is awkward to name the arylamine as a derivative of aniline.

† This product was obtained when 2 equivalents of the diazonium salt were used.

TABLE II—*Continued*

B. β-Keto Esters—Continued

β-Keto Ester	Substituent(s) in Aniline*	Product (Yield, %)	References
Methyl *o*-methoxybenzoylacetate	—	*o*-$CH_3OC_6H_4COC(CO_2CH_3)$=$NNHC_6H_5$	268
	4-Nitro	*o*-$CH_3OC_6H_4COC(CO_2CH_3)$=$NNHC_6H_4NO_2$-*p*	268
Methyl *m*-methoxybenzoylacetate	—	*m*-$CH_3OC_6H_4COC(CO_2CH_3)$=$NNHC_6H_5$	268
	4-Nitro	*m*-$CH_3OC_6H_4COC(CO_2CH_3)$=$NNHC_6H_4NO_2$-*p*	268
Methyl *p*-methoxybenzoylacetate	—	*p*-$CH_3OC_6H_4COC(CO_2CH_3)$=$NNHC_6H_5$	268
	4-Nitro	*p*-$CH_3OC_6H_4COC(CO_2CH_3)$=$NNHC_6H_4NO_2$-*p*	268
Methyl *o*-chlorobenzoylacetate	—	*o*-$ClC_6H_4COC(CO_2CH_3)$=$NNHC_6H_5$	269
	4-Nitro	*o*-$ClC_6H_4COC(CO_2CH_3)$=$NNHC_6H_4NO_2$-*p*	269
Methyl *m*-chlorobenzoylacetate	—	*m*-$ClC_6H_4COC(CO_2CH_3)$=$NNHC_6H_5$	269
	4-Nitro	*m*-$ClC_6H_4COC(CO_2CH_3)$=$NNHC_6H_4NO_2$-*p*	269
Methyl *p*-chlorobenzoylacetate	—	*p*-$ClC_6H_4COC(CO_2CH_3)$=$NNHC_6H_5$	269
	4-Nitro	*p*-$ClC_6H_4COC(CO_2CH_3)$=$NNHC_6H_4NO_2$-*p*	269
Dimethyl oxalacetate	—	$CH_3O_2CCOC(CO_2CH_3)$=$NNHC_6H_5$ (40)	62
	Benzidine	[$CH_3O_2CCOC(CO_2CH_3)$=$NNHC_6H_4$—$]_2$ (65)	270
Diethyl oxalacetate	—	$C_2H_5O_2CCOC(CO_2C_2H_5)$=$NNHC_6H_5$ (75)	62, 61
		C_6H_5N=$NC(CO_2C_2H_5)$=$NNHC_6H_5$† (76)	63, 61
	2-Methyl	$C_2H_5O_2CCOC(CO_2C_2H_5)$=$NNHC_6H_4CH_3$-*o*	62, 271
		o-$CH_3C_6H_4N$=$NC(CO_2C_2H_5)$=$NNHC_6H_4CH_3$-*o*† (81)	63
	4-Bromo	$C_2H_5O_2CCOC(CO_2C_2H_5)$=$NNHC_6H_4Br$-*p* (62)	66
		p-BrC_6H_4N=$NC(CO_2C_2H_5)$=$NNHC_6H_4Br$-*p*† (41)	66
	2,4-Dibromo	$C_2H_5O_2CCOC(CO_2C_2H_5)$=$NNHC_6H_3Br_2$-2,4	272

	Benzidine	4,4′-Biphenylenedihydrazonobis(diethyl dioxosuccinate) (76)	270, 273
	3,3′-Dimethylbenzidine	3,3′-Dimethyl-4,4′-biphenylenedihydrazonobis(diethyl dioxosuccinate) (60)	273, 270
	3,3′-Dimethoxybenzidine	3,3′-Dimethoxy-4,4′-biphenylenedihydrazonobis(diethyl dioxosuccinate) (55–60)	273, 270
Diethyl acetonedicarboxylate	—	$C_2H_5O_2CCH_2COC(CO_2C_2H_5){=}NNHC_6H_5$ (86)	65, 274
	2-Methyl	$C_2H_5O_2CCH_2COC(CO_2C_2H_5){=}NNHC_6H_4CH_3$-*o* (94)	65
	4-Methyl	$C_2H_5O_2CCH_2COC(CO_2C_2H_5){=}NNHC_6H_4CH_3$-*p* (90)	65
	4-Nitro	$C_2H_5O_2CCH_2COC(CO_2C_2H_5){=}NNHC_6H_4NO_2$-*p*	64
	2-Carboxy	$C_2H_5O_2CCH_2COC(CO_2C_2H_5){=}NNHC_6H_4CO_2H$-*o* (70)	65
	2,4-Dimethyl	$C_2H_5O_2CCH_2COC(CO_2C_2H_5){=}NNHC_6H_3(CH_3)_2$-2,4	65
	4-(*p*-Phenylmercaptobenzoyl)	Diethyl α,β-dioxoglutarate α-[*p*-(*p*-phenylmercaptobenzoyl)-phenylhydrazone] (27)	13
	4-(3,4-Dicarbethoxy-5-methyl-1-pyrazolyl)	Diethyl α,β-dioxoglutarate α-[*p*-(3,4-dicarbethoxy-5-methyl-1-pyrazolyl)phenylhydrazone]	253
Diethyl α,α-diethyl-β-oxoglutarate	—	Diethyl α,α-diethyl-β,γ-dioxoglutarate γ-phenylhydrazone	274
5-Hydroxy-3-oxo-4-hexenoic acid lactone	—	5-Hydroxy-3-oxo-2-phenylhydrazono-4-hexenoic acid lactone (60)	275
Diethyl 5-oxo-2-hexendioate	—	$C_6H_5N{=}NC(CH{=}CHCO_2C_2H_5){=}NNHC_6H_5$§ (18)	66
	4-Bromo	$C_2H_5O_2CCOC(CH{=}CHCO_2C_2H_5){=}NNHC_6H_4Br$-*p*‖ (65)	66
		p-$BrC_6H_4N{=}NC(CH{=}CHCO_2C_2H_5){=}NNHC_6H_4Br$-*p*§	66
		p-$BrC_6H_4N{=}NC(CO_2C_2H_5){=}CHC(COCO_2C_2H_5){=}NNHC_6H_4Br$-*p*	66
	4-Ethoxy	$C_2H_5O_2CCOC(CH{=}CHCO_2C_2H_5){=}NNHC_6H_4OC_2H_5$-*p*¶ (36–43)	66

Note: References 177–480 are on pp. 136–142.

* The full name is given when it is awkward to name the arylamine as a derivative of aniline.

† This product was obtained when 2 equivalents of diazonium salt were used.

§ This product was obtained by coupling in the presence of ammonia.

‖ This product was obtained by coupling in alcoholic hydrochloric acid.

¶ This product was obtained by coupling in the presence of sodium carbonate.

TABLE II—*Continued*

B. β-Keto Esters—Continued

β-Keto Ester	Substituent(s) in Aniline*	Product (Yield, %)	References
Oxaldihydrazonobis(ethyl acetoacetate)	—	β,β′-Oxaldihydrazonobis(ethyl α,β-dioxobutyrate) α,α′-diphenylhydrazone**	278
Malondihydrazonobis(ethyl acetoacetate)	—	β,β′-Mesoxaldihydrazonobis(ethyl α,β-dioxobutyrate) α,α′,α″-triphenylhydrazone (72)	280, 279
	4-Methyl	β,β′-Mesoxaldihydrazonobis(ethyl α,β-dioxobutyrate) α,α′,α″-tri-*p*-tolylhydrazone (50)	280

C. β-Keto Amides

β-Keto Amide	Substituent(s) in Aniline*	Product (Yield, %)	References
Acetoacetanilide	—	$CH_3COC(CONHC_6H_5){=}NNHC_6H_5$	281, 282
	2-Methyl	$CH_3COC(CONHC_6H_5){=}NNHC_6H_4CH_3\text{-}o$	283
	4-Methyl	$CH_3COC(CONHC_6H_5){=}NNHC_6H_4CH_3\text{-}p$	283
	2-Methoxy	$CH_3COC(CONHC_6H_5){=}NNHC_6H_4OCH_3\text{-}o$	283
	4-Methoxy	$CH_3COC(CONHC_6H_5){=}NNHC_6H_4OCH_3\text{-}p$	283
	4-Ethoxy	$CH_3COC(CONHC_6H_5){=}NNHC_6H_4OC_2H_5\text{-}p$	283
	3-Chloro	$CH_3COC(CONHC_6H_5){=}NNHC_6H_4Cl\text{-}m$	283
	4-Chloro	$CH_3COC(CONHC_6H_5){=}NNHC_6H_4Cl\text{-}p$	283
	4-Bromo	$CH_3COC(CONHC_6H_5){=}NNHC_6H_4Br\text{-}p$	283
	2-Nitro	$CH_3COC(CONHC_6H_5){=}NNHC_6H_4NO_2\text{-}o$	67, 68
	4-Methyl-2-nitro	$CH_3COC(CONHC_6H_5){=}NNHC_6H_3CH_3\text{-}4\text{-}NO_2\text{-}2$	67, 69
	4-Chloro-2-nitro	$CH_3COC(CONHC_6H_5){=}NNHC_6H_3Cl\text{-}4\text{-}NO_2\text{-}2$	67, 68
	2,4,6-Trimethyl-3-nitro	$CH_3COC(CONHC_6H_5){=}NNHC_6H(CH_3)_3\text{-}2,4,6\text{-}NO_2\text{-}3$	284
	α-Naphthylamine	$CH_3COC(CONHC_6H_5){=}NNHC_{10}H_7\text{-}\alpha$	283

	β-Naphthylamine	$CH_3COC(CONHC_6H_5){=}NNHC_{10}H_7$-β	283
	Anhydrotris-*o*-aminobenzaldehyde	$CH_3COC(CONHC_6H_5){=}NNHC_6H_4CHO$-*o*	285
	4-(3,4-Dicarbethoxy-2,5-dimethyl-pyrrolyl)	α,β-Dioxobutyranilide α-arylhydrazone	286
	4-(3,4-Dicarbethoxy-5-methyl-1-pyrazolyl)	α,β-Dioxobutyranilide α-arylhydrazone	253
	Benzidine	α,α′-(4,4′-Biphenylenedihydrazono)bis-(α,β-dioxobutyranilide)	287
o-Acetoacetotoluide	—	$CH_3COC(CONHC_6H_4CH_3\text{-}o){=}NNHC_6H_5$	282
	Benzidine	$[CH_3COC(CONHC_6H_4CH_3\text{-}o){=}NNHC_6H_4{-}]_2$	287
p-Acetoacetotoluide	—	$CH_3COC(COHNC_6H_4CH_3\text{-}p){=}NNHC_6H_5$	282
	Benzidine	$[CH_3COC(CONHC_6H_4CH_3\text{-}p){=}NNHC_6H_4{-}]_2$	287
o-Acetoacetaniside	—	$CH_3COC(CONHC_6H_4OCH_3\text{-}o){=}NNHC_6H_5$	282
	Benzidine	$[CH_3COC(CONHC_6H_4OCH_3\text{-}o){=}NNHC_6H_4{-}]_2$	287
p-Acetoacetaniside	—	$CH_3COC(CONHC_6H_4OCH_3\text{-}p){=}NNHC_6H_5$	282
	Benzidine	$[CH_3COC(CONHC_6H_4OCH_3\text{-}p){=}NNHC_6H_4{-}]_2$	287
p-Ethoxyacetoacetanilide	—	$CH_3COC(CONHC_6H_4OC_2H_5\text{-}p){=}NNHC_6H_5$	282
	p-(3,4-Dicarbethoxy-2,5-dimethyl-pyrrolyl)	*p*-Ethoxy-α,β-dioxobutyranilide α-arylhydrazone	286
	Benzidine	$[CH_3COC(CONHC_6H_4OC_2H_5\text{-}p){=}NNHC_6H_4{-}]_2$	287
o-Chloroacetoacetanilide	4-Chloro-2-nitro	$CH_3COC(CONHC_6H_4Cl\text{-}o){=}NNHC_6H_3Cl\text{-}4\text{-}NO_2\text{-}2$	67, 68
m-Chloroacetoacetanilide	—	$CH_3COC(CONHC_6H_4Cl\text{-}m){=}NNHC_6H_5$	282
	Benzidine	$[CH_3COC(CONHC_6H_4Cl\text{-}m){=}NNHC_6H_4{-}]_2$	287

Note: References 177–480 are on pp. 136–142.

* The full name is given when it is awkward to name the arylamine as a derivative of aniline.

** Some monophenylhydrazone was isolated.

TABLE II—*Continued*

C. *β-Keto Amides—Continued*

β-Keto Amide	Substituent(s) in Aniline*	Product (Yield, %)	References
p-Chloroacetoacetanilide	—	$CH_3COC(CONHC_6H_4Cl\text{-}p){=}NNHC_6H_5$	282
	Benzidine	$[CH_3COC(CONHC_6H_4Cl\text{-}p){=}NNHC_6H_4{-}]_2$	287
p-Bromoacetoacetanilide	—	$CH_3COC(CONHC_6H_4Br\text{-}p){=}NNHC_6H_5$	282
	Benzidine	$[CH_3COC(CONHC_6H_4Br\text{-}p){=}NNHC_6H_4{-}]_2$	287
p-Sulfamylacetoacetanilide	2-Nitro	$CH_3COC(CONHC_6H_4SO_2NH_2\text{-}p){=}NNHC_6H_4NO_2\text{-}o$	288
	3-Nitro	$CH_3COC(CONHC_6H_4SO_2NH_2\text{-}p){=}NNHC_6H_4NO_2\text{-}m$	288
	4-Nitro	$CH_3COC(CONHC_6H_4SO_2NH_2\text{-}p){=}NNHC_6H_4NO_2\text{-}p$	288
N-(α-Naphthyl)acetoacetamide	—	$CH_3COC(CONHC_{10}H_7\text{-}\alpha){=}NNHC_6H_5$	282
	Benzidine	$[CH_3COC(CONHC_{10}H_7\text{-}\alpha){=}NNHC_6H_4{-}]_2$	285
N-(β-Naphthyl)acetoacetamide	—	$CH_3COC(CONHC_{10}H_7\text{-}\beta){=}NNHC_6H_5$	282
	Benzidine	$[CH_3COC(CONHC_{10}H_7\text{-}\beta){=}NNHC_6H_4{-}]_2$	285
N,N-Diphenylacetoacetamide	2-Nitro	$(C_6H_5)_2NCOC(COCH_3){=}NNHC_6H_4NO_2\text{-}o$ (80–90)	288
	3-Nitro	$(C_6H_5)_2NCOC(COCH_3){=}NNHC_6H_4NO_2\text{-}m$ (80–90)	288
	4-Nitro	$(C_6H_5)_2NCOC(COCH_3){=}NNHC_6H_4NO_2\text{-}p$ (80–90)	288
N-Sulfoacetoacetamide	4-Nitro	$CH_3COC(CONHSO_3H){=}NNHC_6H_4NO_2\text{-}p$	289
N-Sulfamylacetoacetamide	4-Nitro	$CH_3COC(CONHSO_2NH_2){=}NNHC_6H_4NO_2\text{-}p$	289
Acetoacetanilide phenylhydrazone	—	$CH_3C({=}NNHC_6H_5)C({=}NNHC_6H_5)CONHC_6H_5$	281
Benzoylacetanilide	—	$C_6H_5COC(CONHC_6H_5){=}NNHC_6H_5$	282
	4-Methyl	$C_6H_5COC(CONHC_6H_5){=}NNHC_6H_4CH_3\text{-}p$	283
	4-Methoxy	$C_6H_5COC(CONHC_6H_5){=}NNHC_6H_4OCH_3\text{-}p$	283
	4-Ethoxy	$C_6H_5COC(CONHC_6H_5){=}NNHC_6H_4OC_2H_5\text{-}p$	283
	4-Chloro	$C_6H_5COC(CONHC_6H_5){=}NNHC_6H_4Cl\text{-}p$	283
	Benzidine	$[C_6H_5COC(CONHC_6H_5){=}NNHC_6H_4{-}]_2$	287

p-Benzoylacetotoluide	—	$C_6H_5COC(CONHC_6H_4CH_3\text{-}p){=}NNHC_6H_5$	282
	Benzidine	$[C_6H_5COC(CONHC_6H_4CH_3\text{-}p){=}NNHC_6H_4{-}]_2$	287
p-Benzoylacetaniside	—	$C_6H_5COC(CONHC_6H_4OCH_3\text{-}p){=}NNHC_6H_5$	282
	Benzidine	$[C_6H_5COC(CONHC_6H_4OCH_3\text{-}p){=}NNHC_6H_4{-}]_2$	287
p-Benzoylacetophenetide	—	$C_6H_5COC(CONHC_6H_4OC_2H_5\text{-}p){=}NNHC_6H_5$	282
	Benzidine	$[C_6H_5COC(CONHC_6H_4OC_2H_5\text{-}p){=}NNHC_6H_4{-}]_2$	287
N-*p*-Chlorophenylbenzoyl-acetamide	—	$C_6H_5COC(CONHC_6H_4Cl\text{-}p){=}NNHC_6H_5$	282
	Benzidine	$[C_6H_5COC(CONHC_6H_4Cl\text{-}p){=}NNHC_6H_4{-}]_2$	287

Reactant, Substituent R in C_4H_3O-COCH$_2$CONHR	Substituent(s) in Aniline	Substituents in Product, C_4H_3O-COCCONHR(=NNHR′): R	R′	References
Phenyl	—	Phenyl	Phenyl	282
	2-Methyl	Phenyl	*o*-Tolyl	283
	4-Methyl	Phenyl	*p*-Tolyl	283
	2-Methoxy	Phenyl	*o*-Anisyl	283
	4-Methoxy	Phenyl	*p*-Anisyl	283
	4-Ethoxy	Phenyl	*p*-Ethoxyphenyl	283
	3-Chloro	Phenyl	*m*-Chlorophenyl	283
	4-Chloro	Phenyl	*p*-Chlorophenyl	283
	4-Bromo	Phenyl	*p*-Bromophenyl	283
	α-Naphthylamine	Phenyl	α-Naphthyl	283
	β-Naphthylamine	Phenyl	β-Naphthyl	283
	Benzidine	Phenyl	Biphenylene	287

Note: References 177–480 are on pp. 136–142.

* The full name is given when it is awkward to name the arylamine as a derivative of aniline.

TABLE II—*Continued*

C. *β-Keto Amides—Continued*

Reactant, Substituent R in 2-furyl-$COCH_2CONHR$	Substituent(s) in Aniline	Substituents in Product, 2-furyl-$C(=NNHR')COCONHR$: R	R′	References
o-Tolyl	—	*o*-Tolyl	Phenyl	282
	Benzidine	*o*-Tolyl	Biphenylene	287
p-Tolyl	—	*p*-Tolyl	Phenyl	282
	Benzidine	*p*-Tolyl	Biphenylene	287
o-Anisyl	—	*o*-Anisyl	Phenyl	282
	Benzidine	*o*-Anisyl	Biphenylene	287
p-Anisyl	—	*p*-Anisyl	Phenyl	282
	Benzidine	*p*-Anisyl	Biphenylene	287
p-Ethoxyphenyl	—	*p*-Ethoxyphenyl	Phenyl	282
	Benzidine	*p*-Ethoxyphenyl	Biphenylene	287
m-Chlorophenyl	—	*m*-Chlorophenyl	Phenyl	282
	Benzidine	*m*-Chlorophenyl	Biphenylene	287
p-Chlorophenyl	—	*p*-Chlorophenyl	Phenyl	282
	Benzidine	*p*-Chlorophenyl	Biphenylene	287
p-Bromophenyl	—	*p*-Bromophenyl	Phenyl	282
	Benzidine	*p*-Bromophenyl	Biphenylene	287
α-Naphthyl	—	α-Naphthyl	Phenyl	282
	Benzidine	α-Naphthyl	Biphenylene	287
β-Naphthyl	—	*β*-Naphthyl	Phenyl	282
	Benzidine	*β*-Naphthyl	Biphenylene	287

Reactant, Substituent R in 5-methyl-2-furyl–$COCH_2CONHR$ (H$_3$C–furan–$COCH_2CONHR$)		Substituents in Product, H$_3$C–furan–COC(=NNHR′)CONHR: R	R′	
Phenyl	—	Phenyl	Phenyl	290
	2-Methyl	Phenyl	*o*-Tolyl	290
	4-Methyl	Phenyl	*p*-Tolyl	290
	2-Methoxy	Phenyl	*o*-Anisyl	290
	4-Methoxy	Phenyl	*p*-Anisyl	290
	4-Ethoxy	Phenyl	*p*-Ethoxyphenyl	290
	3-Chloro	Phenyl	*m*-Chlorophenyl	290
	4-Chloro	Phenyl	*p*-Chlorophenyl	290
	4-Bromo	Phenyl	*p*-Bromophenyl	290
	α-Naphthylamine	Phenyl	α-Naphthyl	290
	β-Naphthylamine	Phenyl	β-Naphthyl	290
o-Tolyl	—	*o*-Tolyl	Phenyl	290
p-Tolyl	—	*p*-Tolyl	Phenyl	290
o-Anisyl	—	*o*-Anisyl	Phenyl	290
p-Anisyl	—	*p*-Anisyl	Phenyl	290
p-Ethoxyphenyl	—	*p*-Ethoxyphenyl	Phenyl	290
m-Chlorophenyl	—	*m*-Chlorophenyl	Phenyl	290
p-Chlorophenyl	—	*p*-Chlorophenyl	Phenyl	290
p-Bromophenyl	—	*p*-Bromophenyl	Phenyl	290
α-Naphthyl	—	α-Naphthyl	Phenyl	290
β-Naphthyl	—	β-Naphthyl	Phenyl	290

Note: References 177–480 are on pp. 136–142.

TABLE III

Coupling of Diazonium Salts with Malonic Acids, Esters, and Amides

A. Malonic Acids

Malonic Acid	Substituent(s) in Aniline*	Product (Yield, %)	References
Malonic acid	—	$C_6H_5N{=}NCH{=}NNHC_6H_5$ (46)	70
		$C_6H_5N{=}NC(C_6H_5){=}NNHC_6H_5$†	70
	2-Methoxy	o-$CH_3OC_6H_4N{=}NCH{=}NNHC_6H_4OCH_3$-$o$ (67)	290*a*
	4-Methoxy	p-$CH_3OC_6H_4N{=}NCH{=}NNHC_6H_4OCH_3$-$p$	240
	2-Bromo	o-$BrC_6H_4NHN{=}CHCO_2H$ (30–40)	71
	4-Bromo	p-$BrC_6H_4N{=}NCH{=}NNHC_6H_4Br$-$p$	71, 170*a*
	2-Iodo	o-$IC_6H_4N{=}NCH{=}NNHC_6H_4I$-$o$‡	71
	2-Nitro	o-$O_2NC_6H_4NHN{=}CHCO_2H$ (50)§	71, 291
	3-Nitro	m-$O_2NC_6H_4N{=}NCH{=}NNHC_6H_4NO_2$-$m$	240
	4-Nitro	p-$O_2NC_6H_4N{=}NCH{=}NNHC_6H_4NO_2$-$p$	71, 240
Malonic acid and sodium nitrite	—	$C_6H_5N{=}NCH{=}NOH$	71
	2-Methoxy	o-$CH_3OC_6H_4N{=}NCH{=}NOH$	71
	2-Chloro	o-$ClC_6H_4N{=}NCH{=}NOH$	71
	2,4-Dimethyl	2,4-$(CH_3)_2C_6H_3N{=}NCH{=}NOH$	71
	α-Naphthyl	α-$C_{10}H_7N{=}NCH{=}NOH$	71
	β-Naphthyl	β-$C_{10}H_7N{=}NCH{=}NOH$	71
Chloromalonic acid	—	$C_6H_5N{=}NC(Cl){=}NNHC_6H_5$ (40–50)‖	72, 170*a*
	4-Methyl	p-$CH_3C_6H_4N{=}NC(Cl){=}NNHC_6H_4CH_3$-$p$ (40–50)	72
	4-Nitro	p-$O_2NC_6H_4N{=}NC(Cl){=}NNHC_6H_4NO_2$-$p$ (good)	72
	β-Naphthylamine	β-$C_{10}H_7N{=}NC(Cl){=}NNHC_{10}H_7$-β (poor)	72, 170*a*
Ethylmalonic acid	—	$C_6H_5N{=}NC(C_2H_5){=}NNHC_6H_5$ (quant.)	73
Allylmalonic acid	4-Methyl	p-$CH_3C_6H_4N{=}NC(CH_2CH{=}CH_2){=}NNHC_6H_4CH_3$-$p$ (50)	73
Benzylmalonic acid	—	$C_6H_5N{=}NC(CH_2C_6H_5){=}NNHC_6H_5$ (50)	73
Phenacylmalonic acid	—	$C_6H_5N{=}NC(CH_2COC_6H_5){=}NNHC_6H_5$	292

B. Malonic Esters

Malonic Ester	Substituent(s) in Aniline*	Product (Yield, %)	References
Ethyl hydrogen malonate	4-Nitro	p-$O_2NC_6H_4N{=}NC(CO_2C_2H_5){=}NNHC_6H_4NO_2$-$p$ (52)	19*c*
	2-Carboxy-4-chloro	2,4-$HO_2C(Cl)C_6H_3NHN{=}CHCO_2C_2H_5$ (52)	74*a*
	2-Carboxy-5-chloro	2,5-$HO_2C(Cl)C_6H_3NHN{=}CHCO_2C_2H_5$ (72)	74*a*
Dimethyl malonate	—	$C_6H_5NHN{=}C(CO_2CH_3)_2$	74*b*, 293
	2-Methyl	o-$CH_3C_6H_4NHN{=}C(CO_2CH_3)_2$	293
	3-Methyl	m-$CH_3C_6H_4NHN{=}C(CO_2CH_3)_2$	293
	4-Methyl	p-$CH_3C_6H_4NHN{=}C(CO_2CH_3)_2$	293
	2-Methoxy	o-$CH_3OC_6H_4NHN{=}C(CO_2CH_3)_2$	293
	4-Methoxy	p-$CH_3OC_6H_4NHN{=}C(CO_2CH_3)_2$	293
	2-Nitro	o-$O_2NC_6H_4NHN{=}C(CO_2CH_3)_2$	293
	3-Nitro	m-$O_2NC_6H_4NHN{=}C(CO_2CH_3)_2$	293
	4-Nitro	p-$O_2NC_6H_4NHN{=}C(CO_2CH_3)_2$	293
	2-Carboxy	o-$HO_2CC_6H_4NHN{=}C(CO_2CH_3)_2$	293
	3-Carboxy	m-$HO_2CC_6H_4NHN{=}C(CO_2CH_3)_2$	293
	4-Carboxy	p-$HO_2CC_6H_4NHN{=}C(CO_2CH_3)_2$	293
	2,4-Dimethyl	2,4-$(CH_3)_2C_6H_3NHN{=}C(CO_2CH_3)_2$	293
	Benzidine	4,4′-Biphenylenedihydrazonobis(dimethyl mesoxalate)	294, 295

Note: References 177–480 are on pp. 136–142.

* The full name is given when it is awkward to name the arylamine as a derivative of aniline.

† This product was obtained when excess diazonium salt was used.

‡ Glyoxylic acid *o*-iodophenylhydrazone was also formed in 8% yield.

§ N,N′-Di-*o*-nitrophenylformazan was also formed in 5% yield.

‖ With excess chloromalonic acid the corresponding 3-aryl-1,3,4-oxadiazol-2-one was formed.

TABLE III—*Continued*

B. Malonic Esters—Continued

Malonic Ester	Substituent(s) in Aniline*	Product (Yield, %)	References
Dimethyl malonate (*Cont.*)	3,3′-Dimethyl-benzidine	3,3′-Dimethyl-4,4′-biphenylenedihydrazonobis(dimethyl mesoxalate) (84)	294, 295
	3,3′-Dimethoxy-benzidine	3,3′-Dimethoxy-4,4′-biphenylenedihydrazonobis(dimethyl mesoxalate) (71)	294, 295
Diethyl malonate	—	$C_6H_5NHN{=}C(CO_2C_2H_5)_2$	8, 74*c*, 296
	3-Chloro	*m*-$ClC_6H_4NHN{=}C(CO_2C_2H_5)_2$ (78)	74*a*
	4-Bromo	*p*-$BrC_6H_4NHN{=}C(CO_2C_2H_5)_2$	74*c*
	4-Nitro	*p*-$O_2NC_6H_4NHN{=}C(CO_2C_2H_5)_2$ (71)	19*c*
	3-Carboxy	*m*-$HO_2CC_6H_4NHN{=}C(CO_2C_2H_5)_2$	242
	4-Phenyl	*p*-$C_6H_5C_6H_4NHN{=}C(CO_2C_2H_5)_2$ (50)	96
	4-Methoxy-2-nitro	4-CH_3O-2-$O_2NC_6H_3NHN{=}C(CO_2C_2H_5)_2$ (47)	74*a*
	2-Carboxy-5-chloro	2-HO_2C-5-$ClC_6H_3NHN{=}C(CO_2C_2H_5)_2$ (67)	74*a*
	Benzidine	4,4′-Biphenylenedihydrazonobis(diethyl mesoxalate)	294
	3,3′-Dimethyl-benzidine	3,3′-Dimethyl-4,4′-biphenylenedihydrazonobis(diethyl mesoxalate) (80)	294
	3,3′-Dimethoxy-benzidine	3,3′-Dimethoxy-4,4′-biphenylenedihydrazonobis(diethyl mesoxalate)	294
	3,3′-Dicarboxy-benzidine	3,3′-Dicarboxy-4,4′-biphenylenedihydrazonobis(diethyl mesoxalate)	242
Diethyl chloromalonate	4-Nitro	*p*-$O_2NC_6H_4N{=}NCCl(CO_2C_2H_5)_2$ (quant.)	72
Glutaconic acid	—	$C_6H_5N{=}NC(CH{=}CHCO_2H){=}NNHC_6H_5$	297
Diethyl glutaconate	—	$C_6H_5NHN{=}C(CO_2C_2H_5)CH{=}CHCO_2C_2H_5$ (77)	298, 76
		$C_6H_5NHN{=}C(CO_2C_2H_5)CH{=}C(CO_2C_2H_5)N{=}NC_6H_5$¶ (62)	297, 76, 299
	2-Methyl	*o*-$CH_3C_6H_4NHN{=}C(CO_2C_2H_5)CH{=}C(CO_2C_2H_5)N{=}NC_6H_4CH_3$-*o*¶	76

	4-Methyl	p-$CH_3C_6H_4NHN{=}C(CO_2C_2H_5)CH{=}C(CO_2C_2H_5)N{=}NC_6H_4CH_3$-$p$¶	76
	2-Ethoxy	o-$C_2H_5OC_6H_4NHN{=}C(CO_2C_2H_5)CH{=}CHCO_2C_2H_5$	76
		o-$C_2H_5OC_6H_4NHN{=}C(CO_2C_2H_5)$- $CH{=}C(CO_2C_2H_5)N{=}NC_6H_4OC_2H_5$-$o$¶	76
	4-Chloro	p-$ClC_6H_4NHN{=}C(CO_2C_2H_5)CH{=}C(CO_2C_2H_5)N{=}NC_6H_4Cl$-$p$¶	76
	2-Bromo	o-$BrC_6H_4NHN{=}C(CO_2C_2H_5)CH{=}C(CO_2C_2H_5)N{=}NC_6H_4Br$-$o$¶	76
	3-Bromo	m-$BrC_6H_4NHN{=}C(CO_2C_2H_5)CH{=}C(CO_2C_2H_5)N{=}NC_6H_4Br$-$m$¶	76
	4-Bromo	p-$BrC_6H_4NHN{=}C(CO_2C_2H_5)CH{=}C(CO_2C_2H_5)N{=}NC_6H_4Br$-$p$¶	76
	4-Nitro	p-$O_2NC_6H_4NHN{=}C(CO_2C_2H_5)CH{=}CHCO_2C_2H_5$	76
	2,4-Dimethyl	2,4-$(CH_3)_2C_6H_3NHN{=}C(CO_2C_2H_5)CH{=}CHCO_2C_2H_5$	76
		2,4-$(CH_3)_2C_6H_3NHN{=}C(CO_2C_2H_5)$-	76
		$CH{=}C(CO_2C_2H_5)N{=}NC_6H_3(CH_3)_2$-2,4¶	76
	2,4,6-Trimethyl	2,4,6-$(CH_3)_3C_6H_2NHN{=}C(CO_2C_2H_5)CH{=}CHCO_2C_2H_5$	76
		2,4,6-$(CH_3)_3C_6H_2NHN{=}C(CO_2C_2H_5)CH{=}C(CO_2C_2H_5)$- $N{=}NC_6H_2(CH_3)_3$-2,4,6¶	76

C. *Malonic Amides*

Malonic Amide	Substituent in Aniline	Product (Yield, %)	References
Malonamide	—	$C_6H_5NHN{=}C(CONH_2)_2$	75
Diethyl N,N′-malonyl-dicarbamate	—	$C_6H_5NHN{=}C(CONHCO_2C_2H_5)_2$ (67)	75
		$C_6H_5NHN{=}C(CONHCO_2C_2H_5)N{=}NC_6H_5$** (74)	75
	4-Methyl	p-$CH_3C_6H_4NHN{=}C(CONHCO_2C_2H_5)_2$	75
		p-$CH_3C_6H_4NHN{=}C(CONHCO_2C_2H_5)N{=}NC_6H_4CH_3$-$p$**	75

Note: References 177–480 are on pp. 136–142.

* The full name is given when it is awkward to name the arylamine as a derivative of aniline.

¶ This product was obtained when 2 equivalents of diazonium salt were used.

** This product is obtained when 2 equivalents of diazonium salt are used in the presence of sodium carbonate.

TABLE III—*Continued*

C. *Malonic Amides—Continued*

Malonic Amide	Substituent in Aniline	Product (Yield, %)	References
Diethyl N,N′-malonyldicarbamate (*Cont.*)	2-Nitro	*o*-$O_2NC_6H_4NHN{=}C(CONHCO_2C_2H_5)_2$	75
		o-$O_2NC_6H_4NHN{=}C(CONHCO_2C_2H_5)N{=}NC_6H_4NO_2$-*o***	75
	3-Nitro	*m*-$O_2NC_6H_4NHN{=}C(CONHCO_2C_2H_5)_2$	75
	4-Nitro	*p*-$O_2NC_6H_4NHN{=}C(CONHCO_2C_2H_5)_2$	75
Malonamidine	—	$C_6H_5NHN{=}C[C({=}NH)NH_2]_2$	300*a*
$CH_2[CONHN{=}C(CH_3)$-$C(CO_2C_2H_5){=}NNHC_6H_5]_2$	—	$C_6H_5NHN{=}C[CONHN{=}C(CH_3)C(CO_2C_2H_5){=}NNHC_6H_5]_2$	280
Ethyl malonanilate	—	$C_6H_5NHN{=}C(CO_2C_2H_5)CONHC_6H_5$	300*b*
Methyl N-(α-pyridyl) malonamate	—	$C_6H_5NHN{=}C(CO_2CH_3)CONHC_5H_4N$-α (quant.)	300*b*
Ethyl N-(γ-pyridyl)-malonamate	—	$C_6H_5NHN{=}C(CO_2C_2H_5)CONHC_5H_4N$-γ	300*c*
Malonamic acid	4-Nitro	*p*-$O_2NC_6H_4N{=}NC(CONH_2){=}NNHC_6H_4NO_2$-*p* (89)	19*c*
Ethyl malonamate	4-Nitro	*p*-$O_2NC_6H_4NHN{=}C(CO_2C_2H_5)CONH_2$ (36)	19*c*

Note: References 177–480 are on pp. 136–142.

** This product is obtained when 2 equivalents of diazonium salt are used in the presence of sodium carbonate.

TABLE IV

Coupling of Diazonium Salts with Arylacetic Acids and Esters

Acid or Ester	Substituent(s) in Aniline*	Product (Yield, %)	References
2,4-Dinitrophenylacetic acid	—	$2,4\text{-}(O_2N)_2C_6H_3C(N{=}NC_6H_5){=}NNHC_6H_5$	77
	4-Bromo	$2,4\text{-}(O_2N)_2C_6H_3C(N{=}NC_6H_4Br\text{-}p){=}NNHC_6H_4Br\text{-}p$	77
	2,4-Dichloro	$2,4\text{-}(O_2N)_2C_6H_3C(N{=}NC_6H_3Cl_2\text{-}2,4){=}NNHC_6H_3Cl_2\text{-}2,4$	77
	2,4-Dibromo	$2,4\text{-}(O_2N)_2C_6H_3C(N{=}NC_6H_3Br_2\text{-}2,4){=}NNHC_6H_3Br_2\text{-}2,4$	77
Methyl 2,4-dinitrophenylacetate	—	$2,4\text{-}(O_2N)_2C_6H_3C(CO_2CH_3){=}NNHC_6H_5$	79, 80, 301
	2-Methyl	$2,4\text{-}(O_2N)_2C_6H_3C(CO_2CH_3){=}NNHC_6H_4CH_3\text{-}o$ (98)	79
	4-Methyl	$2,4\text{-}(O_2N)_2C_6H_3C(CO_2CH_3){=}NNHC_6H_4CH_3\text{-}p$ (75)	78, 302
	4-Methoxy	$2,4\text{-}(O_2N)_2C_6H_3C(CO_2CH_3){=}NNHC_6H_4OCH_3\text{-}p$	79
	4-Chloro	$2,4\text{-}(O_2N)_2C_6H_3C(CO_2CH_3){=}NNHC_6H_4Cl\text{-}p$	77
	4-Bromo	$2,4\text{-}(O_2N)_2C_6H_3C(CO_2CH_3){=}NNHC_6H_4Br\text{-}p$	77
	4-Acetyl	$2,4\text{-}(O_2N)_2C_6H_3C(CO_2CH_3){=}NNHC_6H_4COCH_3\text{-}p$	78
	2-Nitro	$2,4\text{-}(O_2N)_2C_6H_3C(CO_2CH_3){=}NNHC_6H_4NO_2\text{-}o$ (30)	79
	3-Nitro	$2,4\text{-}(O_2N)_2C_6H_3C(CO_2CH_3){=}NNHC_6H_4NO_2\text{-}m$ (15)	79
	4-Nitro	$2,4\text{-}(O_2N)_2C_6H_3C(CO_2CH_3){=}NNHC_6H_4NO_2\text{-}p$	79
	2-Carboxy	$2,4\text{-}(O_2N)_2C_6H_3C(CO_2CH_3){=}NNHC_6H_4CO_2H\text{-}o$ (quant.)	79
	4-Carboxy	$2,4\text{-}(O_2N)_2C_6H_3C(CO_2CH_3){=}NNHC_6H_4CO_2H\text{-}p$ (quant.)	78
	4-Sulfo	$2,4\text{-}(O_2N)_2C_6H_3C(CO_2CH_3){=}NNHC_6H_4SO_3H\text{-}p$	302
	2,4-Dimethyl	$2,4\text{-}(O_2N)_2C_6H_3C(CO_2CH_3){=}NNHC_6H_3(CH_3)_2\text{-}2,4$	302
	2,4-Dichloro	$2,4\text{-}(O_2N)_2C_6H_3C(CO_2CH_3){=}NNHC_6H_3Cl_2\text{-}2,4$ (55)	78, 77
	2,4-Dibromo	$2,4\text{-}(O_2N)_2C_6H_3C(CO_2CH_3){=}NNHC_6H_3Br_2\text{-}2,4$	77
	2,4,6-Trimethyl	$2,4\text{-}(O_2N)_2C_6H_3C(CO_2CH_3){=}NNHC_6H_2(CH_3)_3\text{-}2,4,6$ (80)	78
	2,4,6-Trichloro	$2,4\text{-}(O_2N)_2C_6H_3C(CO_2CH_3){=}NNHC_6H_2Cl_3\text{-}2,4,6$ (45)	78
	α-Naphthyl	$2,4\text{-}(O_2N)_2C_6H_3C(CO_2CH_3){=}NNHC_{10}H_7\text{-}\alpha$	302
	β-Naphthyl	$2,4\text{-}(O_2N)_2C_6H_3C(CO_2CH_3){=}NNHC_{10}H_7\text{-}\beta$	79
Dimethyl 4-nitrohomophthalate	—	CO_2CH_3; N; O_2N; NC_6H_5; O	79
Methyl 4-carbomethoxy-2-nitrophenylacetate	—	$C_6H_5NHN{=}C(CO_2CH_3)C_6H_3CO_2CH_3\text{-}4\text{-}NO_2\text{-}2$	79
Homophthalic anhydride	—	α-Phenylhydrazonohomophthalic anhydride	81

Note: References 177–480 are on pp. 136–142.

* The full name is given when it is awkward to name the arylamine as a derivative of aniline.

TABLE V

Coupling of Diazonium Salts with Nitriles

Nitrile	Substituent(s) in Aniline*	Product (Yield, %)	References
Cyanoacetaldehyde	—	$CNC(CHO){=}NNHC_6H_5$ (15)	86, 85
	4-Bromo	$CNC(CHO){=}NNHC_6H_4Br$-*p*	86
	4-Nitro	$CNC(CHO){=}NNHC_6H_4NO_2$-*p* (11)	19*c*
Cyanoacetic acid	—	$C_6H_5N{=}NC(CN){=}NNHC_6H_5$	95*a*
	2-Carboxy	*o*-$HO_2CC_6H_4N{=}NC(CN){=}NNHC_6H_4CO_2H$-*o* (65)	303
	4-Nitro	*p*-$O_2NC_6H_4N{=}NC(CN){=}NNHC_6H_4NO_2$-*p*	19*c*
	2-Hydroxy-5-chloro	2-HO-5-$ClC_6H_3N{=}NC(CN){=}NNHC_6H_3Cl$-5-OH-2	232*a*
Methyl cyanoacetate	—	$CNC(CO_2CH_3){=}NNHC_6H_5$	304
	2-Methyl	$CNC(CO_2CH_3){=}NNHC_6H_4CH_3$-*o*	304
	4-Methyl	$CNC(CO_2CH_3){=}NNHC_6H_4CH_3$-*p*	304
	Benzidine	4,4′-Biphenylenedihydrazonobis(methyl cyanoglyoxalate)	305, 306
	3,3′-Dimethylbenzidine	3,3′-Dimethyl-4,4′-biphenylenedihydrazonobis(methyl cyanoglyoxalate)	305, 306
	3,3′-Dimethoxybenzidine	3,3′-Dimethoxy-4,4′-biphenylenedihydrazonobis(methyl cyanoglyoxalate)	305, 306
Ethyl cyanoacetate	—	$CNC(CO_2C_2H_5){=}NNHC_6H_5$ (quant.)	82, 74*c*, 175, 304, 307–309
	2-Methyl	$CNC(CO_2C_2H_5){=}NNHC_6H_4CH_3$-*o*	82, 304
	4-Methyl	$CNC(CO_2C_2H_5){=}NNHC_6H_4CH_3$-*p*	82, 304
	2-Methoxy	$CNC(CO_2C_2H_5){=}NNHC_6H_4OCH_3$-*o*	310
	4-Methoxy	$CNC(CO_2C_2H_5){=}NNHC_6H_4OCH_3$-*p*	310
	4-Ethoxy	$CNC(CO_2C_2H_5){=}NNHC_6H_4OC_2H_5$-*p*	310
	2-Hydroxy	$CNC(CO_2C_2H_5){=}NNHC_6H_4OH$-*o*	311
	3-Hydroxy	$CNC(CO_2C_2H_5){=}NNHC_6H_4OH$-*m*	311
	4-Hydroxy	$CNC(CO_2C_2H_5){=}NNHC_6H_4OH$-*p*	311
	3-Chloro	$CNC(CO_2C_2H_5){=}NNHC_6H_4Cl$-*m* (97)	74*a*

	3-Bromo	$CNC(CO_2C_2H_5)$=$NNHC_6H_4Br$-*m*	311
	2-Nitro	$CNC(CO_2C_2H_5)$=$NNHC_6H_4NO_2$-*o*	312
	3-Nitro	$CNC(CO_2C_2H_5)$=$NNHC_6H_4NO_2$-*m* (76)	312
	4-Nitro	$CNC(CO_2C_2H_5)$=$NNHC_6H_4NO_2$-*p* (97)	312
	2-Carboxy	$CNC(CO_2C_2H_5)$=$NNHC_6H_4CO_2H$-*o*	82
	3-Carboxy	$CNC(CO_2C_2H_5)$=$NNHC_6H_4CO_2H$-*m*	311
	2-Carbomethoxy	$CNC(CO_2C_2H_5)$=$NNHC_6H_4CO_2CH_3$-*o*	310
	4-Sulfo	$CNC(CO_2C_2H_5)$=$NNHC_6H_4SO_3H$-*p*	311
	2,4-Dimethyl	$CNC(CO_2C_2H_5)$=$NNHC_6H_3(CH_3)_2$-2,4	82
	2,4,5-Trimethyl	$CNC(CO_2C_2H_5)$=$NNHC_6H_2(CH_3)_2$-2,4,5	82
	2,4-Dichloro	$CNC(CO_2C_2H_5)$=$NNHC_6H_3Cl_2$-2,4 (96)	313
	2,5-Dichloro	$CNC(CO_2C_2H_5)$=$NNHC_6H_3Cl_2$-2,5 (99)	313
	2,5-Dibromo	$CNC(CO_2C_2H_5)$=$NNHC_6H_3Br_2$-2,5	311
	2,4,6-Tribromo	$CNC(CO_2C_2H_5)$=$NNHC_6H_2Br_3$-2,4,6	311
	2-Chloro-4-methyl	$CNC(CO_2C_2H_5)$=$NNHC_6H_3Cl$-2-CH_3-4 (71)	238
	4-Chloro-2-methyl	$CNC(CO_2C_2H_5)$=$NNHC_6H_3Cl$-4-CH_3-2 (92)	238
	α-Naphthylamine	$CNC(CO_2C_2H_5)$=$NNHC_{10}H_7$-α	311
	β-Naphthylamine	$CNC(CO_2C_2H_5)$=$NNHC_{10}H_7$-β	311
	Benzidine	4,4′-Biphenylenedihydrazonobis(ethyl cyanoglyoxalate)	305, 310
	3,3′-Dimethyl-benzidine	3,3′-Dimethyl-4,4′-biphenylenedihydrazonobis(ethyl cyanoglyoxalate)	305, 310
	3,3′-Dimethoxy-benzidine	3,3′-Dimethoxy-4,4′-biphenylenedihydrazonobis(ethyl cyanoglyoxalate)	305, 310
n-Propyl cyanoacetate	—	$CNC(CO_2C_3H_7$-*n*)=$NNHC_6H_5$	314
n-Butyl cyanoacetate	—	$CNC(CO_2C_4H_9$-*n*)=$NNHC_6H_5$	314
n-Amyl cyanoacetate	—	$CNC(CO_2C_5H_{11}$-*n*)=$NNHC_6H_5$	314
l-Menthyl cyanoacetate	4-Methyl	$CNC(CO_2C_{10}H_{19}$-*l*)=$NNHC_6H_4CH_3$-*p*	315
	4-Bromo	$CNC(CO_2C_{10}H_{19}$-*l*)=$NNHC_6H_4Br$-*p*	315
Cyanoacetamide	4-Nitro	$CNC(CONH_2)$=$NNHC_6H_4NO_2$-*p* (56)	19*c*

Note: References 177–480 are on pp. 136–142.

* The full name is given when it is awkward to name the arylamine as a derivative of aniline.

TABLE V—*Continued*

COUPLING OF DIAZONIUM SALTS WITH NITRILES

Nitrile	Substituent(s) in Aniline*	Product (Yield, %)	References
Cyanoacetanilide	4-Methoxy-2-nitro	$CNC(CONHC_6H_5){=}NNHC_6H_3OCH_3$-4-$NO_2$-2	74*a*
Ethyl α-cyanopropionate	4-Nitro	*p*-$O_2NC_6H_4N{=}NC(CH_3)(CN)CO_2C_2H_5$†	99
Ethyl α-cyanobutyrate	—	$C_6H_5N{=}NC(C_2H_5)(CN)CO_2C_2H_5$‡	99
	4-Bromo	*p*-$BrC_6H_4N{=}NC(C_2H_5)(CN)CO_2C_2H_5$§	99
Ethyl cyanopyruvate	—	$C_6H_5NHN{=}C(CN)COCO_2C_2H_5$ (72)	86, 87
	4-Bromo	*p*-$BrC_6H_4NHN{=}C(CN)COCO_2C_2H_5$ (83)	86, 87
Malononitrile	—	$C_6H_5NHN{=}C(CN)_2$	74*b*, 83
	4-Nitro	*p*-$O_2NC_6H_4NHN{=}C(CN)_2$ (75)	84, 19*c*
Benzylmalononitrile	—	$C_6H_5N{=}NC(CN)_2CH_2C_6H_5$ (84)	96
	4-Nitro	*p*-$O_2NC_6H_4N{=}NC(CN)_2CH_2C_6H_5$ (87)	96
	4-Phenyl	*p*-$C_6H_5C_6H_4N{=}NC(CN)_2CH_2C_6H_5$ (87)	96
Nitroacetonitrile	—	$C_6H_5NHN{=}C(NO_2)CN$	88, 89
	4-Nitro	*p*-$O_2NC_6H_4NHN{=}C(NO_2)CN$ (59)	19*c*
Methylsulfinylacetonitrile	4-Nitro	*p*-$O_2NC_6H_4N{=}NC(CN){=}NNHC_6H_4NO_2$-*p* (72)	19*c*
Methylsulfonylacetonitrile	4-Nitro	*p*-$O_2NC_6H_4NHN{=}C(CN)SO_2CH_3$ (63)	19*c*
p-Nitrophenylacetonitrile	—	*p*-$O_2NC_6H_4C(CN){=}NNHC_6H_5$	316
β-Iminobutyronitrile	—	$CH_3COC(CN){=}NNHC_6H_5$	90
β-Oximinobutyronitrile	—	$CH_3COC(CN){=}NNHC_6H_5$	90
β-Iminovaleronitrile	—	?	90
β-Imino-β-phenyl-propionitrile	—	$C_6H_5COC(CN){=}NNHC_6H_5$	90
β-Phenyliminobutyro-nitrile	—	$C_6H_5N{=}C(CH_3)C(CN){=}NNHC_6H_5$	91
Benzoylacetonitrile	—	$C_6H_5COC(CN){=}NNHC_6H_5$	317
	2-Methyl	$C_6H_5COC(CN){=}NNHC_6H_4CH_3$-*o*	317
	2-Hydroxy-5-sulfo	$C_6H_5COC(CN){=}NNHC_6H_3OH$-2-$SO_3H$-5	94

	2-Carboxy-4-sulfo	$C_6H_5COC(CN){=}NNHC_6H_3CO_2H$-2-$SO_3H$-4	94
	2-Hydroxy-4-sulfo-5-methyl	$C_6H_5COC(CN){=}NNHC_6H_2OH$-2-$SO_3H$-4-$CH_3$-5	94
	2-Hydroxy-3-sulfo-5-chloro	$C_6H_5COC(CN){=}NNHC_6H_2OH$-2-$SO_3H$-3-Cl-5	94
	2-Hydroxy-3-sulfo-5-nitro	$C_6H_5COC(CN){=}NNHC_6H_2OH$-2-$SO_3H$-3-$NO_2$-5	94
	2-Hydroxy-3-carboxy-5-sulfo	$C_6H_5COC(CN){=}NNHC_6H_2OH$-2-$CO_2H$-3-$SO_3H$-5	94
	2-Hydroxy-4-sulfo-1-naphthylamine	α,β-Dioxo-β-phenylpropionitrile α-(2-hydroxy-4-sulfo-1-naphthylhydrazone)	94
	2-Hydroxy-4-sulfo-6-nitro-1-naphthylamine	α,β-Dioxo-β-phenylpropionitrile α-(2-hydroxy-4-sulfo-6-nitro-1-naphthylhydrazone)	94
p-Toluoylacetonitrile	2-Hydroxy-4-sulfo-1-naphthylamine	α,β-Dioxo-*p*-tolylpropionitrile α-(2-hydroxy-4-sulfo-1-naphthylhydrazone)	94
o-Anisoylacetonitrile	2-Hydroxy-4-sulfo-1-naphthylamine	α,β-Dioxo-*o*-anisylpropionitrile α-(2-hydroxy-4-sulfo-1-naphthylhydrazone)	94
o-Ethoxybenzoylacetonitrile	2-Hydroxy-4-sulfo-1-naphthylamine	α,β-Dioxo-*o*-ethoxyphenylpropionitrile α-(2-hydroxy-4-sulfo-1-naphthylhydrazone)	94
o-Propoxybenzoylacetonitrile	2-Hydroxy-4-sulfo-1-naphthylamine	α,β-Dioxo-*o*-propoxyphenylpropionitrile α-(2-hydroxy-4-sulfo-1-naphthylhydrazone)	94
o-Benzyloxybenzoylacetonitrile	2-Hydroxy-4-sulfo-1-naphthylamine	α,β-Dioxo-*o*-benzyloxyphenylpropionitrile α-(2-hydroxy-4-sulfo-1-naphthylhydrazone)	94
p-Chlorobenzoylacetonitrile	2-Hydroxy-4-sulfo-1-naphthylamine	α,β-Dioxo-*p*-chlorophenylpropionitrile α-(2-hydroxy-4-sulfo-1-naphthylhydrazone)	94

Note: References 177–480 are on pp. 136–142.

* The full name is given when it is awkward to name the arylamine as a derivative of aniline.

† Some *p*-$O_2NC_6H_4N(CH_3)N{=}C(CN)CO_2C_2H_5$ was also formed.

‡ Some $C_6H_5N(C_2H_5)N{=}C(CN)CO_2C_2H_5$ was also formed.

§ Some *p*-$BrC_6H_4N(C_2H_5)N{=}C(CN)CO_2C_2H_5$ was also formed.

TABLE V—*Continued*

COUPLING OF DIAZONIUM SALTS WITH NITRILES

Nitrile	Substituent(s) in Aniline*	Product (Yield, %)	References
m-Aminobenzoylacetonitrile	2-Hydroxy-4-sulfo-1-naphthylamine	α,β-Dioxo-*m*-aminophenylpropionitrile α-(2-hydroxy-4-sulfo-1-naphthylhydrazone)	94
m-Nitrobenzoylacetonitrile	2-Hydroxy-4-sulfo-1-naphthylamine	α,β-Dioxo-*m*-nitrophenylpropionitrile α-(2-hydroxy-4-sulfo-1-naphthylhydrazone)	94
m-Carboxybenzoylacetonitrile	2-Hydroxy-4-sulfo-1-naphthylamine	α,β-Dioxo-*m*-carboxyphenylpropionitrile α-(2-hydroxy-4-sulfo-1-naphthylhydrazone)	94
2,4-Dimethoxybenzoylacetonitrile	2-Hydroxy-4-sulfo-1-naphthylamine	α,β-Dioxo-2,4-dimethoxyphenylpropionitrile α-(2-hydroxy-4-sulfo-1-naphthylhydrazone)	94
3,4-Dichlorobenzoylacetonitrile	2-Hydroxy-4-sulfo-1-naphthylamine	α,β-Dioxo-3,4-dichlorophenylpropionitrile α-(2-hydroxy-4-sulfo-1-naphthylhydrazone)	94
3,4,5-Trimethoxybenzoylacetonitrile	2-Hydroxy-4-sulfo-1-naphthylamine	α,β-Dioxo-3,4,5-trimethoxyphenylpropionitrile α-(2-hydroxy-4-sulfo-1-naphthylhydrazone)	94
3,4,5-Triethoxybenzoylacetonitrile	2-Hydroxy-4-sulfo-1-naphthylamine	α,β-Dioxo-3,4,5-triethoxyphenylpropionitrile α-(2-hydroxy-4-sulfo-1-naphthylhydrazone)	94
p-(*p*-Cyanoacetophenyl)-benzoylacetonitrile	2-Hydroxy-4-sulfo-1-naphthylamine	α,β-Dioxo-*p*-(*p*-cyanoacetophenyl)phenylpropionitrile α-(2-hydroxy-4-sulfo-1-naphthylhydrazone)	94
Hexahydrobenzoylacetonitrile	2-Hydroxy-4-sulfo-1-naphthylamine	α,β-Dioxocyclohexylpropionitrile α-(2-hydroxy-4-sulfo-1-naphthylhydrazone)	94
α-Naphthoylacetonitrile	2-Hydroxy-4-sulfo-1-naphthylamine	α,β-Dioxo-1-naphthylpropionitrile α-(2-hydroxy-4-sulfo-1-naphthylhydrazone)	94
β-Naphthoylacetonitrile	2-Hydroxy-4-sulfo-1-naphthylamine	α,β-Dioxo-2-naphthylpropionitrile α-(2-hydroxy-4-sulfo-1-naphthylhydrazone)	94
3-Methoxy-2-naphthoylacetonitrile	2-Hydroxy-4-sulfo-1-naphthylamine	α,β-Dioxo-3-methoxy-2-naphthylpropionitrile α-(2-hydroxy-4-sulfo-1-naphthylhydrazone)	94

	2-Hydroxy-4-sulfo-6-nitro-1-naphthylamine	α,β-Dioxo-3-methoxy-2-naphthylpropionitrile α-(2-hydroxy-4-sulfo-6-nitro-1-naphthylhydrazone)	94
	2-Hydroxy-3-nitro-4-sulfo	α,β-Dioxo-3-methoxy-2-naphthylpropionitrile α-(2-hydroxy-3-nitro-4-sulfophenylhydrazone)	94
5,6,7,8-Tetrahydro-2-naphthoylacetonitrile	2-Hydroxy-4-sulfo-1-naphthylamine	α,β-Dioxo-β-(5,6,7,8-tetrahydro-2-naphthyl)-propionitrile α-(2-hydroxy-4-sulfo-1-naphthylhydrazone)	94
5-Acenaphthenoyl-acetonitrile	2-Hydroxy-4-sulfo-1-naphthylamine	α,β-Dioxo-β-(5-acenaphthyl)propionitrile α-(2-hydroxy-4-sulfo-1-naphthylhydrazone)	94
2-Thenoylacetonitrile	2-Hydroxy-4-sulfo-1-naphthylamine	α,β-Dioxo-β-(2-thienyl)propionitrile α-(2-hydroxy-4-sulfo-1-naphthylhydrazone)	94
2-Furoylacetonitrile	2-Hydroxy-4-sulfo-1-naphthylamine	α,β-Dioxo-β-(2-furyl)propionitrile α-(2-hydroxy-4-sulfo-1-naphthylhydrazone)	94
	2-Carboxy-4-sulfo	α,β-Dioxo-β-(2-furyl)propionitrile α-(2-carboxy-4-sulphophenylhydrazone)	94
	2-Carboxy-3-sulfo-4-chloro	α,β-Dioxo-β-(2-furyl)propionitrile α-(2-carboxy-3-sulfo-4-chlorophenylhydrazone)	94
	2-Hydroxy-4-sulfo-6-nitro-1-naphthylamine	α,β-Dioxo-β-(2-furyl)propionitrile α-(2-hydroxy-4-sulfo-6-nitro-1-naphthylhydrazone)	94
4,4′-Biphenyldicarbonyl-acetonitrile	2-Carboxy-4-sulfo	4,4′-Biphenylenebis-(α,β-dioxopropionitrile) α,α′-di-(2-carboxy-4-sulfophenylhydrazone)	94
Phenylsulfonylacetonitrile	—	$C_6H_5SO_2C(CN){=}NNHC_6H_5$	92
	2-Methyl	$C_6H_5SO_2C(CN){=}NNHC_6H_4CH_3$-*o*	92
	3-Methyl	$C_6H_5SO_2C(CN){=}NNHC_6H_4CH_3$-*m*	92
	2-Methoxy	$C_6H_5SO_2C(CN){=}NNHC_6H_4OCH_3$-*o*	92
	4-Methoxy	$C_6H_5SO_2C(CN){=}NNHC_6H_4OCH_3$-*p*	92

* The full name is given when it is awkward to name the arylamine as a derivative of aniline.

TABLE V—*Continued*

Coupling of Diazonium Salts with Nitriles

Nitrile	Substituent(s) in Aniline*	Product (Yield, %)	References
Phenylsulfonylacetonitrile (*Cont.*)	4-Ethoxy	$C_6H_5SO_2C(CN){=}NNHC_6H_4OC_2H_5$-*p*	92
	2,4-Dimethyl	$C_6H_5SO_2C(CN){=}NNHC_6H_3(CH_3)_2$-2,4	92
p-Tolylsulfonylacetonitrile	—	*p*-$CH_3C_6H_4SO_2C(CN){=}NNHC_6H_5$	92
	2-Methyl	*p*-$CH_3C_6H_4SO_2C(CN){=}NNHC_6H_4CH_3$-*o*	92
	3-Methyl	*p*-$CH_3C_6H_4SO_2C(CN){=}NNHC_6H_4CH_3$-*m*	92
	4-Methyl	*p*-$CH_3C_6H_4SO_2C(CN){=}NNHC_6H_4CH_3$-*p*	92
	2-Methoxy	*p*-$CH_3C_6H_4SO_2C(CN){=}NNHC_6H_4OCH_3$-*o*	92
	4-Methoxy	*p*-$CH_3C_6H_4SO_2C(CN){=}NNHC_6H_4OCH_3$-*p*	92
	4-Ethoxy	*p*-$CH_3C_6H_4SO_2C(CN){=}NNHC_6H_4OC_2H_5$-*p*	92
	2,4-Dimethyl	*p*-$CH_3C_6H_4SO_2C(CN){=}NNHC_6H_3(CH_3)_2$-2,4	92
p-Bromophenylsulfonylacetonitrile	—	*p*-$BrC_6H_4SO_2C(CN){=}NNHC_6H_5$	93
	4-Ethoxy	*p*-$BrC_6H_4SO_2C(CN){=}NNHC_6H_4OC_2H_5$-*p*	93
α-Naphthylsulfonylacetonitrile	—	α-$C_{10}H_7SO_2C(CN){=}NNHC_6H_5$ (67)	93
	2-Methyl	α-$C_{10}H_7SO_2C(CN){=}NNHC_6H_4CH_3$-*o*	93
	4-Methyl	α-$C_{10}H_7SO_2C(CN){=}NNHC_6H_4CH_3$-*p*	93
	4-Methoxy	α-$C_{10}H_7SO_2C(CN){=}NNHC_6H_4OCH_3$-*p*	93

β-Naphthylsulfonylacetonitrile	—	β-$C_{10}H_7SO_2C(CN){=}NNHC_6H_5$	93
	3-Methyl	β-$C_{10}H_7SO_2C(CN){=}NNHC_6H_4CH_3$-*m*	93
	4-Methyl	β-$C_{10}H_7SO_2C(CN){=}NNHC_6H_4CH_3$-*p*	93
	4-Ethoxy	β-$C_{10}H_7SO_2C(CN){=}NNHC_6H_4OC_2H_5$-*p*	93
α-Phenylsulfonylpropionitrile	—	$C_6H_5SO_2C(CN)(CH_3)N{=}NC_6H_5$	93
	4-Methyl	$C_6H_5SO_2C(CN)(CH_3)N{=}NC_6H_4CH_3$-*p*	93
	4-Methoxy	$C_6H_5SO_2C(CN)(CH_3)N{=}NC_6H_4OCH_3$-*p*	93
	4-Ethoxy	$C_6H_5SO_2C(CN)(CH_3)N{=}NC_6H_4OC_2H_5$-*p*	93
α-*p*-Chlorophenylsulfonylpropionitrile	—	*p*-$ClC_6H_4SO_2C(CN)(CH_3)N{=}NC_6H_5$	93
	β-Naphthylamine	*p*-$ClC_6H_4SO_2C(CN)(CH_3)N{=}NC_{10}H_7$-β	93
α-*p*-Bromophenylsulfonylpropionitrile	4-Methyl	*p*-$BrC_6H_4SO_2C(CN)(CH_3)N{=}NC_6H_4CH_3$-*p*	93
	4-Methoxy	*p*-$BrC_6H_4SO_2C(CN)(CH_3)N{=}NC_6H_4OCH_3$-*p*	93
α-(β-Naphthylsulfonyl)-propionitrile	—	β-$C_{10}H_7SO_2C(CN)(CH_3)N{=}NC_6H_5$	93
	4-Methyl	β-$C_{10}H_7SO_2C(CN)(CH_3)N{=}NC_6H_4CH_3$-*p*	93
α-Phenoxyacetyl-β-imino-β-phenylpropionitrile	—	$C_6H_5OCH_2COC(CN)(N{=}NC_6H_5)C({=}NH)C_6H_5$	318
β-Phenoxyacetimido-β-phenylpropionitrile	—	$C_6H_5OCH_2CON{=}C(C_6H_5)C(CN){=}NNHC_6H_5$	319

Note: References 177–480 are on pp. 136–142.

* The full name is given when it is awkward to name the arylamine as a derivative of aniline.

TABLE V—*Continued*

COUPLING OF DIAZONIUM SALTS WITH NITRILES

(General structure: 5-(cyano(RHN–N=)methyl)-3-R′-1,2,4-oxadiazole, drawn as NCC(=NNHR)–C(=N–C(R′)=N–O))

Nitrile	Substituent in Aniline			Yield, %	References
(3-*p*-Tolyl-1,2,4-oxadiazol-5-yl)-acetonitrile	—	R = Phenyl	R′ = *p*-Tolyl	20	32
	2-Methoxy	R = *o*-Anisyl	R′ = *p*-Tolyl	20	32
	4-Nitro	R = *p*-Nitrophenyl	R′ = *p*-Tolyl	20	32
	4-Diethylamino	R = *p*-Diethylaminophenyl	R′ = *p*-Tolyl	20	32
(3-*m*-Nitrophenyl-1,2,4-oxadiazol-5-yl)acetonitrile	4-Diethylamino	R = *p*-Diethylaminophenyl	R′ = *m*-Nitrophenyl	20	32
1,2,3,4-Tetrahydroacridine-4-carbonitrile	4-Methoxy	4-CN, 4-($N{=}NC_6H_4OCH_3$-*p*)-1,2,3,4-tetrahydroacridine		50	98
	4-Bromo	4-CN, 4-($N{=}NC_6H_4Br$-*p*)-1,2,3,4-tetrahydroacridine		56	98
2,3-Dihydro-1-cyclopenta[*b*]-quinoline-3-carbonitrile	4-Bromo	3-CN, 3-($N{=}NC_6H_4Br$-*p*)-2,3-dihydro-1-cyclopenta[*b*]quinoline		61	98

Nitrile	Substituent in Aniline	Product (Yield, %)	References
Benzothiazole-2-acetonitrile	4-Bromo	S, N; CCCN ‖ $NNHC_6H_4Br$-*p* (47)	36*a*
3-Methylquinoxaline-2-acetonitrile	4-Chloro	N, N; CH_3; $C{=}NNHC_6H_4Cl$-*p* | $N{=}NC_6H_4Cl$-*p* (67)	36*a*

TABLE VI

COUPLING OF DIAZONIUM SALTS WITH SULFONES

Sulfone	Substituent(s) in Aniline*	Product (Yield, %)	References
Bis(methylsulfonyl)methane	—	$(CH_3SO_2)_2C{=}NNHC_6H_5$ (56)	101
	2-Methyl	$(CH_2SO_2)_2C{=}NNHC_6H_4CH_3$-*o* (43)	101
	4-Methyl	$(CH_3SO_2)_2C{=}NNHC_6H_4CH_3$-*p* (36)	101
	4-Nitro	$(CH_3SO_2)_2C{=}NNHC_6H_4NO_2$-*p*†	19*c*
Bis(ethylsulfonyl)methane	—	$(C_2H_5SO_2)_2C{=}NNHC_6H_5$ (43)	101
	2-Methyl	$(C_2H_5SO_2)_2C{=}NNHC_6H_4CH_3$-*o* (48)	101
	4-Methyl	$(C_2H_5SO_2)_2C{=}NNHC_6H_4CH_3$-*p* (33)	101
	4-Nitro	$(C_2H_5SO_2)_2C{=}NNHC_6H_4NO_2$-*p*†	19*c*
Methyl (methylsulfonyl)methyl sulfoxide	4-Nitro	*p*-$O_2NC_6H_4N{=}NC(SO_2CH_3){=}NNHC_6H_4NO_2$-*p*†	19*c*
Ethyl methylsulfonylacetate	4-Nitro	$CH_3SO_2C(CO_2C_2H_5){=}NNHC_6H_4NO_2$-*p* (79)	19*c*
2-(Methylsulfonyl)acetamide	4-Nitro	*p*-$O_2NC_6H_4N{=}NC(SO_2CH_3){=}NNHC_6H_4NO_2$-*p* (54)	19*c*
Methyl nitromethyl sulfone	4-Nitro	$CH_3SO_2C(NO_2){=}NNHC_6H_4NO_2$-*p* (35)	19*c*
Bis(phenylsulfonyl)methane	4-Nitro	$(C_6H_5SO_2)_2C{=}NNHC_6H_4NO_2$-*p*†	19*c*
Bis(methylsulfonyl)methylthiomethane	—	$(CH_3SO_2)_2C(SCH_3)N{=}NC_6H_5$ (66)	320
Phenylsulfonylacetic acid	2-Methyl	$C_6H_5SO_2C(N{=}NC_6H_4CH_3$-*o*$){=}NNHC_6H_4CH_3$-*o*	92
	2-Methoxy	$C_6H_5SO_2C(N{=}NC_6H_4OCH_3$-*o*$){=}NNHC_6H_4OCH_3$-*o*	92
Ethyl phenylsulfonylacetate	—	$C_6H_5SO_2C(CO_2C_2H_5){=}NNHC_6H_5$	92
	2-Methyl	$C_6H_5SO_2C(CO_2C_2H_5){=}NNHC_6H_4CH_3$-*o*	92
	3-Methyl	$C_6H_5SO_2C(CO_2C_2H_5){=}NNHC_6H_4CH_3$-*m*	92
	4-Methyl	$C_6H_5SO_2C(CO_2C_2H_5){=}NNHC_6H_4CH_3$-*p*	92
	2-Methoxy	$C_6H_5SO_2C(CO_2C_2H_5){=}NNHC_6H_4OCH_3$-*o*	92
	4-Methoxy	$C_6H_5SO_2C(CO_2C_2H_5){=}NNHC_6H_4OCH_3$-*p*	92
	4-Ethoxy	$C_6H_5SO_2C(CO_2C_2H_5){=}NNHC_6H_4OC_2H_5$-*p*	92
	2,4-Dimethyl	$C_6H_5SO_2C(CO_2C_2H_5){=}NNHC_6H_3(CH_3)_2$-2,4	92

Ethyl *p*-tolylsulfonylacetate	—	$p\text{-}CH_3C_6H_4SO_2C(CO_2C_2H_5){=}NNHC_6H_5$	92
	2-Methyl	$p\text{-}CH_3C_6H_4SO_2C(CO_2C_2H_5){=}NNHC_6H_4CH_3\text{-}o$	92
	3-Methyl	$p\text{-}CH_3C_6H_4SO_2C(CO_2C_2H_5){=}NNHC_6H_4CH_3\text{-}m$	92
	4-Methyl	$p\text{-}CH_3C_6H_4SO_2C(CO_2C_2H_5){=}NNHC_6H_4CH_3\text{-}p$	92
	2-Methoxy	$p\text{-}CH_3C_6H_4SO_2C(CO_2C_2H_5){=}NNHC_6H_4OCH_3\text{-}o$	92
	4-Methoxy	$p\text{-}CH_3C_6H_4SO_2C(CO_2C_2H_5){=}NNHC_6H_4OCH_3\text{-}p$	92
	4-Ethoxy	$p\text{-}CH_3C_6H_4SO_2C(CO_2C_2H_5){=}NNHC_6H_4OC_2H_5\text{-}p$	92
	2,4-Dimethyl	$p\text{-}CH_3C_6H_4SO_2C(CO_2C_2H_5){=}NNHC_6H_3(CH_3)_2\text{-}2,4$	92
Phenylsulfonylacetamide	—	$C_6H_5SO_2C(CONH_2){=}NNHC_6H_5$	92
	2-Methyl	$C_6H_5SO_2C(CONH_2){=}NNHC_6H_4CH_3\text{-}o$	92
	3-Methyl	$C_6H_5SO_2C(CONH_2){=}NNHC_6H_4CH_3\text{-}m$	92
	4-Methyl	$C_6H_5SO_2C(CONH_2){=}NNHC_6H_4CH_3\text{-}p$	92
	2-Methoxy	$C_6H_5SO_2C(CONH_2){=}NNHC_6H_4OCH_3\text{-}o$	92
	4-Methoxy	$C_6H_5SO_2C(CONH_2){=}NNHC_6H_4OCH_3\text{-}p$	92
	4-Ethoxy	$C_6H_5SO_2C(CONH_2){=}NNHC_6H_4OC_2H_5\text{-}p$	92
	2,4-Dimethyl	$C_6H_5SO_2C(CONH_2){=}NNHC_6H_3(CH_3)_2\text{-}2,4$	92
p-Tolylsulfonylacetamide	—	$p\text{-}CH_3C_6H_4SO_2C(CONH_2){=}NNHC_6H_5$	92
	2-Methyl	$p\text{-}CH_3C_6H_4SO_2C(CONH_2){=}NNHC_6H_4CH_3\text{-}o$	92
	3-Methyl	$p\text{-}CH_3C_6H_4SO_2C(CONH_2){=}NNHC_6H_4CH_3\text{-}m$	92
	4-Methyl	$p\text{-}CH_3C_6H_4SO_2C(CONH_2){=}NNHC_6H_4CH_3\text{-}p$	92
	2-Methoxy	$p\text{-}CH_3C_6H_4SO_2C(CONH_2){=}NNHC_6H_4OCH_3\text{-}o$	92
	4-Methoxy	$p\text{-}CH_3C_6H_4SO_2C(CONH_2){=}NNHC_6H_4OCH_3\text{-}p$	92
	4-Ethoxy	$p\text{-}CH_3C_6H_4SO_2C(CONH_2){=}NNHC_6H_4OC_2H_5\text{-}p$	92
	2,4-Dimethyl	$p\text{-}CH_3C_6H_4SO_2C(CONH_2){=}NNHC_6H_3(CH_3)_2\text{-}2,4$	92
Phenylsulfonylnitromethane	—	$C_6H_5SO_2C(NO_2){=}NNHC_6H_5$	102
p-Tolylsulfonylnitromethane	4-Nitro	$p\text{-}CH_3C_6H_4SO_2C(NO_2){=}NNHC_6H_4NO_2\text{-}p$ (22)	19*c*

Note: References 177–480 are on pp. 136–142.

* The full name is given when it is awkward to name the arylamine as a derivative of aniline.

† In addition, some 5-hydroxy-1,3-bis-(*p*-nitrophenyl)tetrazolium betaine was formed.

TABLE VI—*Continued*

COUPLING OF DIAZONIUM SALTS WITH SULFONES

Sulfone	Substituent(s) in Aniline*	Product (Yield, %)	References
p-Bromophenylsulfonylnitromethane	—	*p*-$BrC_6H_4SO_2C(NO_2)=NNHC_6H_5$	102
m-Nitrobenzyl phenyl sulfone	—	*m*-$O_2NC_6H_4C(SO_2C_6H_5)=NNHC_6H_5$	102
Sulfazone, i.e.,	5-Sulfo-1-naphthylamine	2-(5-Sulfo-1-naphthylazo)sulfazone	103
[structure: 1,4-benzothiazin-3-one 1,1-dioxide; positions H, N 4, 3 CO, 2 CH_2, 1 S O_2, 5, 6, 7, 8]	8-Hydroxy-6-sulfo-1-naphthylamine	2-(8-Hydroxy-6-sulfo-1-naphthylazo)sulfazone	103
	3-Sulfo-4-(*p*-sulfophenylazo)	2-[3-Sulfo-4-(*p*-sulfophenylazo)phenylazo]sulfazone	103
	4-[*p*-(4-Hydroxy-3-carboxyphenylazo)-phenyl]	2-{*p*-[*p*-(4-Hydroxy-3-carboxyphenylazo)-phenyl]-phenylazo}sulfazone	103
Sulfazone-7-sulfonylacetic acid	4-Sulfo	2-(*p*-Sulfophenylazo)sulfazone-7-sulfonylacetic acid	321
	3-Carboxy-4-hydroxy	2-(3-Carboxy-4-hydroxyphenylazo)sulfazone-7-sulfonylacetic acid	321
	4-Sulfo-1-naphthylamine	2-(4-Sulfo-1-naphthylazo)sulfazone-7-sulfonylacetic acid	321

Note: References 177–480 are on pp. 136–142.

* The full name is given when it is awkward to name the arylamine as a derivative of aniline.

TABLE VII

COUPLING OF DIAZONIUM SALTS WITH NITRO COMPOUNDS

Nitro Compound	Substituent(s) in Aniline*	Product (Yield, %)	References
Nitromethane	—	$C_6H_5NHN{=}CHNO_2$	104, 105, 107, 322
		$C_6H_5N{=}NC(NO_2){=}NNHC_6H_5$ (56)	20, 3, 104–107, 323
	2-Methyl	*o*-$CH_3C_6H_4N{=}NC(NO_2){=}NNHC_6H_4CH_3$-*o*	106
	4-Methyl	*p*-$CH_3C_6H_4N{=}NC(NO_2){=}NNHC_6H_4CH_3$-*p*	106
	2-Ethoxy	*o*-$C_2H_5OC_6H_4N{=}NC(NO_2){=}NNHC_6H_4OC_2H_5$-*o*	20
	4-Bromo	*p*-$BrC_6H_4N{=}NC(NO_2){=}NNHC_6H_4Br$-*p*	106
	2-Nitro	*o*-$O_2NC_6H_4NHN{=}CHNO_2$ (77)	323*a*, 323*b*
	4-Nitro	*p*-$O_2NC_6H_4N{=}NC(NO_2){=}NNHC_6H_4NO_2$-*p*	106
		p-$O_2NC_6H_4NHN{=}CHNO_2$ (6)	171, 324
	2-Formyl	*o*-$HCOC_6H_4NHN{=}CHNO_2$ (57)	167*d*
	2-Acetyl	*o*-$CH_3COC_6H_4NHN{=}CHNO_2$ (98)	167*d*
	2-Carboxy	*o*-$HO_2CC_6H_4NHN{=}CHNO_2$ (73)	167*d*
	2-Carbomethoxy	*o*-$CH_3O_2CC_6H_4NHN{=}CHNO_2$ (95)	167*d*
	4-Carbethoxy	*p*-$C_2H_5O_2CC_6H_4NHN{=}CHNO_2$ (80)	171
	4-Sulfo	*p*-$HO_3SC_6H_4N{=}NC(NO_2){=}NNHC_6H_4SO_3H$-*p*	325
	4-Sulfamyl	*p*-$H_2NSO_2C_6H_4N{=}NC(NO_2){=}NNHC_6H_4SO_2NH_2$-*p*	106
	2,4-Dimethyl	2,4-$(CH_3)_2C_6H_3N{=}NC(NO_2){=}NNHC_6H_3(CH_3)_2$-2,4 (20)	170
	2-Phenyl	*o*-$C_6H_5C_6H_4N{=}NC(NO_2){=}NNHC_6H_4C_6H_5$-*o*	20
	3-Phenyl	*m*-$C_6H_5C_6H_4N{=}NC(NO_2){=}NNHC_6H_4C_6H_5$-*m*	20
	4-Phenyl	*p*-$C_6H_5C_6H_4N{=}NC(NO_2){=}NNHC_6H_4C_6H_5$-*p*	106
	4-Phenoxy	*p*-$C_6H_5OC_6H_4N{=}NC(NO_2){=}NNHC_6H_4OC_6H_5$-*p*	20

Note: References 177–480 are on pp. 136–142.

* The full name is given when it is awkward to name the arylamine as a derivative of aniline.

TABLE VII—*Continued*

COUPLING OF DIAZONIUM SALTS WITH NITRO COMPOUNDS

Nitro Compound	Substituent(s) in Aniline*	Product (Yield, %)	References
Nitromethane (*Cont.*)	α-Naphthylamine	α-$C_{10}H_7N{=}NC(NO_2){=}NNHC_{10}H_7$-$\alpha$	106
	β-Naphthylamine	β-$C_{10}H_7N{=}NC(NO_2){=}NNHC_{10}H_7$-$\beta$ (63)	106
	2-Phenylthio	*o*-$C_6H_5SC_6H_4N{=}NC(NO_2){=}NNHC_6H_4SC_6H_5$-*o*	20
	2-(*p*-Anisyloxy)	N,N′-Di-*o*-(*p*-anisyloxy)phenyl-C-nitroformazan†	20
	2-Phenoxy-4-phenyl	N,N′-Di-(2-phenoxy-4-phenyl)phenyl-C-nitroformazan†	20
	2-Phenylthio-4-phenyl	N,N′-Di-(2-phenylthio-4-phenyl)phenyl-C-nitroformazan†	20
Nitroethane	—	$CH_3C(NO_2){=}NNHC_6H_5$ (quant.)	326, 1, 2, 107, 171, 324
	2-Methyl	$CH_3C(NO_2){=}NNHC_6H_4CH_3$-*o*	327
	4-Methyl	$CH_3C(NO_2){=}NNHC_6H_4CH_3$-*p*	324, 327
	4-Chloro	$CH_3C(NO_2){=}NNHC_6H_4Cl$-*p* (quant.)	176*b*
	4-Bromo	$CH_3C(NO_2){=}NNHC_6H_4Br$-*p*	328
	3-Nitro	$CH_3C(NO_2){=}NNHC_6H_4NO_2$-*m*	329
	4-Nitro	$CH_3C(NO_2){=}NNHC_6H_4NO_2$-*p*	324
	4-Sulfo	$CH_3C(NO_2){=}NNHC_6H_4SO_3H$-*p*	325
	2,4-Dichloro	$CH_3C(NO_2){=}NNHC_6H_3Cl_2$-2,4 (95)	330
	2,4,6-Trichloro	$CH_3C(NO_2){=}NNHC_6H_2Cl_3$-2,4,6‡	330, 331
	2,4,6-Tribromo	$CH_3C(NO_2){=}NNHC_6H_2Br_3$-2,4,6 (49)‡	331
	α-Naphthylamine	$CH_3C(NO_2){=}NNHC_{10}H_7$-$\alpha$ (5)	332
	β-Naphthylamine	$CH_3C(NO_2){=}NNHC_{10}H_7$-$\beta$	324, 332
1-Nitropropane	—	$C_2H_5C(NO_2){=}NNHC_6H_5$ (87)	326, 4, 107, 324
	4-Methyl	$C_2H_5C(NO_2){=}NNHC_6H_4CH_3$-*p*	324
	4-Nitro	$C_2H_5C(NO_2){=}NNHC_6H_4NO_2$-*p*	324
	β-Naphthylamine	$C_2H_5C(NO_2){=}NNHC_{10}H_7$-$\beta$	324

2-Nitropropane	—	$(CH_3)_2C(NO_2)N{=}NC_6H_5$	2, 333
	4-Methyl	$(CH_3)_2C(NO_2)N{=}NC_6H_4CH_3\text{-}p$	333
	4-Chloro	$(CH_3)_2C(NO_2)N{=}NC_6H_4Cl\text{-}p$	333
	4-Bromo	$(CH_3)_2C(NO_2)N{=}NC_6H_4Br\text{-}p$	333
	2-Nitro	$(CH_3)_2C(NO_2)N{=}NC_6H_4NO_2\text{-}o$	333
	3-Nitro	$(CH_3)_2C(NO_2)N{=}NC_6H_4NO_2\text{-}m$	333
	4-Nitro	$(CH_3)_2C(NO_2)N{=}NC_6H_4NO_2\text{-}p$	324, 333
	2-Carboxy	$(CH_3)_2C(NO_2)N{=}NC_6H_4CO_2H\text{-}o$	333
	4-Carboxy	$(CH_3)_2C(NO_2)N{=}NC_6H_4CO_2H\text{-}p$	333
	4-Sulfo	$(CH_3)_2C(NO_2)N{=}NC_6H_4SO_3H\text{-}p$	325
	4-Acetamido	$(CH_3)_2C(NO_2)N{=}NC_6H_4NHCOCH_3\text{-}p$	333
	2,5-Dichloro	$(CH_3)_2C(NO_2)N{=}NC_6H_3Cl_2\text{-}2,5$	333
	2-Methyl-5-nitro	$(CH_3)_2C(NO_2)N{=}NC_6H_3CH_3\text{-}2\text{-}NO_2\text{-}5$	333
	2,4,6-Tribromo	$(CH_3)_2C(NO_2)N{=}NC_6H_2Br_3\text{-}2,4,6$	333
	β-Naphthylamine	$(CH_3)_2C(NO_2)N{=}NC_{10}H_7\text{-}\beta$	324, 333
	Benzidine	$[(CH_3)_2C(NO_2)N{=}NC_6H_4\text{-}]_2$	333
	4-Phenylazo	$p\text{-}(C_6H_5N{=}N)C_6H_4N{=}NC(CH_3)_2NO_2$	333
1-Nitro-2-propene	—	$CH_2{=}CHC(NO_2){=}NNHC_6H_5$	334
	2-Methyl	$CH_2{=}CHC(NO_2){=}NNHC_6H_4CH_3\text{-}o$	334
	4-Methyl	$CH_2{=}CHC(NO_2){=}NNHC_6H_4CH_3\text{-}p$	334
	4-Methoxy	$CH_2{=}CHC(NO_2){=}NNHC_6H_4OCH_3\text{-}p$	334
	4-Ethoxy	$CH_2{=}CHC(NO_2){=}NNHC_6H_4OC_2H_5\text{-}p$	334
	4-Chloro	$CH_2{=}CHC(NO_2){=}NNHC_6H_4Cl\text{-}p$	334
	3-Bromo	$CH_2{=}CHC(NO_2){=}NNHC_6H_4Br\text{-}m$	334
	4-Carboxy	$CH_2{=}CHC(NO_2){=}NNHC_6H_4CO_2H\text{-}p$	334
1-Nitro-*n*-butane	—	$n\text{-}C_3H_7C(NO_2){=}NNHC_6H_5$	107

Note: References 177–480 are on pp. 136–142.

* The full name is given when it is awkward to name the arylamine as a derivative of aniline.

† The formazan structure is $H_2NN{=}CHN{=}NH$.

‡ In addition, some diarylazonitroethane was formed.

TABLE VII—*Continued*

COUPLING OF DIAZONIUM SALTS WITH NITRO COMPOUNDS

Nitro Compound	Substituent(s) in Aniline*	Product (Yield, %)	References
2-Nitro-*n*-butane	3-Nitro	$C_2H_5C(NO_2)(CH_3)N{=}NC_6H_4NO_2\text{-}m$	333
	4-Carboxy	$C_2H_5C(NO_2)(CH_3)N{=}NC_6H_4CO_2H\text{-}p$	333
	2,5-Dichloro	$C_2H_5C(NO_2)(CH_3)N{=}NC_6H_3Cl_2\text{-}2,5$	333
	2-Methyl-5-nitro	$C_2H_5C(NO_2)(CH_3)N{=}NC_6H_3CH_3\text{-}2\text{-}NO_2\text{-}5$	333
	2,4,6-Tribromo	$C_2H_5C(NO_2)(CH_3)N{=}NC_6H_2Br_3\text{-}2,4,6$	333
	4-Phenylazo	$C_2H_5C(NO_2)(CH_3)N{=}NC_6H_4(N{=}NC_6H_5)\text{-}p$	333
2-Methyl-1-nitropropane	—	$(CH_3)_2CHC(NO_2){=}NNHC_6H_5$	5
	4-Sulfo	$(CH_3)_2CHC(NO_2){=}NNHC_6H_4SO_3H\text{-}p$	325
1-Nitro-*n*-pentane	—	$n\text{-}C_4H_9C(NO_2){=}NNHC_6H_5$ (90–100)	326
Dinitromethane	—	$C_6H_5N{=}NCH(NO_2)_2$	335
	4-Nitro	$p\text{-}O_2NC_6H_4NHN{=}C(NO_2)_2$ (37)	19*c*
1,3-Dinitropropane	—	$C_6H_5NHN{=}C(NO_2)CH_2C(NO_2){=}NNHC_6H_5$	336
	4-Methyl	$p\text{-}CH_3C_6H_4NHN{=}C(NO_2)CH_2C(NO_2){=}NNHC_6H_4CH_3\text{-}p$	336
	4-Methoxy	$p\text{-}CH_3OC_6H_4NHN{=}C(NO_2)CH_2C(NO_2){=}NNHC_6H_4OCH_3\text{-}p$	336
1,5-Dinitro-*n*-pentane	—	$C_6H_5NHN{=}C(NO_2)(CH_2)_3C(NO_2){=}NNHC_6H_5$	337
1,7-Dinitro-*n*-heptane	—	$C_6H_5NHN{=}C(NO_2)(CH_2)_5C(NO_2){=}NNHC_6H_5$	338
Iodonitromethane	—	$IC(NO_2){=}NNHC_6H_5$	339
	4-Methyl	$IC(NO_2){=}NNHC_6H_4CH_3\text{-}p$	339
Methazonic acid	—	$C_6H_5NHN{=}C(NO_2)CH{=}NOH$	340
	4-Methyl	$p\text{-}CH_3C_6H_4NHN{=}C(NO_2)CH{=}NOH$	340
Nitroacetamide	—	$C_6H_5NHN{=}C(NO_2)CONH_2$	89
	4-Nitro	$p\text{-}O_2NC_6H_4NHN{=}C(NO_2)CONH_2$ (66)	19*c*
Methyl nitroacetate	—	$C_6H_5NHN{=}C(NO_2)CO_2CH_3$ (56)	341
Ethyl nitroacetate	—	$C_6H_5NHN{=}C(NO_2)CO_2C_2H_5$	342
	4-Nitro	$p\text{-}O_2NC_6H_4NHN{=}C(NO_2)CO_2C_2H_5$	342

4-Nitro-1-butanesulfonic acid	4-Nitro	p-$O_2NC_6H_4N{=}NC(NO_2)(C_2H_5)CH_2SO_3H$ (51)	343
	4-Phenylazo	p-$(C_6H_5N{=}N)C_6H_4N{=}NC(NO_2)(C_2H_5)CH_2SO_3H$ (56)	343
	3,3′-Dimethoxy-benzidine	2,2′-(3,3′-Dimethoxy-4,4′-biphenylenedisazo)bis-[2-nitro-1-butanesulfonic acid] (77)	343
2-Nitroethanol	—	$HOCH_2C(NO_2){=}NNHC_6H_5$ (94)	107, 344
	4-Sulfo	$HOCH_2C(NO_2){=}NNHC_6H_4SO_3H$-$p$	344
2-Nitropropanol	—	$CH_3C(NO_2){=}NNHC_6H_5$ (78)	107
1-Nitro-2-propanol	—	$CH_3CHOHC(NO_2){=}NNHC_6H_5$	107
2-Nitro-1-butanol	—	$C_2H_5C(NO_2){=}NNHC_6H_5$	107
	4-Methyl	$HOCH_2C(NO_2)(C_2H_5)N{=}NC_6H_4CH_3$-$p$§	108
	2-Chloro	$HOCH_2C(NO_2)(C_2H_5)N{=}NC_6H_4Cl$-$o$§	108
	4-Chloro	$HOCH_2C(NO_2)(C_2H_5)N{=}NC_6H_4Cl$-$p$§ (56)	108
		$C_2H_5C(NO_2){=}NNHC_6H_4Cl$-$p$‖	108
	2-Bromo	$HOCH_2C(NO_2)(C_2H_5)N{=}NC_6H_4Br$-$o$§	108
	4-Bromo	$HOCH_2C(NO_2)(C_2H_5)N{=}NC_6H_4Br$-$p$§	108
		$C_2H_5C(NO_2){=}NNHC_6H_4Br$-$p$‖	108
	2,5-Dichloro	$HOCH_2C(NO_2)(C_2H_5)N{=}NC_6H_3Cl_2$-2,5§	108
	2-Methyl-4-nitro	$C_2H_5C(NO_2){=}NNHC_6H_3CH_3$-2-$NO_2$-4	108
	5-Methyl-3-nitro	$HOCH_2C(NO_2)(C_2H_5)N{=}NC_6H_3CH_3$-5-$NO_2$-3§	108
1-Nitro-2-butanol	—	$C_2H_5CHOHC(NO_2){=}NNHC_6H_5$	107
3-Nitro-2-butanol	—	$CH_3C(NO_2){=}NNHC_6H_5$	107
1,1,1-Trichloro-3-nitro-2-propanol	—	$Cl_3CCHOHC(NO_2){=}NNHC_6H_5$	107

Note: References 177–480 are on pp. 136–142.

* The full name is given when it is awkward to name the arylamine as a derivative of aniline.

§ This product was obtained by acidification of the reaction mixture.

‖ This product was obtained when the alkaline reaction mixture was left for several days.

TABLE VII—*Continued*

COUPLING OF DIAZONIUM SALTS WITH NITRO COMPOUNDS

Nitro Compound	Substituent(s) in Aniline*	Product (Yield, %)	References
1,1,1-Trichloro-3-nitro-2-propyl acetate	—	$Cl_3CCH(O_2CCH_3)C(NO_2){=}NNHC_6H_5$	345
	2-Methyl	$Cl_3CCH(O_2CCH_3)C(NO_2){=}NNHC_6H_4CH_3$-*o*	345
	3-Methyl	$Cl_3CCH(O_2CCH_3)C(NO_2){=}NNHC_6H_4CH_3$-*m*	345
	4-Methyl	$Cl_3CCH(O_2CCH_3)C(NO_2){=}NNHC_6H_4CH_3$-*p*	345
	4-Chloro	$Cl_3CCH(O_2CCH_3)C(NO_2){=}NNHC_6H_4Cl$-*p*	345
	4-Nitro	$Cl_3CCH(O_2CCH_3)C(NO_2){=}NNHC_6H_4NO_2$-*p*	345
	2,4-Dichloro	$Cl_3CCH(O_2CCH_3)C(NO_2){=}NNHC_6H_3Cl_2$-2,4	345
2-Nitro-1,3-propanediol	—	$HOCH_2C(NO_2){=}NNHC_6H_5$ (97)	107
2-Nitro-1-pentanol	—	*n*-$C_3H_7C(NO_2){=}NNHC_6H_5$	107
1-Nitro-2-pentanol	—	*n*-$C_3H_7CHOHC(NO_2){=}NNHC_6H_5$	107
1-Nitro-2-hexanol	—	*n*-$C_4H_9CHOHC(NO_2){=}NNHC_6H_5$	107
2-Nitro-1-phenylethanol	—	$C_6H_5CHOHC(NO_2){=}NNHC_6H_5$	107
3,3,4-Trichloro-1-nitro-2-pentyl acetate	—	$CH_3CHClCCl_2C(O_2CCH_3)C(NO_2){=}NNHC_6H_5$	345
	4-Methyl	$CH_3CHClCCl_2C(O_2CCH_3)C(NO_2){=}NNHC_6H_4CH_3$-*p*	345
	4-Chloro	$CH_3CHClCCl_2C(O_2CCH_3)C(NO_2){=}NNHC_6H_4Cl$-*p*	345
	4-Nitro	$CH_3CHClCCl_2C(O_2CCH_3)C(NO_2){=}NNHC_6H_4NO_2$-*p*	345
1-Benzoyl-2-nitroethanol	4-Nitro	*p*-$O_2NC_6H_4N{=}NC(NO_2){=}NNHC_6H_4NO_2$-*p*	346
2,4-Dinitro-1,3-diphenyl-1-butanol	—	$C_6H_5CHOHCH(NO_2)CH(C_6H_5)C(NO_2){=}NNHC_6H_5$	347
α-Nitrotoluene	—	$C_6H_5C(NO_2){=}NNHC_6H_5$ (80)	171, 348, 349
	4-Methyl	$C_6H_5C(NO_2){=}NNHC_6H_4CH_3$-*p* (40)	171
	4-Methoxy	$C_6H_5C(NO_2){=}NNHC_6H_4OCH_3$-*p* (33)	171
	4-Butoxy	$C_6H_5C(NO_2){=}NNHC_6H_4OC_4H_9$-*p* (34)	171

	4-Benzyloxy	$C_6H_5C(NO_2)=NNHC_6H_4OCH_2C_6H_5\text{-}p$ (39)	171
	3-Nitro	$C_6H_5C(NO_2)=NNHC_6H_4NO_2\text{-}m$ (quant.)	350
	4-Nitro	$C_6H_5C(NO_2)=NNHC_6H_4NO_2\text{-}p$	111, 172, 350
	4-Phenyl	$C_6H_5C(NO_2)=NNHC_6H_4C_6H_5\text{-}p$ (33)	171
	2,4-Dinitro	$C_6H_5C(NO_2)=NNHC_6H_3(NO_2)_2\text{-}2,4$	350
	2-Methyl-4-nitro	$C_6H_5C(NO_2)=NNHC_6H_3CH_3\text{-}2\text{-}NO_2\text{-}4$	172
	4-Methyl-2-nitro	$C_6H_5C(NO_2)=NNHC_6H_3CH_3\text{-}4\text{-}NO_2\text{-}2$	172
	2-Chloro-4-nitro	$C_6H_5C(NO_2)=NNHC_6H_3Cl\text{-}2\text{-}NO_2\text{-}4$	172
	β-Naphthylamine	$C_6H_5C(NO_2)=NNHC_{10}H_7\text{-}\beta$ (34)	171
	2-(*o*-Nitrophenyl)	$C_6H_5C(NO_2)=NNHC_6H_4(C_6H_4NO_2\text{-}o)\text{-}o$ (55)	323*a*
	4-Chloro-2-(4-chloro-2-nitro-phenyl)	$C_6H_5C(NO_2)=NNHC_6H_3Cl\text{-}4\text{-}(C_6H_3Cl\text{-}4\text{-}NO_2\text{-}2)\text{-}2$ (35)	323*a*
	4-Bromo-2-(4-bromo-2-nitro-phenyl)	$C_6H_5C(NO_2)=NNHC_6H_3Br\text{-}4\text{-}(C_6H_3Br\text{-}4\text{-}NO_2\text{-}2)\text{-}2$	323*a*
α-Nitrobenzylcyanide	—	$C_6H_5C(CN)=NNHC_6H_4NO_2\text{-}p$	114
	2-Methyl	$C_6H_5C(CN)=NNHC_6H_3CH_3\text{-}2\text{-}NO_2\text{-}4$	114
	4-Methyl	$C_6H_5C(CN)=NNHC_6H_3CH_3\text{-}4\text{-}NO_2\text{-}2$	114
	2-Chloro	$C_6H_5C(CN)=NNHC_6H_3Cl\text{-}2\text{-}NO_2\text{-}4$	114
	4-Chloro	$C_6H_5C(CN)=NNHC_6H_3Cl\text{-}4\text{-}NO_2\text{-}2$	114
	2-Nitro	$C_6H_5C(CN)=NNHC_6H_3(NO_2)_2\text{-}2,4$	114
	4-Nitro	$C_6H_5C(CN)=NNHC_6H_3(NO_2)_2\text{-}2,4$	114
p-Methoxy-α-nitrotoluene	—	$p\text{-}CH_3OC_6H_4C(NO_2)=NNHC_6H_5$	351
p-Chloro-α-nitrotoluene	2-(*o*-Nitrophenyl)	$p\text{-}ClC_6H_4C(NO_2)=NNHC_6H_4(C_6H_4NO_2\text{-}o)\text{-}o$ (75)	323*a*
α,*m*-Dinitrotoluene	—	$m\text{-}O_2NC_6H_4C(NO_2)=NNHC_6H_5$ (quant.)	352
α,*p*-Dinitrotoluene	—	$p\text{-}O_2NC_6H_4C(NO_2)=NNHC_6H_5$	352
	4-Nitro	$p\text{-}O_2NC_6H_4C(NO_2)=NNHC_6H_4NO_2\text{-}p$	342

Note: References 177–480 are on pp. 136–142.

* The full name is given when it is awkward to name the arylamine as a derivative of aniline.

TABLE VII—*Continued*

COUPLING OF DIAZONIUM SALTS WITH NITRO COMPOUNDS

Nitro Compound	Substituent(s) in Aniline*	Product (Yield, %)	References
α-Nitroacetophenone	—	$C_6H_5COC(NO_2){=}NNHC_6H_5$ (60)	353
	4-Chloro	$C_6H_5COC(NO_2){=}NNHC_6H_4Cl$-*p*	353
	4-Bromo	$C_6H_5COC(NO_2){=}NNHC_6H_4Br$-*p*	353
	2-Nitro	$C_6H_5COC(NO_2){=}NNHC_6H_4NO_2$-*o*	353
	4-Nitro	$C_6H_5COC(NO_2){=}NNHC_6H_4NO_2$-*p*	342, 353
	2,4-Dichloro	$C_6H_5COC(NO_2){=}NNHC_6H_3Cl_2$-2,4	353
	2,5-Dichloro	$C_6H_5COC(NO_2){=}NNHC_6H_3Cl_2$-2,5	353
	2,4-Dibromo	$C_6H_5COC(NO_2){=}NNHC_6H_3Br_2$-2,4	353
	2,4,6-Tribromo	$C_6H_5COC(NO_2){=}NNHC_6H_2Br_3$-2,4,6	353
	2,4,5-Tribromo	$C_6H_5COC(NO_2){=}NNHC_6H_2Br_3$-2,4,5	353
1-Nitro-3-phenylpropane	—	$C_6H_5(CH_2)_2C(NO_2){=}NNHC_6H_5$	354
Diphenylnitromethane	—	$(C_6H_5)_2C{=}NNHC_6H_4NO_2$-*p*	112, 113
α,α-Dinitrotoluene	—	$C_6H_5C(NO_2){=}NNHC_6H_4NO_2$-*p*	109, 111, 355
	2-Methyl	$C_6H_5C(NO_2){=}NNHC_6H_3CH_3$-2-$NO_2$-4	109, 356
	4-Methyl	$C_6H_5CON{=}NC_6H_4CH_3$-*p*	356
	2-Chloro	$C_6H_5C(NO_2){=}NNHC_6H_3Cl$-2-$NO_2$-4	109, 356
	4-Chloro	$C_6H_5CON{=}NC_6H_4Cl$-*p*	356
	2-Bromo	$C_6H_5C(NO_2){=}NNHC_6H_3Br$-2-$NO_2$-4	109, 356
	4-Bromo	$C_6H_5CON{=}NC_6H_4Br$-*p*	356, 357
	2,4-Dimethyl	$C_6H_5CON{=}NC_6H_3(CH_3)_2$-2,4	110

	2-Methyl-4-nitro	$C_6H_5CON{=}NC_6H_3CH_3$-2-NO_2-4	110
	4-Methyl-2-nitro	$C_6H_5CON{=}NC_6H_3CH_3$-4-NO_2-2	110
	4-Methyl-3-nitro	$C_6H_5CON{=}NC_6H_3CH_3$-4-NO_2-3	110
	2,4,6-Tribromo	$C_6H_5CON{=}NC_6H_2Br_3$-2,4,6	110
α,α-Dinitro-*p*-xylene	—	*p*-$CH_3C_6H_4C(NO_2){=}NNHC_6H_4NO_2$-*p*	109, 358
α,α-Dinitro-*p*-methoxytoluene	—	*p*-$CH_3OC_6H_4C(NO_2){=}NNHC_6H_4NO_2$-*p*	109, 358
4-(2-Nitropropyl)morpholine	—	4-(2-Nitro-2-phenylazopropyl)morpholine (22)	176*a*
	4-Chloro	4-[2-Nitro-2-(*p*-chlorophenylazo)propyl]morpholine (26)	176*a*
	2-Nitro	4-[2-Nitro-2-(*o*-nitrophenylazo)propyl]morpholine (32)	176*a*
	3-Nitro	4-[2-Nitro-2-(*m*-nitrophenylazo)propyl]morpholine (41)	176*a*
	4-Nitro	4-[2-Nitro-2-(*p*-nitrophenylazo)propyl]morpholine (46)	176*a*
	2-Carboxy	4-[2-Nitro-2-(*o*-carboxyphenylazo)propyl]morpholine (13)	176*a*
	4-Carboxy	4-[2-Nitro-2-(*p*-carboxyphenylazo)propyl]morpholine (26)	176*a*
	2,4-Dichloro	4-[2-Nitro-2-(2,4-dichlorophenylazo)propyl]morpholine (48)	176*a*
	β-Naphthylamine	4-(2-Nitro-2-β-naphthylazopropyl)morpholine (25)	176*a*
	4-Phenylazo	4-[2-Nitro-2-(*p*-phenylazophenylazo)propyl]morpholine (80)	176*a*
1-Di-*n*-butylamino-2-nitrobutane	4-Chloro	2-(*p*-Chlorophenylazo)-2-nitrotributylamine (7)	176*a*
	β-Naphthylamine	2-β-Naphthylazo-2-nitrotributylamine (17)	176*a*
2,3-Diphenyl-1,4-dinitrobutane	—	2,3-Diphenyl-1,4-dihydrazono-1,4-dinitrobutane (89)	359
2,3-Di-(3,4-methylenedioxyphenyl)-1,4-dinitrobutane	—	2,3-Di-(3,4-methylenedioxyphenyl)-1,4-dihydrazono-1,4-dinitrobutane	359
Nitromethyl *p*-tolyl sulfoxide	4-Nitro	*p*-$CH_3C_6H_4SOC(NO_2){=}NNHC_6H_4NO_2$-*p* (43)	19*c*

Note: References 177–480 are on pp. 136–142.

* The full name is given when it is awkward to name the arylamine as a derivative of aniline.

TABLE VIII

Coupling of Diazonium Salts with Hydrocarbons

A. Unsaturated Hydrocarbons

Hydrocarbon	Substituent(s) in Aniline*	Product (Yield, %)	References
2-Methylpropene	4-Amino	$(CH_3)_2C{=}CHN{=}NC_6H_4N{=}NCH{=}C(CH_3)_2$	116
	2,4-Dinitro	$2,4\text{-}(O_2N)_2C_6H_3N{=}NCH{=}C(CH_3)_2$	116
1,3-Butadiene	4-Nitro	$p\text{-}O_2NC_6H_4N{=}NCH{=}CHCH{=}CH_2$	360
	2,4-Dinitro	$2,4\text{-}(O_2N)_2C_6H_3N{=}NCH{=}CHCH{=}CH_2$ (13)	115
2-Methyl-2-butene	4-Amino	$(CH_3)_2C{=}C(CH_3)N{=}NC_6H_4N{=}NC(CH_3){=}C(CH_3)_2$	116
	2,4-Dinitro	$2,4\text{-}(O_2N)_2C_6H_3N{=}NC(CH_3){=}C(CH_3)_2$	116
1,3-Pentadiene	4-Amino	$CH_2{=}CHCH{=}C(CH_3)N{=}NC_6H_4N{=}NC(CH_3){=}CHCH{=}CH_2$	116
	4-Nitro	$p\text{-}O_2NC_6H_4N{=}NC(CH_3){=}CHCH{=}CH_2$	115, 116
	2,4-Dinitro	$2,4\text{-}(O_2N)_2C_6H_3N{=}NC(CH_3){=}CHCH{=}CH_2$	115, 116
2-Methyl-1,3-butadiene	4-Nitro	$p\text{-}O_2NC_6H_4N{=}NCH{=}C(CH_3)CH{=}CH_2$	361*a*
	2,4-Dinitro	$2,4\text{-}(O_2N)_2C_6H_3N{=}NC(CH_3){=}CHCH{=}CH_2$	115
2,4-Hexadiene	4-Nitro	$p\text{-}O_2NC_6H_4N{=}NC(CH_3){=}CHCH{=}CHCH_3$	116, 360
	2,4-Dinitro	$2,4\text{-}(O_2N)_2C_6H_3N{=}NC(CH_3){=}CHCH{=}CHCH_3$	116
2-Methyl-2,4-pentadiene	2,4-Dinitro	$2,4\text{-}(O_2N)_2C_6H_3N{=}NCH{=}CHCH{=}C(CH_3)_2$ (49)	361*b*
2,3-Dimethyl-1,3-butadiene	4-Nitro	$p\text{-}O_2NC_6H_4N{=}NCH{=}C(CH_3)C(CH_3){=}CH_2$ (47)	115
	2,4-Dinitro	$2,4\text{-}(O_2N)_2C_6H_3N{=}NCH{=}C(CH_3)C(CH_3){=}CH_2$	115
Cyclopentadiene	—	1-Phenylazocyclopentadiene (small)	117, 362
	4-Nitro	1-(*p*-Nitrophenylazo)cyclopentadiene	118
	2,4-Dinitro	1-(2,4-Dinitrophenylazo)cyclopentadiene	118
2,4-Cyclopentadiene-1-carboxylic acid	2-Hydroxy-5-sulfo	1-(2-Hydroxy-5-sulfophenylazo)-2,4-cyclopentadiene-1-carboxylic acid (40)	363
2,5-Dimethyl-2,4-hexadiene	4-Amino	3,3′-(*p*-Phenylenedisazo)bis-(2,5-dimethyl-2,4-hexadiene)	116
	4-Nitro	3-(*p*-Nitrophenylazo)-2,5-dimethyl-2,4-hexadiene	116

	2,4-Dinitro	3-(2,4-Dinitrophenylazo)-2,5-dimethyl-2,4-hexadiene	116
Indene	2,4-Dinitro	1-(2,4-Dinitrophenylazo)indene	118
p-Methoxystyrene	2,4-Dinitro	*p*-$CH_3OC_6H_4CH{=}NNHC_6H_3(NO_2)_2$-2,4 (21)	124
Phenylacetylene	4-Nitro	$C_6H_5COCH{=}NNHC_6H_4NO_2$-*p* (13)	124
p-Methoxyphenylacetylene	4-Nitro	*p*-$CH_3OC_6H_4COCH{=}NNHC_6H_4NO_2$-*p* (33)	124
	2,4-Dinitro	*p*-$CH_3OC_6H_4COCH{=}NNHC_6H_3(NO_2)_2$-2,4 (69)	124
Anethole	4-Nitro	*p*-$CH_3OC_6H_4CH{=}NNHC_6H_4NO_2$-*p* (71)†	127
	2,4-Dinitro	*p*-$CH_3OC_6H_4CH{=}NNHC_6H_3(NO_2)_2$-2,4 (62)†	127
o-Propenylphenol	4-Nitro	*o*-$HOC_6H_4CH{=}NNHC_6H_4NO_2$-*p* (25)†	130
p-Propenylphenol	4-Nitro	*p*-$HOC_6H_4CH{=}NNHC_6H_4NO_2$-*p* (60)†	130
Isosafrole	4-Nitro	Piperonal *p*-nitrophenylhydrazone (72)†	127
	2,4-Dinitro	Piperonal 2,4-dinitrophenylhydrazone†	127
Isoeugenol	4-Nitro	Vanillin *p*-nitrophenylhydrazone (86)†	128
	2,4-Dinitro	Vanillin 2,4-dinitrophenylhydrazone†	128
Isoapiole	4-Nitro	Apiolaldehyde *p*-nitrophenylhydrazone†	127
p-Propenyldimethylaniline	4-Nitro	*p*-$(CH_3)_2NC_6H_4CH{=}NNHC_6H_4NO_2$-*p*†‡	129
1,1-Diphenylethylene	2,4-Dinitro	$(C_6H_5)_2C{=}CHN{=}NC_6H_3(NO_2)_2$-2,4	14
1,1-Bis-(*p*-tolyl)ethylene	4-(*p*-Phenylmercaptobenzoyl)	(*p*-$CH_3C_6H_4)_2C{=}CHN{=}NC_6H_4(COC_6H_4SC_6H_5$-*p*)-*p*	13
1,1-Bis-(*p*-anisyl)ethylene	4-Nitro	(*p*-$CH_3OC_6H_4)_2C{=}CHN{=}NC_6H_4NO_2$-*p* (40)	14
	4-(*p*-Phenylmercaptobenzoyl)	(*p*-$CH_3OC_6H_4)_2C{=}CHN{=}NC_6H_4(COC_6H_4SC_6H_5$-*p*)-*p*	13
1-Phenyl-1-(*p*-anisyl)ethylene	—	*p*-$CH_3OC_6H_4C(C_6H_5){=}CHN{=}NC_6H_5$	14
	2,4-Dinitro	*p*-$CH_3OC_6H_4C(C_6H_5){=}CHN{=}NC_6H_3(NO_2)_2$-2,4 (40)	14

Note: References 177–480 are on pp. 136–142.

* The full name is given when it is awkward to name the arylamine as a derivative of aniline.

† These products were obtained by the addition of the dry diazonium salt to an ethanolic solution of the reactant.

‡ When an alcoholic solution of the reactant was added to the dry diazonium salt, the entire side chain was eliminated to give a nearly quantitative yield of N,N-dimethyl-*p*-(*p*-nitrophenylazo)aniline.[364]

TABLE VIII—*Continued*

A. Unsaturated Hydrocarbons—Continued

Hydrocarbon	Substituent(s) in Aniline*	Product (Yield, %)	References
1,1-Bis-(*p*-dimethylaminophenyl)ethylene	—	$[p\text{-}(CH_3)_2NC_6H_4]_2C{=}CHN{=}NC_6H_5$	14
	4-Nitro	$[p\text{-}(CH_3)_2NC_6H_4]_2C{=}CHN{=}NC_6H_4NO_2\text{-}p$	14
	2,4-Dinitro	$[p\text{-}(CH_3)_2NC_6H_4]_2C{=}CHN{=}NC_6H_3(NO_2)_2\text{-}2,4$	14
	1-Aminoanthraquinone	$[p\text{-}(CH_3)_2NC_6H_4]_2C{=}CHN{=}NC_{14}H_7O_2$ (88)	14
1-Phenyl-1-(*p*-dimethylaminophenyl)ethylene	—	$p\text{-}(CH_3)_2NC_6H_4C(C_6H_5){=}CHN{=}NC_6H_5$	14
	4-Nitro	$p\text{-}(CH_3)_2NC_6H_4C(C_6H_5){=}CHN{=}NC_6H_4NO_2\text{-}p$	14
	2,4-Dinitro	$p\text{-}(CH_3)_2NC_6H_4C(C_6H_5){=}CHN{=}NC_6H_3(NO_2)_2\text{-}2,4$	14
1-Phenyl-1,3-butadiene	4-Nitro	$C_6H_5CH{=}CHCH{=}CHN{=}NC_6H_4NO_2\text{-}p$	365
2,3-Diphenyl-1,3-butadiene	2,4-Dinitro	$2,4\text{-}(O_2N)_2C_6H_3N{=}NCH{=}C(C_6H_5)C(C_6H_5){=}CH_2$	366

B. Compounds Containing a Reactive Methyl Group

Reactive Methyl Compound	Substituent(s) in Aniline	Product (Yield, %)	References
α-Picoline	4-Nitro	α-Picolinaldehyde *p*-nitrophenylhydrazone (58)	132
2,4,6-Trinitrotoluene	4-Nitro	2,4,6-Trinitrobenzaldehyde *p*-nitrophenylhydrazone (86)	132
2-Methylimidazole	4-Nitro	Imidazole-2-carboxaldehyde *p*-nitrophenylhydrazone (64)	132
2,6-Dimethyl-3,5-dicarboxypyridine	4-Nitro	3,5-Dicarboxy-6-methylpyridine-2-carboxaldehyde *p*-nitrophenylhydrazone (94)	132
N-Methylquinaldinium iodide	—	1,2-Dihydro-1-methyl-2-phenylazomethylenequinoline	133, 134
	4-Nitro	1,2-Dihydro-1-methyl-2-(*p*-nitrophenylazomethylene)-quinoline	133, 134

N-Methylquinaldinium methosulfate	4-Nitro	1,2-Dihydro-1-methyl-2-(*p*-nitrophenylazomethylene)-quinoline	132*g*
	2,5-Dichloro	1,2-Dihydro-1-methyl-2-(2,5-dichlorophenylazomethylene)-quinoline	132*g*
	2-Methoxy-5-chloro	1,2-Dihydro-1-methyl-2-(2-methoxy-5-chlorophenylazo-methylene)quinoline	132*g*
	2-Methoxy-4-nitro	1,2-Dihydro-1-methyl-2-(2-methoxy-4-nitrophenylazo-methylene)quinoline	132*g*
N-Ethyllepidinium iodide	4-Nitro	1,4-Dihydro-1-ethyl-4-(*p*-nitrophenylazomethylene)-quinoline	132*g*
	2,5-Dichloro	1,4-Dihydro-1-ethyl-4-(2,5-dichlorophenylazomethylene)-quinoline	132*g*
	2-Methoxy-5-chloro	1,4-Dihydro-1-ethyl-4-(2-methoxy-5-chlorophenylazo-methylene)quinoline	132*g*
	2-Methoxy-4-nitro	1,4-Dihydro-1-ethyl-4-(2-methoxy-4-nitrophenylazo-methylene)quinoline	132*g*
2,3,3-Trimethylindolenine	—	3,3-Dimethylindolenine-2-carboxaldehyde phenyl-hydrazone (60–90)	132*a*
	4-Chloro	3,3-Dimethylindolenine-2-carboxaldehyde *p*-chloro-phenylhydrazone (60–90)	132*a*
	4-Nitro	3,3-Dimethylindolenine-2-carboxaldehyde *p*-nitrophenyl-hydrazone	132*a*
1,2,3,3-Tetramethylindolenium iodide	—	1,2-Dihydro-2-phenylazomethylene-1,3,3-trimethylindoline	133, 135
	4-Nitro	1,2-Dihydro-2-(*p*-nitrophenylazomethylene)-1,3,3-trimethylindoline	133, 135
	4-Iodo	1,2-Dihydro-2-(*p*-iodophenylazomethylene)-1,3,3-trimethylindoline	133
	2-Methoxy-4-nitro	1,2-Dihydro-2-(2-methoxy-4-nitrophenylazomethylene)-1,3,3-trimethylindoline	135

Note: References 177–480 are on pp. 136–142.

* The full name is given when it is awkward to name the arylamine as a derivative of aniline.

TABLE VIII—*Continued*

B. Compounds Containing a Reactive Methyl Group—Continued

Reactive Methyl Compound	Substituent(s) in Aniline	Product (Yield, %)	References
2-Methylbenzothiazole	4-Nitro	Benzothiazole-2-carboxaldehyde *p*-nitrophenylhydrazone (30)	366*a*, *b*
2,3-Dimethylbenzothiazolium iodide	—	2-[Bis(phenylazo)methylene]-3-methylbenzothiazoline	132*c*
	4-Nitro	2-[Bis-(*p*-nitrophenylazo)methylene]-3-methylbenzothiazoline	132*c*
2,3-Dimethylbenzothiazolium methosulfate	—	2-[Bis-(phenylazo)methylene]-3-methylbenzothiazoline (80)	132*d*
	4-Methyl	2-[Bis-(*p*-tolylazo)methylene]-3-methylbenzothiazoline	132*d*
	4-Methoxy	2-[Bis-(*p*-anisylazo)methylene]-3-methylbenzothiazoline	132*d*
	4-Chloro	2-[Bis-(*p*-chlorophenylazo)methylene]-3-methylbenzothiazoline	132*b*, 132*d*
	2-Nitro	2-[Bis-(*o*-nitrophenylazo)methylene]-3-methylbenzothiazoline	132*d*
	4-Nitro	2-(*p*-Nitrophenylazomethylene)-3-methylbenzothiazoline	132*g*
		2-[Bis-(*p*-nitrophenylazo)methylene]-3-methylbenzothiazoline	132*b*, 132*d*
	4-Sulfo	2-[Bis-(*p*-sulfophenylazo)methylene]-3-methylbenzothiazoline	132*d*
	2,5-Dichloro	2-[Bis-(2,5-dichlorophenylazo)methylene]-3-methylbenzothiazoline	132*d*
	2-Methoxy-4-nitro	2-(2-Methoxy-4-nitrophenylazomethylene)-3-methylbenzothiazoline	132*g*
2-Methyl-3-ethylbenzothiazolium iodide	4-Chloro	2-[Bis-(*p*-chlorophenylazo)methylene]-3-ethylbenzothiazoline	132*b*
	4-Nitro	2-[Bis-(*p*-nitrophenylazo)methylene]-3-ethylbenzothiazoline	132*b*, 132*c*

2,3,6-Trimethylbenzothiazolium methosulfate	4-Nitro	2-[Bis-(*p*-nitrophenylazo)methylene]-3,6-dimethylbenzothiazoline	132*e*
2,3-Dimethyl-6-methoxybenzothiazolium methosulfate	4-Nitro	2-[Bis-(*p*-nitrophenylazo)methylene]-6-methoxy-3-methylbenzothiazoline	132*e*
2-Methyl-3-ethyl-5,6-dimethoxybenzothiazolium methosulfate	4-Nitro	2-[Bis-(*p*-nitrophenylazo)methylene]-3-ethyl-5,6-dimethoxybenzothiazoline	132*e*
1,2,3-Trimethylbenzimidazolium methosulfate	—	2-[Bis(phenylazo)methylene]-1,3-dimethylbenzimidazoline	132*e*
	4-Chloro	2-[Bis-(*p*-chlorophenylazo)methylene]-1,3-dimethylbenzimidazoline	132*e*
1,2,3-Trimethyl-5-nitrobenzimidazolium iodide	4-Nitro	1-Methyl-2-(*p*-nitrophenylazomethyl)-5-nitrobenzimidazole (50)	132*f*
1-Phenyl-2,3-dimethyl-5-nitrobenzimidazolium iodide	4-Nitro	1-Phenyl-2-(*p*-nitrophenylazomethyl)-5-nitrobenzimidazole	132*f*
1-Phenyl-2-methyl-3-ethyl-5-nitrobenzimidazolium iodide	4-Nitro	1-Phenyl-2-(*p*-nitrophenylazomethyl)-5-nitrobenzimidazole	132*f*
2,3-Dimethylbenzoselenazolium methosulfate	—	2-[Bis(phenylazo)methylene]-3-methylbenzoselenazoline	132*e*
	4-Chloro	2-[Bis-(*p*-chlorophenylazo)methylene]-3-methylbenzoselenazoline	132*e*
	4-Nitro	2-[Bis-(*p*-nitrophenylazo)methylene]-3-methylbenzoselenazoline	132*e*
1,2-Dimethylnaphtho[1,2]thiazolium methosulfate	—	2-[Bis(phenylazo)methylene]-1-methylnaphtho[1,2]thiazoline	132*e*
	4-Chloro	2-[Bis-(*p*-chlorophenylazo)methylene]-1-methylnaphtho[1,2]thiazoline	132*e*
	4-Nitro	2-[Bis-(*p*-nitrophenylazo)methylene]-1-methylnaphtho[1,2]thiazoline	132*e*
3,3-Diethyl-1,2-dimethyl indolenium iodide	4-Nitro	1,2-Dihydro-1-methyl-2-(*p*-nitrophenylazomethylene)-3,3-diethylindoline	133, 135

Note: References 177–480 are on pp. 136–142.

TABLE VIII—*Continued*

B. Compounds Containing a Reactive Methyl Group—Continued

Reactive Methyl Compound	Substituent(s) in Aniline	Product (Yield, %)	References
9-Methylacridine	—	Acridine-9-carboxaldehyde phenylhydrazone	131
	2-Methyl	Acridine-9-carboxaldehyde *o*-tolylhydrazone	131
	3-Methyl	Acridine-9-carboxaldehyde *m*-tolylhydrazone	131
	4-Methyl	Acridine-9-carboxaldehyde *p*-tolylhydrazone	131
	2-Methoxy	Acridine-9-carboxaldehyde *o*-anisylhydrazone	131
	4-Methoxy	Acridine-9-carboxaldehyde *p*-anisylhydrazone	131
	4-Hydroxy	Acridine-9-carboxaldehyde *p*-hydroxyphenylhydrazone	131
	4-Chloro	Acridine-9-carboxaldehyde *p*-chlorophenylhydrazone	131
	4-Iodo	Acridine-9-carboxaldehyde *p*-iodophenylhydrazone	131
	2-Nitro	Acridine-9-carboxaldehyde *o*-nitrophenylhydrazone	131
	3-Nitro	Acridine-9-carboxaldehyde *m*-nitrophenylhydrazone	131
	4-Nitro	Acridine-9-carboxaldehyde *p*-nitrophenylhydrazone	131
	2-Carboxy	Acridine-9-carboxaldehyde *o*-carboxyphenylhydrazone	131
	3-Carboxy	Acridine-9-carboxaldehyde *m*-carboxyphenylhydrazone	131
	4-Carboxy	Acridine-9-carboxaldehyde *p*-carboxyphenylhydrazone	131
	4-Sulfo	Acridine-9-carboxaldehyde *p*-sulfophenylhydrazone	131
	2,4-Dimethyl	Acridine-9-carboxaldehyde 2,4-dimethylphenylhydrazone	131
	2,4-Dinitro	Acridine-9-carboxaldehyde 2,4-dinitrophenylhydrazone	131
	2,5-Dimethoxy-4-phenylamino	Acridine-9-carboxaldehyde 2,5-dimethoxy-4-(phenylamino)phenylhydrazone (43)	132
9,10-Dimethylacridinium methosulfate	—	9,10-Dihydro-9-methyl-10-phenylazomethyleneacridine	14
	4-Nitro	9,10-Dihydro-9-methyl-10-(*p*-nitrophenylazomethylene)-acridine	14, 132*g*

	2,5-Dichloro	9,10-Dihydro-9-methyl-10-(2,5-dichlorophenylazo-methylene)acridine	132*g*
	2,4-Dinitro	9,10-Dihydro-9-methyl-10-(2,4-dinitrophenylazo-methylene)acridine	14
	2-Methoxy-5-chloro	9,10-Dihydro-9-methyl-10-(2-methoxy-5-chlorophenylazo-methylene)acridine	132*g*
	2-Methoxy-4-nitro	9,10-Dihydro-9-methyl-10-(2-methoxy-4-nitrophenylazo-methylene)acridine	132*g*
2-Acetamido-9-methylacridine	—	2-Acetamidoacridine-9-carboxaldehyde phenylhydrazone (66)	132
	4-Nitro	2-Acetamidoacridine-9-carboxaldehyde *p*-nitrophenyl-hydrazone (55)	132
9-Methylxanthylium perchlorate	—	Xanthene-9-carboxaldehyde phenylhydrazone	14
	4-Nitro	Xanthene-9-carboxaldehyde *p*-nitrophenylhydrazone	14
	2,4-Dinitro	Xanthene-9-carboxaldehyde 2,4-dinitrophenylhydrazone	14
9-Methylthioxanthylium perchlorate	—	Thioxanthene-9-carboxaldehyde phenylhydrazone	14
	4-Nitro	Thioxanthene-9-carboxaldehyde *p*-nitrophenylhydrazone	14
	2,4 Dinitro	Thioxanthene-9-carboxaldehyde 2,4-dinitrophenyl-hydrazone	14
1-Phenyl-3-methyl-4-iso-propylidene-2-pyrazolin-5-one	—	1-Phenyl-3-methyl-4-α-(phenylazomethyl)ethylidene-2-pyrazolin-5-one (57)	135*a*
	4-Nitro	1-Phenyl-3-methyl-4-α-(*p*-nitrophenylazomethyl)-ethylidene-2-pyrazoline-5-one (76)	135*a*
	3-Carboxy	1-Phenyl-3-methyl-4-α-(*m*-carboxyphenylazomethyl)-ethylidene-2-pyrazolin-5-one (62)	135*a*
	2,5-Dichloro	1-Phenyl-3-methyl-4-α-(2,5-dichlorophenylazomethyl)-ethylidene-2-pyrazolin-5-one (51)	135*a*

TABLE VIII—*Continued*

B. Compounds Containing a Reactive Methyl Group—Continued

Reactive Methyl Compound	Substituent(s) in Aniline	Product (Yield, %)	References
1-Phenyl-3-methyl-4-α-methylbenzylidene-2-pyrazolin-5-one	—	1-Phenyl-3-methyl-4-α-phenylazomethylbenzylidene-2-pyrazolin-5-one (70)	135*a*
	4-Nitro	1-Phenyl-3-methyl-4-α-(*p*-nitrophenylazomethyl)benzylidene-2-pyrazolin-5-one (73)	135*a*
	2-Carboxy	1-Phenyl-3-methyl-4-α-(*o*-carboxyphenylazomethyl)-benzylidene-2-pyrazolin-5-one (82)	135*a*
	2,5-Dichloro	1-Phenyl-3-methyl-4-α-(2,5-dichlorophenylazomethyl)-benzylidene-2-pyrazolin-5-one (87)	135*a*
	4-Chloro-2-nitro	1-Phenyl-3-methyl-4-α-(4-chloro-2-nitrophenylazomethyl)-benzylidene-2-pyrazolin-5-one (47)	135*a*
1-Phenyl-3-methyl-4-(α-methyl-*m*-nitrobenzylidene)-2-pyrazolin-5-one	4-Nitro	1-Phenyl-3-methyl-4-[α-(*p*-nitrophenylazomethyl)-*m*-nitrobenzylidene]-2-pyrazoline-5-one (52)	135*a*

C. Cinnolines from o-Aminophenylethylenes

Substituent(s) in Cinnoline (Yield, %)

(Cinnoline ring, positions numbered 1–8: N-1, N-2, 3, 4, 5, 6, 7, 8)

Amine	Substituent(s) in Cinnoline (Yield, %)	References
o-Amino-α-methylstyrene	4-Methyl (90)	368, 369
2-(2′-Amino-5′-chlorophenyl)propene	6-Chloro-4-methyl (28)	369
2-(2′-Amino-4′-chlorophenyl)propene	7-Chloro-4-methyl (55)	369

2-(2′-Amino-3′-chlorophenyl)propene	8-Chloro-4-methyl (29)	370
2-(2′-Amino-3′-methoxyphenyl)propene	8-Methoxy-4-methyl (72)	167*c*, 167*a*
2-(2′-Amino-4′-carboxyphenyl)propene	7-Carboxy-4-methyl (79)	369, 119
α-(*o*-Aminophenyl)styrene	4-Phenyl (quant.)	120
α-(*o*-Aminophenyl)-*β*-bromostyrene	4-Phenyl (22)	120
α-(*o*-Aminophenyl)-*p*-methylstyrene	4-(*p*-Tolyl)	120
α-(*o*-Aminophenyl)-*p*-methoxystyrene	4-(*p*-Anisyl)	121
α-(2-Pyridyl)-*o*-aminostyrene	4-(2′-Pyridyl) (25)	123
α-(2-Amino-5-bromophenyl)styrene	6-Bromo-4-phenyl	122
α-(2-Amino-3-methoxyphenyl)styrene	8-Methoxy-4-phenyl (86)	167*a*
α-(2-Amino-5-chlorophenyl)-2-hydroxystyrene	6-Chloro-4-(*p*-hydroxyphenyl)	122
α-(2-Amino-5-chlorophenyl)-2-hydroxy-5-methylstyrene	6-Chloro-4-(2-hydroxy-5-methylphenyl)	122
1-(*o*-Aminophenyl)-1-phenylpropene	3-Methyl-4-phenyl (84)	371, 120
1-(*o*-Aminophenyl)-1-*p*-anisylpropene	4-(*p*-Anisyl)-3-methyl (90)	371
α-(*o*-Aminophenyl)-*β*-phenylstyrene	3,4-Diphenyl (quant.)	372
β-(*o*-Aminophenyl)-*β*-(*p*-anisyl)styrene	4-(*p*-Anisyl)-3-phenyl (98)	372
α-(*o*-Aminophenyl)-*β*-benzylstyrene	3-Benzyl-4-phenyl (quant.)	372
α-(*o*-Aminophenyl)-*β*-(1-naphthyl)styrene	3-(α-Naphthyl)-4-phenyl*	372
α-(*o*-Aminophenyl)-*β*-(2-pyridyl)styrene	4-Phenyl-3-(2-pyridyl) (25)	123
α-(*o*-Aminophenyl)-*β*-(2-pyridyl)-*p*-methoxystyrene	4-(*p*-Anisyl-3-(2-pyridyl) (70)	123
2-Hydroxy-5-aminolepidine	5-Hydroxy-3-pyrido[4,3,2-*de*]	373

Note: References 177–480 are on pp. 136–142.

* 2-Phenylchrysene is also formed.

TABLE VIII—*Continued*

D. 4-Hydroxycinnolines from o-Aminophenylacetylenes

Amine	Substituent(s) in 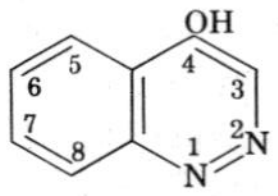 4-hydroxycinnoline (Yield, %)	References
o-Aminophenylacetylene	—	125
2-Amino-5-methoxyphenylacetylene	6-Methoxy	125
2-Amino-5-chlorophenylacetylene	6-Chloro (20*)	23
2-Amino-5-bromophenylacetylene	6-Bromo (20*)	23
1-(*o*-Aminophenyl)-2-phenylacetylene	3-Phenyl (55)	23
1-(2′-Amino-4′-methoxyphenyl)-2-phenylacetylene	6-Methoxy-3-phenyl	23
o-Aminophenylpropiolic acid	3-Carboxy (60)	367, 125, 126
2-Amino-5-chlorophenylpropiolic acid	3-Carboxy-6-chloro (66)	23
2-Amino-5-bromophenylpropiolic acid	3-Carboxy-6-bromo (66)	23
2-Amino-5-methoxyphenylpropiolic acid	3-Carboxy-6-methoxy (68*)	125
2-Amino-4,5-methylenedioxyphenylpropiolic acid	3-Carboxy-6,7-methylenedioxy (37*)	125

E. Indazoles from o-Toluidines

Reactant, Substituent(s) in Aniline	Product, Substituent(s) in Indazole (Yield, %)	References
2-Methyl	— (3–5)	136, 138
2-Cyanomethyl	3-Cyano (71)	95*b*, 168
2-Methyl-3-nitro	4-Nitro (96–98)	137, 376
2,4-Dimethyl	5-Methyl	136
2-Methyl-4-nitro	5-Nitro (82–90)	137, 138, 376
2-Methyl-5-nitro	6-Nitro (90–96)	137, 374, 375, 376
2-Methyl-6-nitro	7-Nitro (80)	137, 376
2,4,6-Trimethyl	5,7-Dimethyl (small)	136
2,4-Dinitro-6-methyl	5,7-Dinitro (34–38)	378
2,3-Dimethyl-4-nitro	4-Methyl-5-nitro (79–86)	137
2,3-Dimethyl-5-nitro	4-Methyl-6-nitro (94)	137
2,3-Dimethyl-6-nitro	4-Methyl-7-nitro (100)	137
2,4-Dimethyl-3-nitro	5-Methyl-4-nitro (79)	137
2,4-Dimethyl-5-nitro	5-Methyl-6-nitro (75–80)	137
2,4-Dimethyl-6-nitro	5-Methyl-7-nitro (48–53)	137, 377
2,5-Dimethyl-3-nitro	6-Methyl-4-nitro (93)	137
2,5-Dimethyl-4-nitro	6-Methyl-5-nitro (83)	137

Note: References 177–480 are on pp. 136–142.

* This is an over-all yield from the nitro compound.

TABLE VIII—*Continued*

E. Indazoles from o-Toluidines—Continued

Reactant, Substituent(s) in Aniline	Product, Substituent(s) in Indazole (Yield, %)	References
2,5-Dimethyl-6-nitro	6-Methyl-7-nitro (81)	137
2,6-Dimethyl-3-nitro	7-Methyl-4-(or 6-)nitro (100)	137
3-Chloro-2-methyl-4-nitro	4-Chloro-5-nitro (86)	380
3-Chloro-2-methyl-6-nitro	4-Chloro-7-nitro	379
4-Chloro-2-methyl-6-nitro	5-Chloro-7-nitro	379
2,3-Dinitro-6-methyl	7-Chloro-6-nitro* (85)	380
3-Methoxy-2-methyl-6-nitro	4-Methoxy-7-nitro	379
3-Methoxy-6-methyl-2-nitro	6-Methoxy-7-nitro (83)	383
3-Diethylsulfamyl-2-methyl-6-nitro	4-Diethylsulfamyl-7-nitro	379
2,4,5-Trimethyl-3-nitro	5,6-Dimethyl-4-nitro (58)	137
3,4,6-Trimethyl-2-nitro	5,6-Dimethyl-7-nitro (20)	137
2,4,6-Trimethyl-3-nitro	5,7-Dimethyl-4-(or 6-)nitro (100)	137
2,4-Dimethyl-3,5-dinitro	5-Methyl-4,6-dinitro (80)	137
2,6-Dimethyl-3,5-dinitro	7-Methyl-4,6-dinitro (86)	137
3,6-Dimethyl-2,4-dinitro	6-Methyl-5,7-dinitro (100)	137
2,4-Dinitro-6-methyl-3-sulfo	5,7-Dinitro-6-sulfo	381
2,4,6-Trimethyl-3-amino	5,7-Dimethyl-4-triazo†	382
2,5-Dinitro-3,4,6-trimethyl	5,6-Dimethyl-4,7-dinitro (75–85)	137
3,5-Dinitro-2,4,6-trimethyl	5,7-Dimethyl-4,6-dinitro (100)	137

Reactant	Product (Yield, %)	Refs.
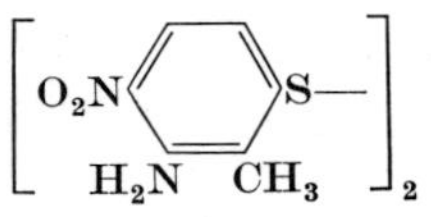 $[O_2N$, S—, H_2N, $CH_3]_2$	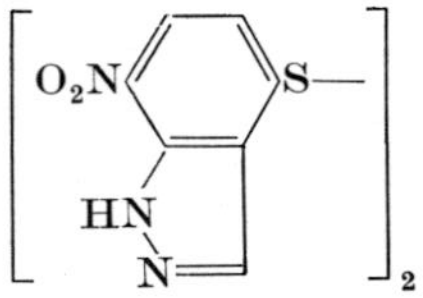 $[O_2N$, S—, HN, N$]_2$ (80)	380
	Substituents X in 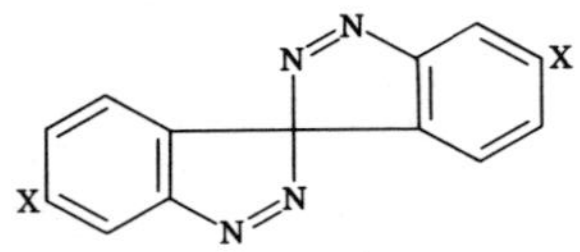 (X, N=N, N=N, X)	
Bis-(2-amino-4-chlorophenyl)methane	Chloro	384
Bis-(2-amino-4-cyanophenyl)methane	Cyano	385
Bis-(2-amino-4-acetylphenyl)methane	Acetyl	385
Bis-(2-amino-4-acetamidophenyl)methane	Acetamido	385
Bis-(2-amino-4-carboxyphenyl)methane	Carboxy	385
Bis-(2-amino-4-carbethoxyphenyl)methane	Carbethoxy	386

Note: References 177–480 are on pp. 136–142.

* One nitro group was replaced by chlorine when the diazotization was run in hydrochloric acid.

† This product was prepared by tetrazotizing the amine and reacting the tetrazonium salt with sodium azide.

TABLE IX

Coupling of Diazonium Salts with Hydrazones

A. Simple Hydrazones

$$RCH{=}NNHR' + R''N_2X \rightarrow \begin{array}{l} RC{=}NNHR' \\ | \\ N{=}NR'' \end{array}$$

R	R′	R″	Yield, %	References
H	Cholyl ($C_{24}H_{39}O_5$)	C_6H_5	—	387
O_2N	C_6H_5	C_6H_5	—	322
CH_3	C_6H_5	C_6H_5	88	139, 144, 388
CH_3	C_6H_5	o-$O_2NC_6H_4$	—	144
CH_3	C_6H_5	m-$O_2NC_6H_4$	—	144
CH_3	C_6H_5	p-$O_2NC_6H_4$	Quant.	139, 144
CH_3	C_6H_5	p-$HO_3SC_6H_4$	Quant.	389
CH_3	C_6H_5	p-$(C_6H_5CH{=}CH)C_6H_4$	68	389*a*
CH_3	C_6H_5	p-$[C_6H_5C(CN){=}CH]C_6H_4$	—	389*b*
CH_3	C_6H_5	p-$(p$-$O_2NC_6H_4CH{=}CH)C_6H_4$	16	389*a*
CH_3	C_6H_5	p-$(p$-$CH_3CONHC_6H_4CH{=}CH)C_6H_4$	12	389*a*
CH_3	C_6H_5	p-$(C_6H_5N{=}N)C_6H_4$	28	389*c*
CH_3	o-$O_2NC_6H_4$	o-$O_2NC_6H_4$	Small	144
CH_3	p-$O_2NC_6H_4$	C_6H_5	—	144
CH_3	p-$O_2NC_6H_4$	o-$O_2NC_6H_4$	—	144
CH_3	p-$O_2NC_6H_4$	m-$O_2NC_6H_4$	—	144
CH_3	p-$O_2NC_6H_4$	p-$O_2NC_6H_4$	48	129, 144
CH_3	p-$O_2NC_6H_4$	2,4-$(O_2N)_2C_6H_3$	—	390
CH_3	2,4-$(O_2N)_2C_6H_3$	C_6H_5	—	391
CH_3	2,4-$(O_2N)_2C_6H_3$	o-$O_2NC_6H_4$	—	390
CH_3	2,4-$(O_2N)_2C_6H_3$	m-$O_2NC_6H_4$	—	390

CH_3	2,4-$(O_2N)_2C_6H_3$	*p*-$O_2NC_6H_4$	—	390
CH_3	$(C_6H_5)_2NCO$	C_6H_5	—	398*d*
CH_3O_2C	C_6H_5	C_6H_5	—	143
CH_3O_2C	C_6H_5	*p*-$O_2NC_6H_4$	—	143
CH_3O_2C	2,4-$(CH_3)_2C_6H_3$*	C_6H_5	—	143
CH_3O_2C	2,4-$(CH_3)_2C_6H_3$*	*p*-BrC_6H_4	—	143
CH_3O_2C	2,4-$(CH_3)_2C_6H_3$*	*p*-$O_2NC_6H_4$	—	143
$C_2H_5O_2C$	C_6H_5	C_6H_5	34	148
$C_2H_5O_2C$	*p*-$HO_3SC_6H_4$†	C_6H_5	80	401
C_2H_5	C_6H_5	C_6H_5	65	393, 392
CH_3CO	C_6H_5	C_6H_5	68–71	52, 226
CH_3CO	C_6H_5	*p*-$CH_3C_6H_4$	—	52
CH_3CO	C_6H_5	*p*-$O_2NC_6H_4$	—	52
n-C_3H_7	C_6H_5	*p*-$HO_3SC_6H_4$	75	389
n-C_3H_7	Cholyl ($C_{24}H_{39}O_5$)	C_6H_5	—	392
i-C_3H_7	C_6H_5	C_6H_5	—	387
$CH_2{=}C(CH_3)$	C_6H_5	C_6H_5	72	393*a*
$(CH_3)_2CHCH_2$	C_6H_5	C_6H_5	—	392
n-C_5H_{11}	C_6H_5	C_6H_5	—	392
n-C_6H_{13}	C_6H_5	C_6H_5	81	148
n-C_6H_{13}	C_6H_5	*p*-$HO_3SC_6H_4$	Quant.	389
Cyclohexyl	$H_2N(HN{=})C$	5-Tetrazolyl	—	19*d*
n-C_7H_{15}	C_6H_5	C_6H_5	46	393, 392
n-C_7H_{15}	C_6H_5	4-$HO_3SC_6H_4$	93	389
n-C_8H_{17}	C_6H_5	C_6H_5	—	392
n-C_9H_{19}	C_6H_5	C_6H_5	—	392
n-$C_{11}H_{23}$	C_6H_5	C_6H_5	77	148

Note: References 177–480 are on pp. 136–142.

* Only the *syn* isomer of methyl glyoxalate 2,4-dimethylphenylhydrazone gave a formazan. The *anti* isomer reacted with the elimination of nitrogen.

† The phenylsulfamyl group was replaced by a phenyl group in the coupling reaction.

TABLE IX—*Continued*

A. Simple Hydrazones—Continued

R	R′	R″	Yield, %	References
n-$C_{11}H_{23}$	C_6H_5	p-BrC_6H_4	82	148
n-$C_{11}H_{23}$	C_6H_5	p-$O_2NC_6H_4$	83	148
n-$C_{11}H_{23}$	C_6H_5	p-$HO_3SC_6H_4$	Quant.	389
n-$C_{11}H_{23}$	C_6H_5	α-$C_{10}H_7$	67	148
n-$C_{11}H_{23}$	p-BrC_6H_4	C_6H_5	63	148
n-$C_{11}H_{23}$	p-$O_2NC_6H_4$	C_6H_5	60	148
C_6H_5	C_6H_5	C_6H_5	50	394, 18, 19, 19*a*, 19*b*, 70 395
C_6H_5	C_6H_5	p-$CH_3C_6H_4$	—	19
C_6H_5	C_6H_5	p-i-$C_3H_7C_6H_4$	—	395*a*
C_6H_5	C_6H_5	p-n-$C_{12}H_{25}C_6H_4$	83	395*a*
C_6H_5	C_6H_5	p-ClC_6H_4	60	395*a*, 393
C_6H_5	C_6H_5	p-BrC_6H_4	50	18, 149
C_6H_5	C_6H_5	p-IC_6H_4	45–60	396
C_6H_5	C_6H_5	o-HOC_6H_4	80	303
C_6H_5	C_6H_5	o-$O_2NC_6H_4$	58	19*b*
C_6H_5	C_6H_5	p-$O_2NC_6H_4$	92	395*a*, 18
C_6H_5	C_6H_5	p-$CH_3CONHC_6H_4$	55	397
C_6H_5	C_6H_5	o-$HO_2CC_6H_4$	75	303
C_6H_5	C_6H_5	p-$HO_3SC_6H_4$	—	147
C_6H_5	C_6H_5	p-$C_6H_5C_6H_4$	44	395*a*, 398
C_6H_5	C_6H_5	4-CH_3CONH-2-ClC_6H_3	76	395*a*
C_6H_5	C_6H_5	4-CH_3CONH-3-ClC_6H_3	44	395*a*
C_6H_5	C_6H_5	4-CH_3CONH-2-$O_2NC_6H_3$	57	395*a*
C_6H_5	C_6H_5	4-CH_3CONH-2-$CH_3CO_2C_6H_3$	39	395*a*
C_6H_5	C_6H_5	p-n-$C_{12}H_{25}CONHC_6H_4$	—	395*a*

C_6H_5	C_6H_5	p-$CH_3CONH(CH_2)_{12}N(COCH_3)C_6H_4$	—	395*a*
C_6H_5	C_6H_5	p-$[(C_2H_5)_2N(CH_2)_2O_2C]C_6H_4$	64	395*a*
C_6H_5	C_6H_5	p-$[(C_2H_5)_2N(CH_2)_3CH(CH_3)NHO_2S]C_6H_4$	47	395*a*
C_6H_5	C_6H_5	p-$(C_6H_5CH{=}CH)C_6H_4$	74	389*a*
C_6H_5	C_6H_5	p-(p-$HOC_6H_4CH{=}CH)C_6H_4$	32	389*a*
C_6H_5	C_6H_5	p-(p-$BrC_6H_4CH{=}CH)C_6H_4$	33	389*a*
C_6H_5	C_6H_5	p-(p-$O_2NC_6H_4CH{=}CH)C_6H_4$	33	389*a*
C_6H_5	C_6H_5	p-(p-$CH_3CONHC_6H_4CH{=}CH)C_6H_4$	14	389*a*
C_6H_5	C_6H_5	p-$(C_6H_5N{=}N)C_6H_4$	50	389*c*
C_6H_5	C_6H_5	p-(p-$CH_3C_6H_4N{=}N)C_6H_4$	53	389*c*
C_6H_5	C_6H_5	p-(p-$ClC_6H_4N{=}N)C_6H_4$	12	389*c*
C_6H_5	C_6H_5	p-(p-$HOC_6H_4N{=}N)C_6H_4$	28	389*c*
C_6H_5	C_6H_5	p-(p-$O_2NC_6H_4N{=}N)C_6H_4$	57	389*c*
C_6H_5	C_6H_5	p-[p-$(CH_3)_2NC_6H_4N{=}N]C_6H_4$	23	389*c*
C_6H_5	C_6H_5	p-(p-$CH_3CONHC_6H_4N{=}N)C_6H_4$	35	389*c*
C_6H_5	C_6H_5	p-(2-Cl-4-$HOC_6H_3N{=}N)C_6H_4$	27	389*c*
C_6H_5	C_6H_5	p-(3-Cl-4-$HOC_6H_3N{=}N)C_6H_4$	8	389*c*
C_6H_5	C_6H_5	2,5-$(CH_3)_2$-4-$(C_6H_5N{=}N)C_6H_2$	50	389*c*
C_6H_5	C_6H_5	α-$C_{10}H_7$	80	150, 147, 149, 390
C_6H_5	C_6H_5	β-$C_{10}H_7$	47	150, 149, 390
C_6H_5	C_6H_5	4-$(C_6H_5N{=}N)$-1-$C_{10}H_6$	9	389*c*
C_6H_5	C_6H_5	3-Pyridyl	53	395*a*
C_6H_5	C_6H_5	6-Quinolyl	—	398*a*
C_6H_5	C_6H_5	7-Quinolyl	—	398*a*
C_6H_5	C_6H_5	6-Ethoxy-2-quinolyl	—	398*a*
C_6H_5	C_6H_5	6-Methoxy-8-quinolyl	20	395*a*
C_6H_5	C_6H_5	2-Quinolylmethyl	—	398*a*
C_6H_5	C_6H_5	2-Thiazolyl	—	398*a*
C_6H_5	C_6H_5	5-Methyl-2-thiazolyl	68	398*b*

Note: References 177–480 are on pp. 136–142.

TABLE IX—*Continued*

A. Simple Hydrazones—Continued

R	R′	R″	Yield, %	References
C_6H_5	C_6H_5	4-Methyl-2-thiazolyl	1–3	398*b*
C_6H_5	C_6H_5	4,5-Dimethyl-2-thiazolyl	69	398*b*
C_6H_5	C_6H_5	2,5-Dimethyl-4-(2-thiazolylazo)phenyl	25	389*c*
C_6H_5	C_6H_5	*p*-(6-Methyl-2-benzothiazolyl)phenyl	—	398*a*
C_6H_5	*o*-$CH_3C_6H_4$	C_6H_5	85	19*b*
C_6H_5	*o*-$CH_3C_6H_4$	*p*-$O_2NC_6H_4$	37	19*b*
C_6H_5	*p*-$CH_3C_6H_4$	C_6H_5	—	19
C_6H_5	*p*-$CH_3C_6H_4$	*p*-$CH_3C_6H_4$	—	19
C_6H_5	*p*-$CH_3C_6H_4$	α-$C_{10}H_7$	—	390
C_6H_5	*p*-$CH_3C_6H_4$	β-$C_{10}H_7$	—	390
C_6H_5	*o*-$CH_3OC_6H_4$	*o*-$CH_3OC_6H_4$	—	290*a*
C_6H_5	*p*-$CH_3OC_6H_4$	*p*-$CH_3OC_6H_4$	60	290*a*
C_6H_5	*o*-$C_2H_5OC_6H_4$	C_6H_5	91	19*b*
C_6H_5	*o*-$C_2H_5OC_6H_4$	*p*-$O_2NC_6H_4$	51	19*b*
C_6H_5	*p*-$C_2H_5OC_6H_4$	C_6H_5	74	19*b*
C_6H_5	*o*-ClC_6H_4	C_6H_5	26	19*b*
C_6H_5	*p*-ClC_6H_4	C_6H_5	55	19*b*
C_6H_5	*p*-ClC_6H_4	*p*-ClC_6H_4	50	19*b*
C_6H_5	*p*-ClC_6H_4	*p*-$(C_6H_5N{=}N)C_6H_4$	18	19*b*
C_6H_5	*p*-BrC_6H_4	C_6H_5	50	18, 149
C_6H_5	*p*-IC_6H_4	*p*-IC_6H_4	42–51	396
C_6H_5	*o*-$C_2NC_6H_4$	C_6H_5	10	19*b*
C_6H_5	*p*-$O_2NC_6H_4$	C_6H_5	46	19*b*
C_6H_5	*p*-$O_2NC_6H_4$	*p*-IC_6H_4	36–58	396
C_6H_5	*p*-$O_2NC_6H_4$	*p*-$O_2NC_6H_4$	8	323*b*
C_6H_5	*p*-$O_2NC_6H_4$	*p*-$C_6H_5C_6H_4$	22	398*c*
C_6H_5	*p*-$O_2NC_6H_4$	α-$C_{10}H_7$	41	150, 390

C_6H_5	p-$O_2NC_6H_4$	β-$C_{10}H_7$	—	390
C_6H_5	p-$O_2NC_6H_4$	p-(p-$C_2H_5OC_6H_4)C_6H_4$	52	398*c*
C_6H_5	p-$O_2NC_6H_4$	3-CH_3O-4-(m-$CH_3OC_6H_4)C_6H_3$	52	398*c*
C_6H_5	p-$O_2NC_6H_4$	3-CH_3O-4-[3,4-$(CH_3O)_2C_6H_3]C_6H_3$	21	398*c*
C_6H_5	p-$O_2NC_6H_4$	2,5-$(CH_3O)_2$-4-(p-$O_2NC_6H_4N{=}N)C_6H_2$	5	398*c*
C_6H_5	o-$HO_2CC_6H_4$	o-$HO_2CC_6H_4$	75–80	303
C_6H_5	m-$HO_2CC_6H_4$	C_6H_5	—	141
C_6H_5	m-$HO_2CC_6H_4$	o-ClC_6H_4	—	141
C_6H_5	m-$HO_2CC_6H_4$	m-$O_2NC_6H_4$	—	141
C_6H_5	m-$HO_2CC_6H_4$	o-$HO_2CC_6H_4$	—	141
C_6H_5	m-$HO_2CC_6H_4$	m-$HO_2CC_6H_4$	—	141
C_6H_5	m-$HO_2CC_6H_4$	p-$HO_2CC_6H_4$	—	141
C_6H_5	p-$HO_2CC_6H_4$	p-$(C_6H_5N{=}N)C_6H_4$	10	389*c*
C_6H_5	p-$CH_3CONHC_6H_4$	p-$(C_6H_5N{=}N)C_6H_4$	26	389*c*
C_6H_5	p-$HO_3SC_6H_4$	C_6H_5	—	147
C_6H_5	p-$H_2NO_2SC_6H_4$	C_6H_5	37	19*b*
C_6H_5	$(C_6H_5)_2NCO$	C_6H_5	—	398*d*
C_6H_5	α-$C_{10}H_7$	C_6H_5‡	—	147, 149, 390
C_6H_5	α-$C_{10}H_7$	p-$CH_3C_6H_4$‡	—	390
C_6H_5	α-$C_{10}H_7$	p-$O_2NC_6H_4$‡	—	390
C_6H_5	β-$C_{10}H_7$	C_6H_5	39§	150, 149
C_6H_5	(β-$C_{10}H_7)_2NCO$	C_6H_5	—	398*d*
C_6H_5	β-$C_{10}H_7(C_6H_5)NCO$	C_6H_5	—	398*d*
C_6H_5	p-$C_6H_5C_6H_4$	p-$C_6H_5C_6H_4$	13	398
C_6H_5	Cholyl ($C_{24}H_{39}O_5$)	C_6H_5	—	387
C_6H_5	p-$(C_6H_5N{=}N)C_6H_4$	p-$(C_6H_5CH{=}CH)C_6H_4$	47	389*a*
C_6H_5	2-Pyridyl	p-ClC_6H_5	—	398*a*
C_6H_5	2-Quinolyl	C_6H_5	—	19*d*

Note: References 177–480 are on pp. 136–142.

‡ These products are probably 4-arylazonaphthylhydrazones rather than formazans. See ref. 150.

§ A 35% yield of the 1-phenylazo-2-naphthylhydrazone of benzaldehyde was obtained also.

TABLE IX—*Continued*

A. Simple Hydrazones—Continued

R	R′	R″	Yield, %	References
C_6H_5	2-Quinolyl	p-ClC_6H_5	—	398*a*
C_6H_5	2-Thiazolyl	C_6H_5	66	398*b*
C_6H_5	4-Methyl-2-thiazolyl	C_6H_5	50	398*b*
C_6H_5	4-Phenyl-2-thiazolyl	C_6H_5	38	398*b*
C_6H_5	4,5-Diphenyl-2-thiazolyl	C_6H_5	22	398*b*
C_6H_5	$H_2N(NH{=})C$	C_6H_5	61	402
C_6H_5	$H_2N(HN{=})C$	m-$O_2NC_6H_4$	—	402
p-$(CH_3)_2CHC_6H_4$	$H_2N(HN{=})C$	5-Tetrazolyl	—	19*d*
p-$CH_3OC_6H_4$	C_6H_5	C_6H_5	—	15
p-$CH_3OC_6H_4$	C_6H_5	p-$(C_6H_5CH{=}CH)C_6H_4$	83	389*a*
p-$CH_3OC_6H_4$	p-ClC_6H_4	p-ClC_6H_4	43	323*b*
p-$CH_3OC_6H_4$	p-$O_2NC_6H_4$	p-$O_2NC_6H_4$	15	323*b*
p-$CH_3OC_6H_4$	2-Pyridyl	p-ClC_6H_4	—	398*a*
p-$CH_3OC_6H_4$	2-Quinolyl	p-ClC_6H_4	—	398*a*
p-$CH_3OC_6H_4$	$H_2N(NH{=})C$	5-Tetrazolyl	—	19*d*
o-ClC_6H_4	2-Pyridyl	5-Tetrazolyl	—	398*a*
o-ClC_6H_4	2-Quinolyl	5-Tetrazolyl	—	398*a*
p-ClC_6H_4	o-$CH_3OC_6H_4$	o-$CH_3OC_6H_4$	44	323*b*
p-ClC_6H_4	$H_2N(NH{=})C$	5-Tetrazolyl	—	19*d*
p-BrC_6H_4	C_6H_5	p-BrC_6H_4	80	395*a*
p-BrC_6H_4	C_6H_5	2,4,6-$Br_3C_6H_2$	10	395*a*
p-BrC_6H_4	C_6H_5	p-$(C_6H_5CH{=}CH)C_6H_4$	47	389*a*
o-HOC_6H_4	$(C_6H_5)_2NCO$	C_6H_5	—	398*d*
o-HOC_6H_4	2-Pyridyl	p-ClC_6H_4	—	398*a*
o-HOC_6H_4	2-Quinolyl	p-ClC_6H_4	—	398*a*
p-HOC_6H_4	C_6H_5	p-$(C_6H_5N{=}N)C_6H_4$	50	389*c*

p-NCC_6H_4	C_6H_5	C_6H_5	65	395*a*
p-NCC_6H_4	C_6H_5	p-NCC_6H_4	80	395*a*
o-$O_2NC_6H_4$	2-Pyridyl	p-ClC_6H_4	—	398*a*
o-$O_2NC_6H_4$	2-Quinolyl	p-ClC_6H_4	—	398*a*
p-$O_2NC_6H_4$	C_6H_5	C_6H_5	40	19*b*, 395*a*
p-$O_2NC_6H_4$	p-$CH_3OC_6H_4$	p-$CH_3OC_6H_4$	51	323*b*
p-$O_2NC_6H_4$	p-$O_2NC_6H_4$	p-$C_6H_5C_6H_4$	49	398*c*
p-$O_2NC_6H_4$	p-$O_2NC_6H_4$	3-CH_3O-4-(m-$CH_3OC_6H_4$)C_6H_3	23	398*c*
p-$O_2NC_6H_4$	$H_2N(HN{=})C$	C_6H_5	—	402
p-$HO_2CC_6H_4$	p-$(C_6H_5N{=}N)C_6H_4$	p-$(C_6H_5CH{=}CH)C_6H_4$	33	389*a*
p-$CH_3CO_2C_6H_4$	p-$(C_6H_5N{=}N)C_6H_4$	p-$(C_6H_5CH{=}CH)C_6H_4$	40	389*a*
p-$CH_3CONHC_6H_4$	C_6H_5	C_6H_5	53	395*a*
p-$CH_3CONHC_6H_4$	C_6H_5	p-$CH_3CONHC_6H_4$	17	395*a*
p-$CH_3CONHC_6H_4$	p-$CH_3CONHC_6H_4$	p-(p-$HOC_6H_4N{=}N$)C_6H_4	—	389*c*
m-$HO_3SC_6H_4$	C_6H_5	C_6H_5	—	147
3,4-$(CH_3O)_2C_6H_3$	C_6H_5	p-$CH_3OC_6H_4$	25	395*a*
$C_6H_5CH_2$	Cholyl ($C_{24}H_{39}O_5$)	C_6H_5	—	387
C_6H_5CO	C_6H_5	C_6H_5	—	70, 204
p-$C_6H_5C_6H_4$	C_6H_5	C_6H_5	43	398
p-$C_6H_5C_6H_4$	p-$C_6H_5C_6H_4$	p-$C_6H_5C_6H_4$	23	398
2-Furyl	C_6H_5	C_6H_5	14	402*a*
2-Furyl	$(C_6H_5)_2NCO$	C_6H_5	—	398*d*
2-Furyl	2-Pyridyl	p-ClC_6H_4	—	398*a*
2-Furyl	2-Quinolyl	p-ClC_6H_4	—	398*a*
2-Furyl	Cholyl ($C_{24}H_{39}O_5$)	C_6H_5	—	387
2-Thienyl	C_6H_5	m-$F_3CC_6H_4$	—	398*a*
2-Pyridyl	C_6H_5	C_6H_5	46	402*a*
2-Pyridyl	C_6H_5	p-$CH_3OC_6H_4$	95	402*a*
2-Pyridyl	C_6H_5	p-ClC_6H_4	40	402*a*
2-Pyridyl	C_6H_5	o-$H_2NC_6H_4$	35	402*b*

Note: References 177–480 are on pp. 136–142.

TABLE IX—*Continued*

A. Simple Hydrazones—Continued

R	R′	R″	Yield, %	References
2-Pyridyl	C_6H_5	p-$(C_6H_5CH{=}CH)C_6H_4$	40	402*a*
2-Pyridyl	C_6H_5	p-$(C_6H_5N{=}N)C_6H_4$	39	402*a*
2-Pyridyl	2-Pyridyl	p-ClC_6H_4	—	398*a*
2-Pyridyl	2-Quinolyl	p-ClC_6H_4	—	398*a*
2-Pyridyl	2-Quinolyl	6-Quinolyl	—	398*a*
4-Pyridyl	2-Quinolyl	p-ClC_6H_4	—	398*a*
4-Pyridyl	2-Quinolyl	6-Quinolyl	—	398*a*
2-Phenyl-1,2,3-triazol-4-yl	C_6H_5	C_6H_5	59	402*a*
2,6-Dioxy-4-pyrimidyl	C_6H_5	C_6H_5	76	399
2-Quinolyl	C_6H_5	C_6H_5	50	402*d*, 139*a*
2-Quinolyl	C_6H_5	o-$HO_2CC_6H_4$	65	400, 402*e*
2-Benzothiazolyl	C_6H_5	C_6H_5	47	402*d*, 402*f*, 402*g*
2-Benzothiazolyl	C_6H_5	p-ClC_6H_4	—	132*b*, 402*f*
2-Benzothiazolyl	C_6H_5	p-$O_2NC_6H_4$	—	132*b*, 402*f*, 402*h*
2-Benzothiazolyl	C_6H_5	o-$HO_2CC_6H_4$	56	402*d*
2-Benzothiazolyl	p-ClC_6H_4	C_6H_5	—	132*b*, 402*f*
2-Benzothiazolyl	p-ClC_6H_4	p-ClC_6H_4	—	132*b*, 402*f*
2-Benzothiazolyl	p-$O_2NC_6H_4$	C_6H_5	—	132*b*, 402*f*, 402*h*
2-Benzothiazolyl	p-$O_2NC_6H_4$	p-$O_2NC_6H_4$	—	132*b*, 402*f*, 402*g*
2-Benzo[*f*]quinolyl	C_6H_5	C_6H_5	48	402*i*
2-Benzo[*f*]quinolyl	C_6H_5	o-$HO_2CC_6H_4$	65	402*i*

B. Hydrazones of Sugars

Hydrazone	Substituent in Aniline	Product (Yield, %)	References
D-Glucose phenylhydrazone	—	D-Glucose diphenylformazan (64)	139*b*, 139*c*
D-Glucose phenylosazone	—	D-Glucose phenylosazone (20)	139*a*
Anhydro-D-glucose phenylosazone	—	Anhydro-D-glucose phenylosazone formazan (27)	139*d*
D-Galactose phenylhydrazone	—	D-Galactose diphenylformazan (73)	139*b*, 139*c*, 139*e*
D-Galactose phenylhydrazone	4-Bromo	D-Galactose phenyl-(*p*-bromophenyl)formazan	139*f*
D-Galactose *p*-bromophenylhydrazone	—	D-Galactose phenyl-(*p*-bromophenyl)formazan	139*f*
D-Mannose phenylhydrazone	—	D-Mannose diphenylformazan (68)	139*b*, 139*c*
L-Arabinose phenylhydrazone	—	L-Arabinose diphenylformazan (51)	139*b*
L-Rhamnose phenylhydrazone	—	L-Rhamnose diphenylformazan (45)	139*b*, 139*e*
D-Xylose phenylhydrazone	—	D-Xylose diphenylformazan (55)	139*b*
D-Mannose pentaacetate phenylhydrazone	—	D-Mannose diphenylformazan pentaacetate (57)	139*e*

Note: References 177–480 are on pp. 136–142.

TABLE IX—*Continued*

C. Diformazans from Hydrazones and Diamines

$$RCH{=}NHNR' + XN_2\text{-}C_6H_3(Y)\text{-}C_6H_3(Y)\text{-}N_2X \rightarrow \left[\begin{array}{l} RC{=}NNHR' \\ \;| \\ N{=}N\text{-}C_6H_3(Y)\text{-} \end{array} \right]_2$$

R	R′	Y	Yield, %	References
CH_3	C_6H_5	H	—	179
C_6H_5	C_6H_5	H	90‖	402*j*
C_6H_5	C_6H_5	CH_3	39‖	402*j*
C_6H_5	C_6H_5	CH_3O	72¶	402*k*, 402*j*
C_6H_5	*p*-$O_2NC_6H_4$	H	11	398*c*
C_6H_5	*p*-$O_2NC_6H_4$	CH_3O	18	398*c*
C_6H_5	2-Pyridyl	CH_3O	—	398*a*
C_6H_5	2-Quinolyl	CH_3O	—	398*a*
p-$CH_3OC_6H_4$	C_6H_5	CH_3O	—	402*k*
o-ClC_6H_4	2-Pyridyl	CH_3O	—	398*a*
o-ClC_6H_4	2-Quinolyl	CH_3O	—	398*a*
o-HOC_6H_4	C_6H_5	CH_3O	—	402*k*
o-$O_2NC_6H_4$	2-Pyridyl	CH_3O	—	398*a*
o-$O_2NC_6H_4$	2-Quinolyl	CH_3O	—	398*a*
p-$O_2NC_6H_4$	*p*-$O_2NC_6H_4$	H	49	398*c*
p-$O_2NC_6H_4$	*p*-$O_2NC_6H_4$	CH_3O	12	398*c*
3,4-$(CH_3O)_2C_6H_3$	C_6H_5	CH_3O	79	402*k*
2-Furyl	C_6H_5	CH_3O	70	402*k*, 398*a*
2-Furyl	2-Pyridyl	CH_3O	—	398*a*
2-Furyl	2-Quinolyl	CH_3O	—	398*a*

2-Pyridyl	C_6H_5	CH_3O	—	398*a*
2-Pyridyl	2-Pyridyl	CH_3O	—	398*a*
4-Pyridyl	C_6H_5	CH_3O	49	402*k*, 398*a*
4-Pyridyl	2-Pyridyl	CH_3O	—	398*a*
2-Thienyl	C_6H_5	H	—	398*a*
2-Thienyl	C_6H_5	CH_3O	61	402*k*, 398*a*
2-Thianaphthenyl	C_6H_5	CH_3O	64	402*k*, 398*a*
2-Thianaphthenyl	2-Pyridyl	CH_3O	—	398*a*
2-Benzothiazolyl	C_6H_5	CH_3O	—	398*a*

D. Diformazans from Dihydrazones

Hydrazone	Substituent in Aniline	Product (Yield, %)	References
Glyoxal dicholylhydrazone	—	Bis-(N-Cholyl-N′-phenylformazan)	387
Dioxosuccinic acid phenylhydrazone	—	Bis-(N,N′-Diphenylformazan) (small)	153, 180
Succinaldehyde bisphenylhydrazone	—	C,C′-Ethylenebis-(N,N′-diphenylformazan) (53)	179
Succinaldehyde bisphenylhydrazone	4-Phenylazo	C,C′-Ethylenebis-[N-phenyl-N′-(*p*-phenylazophenyl)-formazan] (29)	389*c*
Suberaldehyde bisphenylhydrazone	—	C,C′-Hexamethylenebis-(N,N′-diphenylformazan)	395*a*
	4-Phenylazo	C,C′-Hexamethylenebis-[N-phenyl-N′-(*p*-phenylazo-phenyl)formazan] (39)	389*c*
Terephthaldehyde bisphenylhydrazone	—	*p*-Phenylenebis-(N,N′-diphenylformazan) (90)	179
	4-Carbethoxy	*p*-Phenylenebis-[N-phenyl-N′-(*p*-carbethoxyphenyl)-formazan] (47)	179

Note: References 177–480 are on pp. 136–142.

‖ The starting material was phenylglyoxylic acid phenylhydrazone.

¶ The product was also obtained from phenylglyoxylic acid phenylhydrazone in 50% yield.

TABLE IX—*Continued*

E. Diformazans from Dibenzalaminoguanidines

$$RCH{=}NNHC({=}NH)NHN{=}CHR + 2R'N_2X \rightarrow \underset{\displaystyle N{=}NR'}{RC}{=}NNHC({=}NH)NHN{=}\underset{\displaystyle R'N{=}N}{CR}$$

R	R′	References
C_6H_5	C_6H_5	403
C_6H_5	*o*-$O_2NC_6H_4$	19*d*
C_6H_5	*p*-$O_2NC_6H_4$	19*d*
C_6H_5	*p*-$HO_3SC_6H_4$	403
C_6H_5	4-CH_3-2-$(O_2N)C_6H_3$	19*d*
C_6H_5	2-CH_3-6-$(O_2N)C_6H_3$	19*d*
C_6H_5	2-CH_3-4-ClC_6H_3	19*d*
C_6H_5	β-$C_{10}H_7$	19*d*
C_6H_5	4-Antipyryl	19*d*
m-$O_2NC_6H_4$	C_6H_5	403

F. Hydrazones Which Couple with Elimination of a Substituent

$$\underset{\displaystyle R'}{RC}{=}NNHR'' + R'''N_2X \xrightarrow{OH^-} \underset{\displaystyle N{=}NR'''}{RC}{=}NNHR'' + R'OH$$

R	R′	R″	R‴	Yield, %	References
H	HO_2C	C_6H_5	C_6H_5	20	143
H	HO_2C	C_6H_5	2,4-$Br_2C_6H_3$	—	170*a*
Cl	HO_2C	*o*-ClC_6H_4	*p*-$O_2NC_6H_4$	Quant.	145

Cl	HO_2C	o-$CH_3O_2CC_6H_4$	p-$O_2NC_6H_4$	—	145
Cl	HO_2C	2,4-$(CH_3)_2C_6H_3$	p-$O_2NC_6H_4$	—	145
CH_3	HO_2C	C_6H_5	C_6H_5	87–89	27, 153, 95*a*
CH_3	HO_2C	C_6H_5	o-$O_2NC_6H_4$	—	144
CH_3	HO_2C	o-$CH_3OC_6H_4$	o-$CH_3OC_6H_4$	70	290*a*
CH_3	HO_2C	p-$CH_3OC_6H_4$	p-$CH_3OC_6H_4$	—	290*a*
CH_3O_2C	HO_2C	C_6H_5	C_6H_5	—	70
$C_2H_5O_2C$	HO_2C	C_6H_5	C_6H_5	Quant.	70
$C_2H_5O_2C$	HO_2C	C_6H_5	p-$CH_3C_6H_4$	—	19
CH_3CO	HO_2C	C_6H_5	C_6H_5	75	52, 142
C_6H_5	HO_2C	C_6H_5	C_6H_5	—	19
C_6H_5	HO_2C	C_6H_5	o-$CH_3C_6H_4$	—	141
C_6H_5	HO_2C	C_6H_5	o-$O_2NC_6H_4$	—	141
C_6H_5	HO_2C	C_6H_5	m-$O_2NC_6H_4$	—	141
C_6H_5	HO_2C	C_6H_5	p-$O_2NC_6H_4$	—	141
C_6H_5	HO_2C	C_6H_5	2,4-$(CH_3)_2C_6H_3$	—	141
C_6H_5CO	HO_2C	C_6H_5	C_6H_5	—	120
$C_6H_5N{=}N$	HO_2C	C_6H_5	C_6H_5	56	60, 70, 140, 151
$C_6H_5N{=}N$	HO_2C	C_6H_5	p-$CH_3C_6H_4$	—	19
$C_6H_5N{=}N$	HO_2C	p-$CH_3C_6H_4$	C_6H_5	—	19
$HOCH_2CH_2$**	HO_2C	o-$CH_3C_6H_4$	o-ClC_6H_4	23	403*a*
$HOCH_2CH_2$**	HO_2C	o-ClC_6H_4	o-$CH_3C_6H_4$	7	403*a*
$HOCH_2CH_2$**	HO_2C	o-ClC_6H_4	o-ClC_6H_4	38	403*a*
$HOCH_2CH_2$**	HO_2C	o-$O_2NC_6H_4$	o-$O_2NC_6H_4$	4	403*a*

Note: References 177–480 are on pp. 136–142.

** The starting material was the hydrazone of α-oxo-γ-butyrolactone.

TABLE IX—*Continued*

F. Hydrazones Which Couple with Elimination of a Substituent—Continued

R	R′	R″	R‴	Yield, %	References
$CH_3CHOHCH_2$††	HO_2C	C_6H_5	C_6H_5	4	403*a*
$CH_3CHOHCH_2$††	HO_2C	*o*-ClC_6H_4	*o*-ClC_6H_4	15	403*a*
CH_3O_2C	CH_3CO	*p*-$CH_3C_6H_4$	C_6H_5	—	19
$C_2H_5O_2C$	CH_3CO	C_6H_5	C_6H_5	—	60, 151
$C_2H_5O_2C$	CH_3CO	*p*-$CH_3C_6H_4$	C_6H_5	—	19
l-Carbomenthyloxy	CH_3CO	*p*-$CH_3C_6H_4$	*p*-ClC_6H_4	—	146
l-Carbomenthyloxy	CH_3CO	*p*-BrC_6H_4	*p*-$CH_3C_6H_4$	—	146
$C_6H_5N{=}N$	CH_3CO	C_6H_5	C_6H_5	—	52, 142
$C_6H_5N{=}N$	HO_2CCO	C_6H_5	C_6H_5	—	153
$C_2H_5O_2C$	$C_2H_5O_2CCO$	*p*-BrC_6H_4	*p*-BrC_6H_4	—	66
NO_2	$HOCH_2$	C_6H_5	C_6H_5	—	107
NO_2	$CH_3CH(OH)$	C_6H_5	C_6H_5	—	107
NO_2	$Cl_3CCH(OH)$	C_6H_5	C_6H_5	—	107
NO_2	$CH_3CH_2CH(OH)$	C_6H_5	C_6H_5	—	107
NO_2	$CH_3(CH_2)_2CH(OH)$	C_6H_5	C_6H_5	—	107
NO_2	$CH_3(CH_2)_3CH(OH)$	C_6H_5	C_6H_5	—	107
NO_2	$C_6H_5CH(OH)$	C_6H_5	C_6H_5	—	107

Note: References 177–480 are on pp. 136–142.

†† The starting material was the hydrazone of α-oxo-γ-valerolactone.

TABLE X

Coupling of Diazonium Salts with Heterocyclic Compounds

A. 5-*Pyrazolones*

Heterocyclic Compound, Substituent(s) in $O{=}C_5$–N_1H–$N_2{=}C_3H$–C_4H_2	Substituent(s) in Aniline*	Product (Yield, %), Substituent(s) in $O{=}C_5$–N_1H–$N_2{=}C_3H$–C_4H_2	References
—	—	4-Phenylazo (quant.)	405, 404
	4-Methyl	4-(*p*-Tolylazo) (quant.)	405, 404, 406, 407
3-Methyl	—	3-Methyl-4-phenylazo	404, 407, 408
	2-Aminoanthraquinone	3-Methyl-4-(2-anthraquinonylazo) (quant.)	250
3-Carboxy	—	3-Carboxy-4-phenylazo	404
	2-Carboxy	3-Carboxy-4-(*o*-carboxyphenylazo)	404
	2-Carbethoxy	3-Carboxy-4-(*o*-carbethoxyphenylazo)	409
3-Carbomethoxy	—	3-Carbomethoxy-4-phenylazo	404
3-Carbethoxy	—	3-Carbethoxy-4-phenylazo	404
	2-Carboxy	3-Carbethoxy-4-(*o*-carboxyphenylazo)	404
	2-Carbethoxy	3-Carbethoxy-4-(*o*-carbethoxyphenylazo)	409
3-Carbethoxymethyl	4-Methyl	3-Carbethoxymethyl-4-(*p*-tolylazo) (98)	65
3-Phenyl	—	3-Phenyl-4-phenylazo	404, 407, 408, 409
	2-Methyl	3-Phenyl-4-(*o*-tolylazo)	404, 409
	4-Methyl	3-Phenyl-4-(*p*-tolylazo)	404, 409
	α-Naphthylamine	3-Phenyl-4-(α-naphthylazo)	404, 409
	β-Naphthylamine	3-Phenyl-4-(β-naphthylazo)	404, 409

Note: References 177–480 are on pp. 136–142.

* The full name is given when it is awkward to name the arylamine as a derivative of aniline.

TABLE X—*Continued*

A. 5-*Pyrazolones*—*Continued*

Heterocycle Compound, Substituent(s) in 5-pyrazolone (H–N1, 2N=3CH, H$_2$C4, O=C5)	Substituent(s) in Aniline*	Product (Yield, %), Substituent(s) in 5-pyrazolone (H–N1, 2N=3CH, H$_2$C4, O=C5)	References
3-(2-Furyl)	—	3-(2-Furyl)-4-phenylazo	410
1-Methyl-3-amino	4-Methoxy	1-Methyl-3-amino-4-(*p*-anisylazo) (41)	411
1-Methyl-3-carbethoxy	4-Methoxy	1-Methyl-3-carbethoxy-4-(*p*-anisylazo) (88)	411
1-Methyl-3-phenyl	—	1-Methyl-3-phenyl-4-phenylazo	412
1-Acetyl-3-phenyl	—	1-Acetyl-3-phenyl-4-phenylazo	408
1-Phenyl	—	1-Phenyl-4-phenylazo	157
1-Phenyl-3-methyl	—	1-Phenyl-3-methyl-4-phenylazo	413, 414, 415
	2-Methyl	1-Phenyl-3-methyl-4-(*o*-tolylazo)	415, 416, 417
	3-Methyl	1-Phenyl-3-methyl-4-(*m*-tolylazo)	415, 417
	4-Methyl	1-Phenyl-3-methyl-4-(*p*-tolylazo)	415, 417
	2-Methoxy	1-Phenyl-3-methyl-4-(*o*-anisylazo)	415, 417
	4-Methoxy	1-Phenyl-3-methyl-4-(*p*-anisylazo)	415, 417
	2-Ethoxy	1-Phenyl-3-methyl-4-(*o*-ethoxyphenylazo)	415, 417
	4-Ethoxy	1-Phenyl-3-methyl-4-(*p*-ethoxyphenylazo)	415, 417
	2-Chloro	1-Phenyl-3-methyl-4-(*o*-chlorophenylazo)	68, 415
	3-Chloro	1-Phenyl-3-methyl-4-(*m*-chlorophenylazo)	415
	4-Chloro	1-Phenyl-3-methyl-4-(*p*-chlorophenylazo)	415, 417
	4-Bromo	1-Phenyl-3-methyl-4-(*p*-bromophenylazo)	415, 417
	4-Acetyl	1-Phenyl-3-methyl-4-(*p*-acetylphenylazo)	417
	2-Nitro	1-Phenyl-3-methyl-4-(*o*-nitrophenylazo)	415, 417
	3-Nitro	1-Phenyl-3-methyl-4-(*m*-nitrophenylazo)	415, 417

4-Nitro	1-Phenyl-3-methyl-4-(*p*-nitrophenylazo)	415, 417
4-Acetamido	1-Phenyl-3-methyl-4-(*p*-acetamidophenylazo)	417
4-Benzamido	1-Phenyl-3-methyl-4-(*p*-benzamidophenylazo)	417
3-Sulfo	1-Phenyl-3-methyl-4-(*m*-sulfophenylazo)	418
4-Sulfo	1-Phenyl-3-methyl-4-(*p*-sulfophenylazo)	418
2,4-Dimethyl	1-Phenyl-3-methyl-4-(2,4-dimethylphenylazo)	417
2,5-Dimethyl	1-Phenyl-3-methyl-4-(2,5-dimethylphenylazo)	417
2,5-Dichloro	1-Phenyl-3-methyl-4-(2,5-dichlorophenylazo)	67, 415
4-Chloro-2-methyl	1-Phenyl-3-methyl-4-(4-chloro-2-methylphenylazo)	415
5-Chloro-2-methyl	1-Phenyl-3-methyl-4-(5-chloro-2-methylphenylazo)	415
4-Chloro-2-nitro	1-Phenyl-3-methyl-4-(4-chloro-2-nitrophenylazo)	415
3-Methyl-4-sulfo	1-Phenyl-3-methyl-4-(3-methyl-4-sulfophenylazo)	418
4-Chloro-3-sulfo	1-Phenyl-3-methyl-4-(4-chloro-3-sulfophenylazo)	418
3-Chloro-5-sulfo	1-Phenyl-3-methyl-4-(3-chloro-5-sulfophenylazo)	419
α-Naphthylamine	1-Phenyl-3-methyl-4-(α-naphthylazo)	415, 417
β-Naphthylamine	1-Phenyl-3-methyl-4-(β-naphthylazo)	415, 417
1-Nitro-2-naphthylamine	1-Phenyl-3-methyl-4-(1-nitro-2-naphthylazo)	417
4-Nitro-1-naphthylamine	1-Phenyl-3-methyl-4-(4-nitro-1-naphthylazo)	417
1-Sulfo-2-naphthylamine	1-Phenyl-3-methyl-4-(1-sulfo-2-naphthylazo)	418
1-(*p*-Aminophenyl)-piperazine	1-Phenyl-3-methyl-4-(*p*-1-piperazylphenylazo) (66)	420
6-Amino-2,3-dihydro-3-oxobenzo-1,4-thiazine	1-Phenyl-3-methyl-4-(2,3-dihydro-3-oxobenzo-1,4-thiazin-6-ylazo) (88)	421
Benzidine	4,4′-(4,4′-Biphenylenedisazo)bis-[1-phenyl-3-methyl-5-pyrazolone]	417

Note: References 177–480 are on pp. 136–142.

* The full name is given when it is awkward to name the arylamine as a derivative of aniline.

TABLE X—*Continued*

A. 5-Pyrazolones—Continued

Heterocyclic Compound, Substituent(s) in (5-pyrazolone ring: O=C5, N1H, 2N, 3CH, H2C4)	Substituent(s) in Aniline*	Product (Yield, %), Substituent(s) in (5-pyrazolone ring: O=C5, N1H, 2N, 3CH, H2C4)	References
1-Phenyl-3-carbethoxymethyl	4-Methyl	1-Phenyl-3-carbethoxymethyl-4-(*p*-tolylazo) (89)	65
	4-Nitro	1-Phenyl-3-carbethoxymethyl-4-(*p*-nitrophenylazo) (85)	65
1,3-Diphenyl	—	1,3-Diphenyl-4-phenylazo	409, 415, 422
	2-Methyl	1,3-Diphenyl-4-(*o*-tolylazo)	409, 415
	3-Methyl	1,3-Diphenyl-4-(*m*-tolylazo)	415
	4-Methyl	1,3-Diphenyl-4-(*p*-tolylazo)	409, 415
	2-Methoxy	1,3-Diphenyl-4-(*o*-anisylazo)	415
	4-Methoxy	1,3-Diphenyl-4-(*p*-anisylazo)	415
	2-Ethoxy	1,3-Diphenyl-4-(*o*-ethoxyphenylazo)	415
	4-Ethoxy	1,3-Diphenyl-4-(*p*-ethoxyphenylazo)	415
	2-Chloro	1,3-Diphenyl-4-(*o*-chlorophenylazo)	415
	3-Chloro	1,3-Diphenyl-4-(*m*-chlorophenylazo)	415
	4-Chloro	1,3-Diphenyl-4-(*p*-chlorophenylazo)	415
	4-Bromo	1,3-Diphenyl-4-(*p*-bromophenylazo)	415
	2-Nitro	1,3-Diphenyl-4-(*o*-nitrophenylazo)	415
	3-Nitro	1,3-Diphenyl-4-(*m*-nitrophenylazo)	415
	4-Nitro	1,3-Diphenyl-4-(*p*-nitrophenylazo)	415
	3-Sulfo	1,3-Diphenyl-4-(*m*-sulfophenylazo)	418
	4-Sulfo	1,3-Diphenyl-4-(*p*-sulfophenylazo)	418
	2,5-Dichloro	1,3-Diphenyl-4-(2,5-dichlorophenylazo)	415
	4-Chloro-2-methyl	1,3-Diphenyl-4-(4-chloro-2-methylphenylazo)	415

	5-Chloro-2-methyl	1,3-Diphenyl-4-(5-chloro-2-methylphenylazo)	415
	4-Chloro-2-nitro	1,3-Diphenyl-4-(4-chloro-2-nitrophenylazo)	415
	3-Methyl-4-sulfo	1,3-Diphenyl-4-(3-methyl-4-sulfophenylazo)	418
	4-Chloro-3-sulfo	1,3-Diphenyl-4-(4-chloro-3-sulfophenylazo)	418
	α-Naphthylamine	1,3-Diphenyl-4-(α-naphthylazo)	409, 415
	β-Naphthylamine	1,3-Diphenyl-4-(β-naphthylazo)	409, 415
	1-Sulfo-2-naphthylamine	1,3-Diphenyl-4-(1-sulfo-2-naphthylazo)	418
1-Phenyl-3-(2-furyl)	—	1-Phenyl-3-(2-furyl)-4-phenylazo	410, 415
	2-Methyl	1-Phenyl-3-(2-furyl)-4-(*o*-tolylazo)	410, 415
	3-Methyl	1-Phenyl-3-(2-furyl)-4-(*m*-tolylazo)	410, 415
	4-Methyl	1-Phenyl-3-(2-furyl)-4-(*p*-tolylazo)	410, 415
	2-Methoxy	1-Phenyl-3-(2-furyl)-4-(*o*-anisylazo)	410, 415
	4-Methoxy	1-Phenyl-3-(2-furyl)-4-(*p*-anisylazo)	410, 415
	2-Ethoxy	1-Phenyl-3-(2-furyl)-4-(*o*-ethoxyphenylazo)	410, 415
	4-Ethoxy	1-Phenyl-3-(2-furyl)-4-(*p*-ethoxyphenylazo)	410, 415
	2-Chloro	1-Phenyl-3-(2-furyl)-4-(*o*-chlorophenylazo)	410, 415
	3-Chloro	1-Phenyl-3-(2-furyl)-4-(*m*-chlorophenylazo)	410, 415
	4-Chloro	1-Phenyl-3-(2-furyl)-4-(*p*-chlorophenylazo)	410, 415
	4-Bromo	1-Phenyl-3-(2-furyl)-4-(*p*-bromophenylazo)	410, 415
	2-Nitro	1-Phenyl-3-(2-furyl)-4-(*o*-nitrophenylazo)	410, 415
	3-Nitro	1-Phenyl-3-(2-furyl)-4-(*m*-nitrophenylazo)	410, 415
	4-Nitro	1-Phenyl-3-(2-furyl)-4-(*p*-nitrophenylazo)	410, 415
	3-Sulfo	1-Phenyl-3-(2-furyl)-4-(*m*-sulfophenylazo)	418
	4-Sulfo	1-Phenyl-3-(2-furyl)-4-(*p*-sulfophenylazo)	418
	2,5-Dichloro	1-Phenyl-3-(2-furyl)-4-(2,5-dichlorophenylazo)	415
	4-Chloro-2-methyl	1-Phenyl-3-(2-furyl)-4-(4-chloro-2-methylphenylazo)	415
	5-Chloro-2-methyl	1-Phenyl-3-(2-furyl)-4-(5-chloro-2-methylphenylazo)	415
	4-Chloro-2-nitro	1-Phenyl-3-(2-furyl)-4-(4-chloro-2-nitrophenylazo)	415

Note: References 177–480 are on pp. 136–142.

* The full name is given when it is awkward to name the arylamine as a derivative of aniline.

TABLE X—*Continued*

A. 5-*Pyrazolones*—*Continued*

Heterocyclic Compound, Substituent(s) in (5-pyrazolone ring: $O{=}C_5$–N_1H–$N_2{=}C_3H$–C_4H_2)	Substituent(s) in Aniline*	Product (Yield, %), Substituent(s) in (5-pyrazolone ring: $O{=}C_5$–N_1H–$N_2{=}C_3H$–C_4H_2)	References
1-Phenyl-3-(2-furyl) (*Cont.*)	3-Methyl-4-sulfo	1-Phenyl-3-(2-furyl)-4-(3-methyl-4-sulfophenylazo)	418
	4-Chloro-3-sulfo	1-Phenyl-3-(2-furyl)-4-(4-chloro-3-sulfophenylazo)	418
	α-Naphthylamine	1-Phenyl-3-(2-furyl)-4-(α-naphthylazo)	415
	β-Naphthylamine	1-Phenyl-3-(2-furyl)-4-(β-naphthylazo)	410, 415
	1-Sulfo-2-naphthylamine	1-Phenyl-3-(2-furyl)-4-(1-sulfo-2-naphthylazo)	418
1-Phenyl-3-(α-phenylbutyramido)	4-Methoxy	1-Phenyl-3-(α-phenylbutyramido)-4-(*p*-anisylazo) (80)	423
1-*p*-Tolyl-3-methyl	—	1-*p*-Tolyl-3-methyl-4-phenylazo	416
	4-Methyl	1-*p*-Tolyl-3-methyl-4-(*p*-tolylazo)	416
1-(*o*-Chlorophenyl)-3-methyl	2-Chloro	1-(*o*-Chlorophenyl)-3-methyl-4-(*o*-chlorophenylazo)	424
1-(*m*-Chlorophenyl)-3-methyl	2,4-Dichloro	1-(*m*-Chlorophenyl)-3-methyl-4-(2,4-dichlorophenylazo)	424
1-(*p*-Chlorophenyl)-3-methyl	4-Chloro	1-(*p*-Chlorophenyl)-3-methyl-4-(*p*-chlorophenylazo)	424
1-(2,4-Dichlorophenyl)-3-methyl	—	1-(2,4-Dichlorophenyl)-3-methyl-4-phenylazo	424
1-(*m*-Nitrophenyl)-3-phenyl	—	1-(*m*-Nitrophenyl)-3-phenyl-4-phenylazo	425
1-(*p*-Nitrophenyl)-3-methyl	4-Methoxy	1-(*p*-Nitrophenyl)-3-methyl-4-(*p*-anisylazo) (52)	423
	2-Chloro	1-(*p*-Nitrophenyl)-3-methyl-4-(*o*-chlorophenylazo)	68
1-(*o*-Carboxyphenyl)-3-methyl	—	1-(*o*-Carboxyphenyl)-3-methyl-4-phenylazo	426
1-(*o*-Carboxyphenyl)-3-phenyl	—	1-(*o*-Carboxyphenyl)-3-phenyl-4-phenylazo	427
	4-Methyl	1-(*o*-Carboxyphenyl)-3-phenyl-4-(*p*-tolylazo)	427

1-(*m*-Carboxyphenyl)-3-methyl	—	1-(*m*-Carboxyphenyl)-3-methyl-4-phenylazo	428
1-(*p*-Carboxyphenyl)-3-methyl	—	1-(*p*-Carboxyphenyl)-3-methyl-4-phenylazo	428
1-(*o*-Sulfophenyl)-3-methyl	—	1-(*o*-Sulfophenyl)-3-methyl-4-phenylazo	429
1-(*p*-Sulfophenyl)-3-methyl	—	1-(*p*-Sulfophenyl)-3-methyl-4-phenylazo	430, 431
	4-Nitro	1-(*p*-Sulfophenyl)-3-methyl-4-(*p*-nitrophenylazo)	430, 432
	2,5-Dichloro	1-(*p*-Sulfophenyl)-3-methyl-4-(2,5-dichlorophenylazo)	430
	4-Chloro-2-methyl	1-(*p*-Sulfophenyl)-3-methyl-4-(4-chloro-2-methylphenylazo)	430
	5-Chloro-2-methyl	1-(*p*-Sulfophenyl)-3-methyl-4-(5-chloro-2-methylphenylazo)	430
1-(*p*-Sulfophenyl)-3-phenyl	—	1-(*p*-Sulfophenyl)-3-phenyl-4-phenylazo	430
	2-Nitro	1-(*p*-Sulfophenyl)-3-phenyl-4-(*o*-nitrophenylazo)	430
	4-Nitro	1-(*p*-Sulfophenyl)-3-phenyl-4-(*p*-nitrophenylazo)	430
	2,5-Dichloro	1-(*p*-Sulfophenyl)-3-phenyl-4-(2,5-dichlorophenylazo)	430
	4-Chloro-2-methyl	1-(*p*-Sulfophenyl)-3-phenyl-4-(4-chloro-2-methylphenylazo)	430
	5-Chloro-2-methyl	1-(*p*-Sulfophenyl)-3-phenyl-4-(5-chloro-2-methylphenylazo)	430
1-(*p*-Sulfophenyl)-3-(2-furyl)	—	1-(*p*-Sulfophenyl)-3-(2-furyl)-4-phenylazo	430
	2-Nitro	1-(*p*-Sulfophenyl)-3-(2-furyl)-4-(*o*-nitrophenylazo)	430
	4-Nitro	1-(*p*-Sulfophenyl)-3-(2-furyl)-4-(*p*-nitrophenylazo)	430
	2,5-Dichloro	1-(*p*-Sulfophenyl)-3-(2-furyl)-4-(2,5-dichlorophenylazo)	430
	4-Chloro-2-methyl	1-(*p*-Sulfophenyl)-3-(2-furyl)-4-(4-chloro-2-methylphenylazo)	430
	5-Chloro-2-methyl	1-(*p*-Sulfophenyl)-3-(2-furyl)-4-(5-chloro-2-methylphenylazo)	430

Note: References 177–480 are on pp. 136–142.

* The full name is given when it is awkward to name the arylamine as a derivative of aniline.

TABLE X—*Continued*

A. 5-*Pyrazolones*—*Continued*

Heterocyclic Compound, Substituent(s) in $O{=}C_5\text{–}N_1H\text{–}N_2{=}C_3H\text{–}C_4H_2$	Substituent(s) in Aniline*	Product (Yield, %), Substituent(s) in $O{=}C_5\text{–}N_1H\text{–}N_2{=}C_3H\text{–}C_4H_2$	References
1-(*m*-Sulfamylphenyl)-3-methyl	2-Hydroxy-4-sulfo-1-naphthylamine	1-(*m*-Sulfamylphenyl)-3-methyl-4-(2-hydroxy-4-sulfo-1-naphthylazo)	433
	2-Hydroxy-4-sulfo-6-nitro-1-naphthylamine	1-(*m*-Sulfamylphenyl)-3-methyl-4-(2-hydroxy-4-sulfo-6-nitro-1-naphthylazo)	433
1-Diphenylmethyl-3-methyl	4-Methyl	1-Diphenylmethyl-3-methyl-4-(*p*-tolylazo)	434
1-(2-Naphthyl)-3-methyl	2-Amino-anthraquinone	1-(2-Naphthyl)-3-methyl-4-(2-anthraquinonylazo) (quant.)	250
1-(2-Anthraquinonyl)-3-methyl	—	1-(2-Anthraquinonyl)-3-methyl-4-phenylazo	250
	α-Naphthylamine	1-(2-Anthraquinonyl)-3-methyl-4-(α-naphthylazo)	250
	β-Naphthylamine	1-(2-Anthraquinonyl)-3-methyl-4-(β-naphthylazo)	250
	2-Amino-anthraquinone	1-(2-Anthraquinonyl)-3-methyl-4-(2-anthra-quinonylazo)	250
1-(2-Benzothiazolyl)-3-methyl	—	1-(2-Benzothiazolyl)-3-methyl-4-phenylazo	435
	4-Sulfo	1-(2-Benzothiazolyl)-3-methyl-4-(*p*-sulfophenylazo)	435

B. Miscellaneous Heterocyclic Compounds

Heterocyclic Reactant	Substituent(s) in Aniline*	Product (Yield, %)	References
1-Methyl-3-hydroxy-5-pyrazolone imide	4-Methoxy	1-Methyl-3-hydroxy-4-(*p*-methoxyphenylazo)-5-pyrazolone imide (35)	411
3-(*p*-Tolyl)-5-pyrazolone imide	—	3-(*p*-Tolyl)-4-phenylazo-5-pyrazolone imide	318
1-Phenyl-3-methyl-5-pyrazolone imide	—	1-Phenyl-3-methyl-4-phenylazo-5-pyrazolone imide (59)	437, 436
	4-Sulfo	1-Phenyl-3-methyl-4-(*p*-sulfophenylazo)-5-pyrazolone imide	438
	β-Naphthylamine	1-Phenyl-3-methyl-4-(β-naphthylazo)-5-pyrazolone imide	439
1-(*o*-Tolyl)-3-methyl-5-pyrazolone imide	—	1-(*o*-Tolyl)-3-methyl-4-phenylazo-5-pyrazolone imide	440
1-Phenyl-3-methyl-5-thiopyrazolone	—	1-Phenyl-3-methyl-4-phenylazo-5-thiopyrazolone	441, 442
1-Phenyl-5-methyl-3-pyrazolone	—	1-Phenyl-4-phenylazo-5-methyl-3-pyrazolone	443, 444
1-(*o*-Tolyl)-5-methyl-3-pyrazolone	—	1-(*o*-Tolyl)-4-phenylazo-5-methyl-3-pyrazolone	444
1-(*p*-Tolyl)-5-methyl-3-pyrazolone	—	1-(*p*-Tolyl)-4-phenylazo-5-methyl-3-pyrazolone	444
1-(*p*-Bromophenyl)-5-methyl-3-pyrazolone	—	1-(*p*-Bromophenyl)-4-phenylazo-5-methyl-3-pyrazolone	445
1-(*o*-Carboxyphenyl)-5-methyl-3-pyrazolone	—	1-(*o*-Carboxyphenyl)-4-phenylazo-5-methyl-3-pyrazolone	446
Pyrazolidine-3,5-dione	4-Methyl	4-(*p*-Tolylazo)pyrazolidine-3,5-dione	404
1-Phenylpyrazolidine-3,5-dione	—	1-Phenyl-4-phenylazopyrazolidine-3,5-dione	447
	4-Methyl	1-Phenyl-4-(*p*-tolylazo)pyrazolidine-3,5-dione	448
1-Phenyl-4-ethylpyrazolidine-3,5-dione	—	1-Phenyl-4-ethyl-4-phenylazopyrazolidine-3,5-dione	449

Note: References 177–480 are on pp. 136–142.

* The full name is given when it is awkward to name the arylamine as a derivative of aniline.

TABLE X—*Continued*

B. Miscellaneous Heterocyclic Compounds—Continued

Heterocyclic Reactant	Substituent(s) in Aniline*	Product (Yield, %)	References
1-*p*-Tolylpyrazolidine-3,5-dione	—	1-(*p*-Tolyl)-4-phenylazopyrazolidine-3,5-dione	450
3-Methyl-5-isoxazolone	—	3-Methyl-4-phenylazo-5-isoxazolone (quant.)	451, 227, 452
	2-Methyl	3-Methyl-4-(*o*-tolylazo)-5-isoxazolone	227
	4-Methyl	3-Methyl-4-(*p*-tolylazo)-5-isoxazolone	227
	2-Methoxy	3-Methyl-4-(*o*-anisylazo)-5-isoxazolone	227
	α-Naphthylamine	3-Methyl-4-(α-naphthylazo)-5-isoxazolone	227
	β-Naphthylamine	3-Methyl-4-(β-naphthylazo)-5-isoxazolone	227
3-Phenyl-5-isoxazolone	—	3-Phenyl-4-phenylazo-5-isoxazolone	453
3-(*m*-Tolyl)-5-isoxazolone	—	3-(*m*-Tolyl)-4-phenylazo-5-isoxazolone	454
3-(*p*-Tolyl)-5-isoxazolone	—	3-(*p*-Tolyl)-4-phenylazo-5-isoxazolone	454
3-(*m*-Chlorophenyl)-5-isoxazolone	4-Nitro	3-(*m*-Chlorophenyl)-4-(*p*-nitrophenylazo)-5-isoxazolone	455
3-(*m*-Nitrophenyl)-5-isoxazolone	4-Nitro	3-(*m*-Nitrophenyl)-4-(*p*-nitrophenylazo)-5-isoxazolone	455
3-Anilino-5-isoxazolone	—	3-Anilino-4-phenylazo-5-isoxazolone	456
3-Methyl-5-iminoisoxazole	—	3-Methyl-4-phenylazo-5-iminoisoxazole	90
2-Benzyl-4-imidazolone	4-Nitro	3-Benzyl-5-(*p*-nitrophenylazo)-4-imidazolone	457
1,2,3-Triazol-5-one	4-Methyl	4-(*p*-Tolylazo)-1,2,3-triazol-5-one	458
1-Carboxymethyl-1,2,3-triazol-5-one	4-Methyl	1-Carboxymethyl-4-(*p*-tolylazo)-1,2,3-triazol-5-one	458
1-Phenyl-1,2,3-triazol-5-one	—	1-Phenyl-4-phenylazo-1,2,3-triazol-5-one	459
1-Acetylbenzalhydrazide-1,2,3-triazol-5-one	4-Methyl	1-Acetylbenzalhydrazide-4-(*p*-tolylazo)-1,2,3-triazol-5-one	460
1-Acetylglycinbenzalhydrazide-1,2,3-triazol-5-one	4-Methyl	1-Acetylglycinbenzalhydrazide-4-(*p*-tolylazo)-1,2,3-triazol-5-one	460
Barbituric acid	—	5-Oxobarbituric acid phenylhydrazone (quant.)	461
	2-Nitro	5-Oxobarbituric acid *o*-nitrophenylhydrazone	461

	4-Nitro	5-Oxobarbituric acid *p*-nitrophenylhydrazone	461
	4-Sulfamyl	5-Oxobarbituric acid *p*-sulfamylphenylhydrazone	244
	4-(*p*-Dimethylsulfamylphenyl)-sulfamyl	5-Oxobarbituric acid *p*-(*p*-dimethylsulfamylphenyl)-sulfamylphenylhydrazone	244
N,N′-Diphenylbarbituric acid	—	N,N′-Diphenyl-5-oxobarbituric acid phenylhydrazone	462
	4-Nitro	N,N′-Diphenyl-5-oxobarbituric acid *p*-nitrophenylhydrazone	462
N,N′-Diphenyl-5-benzylbarbituric acid	—	N,N′-Diphenyl-5-benzyl-5-phenylazobarbituric acid	462
	4-Nitro	N,N′-Diphenyl-5-benzyl-5-(*p*-nitrophenylazo)-barbituric acid	462
N,N′-Diphenyl-5-diphenylmethylbarbituric acid	4-Nitro	N,N′-Diphenyl-5-diphenylmethyl-5-(*p*-nitrophenylazo)-barbituric acid	462
N,N′-Diphenylthiobarbituric acid	—	N,N′-Diphenyl-5-phenylazothiobarbituric acid	463
	4-Nitro	N,N′-Diphenyl-5-(*p*-nitrophenylazo)thiobarbituric acid	463
N,N′-Diphenyl-5-diphenylmethylthiobarbituric acid	—	N,N′-Diphenyl-5-diphenylmethyl-5-phenylazothiobarbituric acid	463
2-Thianaphthenone	—	3-Phenylazo-2-thianaphthenone	464
	4-Nitro	3-(*p*-Nitrophenylazo)-2-thianaphthenone	464
	α-Naphthylamine	3-(α-Naphthylazo)-2-thianaphthenone	464
	β-Naphthylamine	3-(β-Naphthylazo)-2-thianaphthenone	464
3-Thianaphthenone	4-Nitro	2-(*p*-Nitrophenylazo)-3-thianaphthenone	465
5-Methyl-3-thianaphthenone	—	2-Phenylazo-5-methyl-3-thianaphthenone	466
3-Selenanaphthenone	—	2-Phenylazo-3-selenanaphthenone	467
6-Nitroöxindole	4-Bromo	3-(*p*-Bromophenylazo)-6-nitroöxindole	77
1-Phenyloxindole	—	1-Phenyl-3-phenylazoöxindole	468
Indoxyl	—	2-Phenylazoindoxyl	469

Note: References 177–480 are on pp. 136–142.

* The full name is given when it is awkward to name the arylamine as a derivative of aniline.

TABLE X—*Continued*

B. Miscellaneous Heterocyclic Compounds—Continued

Heterocyclic Reactant	Substituent(s) in Aniline*	Product (Yield, %)	References
Homophthalimide	—	α-Phenylazohomophthalimide	470, 471, 472
	2-Methyl	α-(*o*-Tolylazo)homophthalimide	472
	3-Methyl	α-(*m*-Tolylazo)homophthalimide	472
	4-Methyl	α-(*p*-Tolylazo)homophthalimide	472
	2-Chloro	α-(*o*-Chlorophenylazo)homophthalimide	472
	2-Nitro	α-(*o*-Nitrophenylazo)homophthalimide	472
	4-Nitro	α-(*p*-Nitrophenylazo)homophthalimide	472
	2-Carboxy	α-(*o*-Carboxyphenylazo)homophthalimide	472
	3-Carboxy	α-(*m*-Carboxyphenylazo)homophthalimide	472
	4-Sulfo	α-(*p*-Sulfophenylazo)homophthalimide	473
	2,4-Dimethyl	α-(2,4-Dimethylphenylazo)homophthalimide	472
	4-Methyl-2-nitro	α-(4-Methyl-2-nitrophenylazo)homophthalimide	472
	4-Methyl-3-nitro	α-(4-Methyl-3-nitrophenylazo)homophthalimide	472
	α-Naphthylamine	α-(1-Naphthylazo)homophthalimide	472
	β-Naphthylamine	α-(2-Naphthylazo)homophthalimide	472
	4-Sulfo-1-naphthylamine	α-(4-Sulfo-1-naphthylazo)homophthalimide	473
	6,8-Disulfo-2-naphthylamine	α-(6,8-Disulfo-2-naphthylazo)homophthalimide	473
	2-Hydroxy-4-sulfo-1-naphthylamine	α-(2-Hydroxy-4-sulfo-1-naphthylazo)homophthalimide	473
	Benzidine	α,α′-(4,4′-Biphenylenedisazo)bis(homophthalimide)	472
	3,3′-Dimethylbenzidine	α,α′-(3,3′-Dimethyl-4,4′-biphenylenedisazo)bis-(homophthalimide)	472
	3,3′-Dimethoxybenzidine	α,α′-(3,3′-Dimethoxy-4,4′-biphenylenedisazo)bis-(homophthalimide)	472

N-Phenylhomophthalimide	—	α-Phenylazo-N-phenylhomophthalimide	474
4-Hydroxycoumarin	—	3-Phenylazo-4-hydroxycoumarin (91)	475
	4-Methyl	3-(*p*-Tolylazo)-4-hydroxycoumarin (88)	475
	4-Nitro	3-(*p*-Nitrophenylazo)-4-hydroxycoumarin (75)	475
	4-Sulfo	3-(*p*-Sulfophenylazo)-4-hydroxycoumarin (10)	475
	4-Sulfamyl	3-(*p*-Sulfamylphenylazo)-4-hydroxycoumarin (50)	475
1-Methyl-4-hydroxycarbostyril	3-Nitro	1-Methyl-3-(*m*-nitrophenylazo)-4-hydroxycarbostyril	476*a*
Glutaconic anhydride	—	γ-Ketoglutaconic anhydride phenylhydrazone (87)	475*a*
	2-Methyl	γ-Ketoglutaconic anhydride *o*-tolylhydrazone (57)	475*a*
	4-Methyl	γ-Ketoglutaconic anhydride *p*-tolylhydrazone (79)	475*a*
	2-Methoxy	γ-Ketoglutaconic anhydride *o*-anisylhydrazone (56)	475*a*
	4-Dimethylamino	γ-Ketoglutaconic anhydride *p*-dimethylaminophenylhydrazone (64)	475*a*
	2-Carboxy	γ-Ketoglutaconic anhydride *o*-carboxyphenylhydrazone (80)	475*a*
	α-Naphthylamine	γ-Ketoglutaconic anhydride α-naphthylhydrazone (86)	475*a*
	β-Naphthylamine	γ-Ketoglutaconic anhydride β-naphthylhydrazone (87)	475*a*
β-Methylglutaconic anhydride	—	γ-Keto-β-methylglutaconic anhydride phenylhydrazone (70)	8*b*
	2-Methoxy	γ-Keto-β-methylglutaconic anhydride *o*-anisylhydrazone (62)	8*b*
	4-Methoxy	γ-Keto-β-methylglutaconic anhydride *p*-anisylhydrazone (40)	8*b*
	2-Nitro	γ-Keto-β-methylglutaconic anhydride *o*-nitrophenylhydrazone (64)	8*b*
	4-Dimethylamino	γ-Keto-β-methylglutaconic anhydride *p*-dimethylaminophenylhydrazone (72)	8*b*
	4-Diethylamino	γ-Keto-β-methylglutaconic anhydride *p*-diethylaminophenylhydrazone (71)	8*b*

Note: References 177–480 are on pp. 136–142.

* The full name is given when it is awkward to name the arylamine as a derivative of aniline.

TABLE X—*Continued*

B. Miscellaneous Heterocyclic Compounds—Continued

Heterocyclic Reactant	Substituent(s) in Aniline*	Product (Yield, %)	References
β-Methylglutaconic anhydride (*Cont.*)	4-Sulfo	γ-Keto-β-methylglutaconic anhydride *p*-sulfophenylhydrazone (85)	8*b*
	3-Trifluoromethyl	γ-Keto-β-methylglutaconic anhydride *m*-trifluoromethylphenylhydrazone (65)	8*b*
	2,4-Dinitro	γ-Keto-β-methylglutaconic anhydride 2,4-dinitrophenylhydrazone (69)	8*b*
	α-Naphthylamine	γ-Keto-β-methylglutaconic anhydride α-naphthylhydrazone (85)	8*b*
	β-Naphthylamine	γ-Keto-β-methylglutaconic anhydride β-naphthylhydrazone (85)	8*b*
β-Chloroglutaconic anhydride	—	β-Chloro-γ-ketoglutaconic anhydride phenylhydrazone	476*b*
β-Carboxyglutaconic anhydride (*trans*-aconitic anhydride)	—	β-Carboxy-γ-ketoglutaconic anhydride phenylhydrazone (84)	476*c*
β-Carbomethoxyglutaconic anhydride	—	β-Carbomethoxy-γ-ketoglutaconic anhydride phenylhydrazone (70)	476*c*
Malonyl-α-aminopyridine	—	3-Phenylazo-4H-pyrido[1,2-*a*]pyrimidin-4-one (85)	300*b*
	4-Carboxy	3-(*p*-Carboxyphenylazo)-4H-pyrido[1,2-*a*]pyrimidin-4-one (96)	300*b*
	4-Carbomethoxy	3-(*p*-Carbomethoxyphenylazo)-4H-pyrido[1,2-*a*]-pyrimidin-4-one (70)	300*b*
	4-Carbethoxy	3-(*p*-Carbethoxyphenylazo)-4H-pyrido[1,2-*a*]pyrimidin-4-one	300*b*
	4-Sulfo	3-(*p*-Sulfophenylazo)-4H-pyrido[1,2-*a*]pyrimidin-4-one (93)	300*b*

Note: References 177–480 are on pp. 136–142.

* The full name is given when it is awkward to name the arylamine as a derivative of aniline.

TABLE XI

COUPLING OF DIAZONIUM SALTS WITH MISCELLANEOUS COMPOUNDS

Reactant	Substituent in Aniline	Product (Yield, %)	References
Diazomethane	4-Nitro	Chloroformaldehyde *p*-nitrophenylhydrazone* (85)	476*d*
Acetaldehyde	—	N,N′-Diphenyl-C-phenylazoformazan (20–30)	153, 27
Ketene diethylacetal	—	1-Phenyl-4-ethoxy-6-pyridazone (35)	477
	4-Ethoxy	1-*p*-Ethoxyphenyl-4-ethoxy-6-pyridazone† (21)	477
	4-Nitro	1-*p*-Nitrophenyl-4-ethoxy-6-pyridazone (25)	477
	4-Carbethoxy	1-*p*-Carbethoxyphenyl-4-ethoxy-6-pyridazone (33)	477
Ethyl β-aminocrotonate	—	Ethyl α-phenylazo-β-aminocrotonate (52)	478
Ethyl β-methylaminocrotonate	—	Ethyl α-phenylazo-β-methylaminocrotonate (51)	478
Ethyl β-diethylaminocrotonate	—	1-Phenyl-3-diethylamino-3-methyl-4-phenylazo-5-ethoxypyrazoline (75)	479
Bis(phenylsulfinyl)methane	—	Bis(phenylsulfinyl)formaldehyde phenylhydrazone	480
1-(2-Methylpropenyl)piperidine	4-Chloro	Acetone *p*-chlorophenylhydrazone	130*a*
	4-Nitro	Acetone *p*-nitrophenylhydrazone	130*a*
1-(1-Butenyl)piperidine	4-Methoxy	1,2-Butanedione 2-*p*-anisylhydrazone (53)	130*a*
	4-Chloro	1,2-Butanedione 2-*p*-chlorophenylhydrazone (65)	130*a*
	4-Nitro	1,2-Butanedione 2-*p*-nitrophenylhydrazone (41)	130*a*
N,N-Diethylstyrylamine	4-Methoxy	Phenylglyoxal β-*p*-anisylhydrazone (76)	130*a*
	4-Chloro	Phenylglyoxal β-*p*-chlorophenylhydrazone (90)	130*a*
	4-Nitro	Phenylglyoxal β-*p*-nitrophenylhydrazone (94)	130*a*
	4-Carboxy	Phenylglyoxal β-*p*-carboxyphenylhydrazone (89)	130*a*
1-(β-Methylstyryl)piperidine	4-Nitro	Acetophenone *p*-nitrophenylhydrazone (87)	130*a*
	4-Carboxy	Acetophenone *p*-carboxyphenylhydrazone (95)	130*a*
	2,4-Dinitro	Acetophenone 2,4-dinitrophenylhydrazone (97)	130*a*

Note: References 177–480 are on pp. 136–142.

* The reaction was run in methanol saturated with lithium chloride.

† Nineteen per cent of N,N′-di-*p*-ethoxyphenyl-C-carbethoxyformazan was also formed.

REFERENCES FOR TABLES I-XI

[177] Favrel, *Bull. soc. chim. France,* [5], **1,** 981 (1934).
[178] Benary, Reiter, and Soenderop, *Ber.*, **50,** 65 (1917).
[179] Jerchel and Fischer, *Ann.*, **563,** 208 (1949).
[180] Bamberger and Kuhlemann, *Ber.*, **26,** 2978 (1893).
[181] Wolff, *Ann.*, **317,** 1 (1901).
[182] Wislicenus and Schöllkopf, *J. prakt. Chem.*, [2], **95,** 269 (1917).
[183] Borsche, Stackmann, and Makaroff-Semljanski, *Ber.*, **49,** 2222 (1916).
[184] Kröhnke and Kübler, *Ber.*, **70,** 538 (1937).
[185] Kowjalgi and Iyer, *Current Sci. India,* **19,** 210 (1950) [*C. A.*, **45,** 863 (1951)].
[186] Iyer and Kowjalgi, *J. Indian Inst. Sci.*, **34,** 81 (1952) [*C. A.*, **46,** 8857 (1952)].
[187] Beyer and Claisen, *Ber.*, **21,** 1697 (1888).
[188] Bülow and Schlotterbeck, *Ber.*, **35,** 2187 (1902).
[189] Bülow and Spengler, *Ber.*, **58,** 1375 (1925).
[190] Chattaway and Ashworth, *J. Chem. Soc.*, **1934,** 930.
[191] Favrel, *Bull. soc. chim. France,* [3], **27,** 328 (1902).
[192] Favrel, *Compt. rend.*, **128,** 318 (1899).
[193] Reilly, Daly, and Drumm, *Proc. Roy. Irish Acad.*, **40B,** 94 (1931) [*C. A.*, **26,** 452 (1932)].
[194] Morgan and Reilly, *J. Chem. Soc.*, **103,** 808 (1913).
[195] Reilly and MacSweeney, *Proc. Roy. Irish Acad.*, **39B,** 497 (1930) [*C. A.*, **25,** 1523 (1931)].
[196] Morgan and Ackerman, *J. Chem. Soc.*, **123,** 1308 (1923).
[197] Reilly and Drumm, *J. Chem. Soc.*, **1926,** 1729.
[198] Morgan and Drew, *J. Chem. Soc.*, **119,** 610 (1921).
[199] Sieglitz and Horn, *Chem. Ber.*, **84,** 607 (1951).
[200] Claisen and Ehrhardt, *Ber.*, **22,** 1009 (1889).
[201] Feist and Belart, *Ber.*, **28,** 1817 (1895).
[202] Mullen and Crowe, *J. Chem. Soc.*, **1927,** 1751.
[203] Bamberger and Witter, *Ber.*, **26,** 2786 (1893).
[204] Bamberger and Witter, *J. prakt. Chem.*, [2], **65,** 139 (1902).
[205] Chattaway and Ashworth, *J. Chem. Soc.*, **1933,** 1624.
[206] Bülow, *Ber.*, **32,** 2637 (1899).
[207] Bülow and Busse, *Ber.*, **39,** 2459 (1906).
[208] Sachs and Herold, *Ber.*, **40,** 2714 (1907).
[209] Kostanecki and Tambor, *Ber.*, **35,** 1679 (1902).
[210] Bülow and Sautermeister, *Ber.*, **37,** 354 (1904).
[211] Morgan and Porter, *J. Chem. Soc.*, **125,** 1269 (1924).
[212] Bülow and Riess, *Ber.*, **35,** 3900 (1902).
[213] Bülow and Grotowsky, *Ber.*, **34,** 1479 (1901).
[214] Anand, Patel, and Venkataraman, *Proc. Indian Acad. Sci.*, **28A,** 545 (1948) [*C. A.*, **43,** 5778 (1949)].
[215] Claisen and Roosen, *Ann.*, **278,** 274 (1894).
[216] Favrel and Jean, *Bull. soc. chim. France,* [4], **37,** 1238 (1925).
[217] Bülow, *Ber.*, **37,** 2198 (1904).
[218] Bülow and Nottbohm, *Ber.*, **36,** 2695 (1903).
[219] Bülow and Nottbohm, *Ber.*, **36,** 392 (1903).
[220] Krishnan, Iyer, and Guha, *Science and Culture India,* **11,** 567 (1946) [*C. A.*, **40,** 5712 (1946)].
[221] Vorländer and Erig, *Ann.*, **294,** 302 (1897).
[222] Boehm, *Ann.*, **318,** 230 (1901).
[223] Boehm, *Ann.*, **329,** 269 (1903).
[224] Rabe, *Ber.*, **31,** 1896 (1898).
[224a] Osborn and Schofield, *J. Chem. Soc.*, **1955,** 2100.
[225] den Otter, *Rec. trav. chim.*, **57,** 427 (1938).
[226] Bamberger, *Ber.*, **24,** 3260 (1891).

[227] Schiff and Viciani, *Gazz. chim. ital.*, **27,** II, 70 (1897).
[228] Chattaway and Ashworth, *J. Chem. Soc.*, **1933,** 475.
[229] Bamberger, *Ber.*, **17,** 2415 (1884).
[230] Chattaway and Lye, *Proc. Roy. Soc. London,* **A135,** 282 (1932) [*C. A.*, **26,** 5074 (1932)].
[231] Wolff and Lüttringhaus, *Ann.*, **312,** 155 (1900).
[232] Bamberger and Schmidt, *Ber.*, **34,** 2001 (1901).
[232a] Wizinger and Herzog, *Helv. Chim. Acta,* **36,** 531 (1953).
[233] Michael, *Ber.*, **38,** 2096 (1905).
[234] von Richter and Münzer, *Ber.*, **17,** 1926 (1884).
[235] Bülow and Neber, *Ber.*, **45,** 3732 (1912).
[236] Goldberg and Kelly, *J. Chem. Soc.*, **1948,** 1919.
[237] Bülow and Schaub, *Ber.*, **41,** 2355 (1908).
[238] Bülow and Engler, *Ber.*, **51,** 1246 (1918).
[239] Kjellin, *Ber.*, **30,** 1965 (1897).
[239a] Le Bris and Wahl, *Compt. rend.*, **241,** 1143 (1955).
[240] von Pechmann and Wedekind, *Ber.*, **28,** 1688 (1895).
[241] Bülow, *Ber.*, **31,** 3122 (1898).
[242] Griess, *Ber.*, **18,** 960 (1885).
[243] Bülow, *Ber.*, **33,** 187 (1900).
[244] Mossini, *Ann. chim. farm.*, Dec. **1939,** 47 [*C. A.*, **34,** 2175 (1940)].
[245] Chattaway and Parkes, *J. Chem. Soc.*, **1935,** 1005.
[246] Chattaway and Daldy, *J. Chem. Soc.*, **1928,** 2756.
[247] Chattaway, Ashworth, and Grimwade, *J. Chem. Soc.*, **1935,** 117.
[248] Chattaway and Ashworth, *J. Chem. Soc.*, **1933,** 475.
[249] Oddo, *Gazz. chim. ital.*, **21,** I, 264 (1891).
[250] Saunders, *J. Chem. Soc.*, **117,** 1264 (1920).
[251] Morgan and Read, *J. Chem. Soc.*, **121,** 2709 (1922).
[252] Bülow, *Ber.*, **44,** 601 (1911).
[253] Bülow and Baur, *Ber.*, **58,** 1926 (1925).
[254] Wedekind, *Ann.*, **295,** 324 (1897).
[255] Wizinger and Herzog, *Helv. Chim. Acta,* **34,** 1202 (1951).
[256] Bülow and von Reden, *Ber.*, **31,** 2574 (1898).
[257] Favrel, *Compt. rend.*, **145,** 194 (1907).
[258] Favrel, *Bull. soc. chim. France,* [4], **1,** 1238 (1907).
[259] Wolff and Fertig, *Ann.*, **313,** 12 (1900).
[260] Wahl and Doll, *Bull. soc. chim. France,* [4], **13,** 265 (1913).
[261] Wahl, *Compt. rend.*, **147,** 72 (1908).
[262] Wahl, *Bull. soc. chim. France,* [4], **3,** 946 (1908).
[263] Bamberger and Calman, *Ber.*, **18,** 2563 (1885).
[264] Stierlin, *Ber.*, **21,** 2120 (1888).
[265] Wahl, *Bull. soc. chim. France,* [4], **1,** 729 (1907).
[266] Ciusa, *Gazz. chim. ital.*, **50,** I, 194 (1920).
[267] Bülow and Busse, *Ber.*, **39,** 3861 (1906).
[268] Wahl and Silberzweig, *Bull. soc. chim. France,* [4], **11,** 61 (1912).
[269] Wahl and Rolland, *Ann. chim. Paris,* [10], **10,** 5 (1928).
[270] Rabischong, *Bull. soc. chim. France,* [3], **31,** 87 (1904).
[271] Chattaway and Humphrey, *J. Chem. Soc.*, **1927,** 2793.
[272] Chattaway and Humphrey, *J. Chem. Soc.*, **1927,** 1323.
[273] Rabischong, *Bull. soc. chim. France,* [3], **27,** 982 (1902).
[274] Sonn, *Ann.*, **518,** 290 (1935).
[275] Tamburello and Carapelle, *Gazz. chim. ital.*, **37,** I, 561 (1907).
[276] Dieckmann, *Ber.*, **45,** 2689 (1912).
[277] Dieckmann, *Ber.*, **44,** 975 (1911).
[278] Bülow, *Ber.*, **40,** 3787 (1907).
[279] Bülow, *Ber.*, **41,** 641 (1908).
[280] Bülow and Bozenhardt, *Ber.*, **43,** 234 (1910).

[281] Knorr and Reuter, *Ber.*, **27**, 1169 (1894).
[282] Andrisano and Pentimalli, *Ann. chim. Rome*, **40**, 292 (1950) [*C. A.*, **45**, 6384 (1951)].
[283] Andrisano, *Boll. sci. fac. chim. ind. Bologna*, **7**, 58 (1949) [*C. A.*, **44**, 9404 (1950)].
[284] Morgan and Davies, *J. Chem. Soc.*, **123**, 228 (1923).
[285] Seidel, *Ber.*, **59**, 1894 (1926).
[286] Bülow and Dick, *Ber.*, **57**, 1281 (1924).
[287] Andrisano and Passerini, *Ann. chim. Rome*, **40**, 439 (1950) [*C. A.*, **45**, 8775 (1951)].
[288] Chelintsev, *J. Gen. Chem. U.S.S.R.*, **14**, 941 (1944) [*C. A.*, **39**, 4611 (1945)].
[289] Petersen, *Chem. Ber.*, **83**, 551 (1950).
[290] Andrisano and Maioli, *Ann. chim. Rome*, **40**, 442 (1950) [*C. A.*, **45**, 8775 (1951)].
[290a] Abramovitch and Schofield, *J. Chem. Soc.*, **1955**, 2326.
[291] Busch and Frey, *Ber.*, **36**, 1362 (1903).
[292] Fusco and Romani, *Gazz. chim. ital.*, **78**, 332 (1948).
[293] Bülow and Ganghofer, *Ber.*, **37**, 4169 (1904).
[294] Favrel, *Bull. soc. chim. France*, [3], **27**, 313 (1902).
[295] Favrel, *Compt. rend.*, **128**, 829 (1899).
[296] Meyer, *Ber.*, **24**, 1241 (1891).
[297] Henrich and Thomas, *Ber.*, **40**, 4924 (1907).
[298] Henrich, *Monatsh.*, **20**, 537 (1899).
[299] Henrich, *Ber.*, **35**, 1663 (1902).
[300a] Shaw, *J. Biol. Chem.*, **185**, 439 (1950).
[300b] Snyder and Robison, *J. Am. Chem. Soc.*, **74**, 4910 (1952).
[300c] Snyder and Robison, *J. Am. Chem. Soc.*, **74**, 5945 (1952).
[301] Meyer, *Ber.*, **21**, 1306 (1888).
[302] Hausknecht, *Ber.*, **22**, 324 (1889).
[303] Wizinger and Biro, *Helv. Chim. Acta*, **32**, 901 (1949).
[304] Haller, *Compt. rend.*, **106**, 1171 (1888).
[305] Favrel, *Bull. soc. chim. France*, [3], **27**, 104 (1902).
[306] Favrel, *Compt. rend.*, **127**, 116 (1898).
[307] Krückeberg, *J. prakt. Chem.*, [2], **46**, 579 (1892).
[308] Krückeberg, *J. prakt. Chem.*, [2], **47**, 591 (1893).
[309] Weissbach, *J. prakt. Chem.*, [2], **57**, 206 (1898).
[310] Lax, *J. prakt. Chem.*, [2], **63**, 1 (1901).
[311] Marquardt, *J. prakt. Chem.*, [2], **52**, 160 (1895).
[312] Uhlmann, *J. prakt. Chem.*, [2], **51**, 217 (1895).
[313] Bülow and Neber, *Ber.*, **49**, 2179 (1916).
[314] Favrel, *Compt. rend.*, **122**, 844 (1896).
[315] Bowack and Lapworth, *J. Chem. Soc.*, **85**, 42 (1904).
[316] Perkin, *J. Chem. Soc.*, **43**, 111 (1883).
[317] Haller, *Compt. rend.*, **108**, 1116 (1889).
[318] von Meyer, *J. prakt. Chem.*, [2], **90**, 1 (1914).
[319] Benary and Hosenfeld, *Ber.*, **55**, 3417 (1922).
[320] Backer, *Rec. trav. chim.*, **70**, 892 (1951).
[321] Finzi and Bottiglieri, *Gazz. chim. ital.*, **48**, II, 113 (1918).
[322] Bamberger and Schmidt, *Ber.*, **34**, 574 (1901).
[323] Bamberger, Padova, and Ormerod, *Ann.*, **446**, 260 (1925).
[323a] Jerchel and Elder, *Chem. Ber.*, **88**, 1284 (1955).
[323b] Robbins and Schofield, *J. Chem. Soc.*, **1957**, 3186.
[324] Dermer and Hutcheson, *Proc. Oklahoma Acad. Sci.*, **23**, 60 (1943) [*C. A.*, **38**, 2006 (1944)].
[325] Kappeler, *Ber.*, **12**, 2285 (1879).
[326] Bamberger, *Ber.*, **31**, 2626 (1898).
[327] Barbieri, *Ber.*, **9**, 386 (1876).
[328] Wald, *Ber.*, **9**, 393 (1876).
[329] Hallmann, *Ber.*, **9**, 389 (1876).
[330] Bamberger and Frei, *Ber.*, **35**, 82 (1902).

[331] Bamberger and Frei, *Ber.*, **36,** 3833 (1903).
[332] Oddo and Ampola, *Gazz. chim. ital.*, **23,** I, 257 (1893).
[333] Feasley and Degering, *J. Org. Chem.*, **8,** 12 (1943).
[334] Askenasy and Meyer, *Ber.*, **25,** 1701 (1892).
[335] Duden, *Ber.*, **26,** 3003 (1893).
[336] Keppler and Meyer, *Ber.*, **25,** 1709 (1892).
[337] von Braun and Sobecki, *Ber.*, **44,** 2526 (1911).
[338] von Braun and Danziger, *Ber.*, **46,** 103 (1913).
[339] Russanow, *Ber.*, **25,** 2635 (1892).
[340] Kimich, *Ber.*, **10,** 140 (1877).
[341] Wieland, *Ann.*, **328,** 250 (1903).
[342] Meyer and Wertheimer, *Ber.*, **47,** 2374 (1914).
[343] Gold and Levine, *J. Org. Chem.*, **16,** 1507 (1951).
[344] Demuth and Meyer, *Ann.*, **256,** 28 (1890).
[345] Chattaway, Drewitt, and Parkes, *J. Chem. Soc.*, **1936,** 1693.
[346] Canonica, *Gazz. chim. ital.*, **79,** 738 (1949).
[347] Meisenheimer and Heim, *Ber.*, **38,** 466 (1905).
[348] Holleman, *Rec. trav. chim.*, **13,** 403 (1894).
[349] Bamberger, *Ber.*, **33,** 1781 (1900).
[350] Ponzio, *Gazz. chim. ital.*, **42,** I, 525 (1912).
[351] Bamberger and Scheutz, *Ber.*, **34,** 2023 (1901).
[352] Bamberger and Pemsel, *Ber.*, **36,** 57 (1903).
[353] Parkes and Williams, *J. Chem. Soc.*, **1934,** 67.
[354] von Braun and Kruber, *Ber.*, **45,** 384 (1912).
[355] Ponzio, *Gazz. chim. ital.*, **38,** I, 509 (1908).
[356] Ponzio and Charrier, *Gazz. chim. ital.*, **39,** I, 625 (1909).
[357] Ponzio, *Gazz. chim. ital.*, **39,** I, 559 (1909).
[358] Ponzio and Charrier, *Gazz. chim. ital.*, **38,** I, 526 (1908).
[359] Sonn and Schellenberg, *Ber.*, **50,** 1513 (1917).
[360] Arbuzov and Rafikov, *J. Gen. Chem. U.S.S.R.*, **7,** 2195 (1937) [*C. A.*, **32,** 515 (1938)].
[361a] Meyer, Irschick, and Schlösser, *Ber.*, **47,** 1741 (1914).
[361b] Bachman and Hatton, *J. Am. Chem. Soc.*, **66,** 1513 (1944).
[362] Thiele, *Ber.*, **33,** 666 (1900).
[363] Süs, *Ann.*, **556,** 85 (1944).
[364] Quilico and Freri, *Gazz. chim. ital.*, **62,** 253 (1932).
[365] Terent'ev and Zegelman, *Sci. Repts. Moscow State Univ.*, **1936,** No. 6, 257 [*C. A.*, **32,** 2516 (1938)].
[366] Allen, Eliot, and Bell, *Can. J. Res.*, **17B,** 75 (1939).
[366a] Pierrot and Wahl, *Compt. rend.*, **240,** 879 (1955).
[366b] Pierrot and Wahl, *Compt. rend.*, **239,** 1049 (1954).
[367] Busch and Klett, *Ber.*, **25,** 2847 (1892).
[368] Jacobs, Winstein, Henderson, and Spaeth, *J. Am. Chem. Soc.*, **68,** 1310 (1946).
[369] Atkinson and Simpson, *J. Chem. Soc.*, **1947,** 808.
[370] Schofield and Swain, *J. Chem. Soc.*, **1949,** 1367.
[371] Simpson, *J. Chem. Soc.*, **1946,** 673.
[372] Simpson, *J. Chem. Soc.*, **1943,** 447.
[373] Krahler and Burger, *J. Am. Chem. Soc.*, **63,** 2367 (1941).
[374] Witt, Nölting, and Grandmougin, *Ber.*, **23,** 3635 (1890).
[375] Michel and Grandmougin, *Ber.*, **26,** 2349 (1893).
[376] von Auwers and Schwegler, *Ber.*, **53,** 1211 (1920).
[377] Gabriel and Stelzner, *Ber.*, **29,** 303 (1896).
[378] Zincke and Malkomesius, *Ann.*, **339,** 218 (1905).
[379] Soc. anon. de mat. color. et prod. chim. Francolor, Brit. pat. 599834 [*C. A.*, **42,** 7538 (1948)].
[380] Petitcolas and Sureau, *Bull. soc. chim. France*, **1950,** 466.
[381] Zincke and Kuchenbecker, *Ann.*, **339,** 226 (1905).

[382] Morgan and Davies, *J. Chem. Soc.*, **123,** 228 (1923).
[383] Dadswell and Kenner, *J. Chem. Soc.*, **1927,** 580.
[384] Duval, *Compt. rend.*, **154**, 780 (1912).
[385] Duval, *Compt. rend.*, **146,** 1407 (1908).
[386] Duval, *Compt. rend.*, **144,** 1222 (1907).
[387] Capka, *Chem. Zvesti*, **2,** 1 (1948) [*C. A.*, **44,** 1523 (1950)].
[388] Bamberger and Pemsel, *Ber.*, **36,** 85 (1903).
[389] Jerchel, *Ber.*, **75B,** 75 (1942).
[389a] Nineham, Pain, and Slack, *J. Chem. Soc.*, **1954,** 1568.
[389b] Lettré, Haede, and Schäfer, *Hoppe-Seyler's Z., physiol. Chem.*, **289,** 298 (1952) [*C. A.*, **48,** 10677 (1954)].
[389c] Libman, Nineham, and Slack, *J. Chem. Soc.* **1954,** 1565.
[390] Ragno and Oreste, *Gazz. chim. ital.*, **78,** 228 (1948).
[391] Ragno and Bruno, *Gazz. chim. ital.*, **77,** 12 (1947).
[392] Breusch and Keskin, *Rev. fac. sci. univ. Istanbul*, **9A,** No. 1, 30 (1944) [*C. A.*, **40,** 1319 (1946)].
[393] Hausser, Jerchel, and Kuhn, *Chem. Ber.*, **82,** 515 (1949).
[393a] Duffin and Kendall, *J. Chem. Soc.*, **1954,** 408.
[394] Wislicenus, *Ber.*, **25,** 3456 (1892).
[395] Mattson, Jensen, and Dutcher, *J. Am. Chem. Soc.*, **70,** 1284 (1948).
[395a] Ashley, Davis, Nineham, and Slack, *J. Chem. Soc.*, **1953,** 3881.
[396] Fox and Atkinson, *J. Am. Chem. Soc.*, **72,** 3629 (1950).
[397] Wedekind, *Ber.*, **32,** 1918 (1899).
[398] Jerchel and Fischer, *Ann.*, **563,** 200 (1949).
[398a] Ried, Gick, and Oertel, *Ann.*, **581,** 29 (1953).
[398b] Beyer and Pyl, *Chem. Ber.*, **87,** 1505 (1954).
[398c] Tsou, Cheng, Nachlas, and Seligman, *J. Am. Chem. Soc.*, **78,** 6139 (1956).
[398d] Ried and Hillenbrand, *Ann.*, **581,** 44 (1953).
[399] Ludolphy, *Chem. Ber.*, **84,** 385 (1951).
[400] Seyhan, *Rev. fac. sci. univ. Istanbul*, **17A,** 182 (1952) [*C. A.*, **47,** 12390 (1953)].
[401] von Pechmann, *Ber.*, **29,** 2161 (1896).
[402] Wedekind, *Ber.*, **30,** 444 (1897).
[402a] Cottrell, Pain, and Slack, *J. Chem. Soc.*, **1954,** 2968.
[402b] Seyhan, *Chem. Ber.*, **87,** 1124 (1954).
[402d] Seyhan, *Chem. Ber.*, **88,** 646 (1955).
[402e] Seyhan, *Chem. Ber.*, **87,** 396 (1954).
[402f] Wahl and Le Bris, *Bull. soc. chim. France*, **1954,** 1281.
[402g] Wahl and Le Bris, *Compt. rend.*, **235,** 1405 (1952).
[402h] Wahl and Le Bris, *Compt. rend.*, **236,** 294 (1953).
[402i] Seyhan, *Chem. Ber.*, **88,** 212 (1955).
[402j] Seiler and Schmid, *Helv. Chim. Acta*, **37,** 1 (1954).
[402k] Ried and Gick, *Ann.*, **581,** 16 (1953).
[403] Scott, O'Sullivan, and Reilly, *J. Chem. Soc.*, **1951,** 3508.
[403a] Duffin and Kendall, *J. Chem. Soc.*, **1955,** 3470.
[404] von Rothenburg, *J. prakt. Chem.*, [2], **51,** 43 (1895).
[405] Knorr, *Ber.*, **29,** 249 (1896).
[406] von Rothenburg, *Ber.*, **26,** 2972 (1893).
[407] von Rothenburg, *Ber.*, **27,** 790 (1894).
[408] von Rothenburg, *J. prakt. Chem.*, [2], **52,** 23 (1895).
[409] von Rothenburg, *Ber.*, **27,** 783 (1894).
[410] Torrey and Zanetti, *Am. Chem. J.*, **44,** 391 (1910).
[411] Graham, Porter, and Weissberger, *J. Am. Chem. Soc.*, **71,** 983 (1949).
[412] Michaelis and Dorn, *Ann.*, **352,** 163 (1907).
[413] Knorr, *Ann.*, **238,** 183 (1887).
[414] Eibner, *Ber.*, **36,** 2687 (1903).
[415] Casoni, *Boll. sci. fac. chim. ind. Bologna*, **9,** 4 (1951) [*C. A.*, **45,** 7353 (1951)].

[416] Michaelis, *Ann.*, **338,** 183 (1905).

[417] Crippa, Long, and Perroncito, *Gazz. chim. ital.*, **62,** 944 (1932).

[418] Casoni, *Boll. sci. fac. chim. ind. Bologna,* **9,** 13 (1951) [*C. A.*, **45,** 7355 (1951)].

[419] Hayashi, Oshima, Tsuruoka, and Seo, *Rept. Japan Assoc. Advance. Sci.*, **17,** 47 (1942) [*C. A.*, **44,** 3258 (1950)].

[420] Kohlbach, *Arch. Hem. Farm.*, **11,** 99 (1937) [*C. A.*, **33,** 2897 (1939)].

[421] Mackie and Cutler, *Rec. trav. chim.*, **71,** 1198 (1952).

[422] Knorr and Klotz, *Ber.*, **20,** 2545 (1887).

[423] Vittum, Sawdey, Herdle, and Scholl, *J. Am. Chem. Soc.*, **72,** 1533 (1950).

[424] Chattaway and Strouts, *J. Chem. Soc.*, **125,** 2423 (1924).

[425] Michaelis and Willert, *Ann.*, **358,** 171 (1908).

[426] Michaelis, *Ann.*, **373,** 129 (1910).

[427] Michaelis, *Ann.*, **373,** 196 (1910).

[428] Michaelis and Horn, *Ann.*, **373,** 213 (1910).

[429] Sharvin, Arbuzov, and Varshavskii, *J. Chem. Ind. Moscow,* **6,** 1409 (1929) [*C. A.*, **25,** 501 (1931)].

[430] Casoni, *Boll. sci. fac. chim. ind. Bologna,* **9,** 9 (1951) [*C. A.*, **45,** 7355 (1951)].

[431] Möllenhoff, *Ber.*, **25,** 1941 (1892).

[432] Ioffe and Khavin, *J. Gen. Chem. U.S.S.R.*, **17,** 522 (1947) [*C. A.*, **42,** 903 (1948)].

[433] Hayashi, Hagiyama, and Seo, *Rept. Japan Assoc. Advance. Sci.*, **17,** 253, 257 (1942) [*C. A.*, **44,** 3259 (1950)].

[434] Darapsky, *J. prakt. Chem.*, [2], **67,** 175 (1903).

[435] Efros and Davidenkov, *J. Gen. Chem. U.S.S.R.*, **21,** 2046 (1951) [*C. A.*, **46,** 8100 (1952)].

[436] Michaelis and Brust, *Ann.*, **339,** 134 (1905).

[437] Mohr, *J. prakt. Chem.*, [2], **79,** 1 (1909).

[438] Michaelis and Klopstock, *Ann.*, **354,** 102 (1907).

[439] Michaelis and Schäfer, *Ann.*, **397,** 119 (1913).

[440] Michaelis and Klappert, *Ann.*, **397,** 149 (1913).

[441] Michaelis and Pander, *Ber.*, **37,** 2774 (1904).

[442] Michaelis and Pander, *Ann.*, **361,** 251 (1908).

[443] Michaelis, *Ber.*, **38,** 154 (1905).

[444] Michaelis and Behrens, *Ann.*, **338,** 228 (1905).

[445] Michaelis, *Ann.*, **358,** 127 (1907).

[446] Michaelis, *Ann.*, **373,** 209 (1910).

[447] Michaelis and Burmeister, *Ber.*, **25,** 1502 (1892).

[448] Michaelis and Simon, *Ann.*, **338,** 217 (1905).

[449] Michaelis and Schenk, *Ber.*, **41,** 3865 (1908).

[450] Asher, *Ber.*, **30,** 1018 (1897).

[451] Schiff, *Ber.*, **28,** 2731 (1895).

[452] Schiff and Viciani, *Ber.*, **30,** 1159 (1897).

[453] Claisen and Zedel, *Ber.*, **24,** 140 (1891).

[454] Posner and Schreiber, *Ber.*, **57,** 1127 (1924).

[455] Khromov and Poraĭ-Koshits, *J. Gen. Chem. U.S.S.R.*, **17,** 1828 (1947) [*C. A.*, **42,** 4171 (1948)].

[456] Worrall, *J. Am. Chem. Soc.*, **44,** 1551 (1922).

[457] Finger and Zeh, *J. prakt. Chem.*, [2], **82,** 50 (1910).

[458] Curtius and Thompson, *Ber.*, **39,** 4140 (1906).

[459] Dimroth, *Ann.*, **335,** 86 (1904).

[460] Curtius and Callan, *Ber.*, **43,** 2447 (1910).

[461] Kühling, *Ber.*, **31,** 1972 (1898).

[462] Whiteley, *J. Chem. Soc.*, **91,** 1330 (1907).

[463] Whiteley and Mountain, *Chem. News*, **99,** 234 (1909).

[464] Marschalk, *J. prakt. Chem.*, [2], **88,** 227 (1913).

[465] Friedländer, *Monatsh.*, **30,** 347 (1909).

[466] Auwers and Arndt, *Ann.*, **381,** 299 (1911).

[467] Lesser and Schoeller, *Ber.*, **47,** 2292 (1914).

[468] Stollé, Hecht, and Becker, *J. prakt. Chem.*, [2], **135**, 345 (1932).
[469] Baeyer, *Ber.*, **16**, 2188 (1883).
[470] Gabriel, *Ber.*, **20**, 1198 (1887).
[471] Pulvermacher, *Ber.*, **20**, 2492 (1887).
[472] Meyer and Vittenet, *Compt. rend.*, **192**, 885 (1931).
[473] Meyer and Vittenet, *Compt. rend.*, **193**, 344 (1931).
[474] Dieckmann, *Ber.*, **47**, 1428 (1914).
[475] Huebner and Link, *J. Am. Chem. Soc.*, **67**, 99 (1945).
[475a] Wiley and Ellert, *J. Am. Chem. Soc.*, **77**, 5187 (1955).
[476a] Waldmann, *J. prakt. Chem.*, [2], **147**, 321 (1937).
[476b] Malachowski and Kalinski, *Roczniki Chem.*, **6**, 768 (1926) [*C. A.*, **21**, 3615 (1927)].
[476c] Malachowski, Giedroyc, and Jerzmanowska, *Ber.*, **61**, 2525 (1928).
[476d] Huisgen and Koch, *Naturwiss.*, **41**, 16 (1954) [*C. A.*, **49**, 5344 (1955)].
[477] McElvain and Jelinek, *J. Am. Chem. Soc.*, **65**, 2236 (1943).
[478] Prager, *Ber.*, **34**, 3600 (1901).
[479] Prager, *Ber.*, **36**, 1451 (1903).
[480] Hinsberg, *J. prakt. Chem.*, [2], **85**, 337 (1912).

CHAPTER 2

THE JAPP-KLINGEMANN REACTION

ROBERT R. PHILLIPS

Eastman Kodak Company

CONTENTS

INTRODUCTION

In an attempt to prepare the azo ester I by coupling benzenediazonium chloride with ethyl 2-methylacetoacetate, Japp and Klingemann[1] obtained a product which was soon recognized[1–4] as the phenylhydrazone of ethyl pyruvate (II). It thus appeared that the acetyl group had been dis-

$$CH_3COCH(CH_3)CO_2C_2H_5 + C_6H_5N_2^+Cl^- \rightarrow \left[CH_3COC(CO_2C_2H_5)(CH_3){-}N{=}NC_6H_5 \right]_{\text{I}} \xrightarrow{H_2O}$$

$$CH_3CO_2H + \underset{\text{II}}{CH_3C(CO_2C_2H_5){=}N{-}NHC_6H_5}$$

placed; actually the coupling product I was unstable under the conditions of its formation, undergoing hydrolytic scission of the acetyl group and rearrangement of the azo structure. A year later the same authors discovered that, if the substituted acetoacetic ester was saponified and the coupling carried out on the sodium salt, the carboxylate function, rather than the acetyl group, was lost and the product isolated was the phenylhydrazone of biacetyl.[4,5]

$$CH_3COCH(CH_3)CO_2^- \xrightarrow{C_6H_5N_2^+} \left[CH_3COC(CO_2^-)(CH_3){-}N{=}NC_6H_5 \right] \xrightarrow{H_2O}$$

$$CH_3COC(CH_3){=}NNHC_6H_5 + HCO_3^-$$

In later years the reaction has been extended to other systems containing activated methinyl groups. The process can be generalized as shown in the following equation, in which x and y are electron-withdrawing groups.

[1] Japp and Klingemann, *Ber.*, **20,** 2942 (1887).
[2] Japp and Klingemann, *Ber.*, **20,** 3284 (1887).
[3] Japp and Klingemann, *Ber.*, **20,** 3398 (1887).
[4] Japp and Klingemann, *Ber.*, **21,** 549 (1888).
[5] Japp and Klingemann, *Ann.*, **247,** 190 (1888); *J. Chem. Soc.*, **53,** 519 (1888).

$$\begin{matrix} x & & H \\ & \diagdown\!\!\diagup & \\ & C & \\ & \diagup\!\!\diagdown & \\ y & & R \end{matrix} + ArN_2^+ \rightarrow \left[\begin{matrix} x & & N{=}N{-}Ar \\ & \diagdown\!\!\diagup & \\ & C & \\ & \diagup\!\!\diagdown & \\ y & & R \end{matrix}\right] \xrightarrow{H_2O} yOH + x{-}\underset{\displaystyle R}{\underset{|}{C}}{=}N{-}NHAr$$

MECHANISM

As is apparent from the above equations the Japp-Klingemann reaction is a special case of the coupling of diazonium salts with aliphatic compounds (see Chapter 1), distinguished by the fact that the coupling product ordinarily undergoes solvolysis as rapidly, or almost as rapidly, as it is formed. It resembles very closely the nitrosation and cleavage of active methinyl compounds discussed in an earlier volume of this series.[6] The first step undoubtedly occurs by the same mechanism as the similar coupling with an active methylene compound (for a discussion see p. 6), and is probably best represented as a direct union of the anion of the active methinyl compound and the diazonium cation, which are shown in the accompanying equation as the forms carrying full unit charges on the atoms that unite in the process.

$$C_6H_5N{=}N^{\oplus} + {}^{\ominus}{:}\overset{\displaystyle x}{\overset{|}{\underset{\displaystyle R}{\underset{|}{C}}}}{-}y \rightarrow C_6H_5N{=}N{-}\overset{\displaystyle x}{\overset{|}{\underset{\displaystyle R}{\underset{|}{C}}}}{-}y$$

Much of the early concern[7–9] about the mechanism of such couplings dealt with the question of the participation of the enolic forms of the active methinyl compounds and with the status of O-azo compounds as possible intermediates (p. 4). Although the mechanism just shown is probably an accurate representation of the coupling of mono-β-keto esters, there can be little doubt but that O-azo compounds are sometimes first formed from di-β-keto esters and triketones. Thus tribenzoylmethane yields a coupling product that generates an azo dye upon treatment with β-naphthol and undoubtedly is the derivative of the enol.[10]

[6] Touster, in Adams, *Organic Reactions*, Vol. 7, Chapter 6, John Wiley & Sons, 1953.

[7] Dimroth and Hartmann, *Ber.*, **41**, 4012 (1908).

[8] Dimroth, *Ber.*, **40**, 2404 (1907).

[9] Dimroth and Hartmann, *Ber.*, **40**, 4460 (1907).

[10] Dimroth, Leichtlin, and Friedemann, *Ber.*, **50**, 1534 (1917).

When it is heated to its melting point it changes to an isomer that does not have this property and must be the C-azo compound.

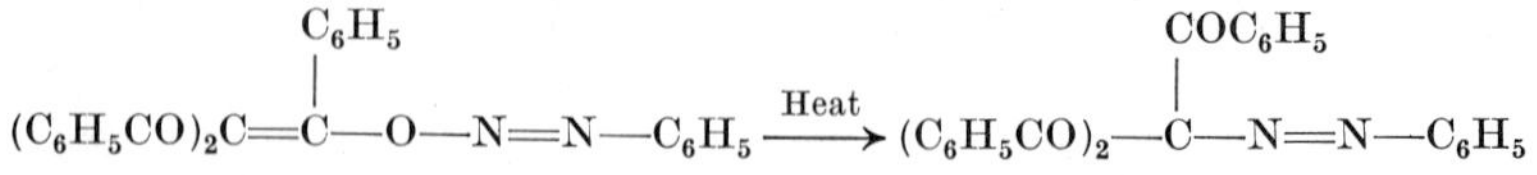

$$(C_6H_5CO)_2C{=}\underset{}{\overset{C_6H_5}{\overset{|}{C}}}{-}O{-}N{=}N{-}C_6H_5 \xrightarrow{\text{Heat}} (C_6H_5CO)_2{-}\overset{COC_6H_5}{\overset{|}{C}}{-}N{=}N{-}C_6H_5$$

The cleavage step is closely similar to the scission of triacylmethanes and of nitroso derivatives of monosubstituted active methylene compounds.[7] The cleavage is favored by increasing alkalinity of the solution; for example the azo compound III can be obtained from the diazonium salt prepared from 2,4-dinitroaniline and ethyl cyclopentanone-2-carboxylate by coupling in acetic acid solution, but it is rapidly cleaved by aqueous base, yielding IV.[11] In analogy with the base-catalyzed

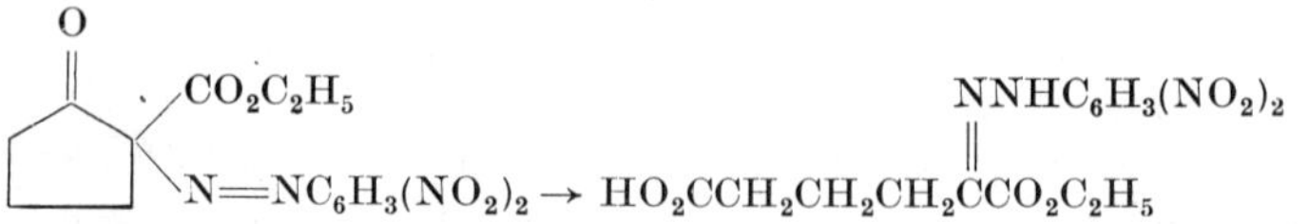

$$\underset{\text{III}}{\text{2-}CO_2C_2H_5\text{-2-}(N{=}NC_6H_3(NO_2)_2)\text{cyclopentanone}} \rightarrow \underset{\text{IV}}{HO_2CCH_2CH_2CH_2\overset{NNHC_6H_3(NO_2)_2}{\overset{\|}{C}}CO_2C_2H_5}$$

cleavage of nitroso esters[6] the second step of the Japp-Klingemann reaction can be represented as shown. In the decomposition of the

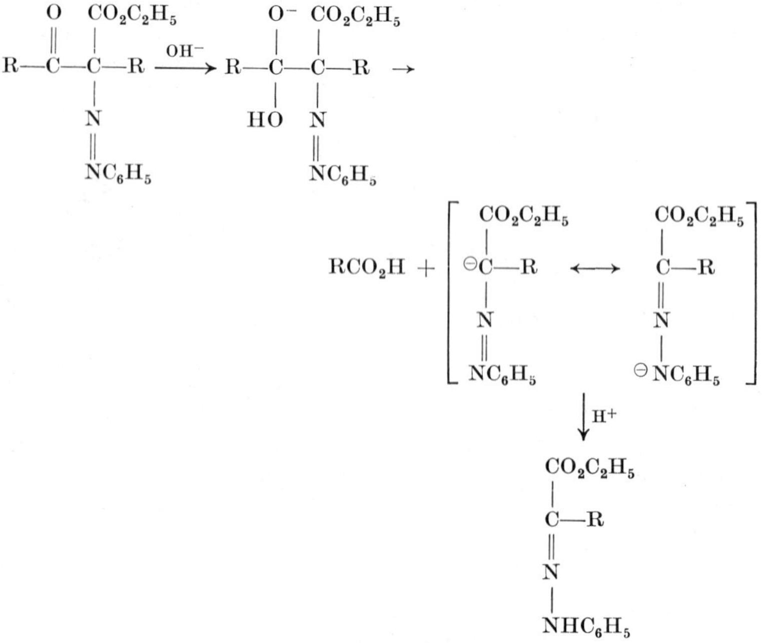

$$R{-}\overset{O}{\overset{\|}{C}}{-}\overset{CO_2C_2H_5}{\overset{|}{\underset{\underset{NC_6H_5}{\overset{\|}{N}}}{\underset{|}{C}}}}{-}R \xrightarrow{OH^-} R{-}\overset{O^-}{\overset{|}{\underset{HO}{\underset{|}{C}}}}{-}\overset{CO_2C_2H_5}{\overset{|}{\underset{\underset{NC_6H_5}{\overset{\|}{N}}}{\underset{|}{C}}}}{-}R \rightarrow$$

$$RCO_2H + \left[\ominus\overset{CO_2C_2H_5}{\overset{|}{\underset{\underset{NC_6H_5}{\overset{\|}{N}}}{\underset{|}{C}}}}{-}R \longleftrightarrow \overset{CO_2C_2H_5}{\overset{|}{\underset{\underset{\ominus NC_6H_5}{\overset{|}{N}}}{\underset{\|}{C}}}}{-}R\right] \xrightarrow{H^+} \overset{CO_2C_2H_5}{\overset{|}{\underset{\underset{NHC_6H_5}{\overset{|}{N}}}{\underset{\|}{C}}}}{-}R$$

[11] Linstead and Wang, *J. Chem. Soc.*, **1937**, 807.

product obtained by coupling with a salt of a keto acid, the resonating anion which gives rise to the phenylhydrazone probably results from the loss of carbon dioxide from the carboxylate anion.

Support for the above interpretation of the Japp-Klingemann process can be found in the isolation of many intermediate azo compounds,[7,11–14] although not all attempts to obtain these intermediates have been successful.[12] That the coupling with salts of β-keto acids and malonic acids does not proceed by a direct displacement of the carboxyl group is indicated by the observation that malonate salts of the type V react much more slowly than their decarboxylation products VI.[15] Thus it appears likely that the malonate salt V undergoes decarboxylation before it reacts with the diazonium salt.

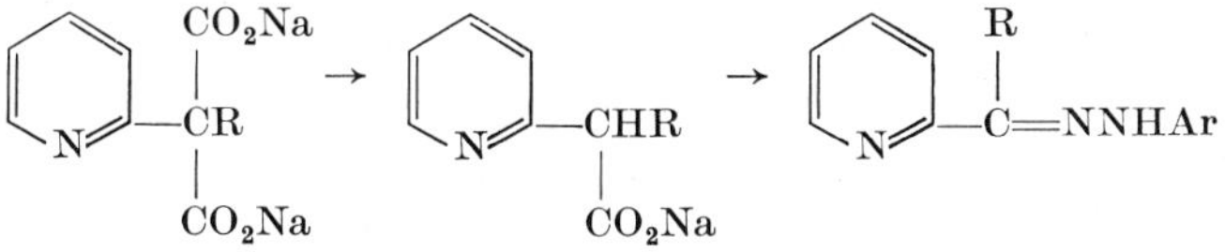

$$\text{C}_5\text{H}_4\text{N}\text{—CR(CO}_2\text{Na)}_2 \;(\text{V}) \rightarrow \text{C}_5\text{H}_4\text{N}\text{—CHR(CO}_2\text{Na)} \;(\text{VI}) \rightarrow \text{C}_5\text{H}_4\text{N}\text{—C(R)=NNHAr}$$

Azo derivatives of cyclohexanone-2-carboxanilide are relatively stable and can be isolated from coupling reactions of the anilide.[11] However,

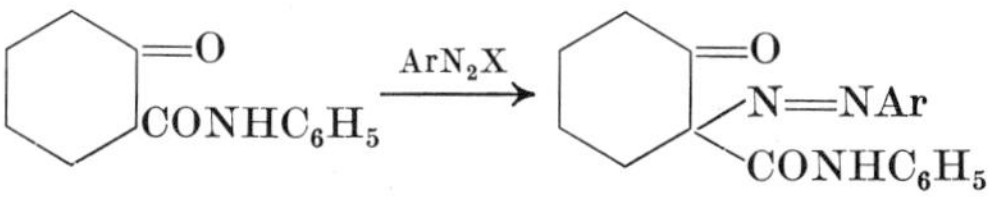

$$\text{2-(CONHC}_6\text{H}_5\text{)cyclohexanone} \xrightarrow{\text{ArN}_2\text{X}} \text{2-(N=NAr)-2-(CONHC}_6\text{H}_5\text{)cyclohexanone}$$

some of the monoarylhydrazone of cyclohexanedione was formed along with the azoanilide, presumably as a result of hydrolysis followed by decarboxylation.

The phenylpyrazolone obtained from ethyl cyclohexanone-2-carboxylate couples with diazotized p-nitroaniline to give the unusually interesting azo derivative VII. Although quite unstable, VII does not undergo the

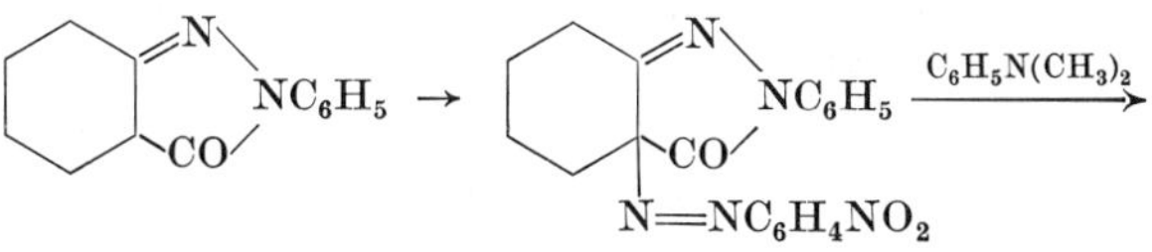

$$\text{(tetrahydroindazolone, N=, NC}_6\text{H}_5\text{, CO)} \rightarrow \text{VII (N=NC}_6\text{H}_4\text{NO}_2\text{ at ring junction)} \xrightarrow{\text{C}_6\text{H}_5\text{N(CH}_3\text{)}_2} \text{(tetrahydroindazolone)} + p\text{-O}_2\text{NC}_6\text{H}_4\text{N=NC}_6\text{H}_4\text{N(CH}_3\text{)}_2$$

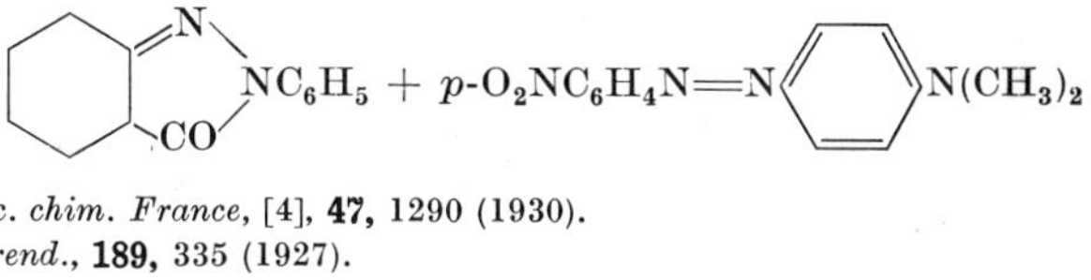

[12] Favrel, *Bull. soc. chim. France*, [4], **47,** 1290 (1930).

[13] Favrel, *Compt. rend.*, **189,** 335 (1927).

[14] Kalb, Schweitzer, Zellner, and Berthold, *Ber.*, **59,** 1860 (1926).

[15] Frank and Phillips, *J. Am. Chem. Soc.*, **71,** 2804 (1949).

Japp-Klingemann transformation, but instead loses the azo function in a reversal of the coupling reaction. Thus it reacts as shown with dimethylaniline; similarly, it reacts with ethanol to regenerate the original pyrazolone and to form nitrobenzene, acetaldehyde, and nitrogen.[11]

Most of the compounds that have been subjected to the Japp-Klingemann reaction can be classified as substituted β-diketones, β-keto esters (acyclic or cyclic), cyanoacetic esters, or salts of the corresponding acids. The cleavage of the coupling products apparently represents a special case of the cleavage of diketones, β-keto esters, and similar compounds. Nearly all of the recorded examples of the reaction concern derivatives of β-keto esters; as indicated above, in the scission of these substances an aliphatic acyl group is much more labile than a carbalkoxyl group, but, if the carbalkoxyl group is first saponified, then the carboxylate ion is eliminated in preference to the acyl group.

Although no direct comparison of a formyl group and an acetyl group in a Japp-Klingemann cleavage appears to have been made, the formyl group would be expected to be the more labile. Ethyl formylpropionate[16] undergoes the reaction with the fission of the formyl group, as expected, and certain formyl derivatives of cyclanones, such as 2-formylcyclohexanone,[17] undergo the reaction with loss of the formyl group under conditions which bring about ring opening (the alternative scission) with the corresponding acetyl derivatives.

$$\text{2-CHO-cyclohexanone }(\text{CHO}, =\!\text{O}) \xrightarrow{C_6H_5N_2^+} \text{cyclohexanone with } =\!NNHC_6H_5,\ =\!O$$

$$\text{2-COCH}_3\text{-cyclohexanone }(COCH_3, =\!\text{O}) \xrightarrow{C_6H_5N_2^+} CH_3CO\overset{\overset{NNHC_6H_5}{\|}}{C}CH_2CH_2CH_2CH_2CO_2H$$

Little is known about the cleavage of aromatic acyl groups, but they appear to be much more firmly bound than their aliphatic analogs. α,α-Dibenzoylacetone undergoes the reaction with loss of the acetyl group.[19] Ethyl dibenzoylacetate[9] reacts with diazotized aniline in a

$$(C_6H_5CO)_2CHCOCH_3 \xrightarrow{ArN_2^+} C_6H_5CO\overset{\overset{N—NHAr}{\|}}{C}COC_6H_5$$

buffered solution (sodium acetate) to give the oxygen-azo compound IX under conditions which cause the cleavage of the coupling product VIII

[16] Michael, *Ber.*, **38**, 2096 (1905).

[17] Coffey, *Rec. trav. chim.*, **42**, 528 (1923); Sen and Ghosh, *J. Indian Chem. Soc.*, **4**, 477 (1927).

$$C_6H_5COCH(COCH_3)CO_2C_2H_5 \xrightarrow{C_6H_5N_2^+} C_6H_5COC(=NNHC_6H_5)CO_2C_2H_5$$

VIII

$$(C_6H_5CO)_2CHCO_2C_2H_5 \xrightarrow{C_6H_5N_2^+} C_6H_5C(ON{=}NC_6H_5){=}C(COC_6H_5)(CO_2C_2H_5)$$

IX

from ethyl benzoylacetoacetate.[18] Warm dilute alkali brings about the cleavage of IX, and, since benzoic acid is eliminated, it is probable that rearrangement and scission precede hydrolysis; the product isolated is the acid corresponding to the salt shown.[9]

$$\underset{\text{IX}}{C_6H_5C(ON{=}NC_6H_5){=}C(COC_6H_5)(CO_2C_2H_5)} \xrightarrow[H_2O]{NaOH} (C_6H_5CO)_2C(N{=}NC_6H_5)CO_2C_2H_5 \xrightarrow[H_2O]{NaOH} C_6H_5CO_2Na +$$

$$C_6H_5COC(=NNHC_6H_5)CO_2C_2H_5 \xrightarrow[H_2O]{NaOH} C_6H_5COC(=NNHC_6H_5)CO_2Na$$

Nevertheless, there are examples of the facile cleavage of a benzoyl group. For example, von Auwers and Pohl[19] used the Japp-Klingemann reaction to prepare a derivative of 2-benzoyl-6-methylcoumaran-3-one. It is especially interesting that the cleavage of the benzoyl group occurred in preference to ring opening.

$$\text{2-benzoyl-6-methylcoumaran-3-one } (H_3C\text{–}C_6H_3\text{–O–}CHCOC_6H_5\text{–}C{=}O) \xrightarrow{C_6H_5N_2^+} H_3C\text{–}C_6H_3\text{–O–}C{=}NNHC_6H_5\text{–}C{=}O$$

The benzoyl group is eliminated in preference to a cyano group. Thus ethyl benzoylcyanoacetate leads to a derivative of mesoxalic acid.[20,21]

$$C_6H_5COCH(CN)CO_2C_2H_5 \xrightarrow{C_6H_5N_2^+} N{\equiv}C{-}C(=NNHC_6H_5)CO_2C_2H_5$$

[18] Bülow and Hailer, *Ber.*, **35**, 915 (1902).
[19] von Auwers and Pohl, *Ann.*, **405**, 243 (1914).
[20] Favrel, *Bull. soc. chim. France*, [3], **27**, 200 (1902).
[21] Favrel, *Compt. rend.*, **131**, 190 (1900).

Bülow and Hailer applied the Japp-Klingemann reaction to the ethyl esters of several diacylacetic acids.[18] From ethyl propionylacetoacetate they isolated the phenylhydrazone corresponding to cleavage of the propionyl group. The product from ethyl benzoylacetoacetate contained the benzoyl group (loss of acetyl) and that from ethyl phenacetylacetoacetate contained the phenacetyl group (loss of acetyl). It was concluded that in such cleavages the acyl group corresponding to the weaker acid is liberated the more readily (the corrected acidity constants,[22] $10^5\ K_a$, of the acids concerned are: propionic acid, 1.33; acetic acid, 1.75; phenylacetic acid, 4.88; benzoic acid, 6.27). In a study of the cleavage of unsymmetrical 1,3-diketones of the type $RCOCH_2COR'$, Hauser, Swamer, and Ringler[23] found a correlation of the relative yields of the acids RCO_2H and $R'CO_2H$ with the rates of saponification of the ethyl esters of these acids, although the relationship did not hold well with purely aliphatic compounds. On this basis the acetyl group would be expected, contrary to observation, to undergo cleavage in either ethyl benzoylacetoacetate or ethyl propionylacetoacetate (the rate constants, $10^4\ k$, for the alkaline hydrolysis of the ethyl esters of the acids are:[24] $C_6H_5CO_2C_2H_5$, 5.50; $CH_3CH_2CO_2C_2H_5$, 35.5; $CH_3CO_2C_2H_5$, 69.5).

In the cleavage of substituted cyanoacetic esters during the second stage of the Japp-Klingemann reaction, saponification and decarboxylation invariably occur leading to the phenylhydrazones of α-ketonitriles. Apparently no instance of the scission of the nitrile group has been recorded.

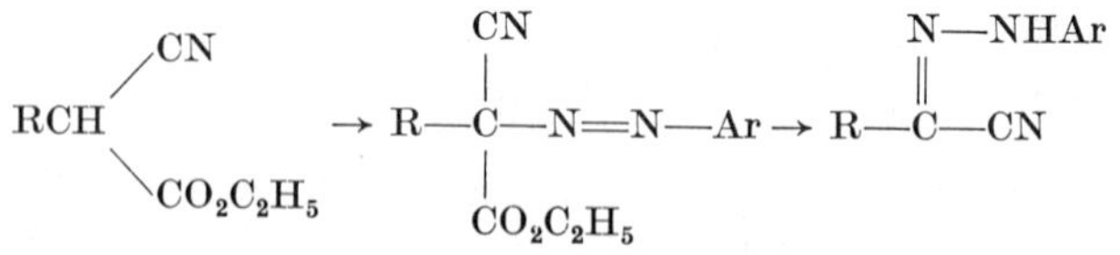

$$RCH(CN)(CO_2C_2H_5) \rightarrow R{-}C(CN)(CO_2C_2H_5){-}N{=}N{-}Ar \rightarrow R{-}C({=}N{-}NHAr){-}CN$$

Perhaps one reason why more precise information is lacking on the direction of cleavage of azodiketones in the Japp-Klingemann reaction is that the arylhydrazones produced in the process usually are capable of existing in geometrically isomeric forms (e.g., X and XI). Both isomers often are produced, and it may be economical to subject the crude

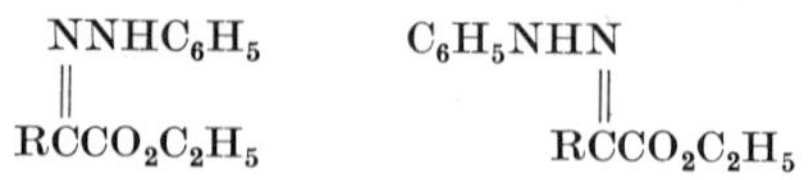

$$\underset{\text{X}}{RC(=NNHC_6H_5)CO_2C_2H_5} \qquad \underset{\text{XI}}{RC(=NNHC_6H_5)CO_2C_2H_5}$$

[22] Ingold, *Structure and Mechanism in Organic Chemistry*, p. 734, Cornell University Press, Ithaca, N. Y., 1953.

[23] Hauser, Swamer, and Ringler, *J. Am. Chem. Soc.*, **70**, 4023 (1948).

[24] Hammett, *Physical Organic Chemistry*, p. 121, McGraw-Hill Book Co., New York, 1940.

material to the next reaction in a sequence, with purification at a later stage, rather than to isolate the pure arylhydrazone. As a result, yields of the arylhydrazones often are not reported.

SCOPE AND APPLICATION

The first requirement for the occurrence of the Japp-Klingemann reaction is the presence of a hydrogen atom of sufficient activity to permit the coupling with the diazonium salt. Although normally two or three electron-withdrawing groups, such as carbonyl, carbethoxyl, cyano, etc., are present in the molecule, only one such group is required if other labilizing influences are operative upon the hydrogen atom concerned. For example, 9-ethoxalylfluorene reacts in the typical fashion.[25] A

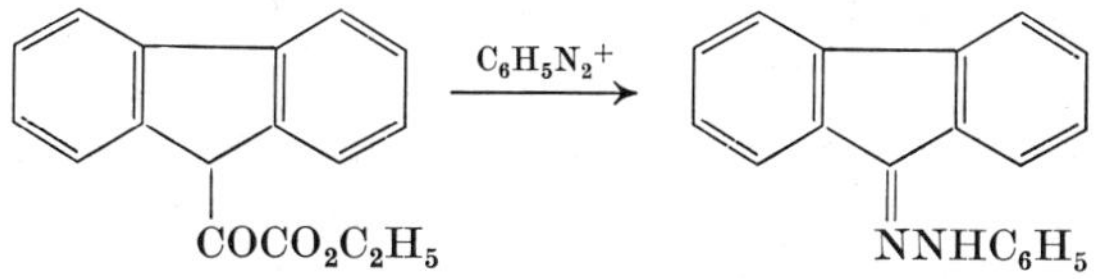

$COCO_2C_2H_5$ $\xrightarrow{C_6H_5N_2^+}$ $NNHC_6H_5$

particularly interesting reaction is that of 9-nitrofluorene;[26] in the coupling with diazotized aniline the displaced nitro group appears in the para position of the phenylhydrazine residue of the product.

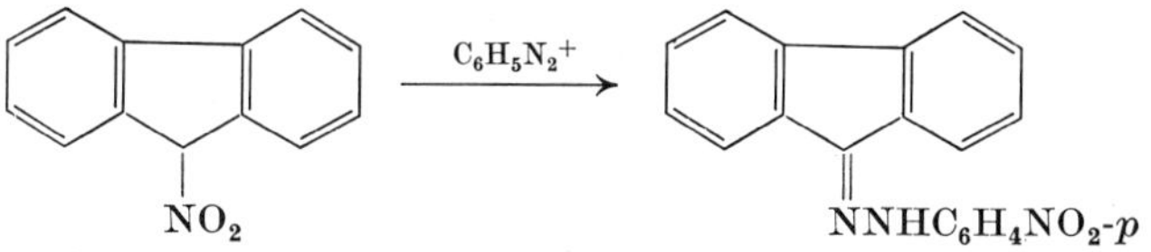

NO_2 $\xrightarrow{C_6H_5N_2^+}$ $NNHC_6H_4NO_2$-*p*

A methinyl group in the α-position of a pyridine compound also is reactive enough to participate in the Japp-Klingemann process if one additional activating group is present. For example, 2-*n*-butyrylpyridine has been prepared in good yield from 2-(2′-pyridyl)pentanoic acid by the process shown.[15] A somewhat similar reaction is that of 1-ethoxalyl-1,2,3,4-tetrahydroacridine and the analogous cyclopenteno derivative.[27]

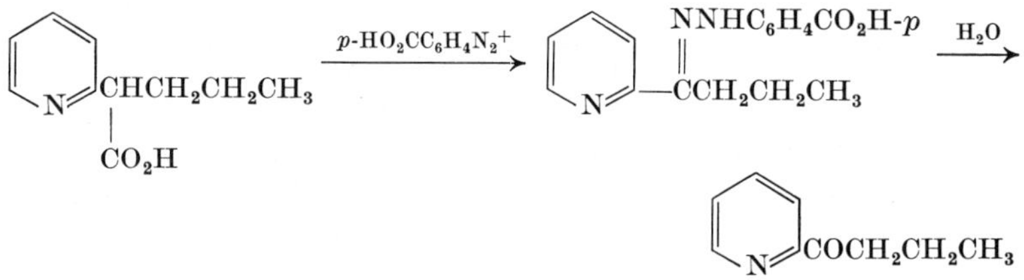

N $CHCH_2CH_2CH_3$ (CO_2H) $\xrightarrow{p\text{-}HO_2CC_6H_4N_2^+}$ N —$C(=NNHC_6H_4CO_2H\text{-}p)CH_2CH_2CH_3$ $\xrightarrow{H_2O}$ N $COCH_2CH_2CH_3$

[25] Kuhn and Levy, *Ber.*, **61,** 2240 (1928).

[26] Ponzio, *Gazz. chim. ital.*, **42,** [II], 55 (1912).

[27] Borsche and Manteuffel, *Ann.*, **534,** 56 (1938).

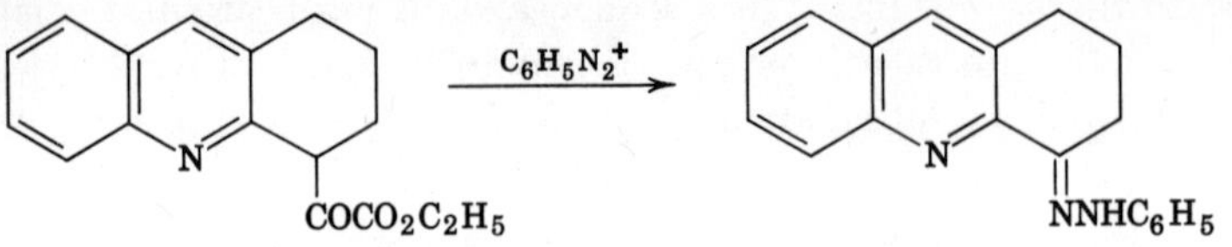

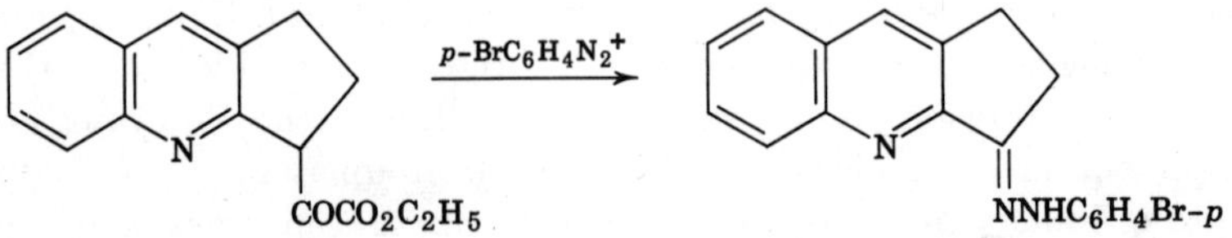

$$\text{(tetrahydroacridine with } COCO_2C_2H_5\text{)} \xrightarrow{C_6H_5N_2^+} \text{(tetrahydroacridine with } =NNHC_6H_5\text{)}$$

$$\text{(cyclopenta[b]quinoline with } COCO_2C_2H_5\text{)} \xrightarrow{p\text{-}BrC_6H_4N_2^+} \text{(cyclopenta[b]quinoline with } =NNHC_6H_4Br\text{-}p\text{)}$$

In contrast with 9-nitrofluorene, α-nitropropionic acid retains the nitro group in the reaction. Decarboxylation takes place to yield the phenylhydrazone, $CH_3C(NO_2){=}NNHC_6H_5$, identical with the product obtained from nitroethane and benzenediazonium chloride.[28]

Esters of a great variety of monosubstituted acetoacetic acids have been subjected to the reaction. Chlorine and bromine atoms may serve as the third substituent on the methinyl carbon. These halogen atoms are not removed during the reaction but appear in the products, which are phenylhydrazones of unusual structure, as shown in the equation.[29,30]

$$CH_3COCH(Cl)CO_2C_2H_5 \xrightarrow{C_6H_5N_2^+} C_6H_5NHN{=}C(Cl)CO_2C_2H_5$$

One exception to the statement that halogen is not removed is the coupling of 3-bromotriacetic lactone (XII), which furnishes the same arylhydrazone XIII as that obtained from triacetic lactone itself.[30a] Methylene bis(triacetic lactone) (XIV) on coupling also yields the arylhydrazone XIII.

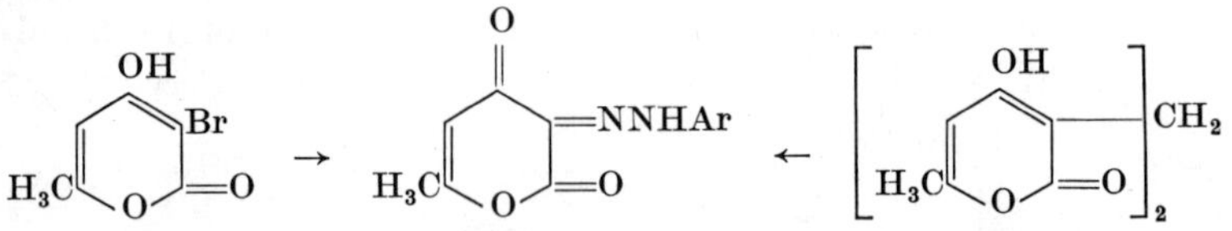

$$\text{XII (OH, Br, } H_3C\text{, =O)} \rightarrow \text{XIII (O, =NNHAr, } H_3C\text{, =O)} \leftarrow \text{XIV } [\text{(OH, } H_3C\text{, =O)}]_2CH_2$$

Alkyl-substituted acetoacetic esters are more commonly encountered. The products from such esters are readily reduced and hydrolyzed, and

[28] Steinkopf and Supan, *Ber.*, **43**, 3239 (1910).
[29] Favrel, *Compt. rend.*, **134**, 1312 (1902).
[30] Favrel, *Bull. soc. chim. France*, [3], **31**, 150 (1904).
[30a] Wiley and Jarboe, *J. Am. Chem. Soc.*, **78**, 624 (1956).

this method of synthesis of α-amino acids has been employed extensively. Examples are the syntheses of alanine[5,31–34] and methionine.[35]

$$CH_3COCH(CH_3)CO_2C_2H_5 \xrightarrow{C_6H_5N_2^+} CH_3C(=NNHC_6H_5)CO_2C_2H_5 \xrightarrow[\text{then } H_2O]{4H,} CH_3CH(NH_2)CO_2H$$

$$CH_3SCH_2CH_2CH(COCH_3)CO_2C_2H_5 \rightarrow CH_3SCH_2CH_2C(=NNHC_6H_5)CO_2C_2H_5 \xrightarrow[\text{then } H_2O]{4H,} CH_3SCH_2CH_2CH(NH_2)CO_2H$$

The phenylhydrazones from the Japp-Klingemann reaction on simply substituted acetoacetic esters also have been used extensively in the synthesis of indoles. The Fischer cyclization converts them to esters of substituted indole-2-carboxylic acids. The preparation of ethyl 3-phenylindole-2-carboxylate is illustrative.[36]

$$CH_3COCH(CH_2C_6H_5)CO_2C_2H_5 \rightarrow C_6H_5CH_2C(=NNHC_6H_5)CO_2C_2H_5 \xrightarrow{H^+} \text{3-}C_6H_5\text{-indole-2-}CO_2C_2H_5 \text{ (N–H)}$$

Substituents in the benzene ring of the indole may be introduced through the use of a substituted benzenediazonium salt in the coupling. Diazonium salts from 2- and 4-substituted anilines can give only one product in a simple Fischer cyclization, but two different indoles may be obtained from a *m*-substituted aniline,[37] and consequently these have been employed infrequently. Examples of the products obtained from 2- and 4-substituted anilines are shown.[38,39]

[31] Feofilaktov, *Compt. rend. acad. sci. U.R.S.S.*, **24,** 755 (1939) [*C. A.*, **34,** 1971 (1940)].

[32] Feofilaktov and others, *Bull. acad. sci. U.R.S.S. Classe sci. chim.*, **1940,** 259 [*C. A.*, **35,** 3606 (1941)].

[33] Bamberger, *Ber.*, **25,** 3547 (1892).

[34] Feofilaktov and Zaitseva, *J. Gen. Chem. U.S.S.R.*, **10,** 258 (1940) [*C. A.*, **34,** 7283 (1940)].

[35] Feofilaktov and Ivanova, *J. Gen. Chem. U.S.S.R.*, **21,** 1684 (1951) [*C. A.*, **46,** 3955 (1952)].

[36] Manske, Perkin, and Robinson, *J. Chem. Soc.*, **1927,** 1.

[37] Koelsch, *J. Org. Chem.*, **8,** 295 (1943).

[38] Hughes, Lions, and Ritchie, *J. Proc. Roy. Soc. N. S. Wales*, **72,** 209 (1938) [*C. A.*, **33,** 6837 (1939)].

[39] Hughes and others, *J. Proc. Roy. Soc. N. S. Wales*, **71,** 475 (1937) [*C. A.*, **33,** 587 (1939)].

$$CH_3COCH(CH_2CH_3)CO_2C_2H_5 \xrightarrow{o\text{-}O_2NC_6H_4N_2^+} o\text{-}O_2NC_6H_4NHN{=}C(CH_2CH_3)CO_2C_2H_5 \rightarrow$$

$$\text{7-nitro-3-methyl-2-carbethoxyindole } (NO_2,\ CH_3,\ CO_2C_2H_5,\ NH)$$

$$CH_3COCH(CH_2CH_3)CO_2C_2H_5 \xrightarrow{p\text{-}CH_3OC_6H_4N_2^+} p\text{-}CH_3OC_6H_4NHN{=}C(CH_2CH_3)CO_2C_2H_5 \rightarrow$$

$$\text{5-methoxy-3-methyl-2-carbethoxyindole } (CH_3O,\ CH_3,\ CO_2C_2H_5,\ NH)$$

If the substituent in the acetoacetic ester has a carbonyl group attached to the first carbon atom, the phenylhydrazone from the Japp-Klingemann reaction will readily cyclize to a pyrazole. Acetonyl[40] and phenacyl[41]

$$CH_3COCH_2CH(COCH_3)CO_2C_2H_5 \rightarrow CH_3C(=O)CH_2C(CO_2C_2H_5){=}N{-}NHC_6H_5 \rightarrow H_3CC{=}CH{-}C(CO_2C_2H_5){=}N{-}NC_6H_5 \text{ (ring)}$$

groups, which may bear additional substituents, have been employed in this way.

Acyl derivatives of acetoacetic ester also may be employed. The products are monophenylhydrazones of α,β-diketo esters. Thus ethyl benzoylacetoacetate reacts as shown.[18]

$$C_6H_5COCH(COCH_3)CO_2C_2H_5 \xrightarrow{C_6H_5N_2^+} C_6H_5C(=O){-}C(=NNHC_6H_5)CO_2C_2H_5$$

[40] Bischler, *Ber.*, **26,** 1881 (1893).
[41] Bischler, *Ber.*, **25,** 3143 (1892).

Probably because they have been less readily available than acetoacetic esters, 1,3-diketones have not been extensively employed in the Japp-Klingemann reaction. Among those which have been examined are α-chloro-,[42] α-methyl-[43] and α-ethyl-acetylacetone.[43] The products are monophenylhydrazones of 1,2-diketones, as illustrated for the methyl derivative. The same products are available from the substituted β-keto

$$\underset{\displaystyle CH_3}{CH_3COCHCOCH_3} \xrightarrow{C_6H_5N_2^+} CH_3CO\overset{\displaystyle NNHC_6H_5}{\overset{\|}{C}}CH_3$$

esters, provided the ester group is saponified before the coupling is performed (p. 144). Such monophenylhydrazones have been prepared from several substituted acetoacetic esters.

When the Japp-Klingemann reaction is applied to a cyclic β-keto ester, the ring is opened in the second stage of the process. The reaction of ethyl cyclohexanone-2-carboxylate is illustrative.[11,44] Cyclopentanone

$$\text{(cyclohexanone-2-)}CO_2C_2H_5 \xrightarrow{C_6H_5N_2^+} HO_2CCH_2CH_2CH_2CH_2\overset{\displaystyle NNHC_6H_5}{\overset{\|}{C}}CO_2H$$

derivatives undergo similar ring opening. The products from both series have been employed in the synthesis of amino acids and indoles. The ring opened may be that of a lactone, as in acetobutyrolactone, which yields the phenylhydrazone of ketobutyrolactone.[45] This product also

$$\begin{array}{ccc} CH_2\text{—}CHCOCH_3 & & CH_2\text{—}C{=}NNHC_6H_5 \\ | \qquad | & & | \qquad | \\ CH_2 \quad CO & \rightarrow & CH_2 \quad CO \\ \diagdown \; \diagup & & \diagdown \; \diagup \\ O & & O \end{array}$$

has found use in the synthesis of amino acids.[46,47] Alternatively the ring opened may be that of a lactam, as in the elegant synthesis of tryptamine

[42] Dieckmann and Platz, *Ber.*, **38**, 2986 (1905).

[43] Favrel, *Bull. soc. chim. France*, [3], **27**, 336 (1902); *Compt. rend.*, **132**, 41 (1901).

[44] Feofilaktov and Ivanov, *J. Gen. Chem. U.S.S.R.*, **13**, 457 (1943) [*C. A.*, **38**, 3255 (1944)].

[45] Harradence and Lions, *J. Proc. Roy. Soc. N. S. Wales*, **72**, 221 (1938) [*C. A.*, **33**, 6838 (1939)].

[46] Feofilaktov and Onishchenko, *J. Gen. Chem. U.S.S.R.*, **9**, 314 (1939) [*C. A.*, **34**, 378 (1940)].

[47] Snyder, Andreen, Cannon, and Peters, *J. Am. Chem. Soc.*, **64**, 2082 (1942).

and serotonin (5-hydroxytryptamine) based on the coupling with a salt of α-carboxy-α-valerolactone and a Fischer cyclization of the products.[47a]

As in the reactions of acyclic β-keto esters, the reaction takes the decarboxylation course if the ester is saponified before the coupling. Thus a monophenylhydrazone of cyclohexane-1,2-dione is obtained from ethyl cyclohexanone-2-carboxylate.[11]

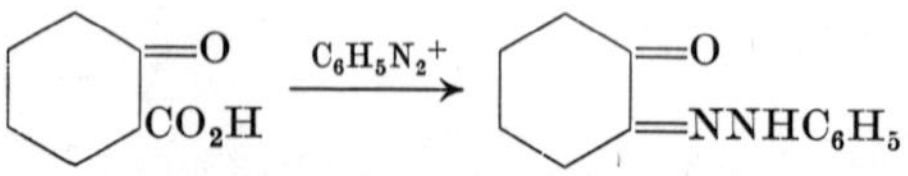

$$\text{(cyclohexane ring)}\begin{matrix}=O\\ CO_2H\end{matrix} \xrightarrow{C_6H_5N_2^+} \text{(cyclohexane ring)}\begin{matrix}=O\\ =NNHC_6H_5\end{matrix}$$

Such compounds may serve as sources of derivatives of ω-aldehydo acids. When the o-nitrophenylhydrazone obtained from cyclopentanone-2-carboxylic acid was allowed to stand in aqueous alcoholic potassium hydroxide for five days it was converted to the o-nitrophenylhydrazone of δ-formylbutyric acid in about 35% yield.[11]

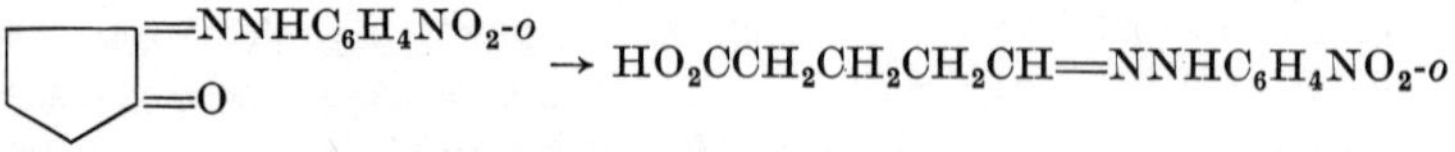

$$\text{(cyclopentane ring)}\begin{matrix}=NNHC_6H_4NO_2\text{-}o\\ =O\end{matrix} \rightarrow HO_2CCH_2CH_2CH_2CH{=}NNHC_6H_4NO_2\text{-}o$$

Monosubstituted cyanoacetic esters couple readily. When the products are hydrolyzed, decarboxylation ensues leading to hydrazones of α-keto nitriles. Substituted malonic esters yield phenylhydrazones of α-keto acids, identical to those which can be obtained from similarly substituted acetoacetic esters.

The diazonium salts used in the reaction include those derived from aniline and its simple substitution products, polysubstituted anilines, benzidine and substituted benzidines, and even antipyrine. The diazonium salt related to the last substance has been coupled with 3-methylpentane-2,4-dione[48] to give the hydrazone shown in the equation.

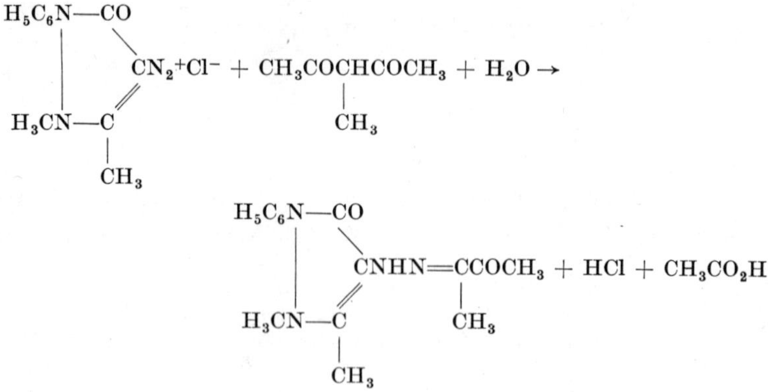

$$\begin{matrix}H_5C_6N\text{—}CO & \\ | \quad\quad \diagdown & \\ | \quad\quad\quad CN_2^+Cl^- & + \; CH_3COCHCOCH_3 + H_2O \rightarrow \\ | \quad\quad /\!/ & \quad\quad | \\ H_3CN\text{—}C & \quad\quad CH_3 \\ \quad\quad | & \\ \quad\quad CH_3 & \end{matrix}$$

$$\begin{matrix}H_5C_6N\text{—}CO & \\ | \quad\quad \diagdown & \\ | \quad\quad\quad CNHN{=}CCOCH_3 & + \; HCl + CH_3CO_2H \\ | \quad\quad /\!/ \quad\quad\quad | & \\ H_3CN\text{—}C \quad\quad\quad CH_3 & \\ \quad\quad | & \\ \quad\quad CH_3 & \end{matrix}$$

[47a] Abramovitch and Shapiro, *Chemistry & Industry*, **1955,** 1255.

[48] Morgan and Reilly, *J. Chem. Soc.*, **103,** 808 (1913).

It might be expected that diazonium salts in which electron-withdrawing groups are located in ortho or para positions, so that they accentuate the positive character of the diazonium cation, would be most active in the coupling. In couplings with 2-pyridylacetic acid, diazotized *p*-aminobenzoic acid gave the best results, and diazotized *p*-nitroaniline and sulfanilic acid were superior, both with regard to the yield and the purity of the products, to diazotized aniline.[15] Although few experiments have been carried out with a single active methinyl compound and a variety of diazonium salts in the Japp-Klingemann reaction under identical conditions, the yields from substituted anilines appear to run higher than those from aniline. It is possible that substituents such as the nitro and carboxyl groups may give rise to higher melting and less soluble products, leading to easier isolation as well as to more complete reaction.

If the arylamino portion of a Japp-Klingemann product is to be removed, as in a reduction to an α-amino acid (pp. 152–153), the diazonium salt should be selected not only on the basis of the probable yield in the coupling but also with consideration of the character of the second product in the further reaction. For example, if a diazotized aminobenzoic acid were used in a coupling carried out as part of a sequence to an α-amino acid, the difficulty of separating this product from the regenerated aminobenzoic acid might outweigh any advantage gained in the coupling.

In the preparation of arylhydrazones to be employed in the synthesis of indoles and pyrazoles the choice of the diazonium salt is dictated by the substituents desired in the final product.

EXPERIMENTAL CONDITIONS

Most of the reactions have been run in aqueous medium at about 0°. Occasionally ethanol has been added to increase the solubility.[49] In the coupling of 1-ethoxalyl-1,2,3,4-tetrahydroacridine (p. 151) the medium was pyridine diluted with the water in which the diazonium salt was prepared.[27] The aqueous solutions usually are buffered with sodium acetate in reactions in which an acyl group is to be cleaved.[20,50] Stronger bases have been used, however. In the conversion of ethyl cyclopentanone-2-carboxylate to the phenylhydrazone of ethyl hydrogen α-ketoadipate, Manske and Robinson[51] employed potassium hydroxide; for the preparation of the similar product from diazotized *m*-aminobenzoic acid,

[49] Lions and Spruson, *J. Proc. Roy. Soc. N. S. Wales*, **66**, 171 (1932) [*C. A.*, **27**, 291 (1933)].

[50] Favrel and Chrz, *Bull. soc. chim. France*, [4], **37**, 1238 (1925).

[51] Manske and Robinson, *J. Chem. Soc.*, **1927**, 240.

Koelsch[37] preferred to carry out the coupling in acid solution and to convert the azo compound so obtained to the substituted hydrazone by a two-minute treatment with boiling 7% aqueous sodium carbonate. Other couplings also have been found to occur under either acid or basic conditions,[8,43,52] and even sodium ethoxide has been used as the base.[53]

If the cleavage of the acyl group from a β-keto ester is desired, the basic solution of the ester should be treated with the diazonium salt immediately.[54] If such basic solutions are allowed to stand at 0° for periods up to twenty-four hours before the treatment with the diazonium salt, the ester group is removed and the product obtained is a derivative of a 1,2-diketone.[11,55,56]

The time required for the Japp-Klingemann process varies, with the activity of the methinyl group, from a few seconds to as much as four days.[15] When aqueous solutions are employed the products often separate, and the mixture can be stirred until no further change occurs. The azo compounds, sometimes encountered as intermediates (p. 147), are much more deeply colored (usually red) than the arylhydrazones. Accordingly, a color change sometimes furnishes a useful guide to the course of the reaction.

Most of the reactions have been run with equivalent amounts of the methinyl component and the diazonium salt. The use of excess diazonium salt may result in the loss of some of the product by conversion to the formazyl, as shown in the equation.[33,57] This appears to be the only

$$\underset{\displaystyle CH_3}{CH_3CO\overset{}{C}}{=}NNHC_6H_5 + C_6H_5N_2^+Cl^- \rightarrow$$

$$C_6H_5N{=}N\underset{\displaystyle CH_3}{C}{=}NNHC_6H_5 + CH_3CO_2H + HCl$$

serious side reaction in the Japp-Klingemann process, aside from the alternative cleavage of keto esters (above). Another disadvantage to the use of an excess of the diazonium salt is the formation of colored materials and tars as a result of its decomposition when the reaction mixture is allowed to warm.

The products from the Japp-Klingemann reaction usually have been

[52] Findlay and Dougherty, *J. Org. Chem.*, **13**, 560 (1948).
[53] Feofilaktov, *J. Gen. Chem. U.S.S.R.*, **17**, 993 (1947) [*C. A.*, **42**, 4537 (1948)].
[54] Jackson and Manske, *J. Am. Chem. Soc.*, **52**, 5029 (1930).
[55] Manske, *Can. J. Research*, **4**, 591 (1931).
[56] Lions, *J. Proc. Roy. Soc. N. S. Wales*, **66**, 516 (1932) [*C. A.*, **27**, 2954 (1933)].
[57] Walker, *J. Chem. Soc.*, **123**, 2775 (1923).

recrystallized from ethanol or benzene; 80% acetic acid has been employed in some instances.[58]

EXPERIMENTAL PROCEDURES

Ethyl Pyruvate *o*-Nitrophenylhydrazone.[38] To an ice-cold solution of 20.5 g. (0.14 mole) of ethyl 2-methylacetoacetate in 150 ml. of ethanol is added 51 ml. of 50% aqueous potassium hydroxide. This mixture is then diluted with 300 ml. of ice water; and the cold diazonium salt solution, prepared from 20.0 g. (0.14 mole) of *o*-nitroaniline, 60 ml. of concentrated hydrochloric acid, 90 ml. of water, and 10.5 g. of sodium nitrite, is rapidly run in with stirring. Stirring is continued for five minutes, at the end of which time the separated ethyl pyruvate *o*-nitrophenylhydrazone is collected by filtration. It melts at 106°, after recrystallization from ethanol. The yield is 30.0 g. (83%).

1,2-Cyclohexanedione Monophenylhydrazone.[56] To an ice-cold solution of 36.0 g. (0.21 mole) of ethyl cyclohexanone-2-carboxylate in 40 ml. of ethanol is added an ice-cold solution of 12.0 g. of potassium hydroxide in 60 ml. of water. The reaction mixture is held at 0° for twenty-four hours and then diluted with 1 l. of ice water. A benzenediazonium chloride solution is prepared from 18.6 g. (0.2 mole) of aniline, 50 ml. of concentrated hydrochloric acid in 100 ml. of water, and 13.8 g. of sodium nitrite. The cold diazonium solution is then added to the first solution with vigorous stirring and continued cooling in ice, followed immediately by the addition of 30.0 g. of sodium acetate. Carbon dioxide is seen to evolve, and the reaction is allowed to continue at 0° until the gas evolution ceases. The solid product which separates is 1,2-cyclohexanedione monophenylhydrazone. It is collected by filtration and recrystallized from ethanol. It melts at 185–186°. The yield is almost quantitative.

TABULAR SURVEY OF THE JAPP-KLINGEMANN REACTION

The following list of Japp-Klingemann reactions includes many examples in which the products were further modified, so that yields are not available. The list is based on a literature survey to January 1, 1956, but because of the difficulties of locating scattered instances of the reaction in the literature, especially when the products are chiefly of interest as intermediates in further reactions, it probably does not include

[58] Feofilaktov and Vinogradova, *Compt. rend. acad. sci. U.R.S.S.*, **24,** 759 (1939) [*C. A.*, **34,** 1971 (1940)].

all recorded applications of the Japp-Klingemann reaction. For convenience the reactions in which an acyl group is cleaved are listed separately (section A) from those accompanied by decarboxylation (section B). Accordingly, some compounds will be found in both sections. Section A is subdivided as follows:

I. Derivatives of nitropropionic, formylpropionic, and haloacetoacetic acids.
II. Monosubstituted acetoacetic esters.
III. Acylacetoacetic esters.
IV. Acylcyanoacetic esters.
V. Cyclic compounds.
VI. 1,3-Dicarbonyl compounds.
VII. Miscellaneous compounds.

Section B is subdivided as follows:

VIII. Acetoacetic acid derivatives.
IX. Cyanoacetic acid derivatives.
X. Malonic acid derivatives.
XI. Miscellaneous reactions.

A. Reactions in Which an Acyl Group Is Cleaved

TABLE I

DERIVATIVES OF FORMYLPROPIONIC AND HALOACETOACETIC ACIDS

(The group lost in the cleavage is italic.)

Substance	Substituent in (benzene ring)N_2^+ or [Other Diazonium Ion]	Yield, %	References	Conversion Product
$CH_3CHCO_2C_2H_5$	—	—	16	—
CHO				
$\mathit{CH_3CO}CHCO_2CH_3$	—	—	30	—
	—	—	59	—
Cl	2-CH_3	—	30	—
	4-CH_3	—	30	—
$\mathit{CH_3CO}CHCO_2C_2H_5$	—	—	29, 30	—
	—*	—	59	—
Cl	2-CH_3	—	29, 30	—
	4-CH_3*	—	29, 30	—
	4-Br*	—	60	—
	[Certain benzidine derivatives]	—	30	—
$\mathit{CH_3CO}CHCONHC_6H_5$	4-CH_3	80	61	—
	3-CH_3, 4-CH_3	—	61	—
Cl	3-CH_3, 5-CH_3	—	61	—
	[α-$C_{10}H_7N_2^+$]	—	61	—
	[β-$C_{10}H_7N_2^+$]	—	61	—
$\mathit{CH_3CO}CHCO_2C_{10}H_{19}$†‡	—	—	62	—
	4-Br	—	62	—
Br	4-CH_3	—	62	—

Note: References 59–118 are on pp. 177–178.

* These reagents have also been coupled with ethyl α-bromoacetoacetate, ref. 60.

† The (−)-menthyl ester.

‡ Certain reactions of the ethyl ester are entered under ethyl α-chloroacetoacetate.

TABLE II

MONOSUBSTITUTED ACETOACETIC ESTERS IN THE REACTION:

$$CH_3COCH(R)CO_2C_2H_5 + ArN_2^+X^- \rightarrow [CH_3COC(R)(N{=}NAr)CO_2C_2H_5] \xrightarrow{H_2O} CH_3CO_2H + RC({=}NNHAr)CO_2C_2H_5$$

Substituent R in $CH_3COCH(R)CO_2C_2H_5$	Substituent in $C_6H_5N_2^+$ or [Other Diazonium Ion]	Yield, %	References	Conversion Product
CH_3	—	38	5, 31–34	Amino acid
	2-CH_3	—	1, 5	—
	4-CH_3	—	1, 5	—
	2-NO_2	83	38	Indole
	3-NO_2	—	12	—
		84	63	—
	4-NO_2	78	63	—
	4-Br	—	39	Indole
	4-OCH_3	—	39	Indole
	2-OC_2H_5	—	39	Indole
	4-OC_2H_5	—	39	Indole
	4-$CO_2C_2H_5$	—	39	Indole
	3-OCH_3, 4-OCH_3	73	49	Indole
	[α-$C_{10}H_7N_2^+$]	—	39	Indole
	[β-$C_{10}H_7N_2^+$]	—	39	Indole
C_2H_5	—	—	1, 5	—
	2-NO_2	90	38	Indole
	3-NO_2	—	12	—
	4-Br	—	39	—
	4-OCH_3	—	39	Indole
	4-OC_2H_5	—	39	Indole
	4-$CO_2C_2H_5$	—	39	Indole
	3-OCH_3, 4-OCH_3	70	49	Indole
	[α-$C_{10}H_7N_2^+$]	—	39	Indole
	[β-$C_{10}H_7N_2^+$]	—	39	Indole
$CH_3SCH_2CH_2$	—	73	35, 117	Amino acid
$(C_2H_5)_2NCH_2CH_2$	—	76	64	Indole
n-C_3H_7	—	35	65	Amino acid
	4-CH_3	43	65	Amino acid
	2-NO_2	97	38	Indole
i-C_3H_7	—	55	66	Amino acid

Note: References 59–118 are on pp. 177–178.

TABLE II—*Continued*

MONOSUBSTITUTED ACETOACETIC ESTERS IN THE REACTION:

$$CH_3COCH(R)CO_2C_2H_5 + ArN_2^+X^- \rightarrow [CH_3COC(R)(N{=}NAr)CO_2C_2H_5] \xrightarrow{H_2O} CH_3CO_2H + RC({=}NNHAr)CO_2C_2H_5$$

Substituent R in $CH_3COCH(R)CO_2C_2H_5$	Substituent in $C_6H_5N_2^+$ or [Other Diazonium Ion]	Yield, %	References	Conversion Product
CH_3COCH_2	—	—	40	Pyrazole
	4-NO_2*	—	67	Pyrazole
$C_2H_5O_2CCH_2CH_2$	—	74	113	—
	2-CH_3	88	113	—
	3-CH_3	34	113	—
	2-Cl	60	113	—
	3-Cl	72	113	—
	4-Cl	81	113	—
	2-CO_2H	90	113	—
	4-SO_3H	95	113	—
	4-NO_2	87	113	—
	(α-$C_{10}H_7N_2$)	47	113	—
	(β-$C_{10}H_7N_2$)	33	113	—
$NCCH_2CH_2$	—	98	112, 113	Indole
	4-NO_2	98	113	—
$C_2H_5O_2CCH_2CH_2$	—	—	68, 69	Indole
	2-Cl	—	52	—
	3-Cl	—	52	—
	4-Cl	—	52	—
	2-CH_3	—	111	Amino acid
	2-OCH_3	—	52	Indole
	3-OCH_3	—	52	Indole
	4-OCH_3	—	52	Indole
$C_6H_5OCH_2CH_2CH_2$	—	15	70	Indole
$C_2H_5O_2CCH(NHCO_2C_2H_5)CH_2CH_2$	—	Good	71	Indole

Note: References 59–118 are on pp. 177–178.

* The azo compound was isolated; upon standing or upon treatment with aqueous alkali, followed by acidification, it underwent loss of the acetyl group and cyclization to the pyrazole.

TABLE II—*Continued*

MONOSUBSTITUTED ACETOACETIC ESTERS IN THE REACTION:

$$CH_3COCH(R)CO_2C_2H_5 + ArN_2^+X^- \rightarrow [CH_3COC(R)(N{=}NAr)CO_2C_2H_5] \xrightarrow{H_2O} CH_3CO_2H + RC({=}NNHAr)CO_2C_2H_5$$

Substituent R in $CH_3COCH(R)CO_2C_2H_5$	Substituent in $C_6H_5N_2^+$ or [Other Diazonium Ion]	Yield, %	References	Conversion Product
n-C_4H_9	—	65	72	Amino acid
	2-NO_2	—	38	Indole
	4-Br	—	39	Indole
	4-OCH_3	—	39	Indole
	2-OC_2H_5	—	39	Indole
	4-OC_2H_5	—	39	Indole
	4-$CO_2C_2H_5$	—	39	Indole
	[α-$C_{10}H_7N_2^+$]	—	39	Indole
$(CH_3)_2CHCH_2$	—	72	31, 32, 73	Amino acid
$CH_3CH_2CH(CH_3)$	—	63	31, 32, 73	Amino acid
$CH_3COCH(CO_2C_2H_5)$	—	Quant.	74, 75, 76	Pyrazole
	4-CH_3	Quant.	77	Pyrazole
	4-CH_3CONH†	—	78	Pyrazole
	4-(p-$H_2NC_6H_4$)†	—	78	Pyrazole
	4-(p-$CH_3CONHC_6H_4$)†	—	78	Pyrazole
	[β-$C_{10}H_7N_2^+$]	—	77	Pyrazole
$C_6H_5CH_2$	—	68	31, 32, 79	Amino acid
	—	Quant.	80	Azoformal-doxime
	2-NO_2	90	38	Indole
	4-Br	—	39	Indole
	4-OCH_3	—	39	Indole
	2-OC_2H_5	—	39	Indole
	4-OC_2H_5	—	39	Indole
	4-$CO_2C_2H_5$	—	39	Indole
	3-OCH_3, 4-OCH_3	70	49	Indole
	[α-$C_{10}N_7N_2^+$]	—	39	Indole
	[β-$C_{10}H_7N_2^+$]	—	39	Indole
4-$CH_3OC_6H_4CH_2$	—	75	81	Amino acid

Note: References 59–118 are on pp. 177–178.

† The azo compound could be isolated.

TABLE II—*Continued*

MONOSUBSTITUTED ACETOACETIC ESTERS IN THE REACTION:

$$CH_3COCH(R)CO_2C_2H_5 + ArN_2^+X^- \rightarrow [CH_3COC(R)(N{=}NAr)CO_2C_2H_5] \xrightarrow{H_2O} CH_3CO_2H + RC({=}NNHAr)CO_2C_2H_5$$

Substituent R in $CH_3COCH(R)CO_2C_2H_5$	Substituent in $C_6H_5N_2^+$ or [Other Diazonium Ion]	Yield, %	References	Conversion Product
2-Naphthylmethyl ($C_{10}H_7CH_2$)	—	70	82	Indole
1-Bromo-2-naphthylmethyl (Br-$C_{10}H_6CH_2$)	—	50	82	Indole
$C_6H_5COCH_2$	—	—	41	Pyrazole
	2-CH_3	—	40	Pyrazole
	4-CH_3	—	40	Pyrazole
$C_6H_5COCH(C_6H_5)$	—	—	40	Pyrazole

Note: References 59–118 are on pp. 177–178.

TABLE III

Acylacetoacetic Esters in the Reaction:

$$RCOCH(COCH_3)CO_2C_2H_5 + ArN_2^+X^- \rightarrow [RCOC(CO_2C_2H_5)(COCH_3)N{=}NAr] \xrightarrow{H_2O} RCOC({=}NNHAr)CO_2C_2H_5 + CH_3CO_2H \quad (a)$$

or

$$\rightarrow CH_3COC({=}NNHAr)CO_2C_2H_5 + RCO_2H \quad (b)$$

R in $RCOCH(COCH_3)CO_2C_2H_5$	Substituent in $C_6H_5N_2^+$ or [Other Diazonium Ion]	Yield, %	References	Conversion Product
CH_3	—	—	18	—
CH_3CH_2*	—	—	18	—
C_2H_5O†	2-CO_2H	—	18	—
C_2H_5OCO†	—	—	83	—
C_6H_5†	—	—	18	—
	2-CH_3	—	18	—
	4-NO_2	—	18	—
	2-CO_2H	—	18	—
	[$^+N_2C_6H_4$—$C_6H_4N_2^+$] (4,4′-biphenylbis(diazonium))	—	18	—
3-$O_2NC_6H_4$†	—	—	18	—
4-$O_2NC_6H_4$†	—	—	18	—
$C_6H_5CH_2CO$†	2-CO_2H	—	18	—

Note: References 59–118 are on pp. 177–178.

* Reaction course *b*.

† Reaction course *a*.

TABLE IV

Acylcyanoacetic Esters in the Reaction:

$$\underset{\displaystyle \mathrm{CN}}{\mathrm{RCOCHCO_2C_2H_5}} + \mathrm{ArN_2^+X^-} \rightarrow \left[\mathrm{RCO}\overset{\displaystyle \mathrm{CO_2C_2H_5}}{\underset{\displaystyle \mathrm{CN}}{\mathrm{C}}}\mathrm{—N{=}N—Ar}\right] \xrightarrow{\mathrm{H_2O}}$$

$$\mathrm{RCO_2H} + \overset{\displaystyle \mathrm{CO_2C_2H_5}}{\underset{\displaystyle \mathrm{CN}}{\mathrm{C}}}\mathrm{{=}NNHC_6H_5}$$

R in Ester	Substituent in $C_6H_5N_2^+$ or [Other Diazonium Ion]	Yield, %	References	Conversion Product
CH_3	—	—	20, 21	—
	[$^+N_2$–C_6H_4–C_6H_4–N_2^+]	—	20	—
CH_3CH_2	—	—	20, 21	—
$(CH_3)_2CH$	—	—	20, 21	—
	[$^+N_2$–C_6H_4–C_6H_4–N_2^+]	—	20	—
$(CH_3)_2CHCH_2$	—	—	20, 21	—
C_6H_5	—	—	20, 21	—

TABLE V

Cyclic Compounds in Ring-Opening Reactions*

Cyclic Compound†	Substituent in  $C_6H_5N_2^+$ or [Other Diazonium Ion]	Yield, %	References	Conversion Product
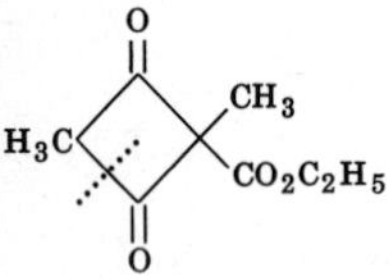 O, O, H_3C, CH_3, $CO_2C_2H_5$	4-NO_2	Good‡	84	—
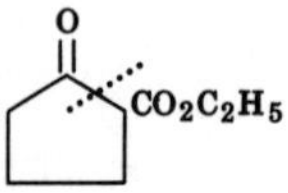 O, $CO_2C_2H_5$	—	96	11, 51, 53, 85, 114	Indole
	2-NO_2	—	11	Indole
	4-NO_2	—	11, 14	Indole
	3-CO_2H	70	37	Indole
	4-I	65	14	Indole
	4-OCH_3	71	86	Indole
	3-I, 4-I, 5-I	95	14	—
	3-I, 4-OCH_3, 5-I	88	14	—
	[α-$C_{10}H_7N_2^+$]	94	53	Indole
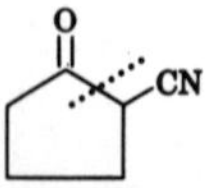 O, CN	—	—	87	—
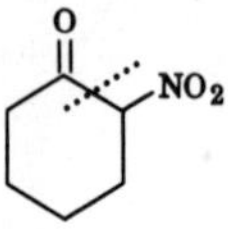 O, NO_2	—	—	88	—

Note: References 59–118 are on pp. 177–178.

* See p. 155.

† The bond broken in the ring opening is indicated by the dotted line.

‡ The reported product is $O_2NC_6H_4N{=}N{-}C(CH_3)(CO_2H){-}CO{-}CH(CH_3)CO_2C_2H_5$.

TABLE V—*Continued*

CYCLIC COMPOUNDS IN RING-OPENING REACTIONS*

Cyclic Compound†	Substituent in  $C_6H_5N_2^+$ or [Other Diazonium Ion]	Yield, %	References	Conversion Product
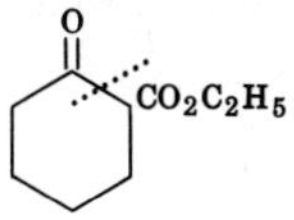 Ethyl cyclohexanone-2-carboxylate (structure; O, $CO_2C_2H_5$)	—	—	44	Amino acid
	—	97	115, 118	Indole
	—§	87	11, 54	—
	2-NO_2	—	38	Indole
	4-NO_2	—	11	—
	3-OCH_3, 4-OCH_3	90	49	Indole
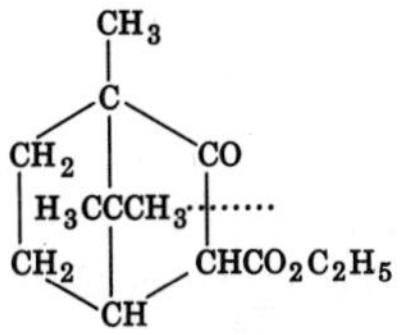 (structure: CH_3, C, CH_2, CO, H_3CCCH_3, CH_2, $CHCO_2C_2H_5$, CH)	—	89	89, 116	—

Note: References 59–118 are on pp. 177–178.

* See p. 155.

† The bond broken in the ring opening is indicated by the dotted line.

§ Methyl cyclohexanone-2-carboxylate was also coupled.

TABLE VI

1,3-Dicarbonyl Compounds

(The group that is lost is italic.)

Carbonyl Compound	Substituent in  N_2^+ or [Other Diazonium Ion]	Yield, %	References	Conversion Product
$\mathit{CH_3CO}\mathrm{CHCOCH_3}$ Cl	—	—	42	—
	—	69	90	—
$\mathrm{CH_3COCH}\mathit{COCO_2C_2H_5}$ Cl	—	—	91	—
$\mathrm{CH_3COCH}\mathit{COCH_3}$ CH_3	—	—	43	—
	2-CH_3	—	43	—
	4-CH_3	—	43	—
	4-NO_2	—	13	—
	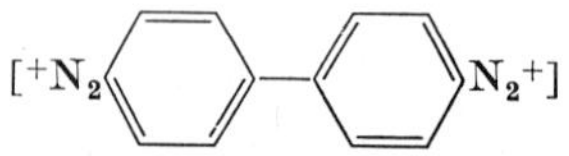	—	43	—
	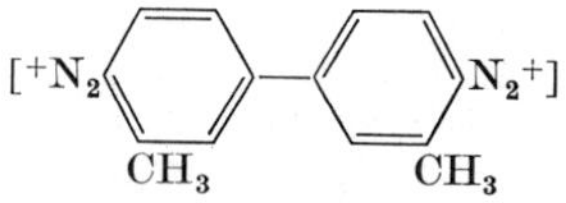	—	43	—
	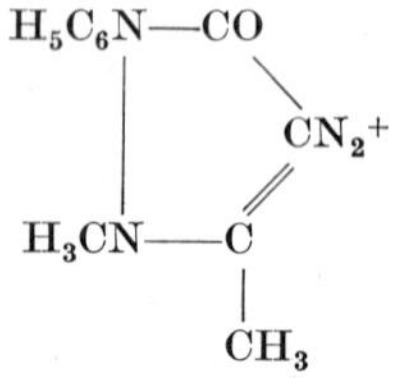	—	48	—
$\mathrm{CH_3COCH}\mathit{COCH_3}$ CH_2CH_3	—	—	43	—
	2-CH_3	—	43	—
	4-CH_3	—	43	—
	4-NO_2	—	13	—
	4-Cl	—	13	—
	4-Br	—	13	—
	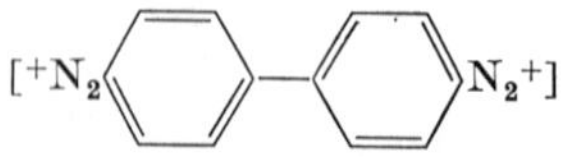	—	43	—

Note: References 59–118 are on pp. 177–178.

TABLE VI—*Continued*

1,3-DICARBONYL COMPOUNDS

(The group that is lost is italic.)

Carbonyl Compound	Substituent in  $C_6H_5N_2^+$ or [Other Diazonium Ion]	Yield, %	References	Conversion Product
$CH_3COCH\mathit{COCH_3}$ / $CH_2CH_2CO_2C_2H_5$	—	90 (as acid)	113	—
	2-CH_3	72 (as acid)	113	—
	3-CH_3	85 (as acid)	113	—
	4-CH_3	81 (as acid)	113	—
	4-NO_2	85 (as acid)	113	—
$C_6H_5COCH\mathit{CHO}$ / C_6H_5	—	—	92, 93	—
	4-Br	—	9	—
	4-NO_2	—	8	—
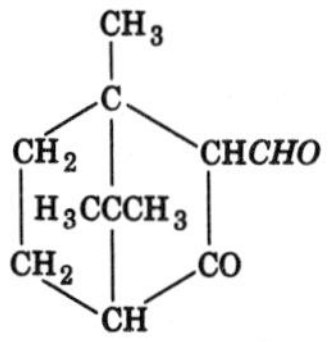 CH_3; C; CH_2; $CH\mathit{CHO}$; H_3CCCH_3; CH_2; CO; CH	—	—	94	—
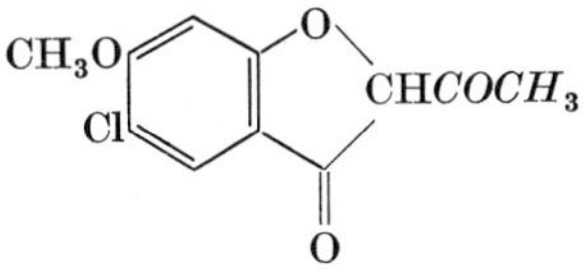 CH_3O; Cl; O; $CH\mathit{COCH_3}$; O	—	—	19	—
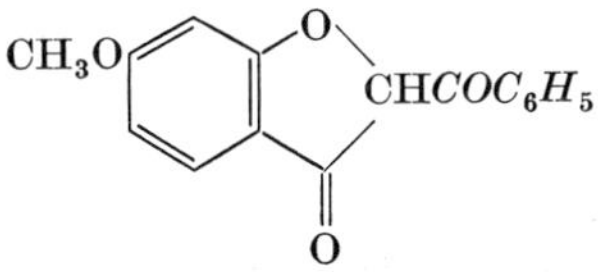 CH_3O; O; $CH\mathit{COC_6H_5}$; O	—	—	19	—
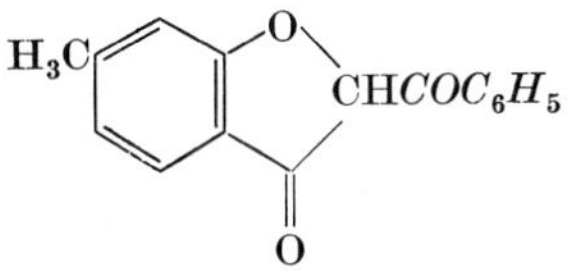 H_3C; O; $CH\mathit{COC_6H_5}$; O	—	—	19	—

Note: References 59–118 are on pp. 177–178.

TABLE VII

Miscellaneous Compounds

Starting Material	Substituent in $C_6H_5N_2^+$	Yield, %	References	Conversion Product
N; $COCO_2C_2H_5$	—*	—	27	—
	4-OCH_3*	—	27	—
	4-Br*	—	27	—
NO_2	—†	—	26	—
$COCO_2C_2H_5$	—‡	—	95	—
	4-NO_2‡	—	25	—
$COCH_3$; O; =O	—	90–96	45, 46, 47	Amino acid
$ClCH_2$; $COCH_3$; O; =O	—	83	96, 97	Amino acid
O; CH_2—CO; CO—$CHCH_3$	—	—	98	—

Note: References 59–118 are on pp. 177–178.

* The reaction was run in pyridine solution.

† The nitro group eliminated from the 9 position of fluorene apparently attacked the coupling product, since the *p-nitro*-phenylhydrazone of fluorenone was isolated.

‡ The ethoxalyl group was eliminated.

B. Reactions Accompanied by Decarboxylation

TABLE VIII

ACETOACETIC ACID DERIVATIVES

R in $RCH(COCH_3)CO_2H$	Substituent in $C_6H_5N_2^+$	Yield, %	References	Conversion Product
CH_3	—	Quant.	4, 5, 33	—
C_2H_5	—	—	4, 5	—
$KO_2CCH_2CH_2$	—	80	99	—
$C_6H_5CH_2$	—	86	36	Indole
	3-NO_2	80	36	—
	2-OCH_3, 5-OCH_3	80	36	—
	3-OCH_3, 4-OCH_3	Quant.	49	—
$C_6H_5COCH_2$	—	—	40	Pyrazole
$C_6H_4(CO)_2NCH_2CH_2CH_2$	—	86	36	Indole
	3-OCH_3	85	36	Indole
	3-Cl	—	36	—

Note: References 59–118 are on pp. 177–178.

TABLE IX

Cyanoacetic Acid Derivatives

R in $RCH(CN)CO_2H$	Substituent in $C_6H_5N_2^+$	Yield, %	References	Conversion Product
CH_3	—	—	100, 101	—
	2-CH_3	25	100, 101	—
	4-CH_3	28	100, 101	—
C_2H_5	—	31	100, 101	—
	2-CH_3	25	100, 101	—
	4-CH_3	15	100, 101, 102	—
	4-Cl	Quant.	102	—
C_6H_5	—	—	102	—
$C_6H_5CH_2$	—	30	58, 103	Amino acid
	—	Quant.	102	—
	4-CH_3	25	102	—
	4-NO_2	—	102	—

Note: References 59–118 are on pp. 177–178.

TABLE X

Malonic Acid Derivatives

R in $RCH(CO_2H)_2$	Substituent in $C_6H_5N_2^+$	Yield, %	References	Conversion Product
Cl	—	—	59	—
	2-CO_2CH_3	—	59	—
CH_3	—	—	104, 105	—
	4-CH_3	—	104, 105	—
C_2H_5	—	—	104, 105	—
	2-CH_3	—	104, 105	—
$HO_2CCH_2CH_2$	—	49	113	—
$C_6H_5CH_2$	—	—	58, 103	Amino acid
	—	—	80	Azoformaldoxime

Note: References 59–118 are on pp. 177–178.

TABLE XI

MISCELLANEOUS REACTIONS

Starting Material	Substituent in  $C_6H_5N_2^+$ or [Other Diazonium Ion]	Yield, %	References	Conversion Product
CH_3CHCO_2H | NO_2	—	—	28	—
CH_2 / \\ CH_2 CO | | CH_2—$CHCO_2H$	—	Quant.	11, 56, 106	Indole
	$2\text{-}NO_2$	—	11	—
	$4\text{-}NO_2$	—	11	—
CH_2 / \\ CH_2 CO | | CH_2—$CHCONHC_6H_5$	$2\text{-}NO_2$*	—	11	—
	$4\text{-}NO_2$*	—	11	—
CH_2 / \\ CH_2 CO | | CH_2 $CHCO_2H$ \\ / CH_2	—	Quant.	11, 56	Indole
	$4\text{-}CH_3$	Quant.	56	Indole
	$4\text{-}NO_2$	—	11	Indole
	[$\alpha\text{-}C_{10}H_7N_2^+$]	—	56	Indole
	[$\beta\text{-}C_{10}H_7N_2^+$]	Quant.	56	Indole
CH_3 | C CH_2 CO H_3CCCH_3 CH_2 $CHCO_2H$ CH	—	—	107	—
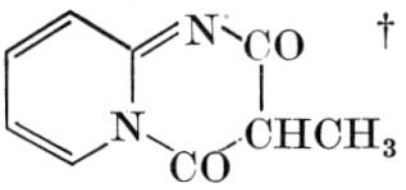 (pyrido-pyrimidine: =N–CO, N–CO, $CHCH_3$) †	$4\text{-}CO_2C_2H_5$	89	108	—

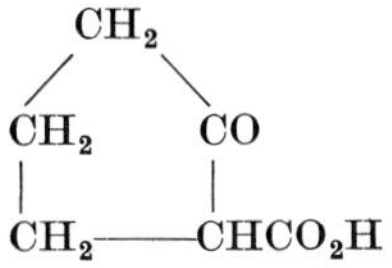

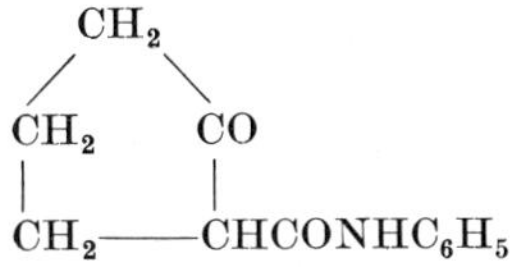

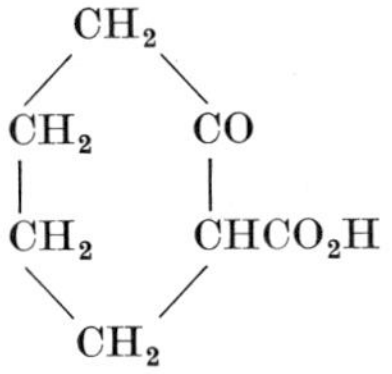

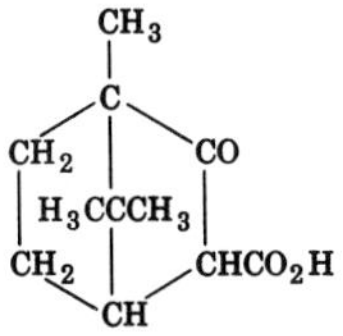

Note: References 59–118 are on pp. 177–178.

* The azo compound was isolated also.

† The product was $\alpha\text{-}C_5H_4NNHCOCH(CH_3){=}NNHC_6H_4CO_2C_2H_5\text{-}(p)$.

TABLE XI—*Continued*

MISCELLANEOUS REACTIONS

Starting Material	Substituent in  $C_6H_5N_2^+$ or [Other Diazonium Ion]	Yield, %	References	Conversion Product
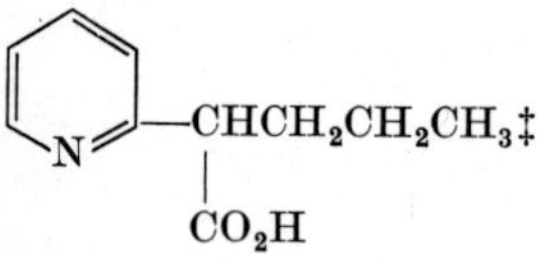 2-Pyridyl—$CH(CO_2H)CH_2CH_2CH_3$‡	4-CO_2H	94	15	—
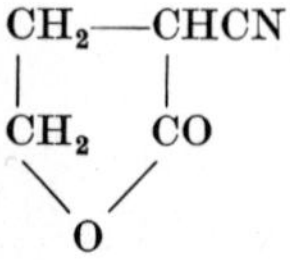 CH_2—CHCN, CH_2 CO, O (ring: $CH_2CH_2OCOCHCN$)	—	88	109	—
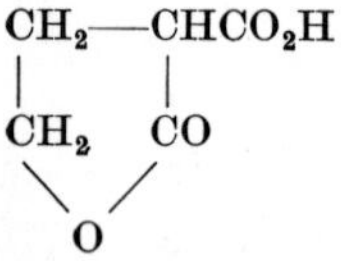 CH_2—$CHCO_2H$, CH_2 CO, O (ring: $CH_2CH_2OCOCHCO_2H$)	—	83	46	Amino acid
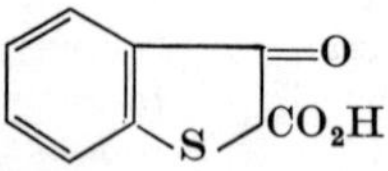 3-Oxo-2,3-dihydrobenzothiophene-2-carboxylic acid (=O, S, CO_2H)	—	Quant.	110	—

Note: References 59–118 are on pp. 177–178.

‡ The product was 2-*n*-butyrylpyridine.

REFERENCES FOR TABLES I-XI

[59] Fusco and Romani, *Gazz. chim. ital.*, **76**, 419 (1946); **78**, 342 (1948).
[60] Bowack and Lapworth, *J. Chem. Soc.*, **87**, 1854 (1905).
[61] Bülow and King, *Ann.*, **439**, 211 (1924).
[62] Lapworth, *J. Chem. Soc.*, **83**, 1114 (1903).
[63] Rydon and Siddappa, *J. Chem. Soc.*, **1951**, 2462.
[64] Hegedus, *Helv. Chim. Acta*, **29**, 1499 (1946).
[65] Feofilaktov and Zaitseva, *J. Gen. Chem. U.S.S.R.*, **13**, 358 (1943) [*C. A.*, **38**, 1211 (1944)].
[66] Feofilaktov and Zaitseva, *J. Gen. Chem. U.S.S.R.*, **10**, 1391 (1940) [*C. A.*, **35**, 3606 (1941)].
[67] Eastman and Detert, *J. Am. Chem. Soc.*, **70**, 962 (1948).
[68] Tanaka, *J. Pharm. Soc. Japan*, **60**, 74 (1940) [*C. A.*, **34**, 3735 (1940)].
[69] King and L'Ecuyer, *J. Chem. Soc.*, **1934**, 1901.
[70] Manske, *Can. J. Research*, **4**, 591 (1931).
[71] Plieninger, *Ber.*, **83**, 268 (1950).
[72] Feofilaktov and Blanko, *J. Gen. Chem. U.S.S.R.*, **11**, 859 (1941) [*C. A.*, **36**, 4096 (1942)].
[73] Feofilaktov, *J. Gen. Chem. U.S.S.R.*, **10**, 247 (1940) [*C. A.*, **34**, 7283 (1940)].
[74] Bülow and Schlesinger, *Ber.*, **32**, 2880 (1899).
[75] Bülow, *Ber.*, **33**, 3266 (1900).
[76] Stolz, *Ber.*, **33**, 262 (1900).
[77] Bülow and Schlesinger, *Ber.*, **33**, 3362 (1900).
[78] Bülow and Baur, *Ber.*, **58**, 1926 (1925).
[79] Feofilaktov and Vinogradova, *J. Gen. Chem. U.S.S.R.*, **10**, 255 (1940) [*C. A.*, **34**, 7283 (1940)].
[80] Walker, *J. Chem. Soc.*, **127**, 1860 (1925).
[81] Feofilaktov, Zaitseva, and Surotkina, *J. Gen. Chem. U.S.S.R.*, **13**, 362 (1943) [*C. A.*, **38**, 1211 (1944)].
[82] Sempronj, *Gazz. chim. ital.*, **68**, 263 (1938).
[83] Rabischong, *Bull. soc. chim. France*, [3], **31**, 91 (1904).
[84] Schroeter, *Ber.*, **49**, 2697 (1916).
[85] Kalb, Schweizer, and Schimpf, *Ber.*, **59**, 1858 (1926).
[86] Barrett, Perkin, and Robinson, *J. Chem. Soc.*, **1929**, 2942.
[87] Feofilaktov, *Bull. acad. sci. U.R.S.S. Classe sci. chim.*, **1941**, 521 [*C. A.*, **37**, 2347 (1943)].
[88] Wieland, Garbsch, and Chavan, *Ann.*, **461**, 295 (1928).
[89] Feofilaktov, *J. Gen. Chem. U.S.S.R.*, **21**, 362 (1951) [*C. A.*, **45**, 7551 (1951)].
[90] Neber and Worner, *Ann.*, **526**, 173 (1936).
[91] Favrel and Chrz, *Bull. soc. chim. France*, [4], **41**, 1603 (1927).
[92] Wislicenus and Ruthing, *Ann.*, **379**, 229 (1911).
[93] Roy and Sen, *J. Indian Chem. Soc.*, **10**, 347 (1933).
[94] Bishop, Claisen, and Sinclair, *Ann.*, **281**, 314 (1894).
[95] Wislicenus and Densch, *Ber.*, **35**, 759 (1902).
[96] Feofilaktov and Onishchenko, *Compt. rend. acad. sci. U.R.S.S.*, **20**, 133 (1938) [*C. A.*, **33**, 1725 (1939)].
[97] Feofilaktov and Onishchenko, *J. Gen. Chem. U.S.S.R.*, **9**, 331 (1939) [*C. A.*, **34**, 379 (1940)].
[98] Wolff, *Ann.*, **312**, 119 (1900).
[99] Clemo and Welch, *J. Chem. Soc.*, **1928**, 2621.
[100] Favrel, *Compt. rend.*, **132**, 983 (1901).
[101] Favrel, *Bull. soc. chim. France*, [3], **27**, 193 (1902).
[102] Walker, *J. Chem. Soc.*, **125**, 1622 (1924).
[103] Feofilaktov and Vinogradova, *Compt. rend. acad. sci. U.R.S.S.*, **24**, 759 (1939) [*C. A.*, **34**, 1971 (1940)]; *J. Gen. Chem. U.S.S.R.*, **10**, 260 (1940) [*C. A.*, **34**, 7283 (1940)].
[104] Favrel, *Compt. rend.*, **132**, 1336 (1901).

[105] Favrel, *Bull. soc. chim. France*, [3], **27**, 324 (1902).

[106] Dieckmann, *Ann.*, **317**, 27 (1901).

[107] Betti, *Ber.*, **32**, 1995 (1899).

[108] Snyder and Robison, *J. Am. Chem. Soc.*, **74**, 4910 (1952).

[109] Feofilaktov and Onishchenko, *J. Gen. Chem. U.S.S.R.*, **9**, 325 (1939) [*C. A.*, **34**, 379 (1940)].

[110] Friedlander, *Monatsh.*, **30**, 347 (1909).

[111] Feofilaktov and Semenova, *Akad. Nauk S.S.S.R. Inst. Org. Khim. Sintezy Org. Soedinenii, Sbornik*, **2**, 74 (1952) [*C. A.*, **48**, 592 (1954)].

[112] Feofilaktov and Semenova, *Akad. Nauk S.S.S.R. Inst. Org. Khim. Sintezy Org. Soedinenii, Sbornik*, **2**, 63 (1952) [*C. A.*, **48**, 666 (1954)].

[113] Feofilaktov and Semenova, *Zhur. Obshchei Khim.*, **23**, 450 (1953) [*C. A.*, **48**, 4443 (1954)].

[114] Feofilaktov, *Akad. Nauk S.S.S.R. Inst. Org. Khim. Sintezy Org. Soedinenii, Sbornik*, **2**, 103 (1952) [*C. A.*, **48**, 666 (1954)].

[115] Polaczkowa and Porowska, *Przemysl Chem.*, **6**, 340 (1950) [*C. A.*, **46**, 3039 (1952)].

[116] Feofilaktov, *J. Gen. Chem. U.S.S.R.*, **21**, 399 (1951) [*C. A.*, **46**, 2014 (1952)].

[117] Feofilaktov and Ivanova, *J. Gen. Chem. U.S.S.R.*, **21**, 1851 (1951) [*C. A.*, **47**, 2698 (1953)].

[118] Feofilaktov and Semenova, *Akad. Nauk S.S.S.R. Inst. Org. Khim. Sintezy Org. Soedinenii, Sbornik*, **2**, 98 (1952) [*C. A.*, **48**, 668 (1954)].

CHAPTER 3

THE MICHAEL REACTION*

Ernst D. Bergmann
Scientific Department, Ministry of Defence, Tel-Aviv

David Ginsburg
Chemistry Department, Israel Institute of Technology, Haifa

Raphael Pappo
Department of Organic Chemistry, Hebrew University, Jerusalem

CONTENTS

* This cooperative study was begun when the three authors were working at the Weizmann Institute of Science, Rehovoth.

INTRODUCTION

The Michael condensation in its original scope[1–21] is the addition of an addend or donor (A) containing an α-hydrogen atom in the system O=C—CH to a carbon-carbon double bond that forms part of a conjugated system of the general formulation C=C—C=O in an acceptor (B).

$$\underset{\text{A}}{\mathrm{O{=}C(R){-}CH(R^{I})(R^{II})}} + \underset{\text{B}}{\mathrm{C(R^{III})(R^{IV}){=}C(R^{V}){-}C(R^{VI}){=}O}} \xrightarrow{\text{Base}} \mathrm{O{=}C(R){-}C(R^{I})(R^{II}){-}C(R^{III})(R^{IV}){-}C(R^{V})(H){-}C(R^{VI}){=}O}$$

The condensation takes place under the influence of alkaline reagents, typically alkali metal alkoxides.

The range of addends is very broad. Generally speaking, all structures O=C—CH in which the hydrogen is active by the Zerewitinoff test will serve as donors in the Michael condensation. In addition, many compounds that do not meet this test of hydrogen activity, such as acetophenone, are effective Michael reactants.

Typical acceptors are α,β-unsaturated aldehydes, ketones, and acid derivatives.

By extension of the original scope, the Michael condensation has come to be understood to include addends and acceptors activated by groups other than carbonyl and carbalkoxyl. The wider scope is encompassed

[1] Michael, *J. prakt. Chem.*, [2], **35**, 349 (1887).
[2] Michael, *Am. Chem. J.*, **9**, 115 (1887).
[3] Michael, *J. prakt. Chem.*, [2], **49**, 20 (1894).
[4] Michael, *Ber.*, **27**, 2126 (1894).
[5] Michael, *Ber.*, **33**, 3731 (1900).
[6] Michael and Schulthess, *J. prakt. Chem.*, [2], **45**, 55 (1892).
[7] von Auwers, *Ber.*, **24**, 307 (1891).
[8] von Auwers, Koebner, and v. Meyenburg, *Ber.*, **24**, 2887 (1891).
[9] von Auwers, *Ber.*, **26**, 364 (1893).
[10] von Auwers and Jacob, *Ber.*, **27**, 1115 (1894).
[11] von Auwers, *Ber.*, **28**, 1130 (1895).
[12] Knoevenagel, *Ann.*, **281**, 25 (1894), especially p. 33.
[13] Knoevenagel, *Ann.*, **281**, 25 (1894), especially p. 53.
[14] Knoevenagel, *Ann.*, **289**, 131 (1896), especially p. 170.
[15] Knoevenagel, *Ann.*, **297**, 185 (1897).
[16] Merling, *Ber.*, **38**, 979 (1905).
[17] Knoevenagel and Schwartz, *Ber.*, **39**, 3441 (1906).
[18] Knoevenagel and Mottek, *Ber.*, **37**, 4464 (1904).
[19] Knoevenagel and Speyer, *Ber.*, **35**, 395 (1902).
[20] Connor and McClellan, *J. Org. Chem.*, **3**, 570 (1938).
[21] H. Henecka, *Chemie der Beta-Dicarbonyl-Verbindungen*, Berlin-Goettingen-Heidelberg, 1950.

by this survey, which therefore includes as donors nitriles, nitro compounds, sulfones, and certain hydrocarbons such as cyclopentadiene, indene, and fluorene that contain sufficiently reactive hydrogen atoms. It also includes as acceptor molecules a vinylsulfonium compound[22] and certain hydrocarbons of permanent polar character (finite dipole moment) such as fulvenes. Another hydrocarbon acceptor is the conjugated tetra-acetylenic compound which adds diethyl sodiomalonate as shown.[22a]

$$CH_3C{\equiv}C{-}C{\equiv}C{-}C{\equiv}C{-}C{\equiv}CCH_3 + CH_2(CO_2C_2H_5)_2 \rightarrow CH_3C{\equiv}C{-}C{\equiv}C{-}C{\equiv}C{-}CH{=}C(CH_3)CH(CO_2C_2H_5)_2$$

The relatively few Michael condensations in which acetylenic aldehydes, ketones, and esters serve as acceptors are also considered.

The interesting examples of activation of an ethylenic double bond by a neighboring sulfonium group provided by the observation[22] that vinyldimethylsulfonium bromide adds methyl acetoacetate and diethyl malonate in the presence of aqueous sodium hydroxide, according to the following equation,

$$(CH_3)_2\overset{\oplus}{S}{-}CH{=}CH_2 + CH_3COCH_2CO_2C_2H_5 \rightarrow (CH_3)_2\underset{\oplus}{S}CH_2CH_2CH(COCH_3)CO_2C_2H_5$$

are good illustrations of the mechanism of the Michael reaction, as set out in the following section.

Unsaturated cyclic quaternary ammonium salts can also act as acceptors in the presence of bases. A recent example is furnished by the 2,7,10-trimethylacridinium halides which react with diethyl malonate in the presence of sodium ethoxide as shown in the accompanying equation.[22b]

H₃C–(acridinium ring, N⊕–CH₃)–CH₃ $\xrightarrow[NaOC_2H_5]{CH_2(CO_2C_2H_5)_2}$ H₃C–(9-H, 9-CH(CO₂C₂H₅)₂ acridan ring, N–CH₃)–CH₃

[22] Doering and Schreiber, *J. Am. Chem. Soc.*, **77**, 514 (1955).

[22a] Bohlmann, Inhoffen, and Politt, *Ann.*, **604**, 207 (1957).

[22b] Dimroth and Criegee, *Chem. Ber.*, **90**, 2207 (1957). Other examples are given by Kroehnke and Honig, *Chem. Ber.*, **90**, 2215 (1957); Kroehnke and Vogt, *Ann.*, **600**, 211 (1956), and *Chem. Ber.*, **90**, 2227 (1957). These reactions recall older observations of the reactions of unsaturated cyclic quaternary ammonium pseudo bases with ethyl acetoacetate and with nitroparaffins: Kaufmann, *Chem. Zentr.*, **1912, II**, 978; Leonard and Leubner, *J. Am. Chem. Soc.*, **71**, 3405 (1949); Leonard, Leubner, and Burk, *J. Org. Chem.*, **15**, 979 (1950).

MECHANISMS OF THE PROCESSES INVOLVED IN THE MICHAEL REACTION

The Normal Reaction

From the nature of the alkaline reagents that cause the Michael condensation to occur, it is logical to suppose that they act by removing the α-hydrogen atom from the donor as a proton. The residual anion is

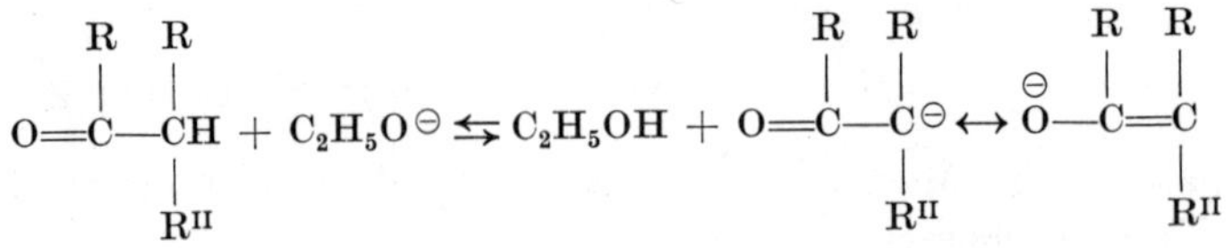

$$\underset{\text{A}}{\mathrm{O{=}\overset{R}{\overset{|}{C}}{-}\underset{R^{II}}{\underset{|}{\overset{R}{\overset{|}{C}}H}}}} + C_2H_5O^{\ominus} \rightleftarrows C_2H_5OH + \mathrm{O{=}\overset{R}{\overset{|}{C}}{-}\underset{R^{II}}{\underset{|}{\overset{R}{\overset{|}{C}}}}^{\ominus}} \leftrightarrow \mathrm{\overset{\ominus}{O}{-}\overset{R}{\overset{|}{C}}{=}\underset{R^{II}}{\underset{|}{\overset{R}{\overset{|}{C}}}}}$$

presumably to be viewed as a hybrid of the enolate ion form and the carbanion form, as depicted here, though the subsequent condensation is most readily visualized as involving the carbanion.

The condensation proper occurs when a new bond is formed between the electron-rich carbon of this ion and the most electron-poor carbon of the conjugated system in the acceptor, namely, the β-carbon atom. Where the acceptor has (as shown) carbonyl activation of the α,β double bond, the carbanion product C is a resonance hybrid. It is noteworthy that ability of acceptors to serve in the Michael condensation is enhanced by polarizing substituents (R^{III}, R^{IV}, R^{V}) that stabilize the ions C.

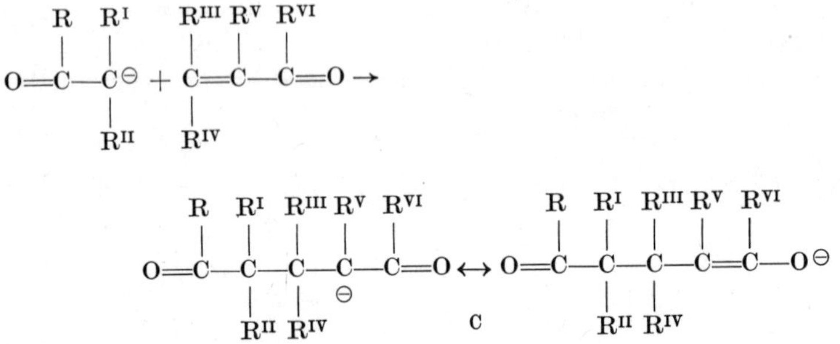

$$\mathrm{O{=}\overset{R}{\overset{|}{C}}{-}\underset{R^{II}}{\underset{|}{\overset{R^{I}}{\overset{|}{C}}}}^{\ominus}} + \mathrm{\underset{R^{IV}}{\underset{|}{\overset{R^{III}}{\overset{|}{C}}}}{=}\overset{R^{V}}{\overset{|}{C}}{-}\overset{R^{VI}}{\overset{|}{C}}{=}O} \rightarrow$$

$$\underset{\text{C}}{\mathrm{O{=}\overset{R}{\overset{|}{C}}{-}\underset{R^{II}}{\underset{|}{\overset{R^{I}}{\overset{|}{C}}}}{-}\underset{R^{IV}}{\underset{|}{\overset{R^{III}}{\overset{|}{C}}}}{-}\underset{\ominus}{\overset{R^{V}}{\overset{|}{C}}}{-}\overset{R^{VI}}{\overset{|}{C}}{=}O}} \leftrightarrow \mathrm{O{=}\overset{R}{\overset{|}{C}}{-}\underset{R^{II}}{\underset{|}{\overset{R^{I}}{\overset{|}{C}}}}{-}\underset{R^{IV}}{\underset{|}{\overset{R^{III}}{\overset{|}{C}}}}{-}\overset{R^{V}}{\overset{|}{C}}{=}\overset{R^{VI}}{\overset{|}{C}}{-}O^{\ominus}}$$

The proton that converts the ionized product (C) into the keto form isolated (D) may come from another donor molecule. This interpretation accounts for the fact that much less than the equivalent amount of basic reagent often suffices to bring about the condensation. Where a full equivalent of base is employed, the proton is supplied by neutralization of the reaction system.

The over-all reaction has, then, the effect of 1,4 addition of the donor (in fragments O═C—C— and —H) to the conjugated system of the acceptor.

$$\underset{\mathbf{C}}{O{=}\overset{R}{\overset{|}{C}}{-}\underset{\underset{R^{II}}{|}}{\overset{R^{I}}{\overset{|}{C}}}{-}\underset{\underset{R^{IV}}{|}}{\overset{R^{III}}{\overset{|}{C}}}{-}\overset{R^{V}}{\overset{|}{C}}{=}\overset{R^{VI}}{\overset{|}{C}}{-}O^{\ominus}} + \underset{\mathbf{A}}{O{=}\overset{R}{\overset{|}{C}}{-}\underset{\underset{R^{II}}{|}}{\overset{R^{I}}{\overset{|}{C}}}H} \rightleftarrows$$

$$\underset{\mathbf{D}}{O{=}\overset{R}{\overset{|}{C}}{-}\underset{\underset{R^{II}}{|}}{\overset{R^{I}}{\overset{|}{C}}}{-}\underset{\underset{R^{IV}}{|}}{\overset{R^{III}}{\overset{|}{C}}}{-}\underset{\underset{H}{|}}{\overset{R^{V}}{\overset{|}{C}}}{-}\overset{R^{VI}}{\overset{|}{C}}{=}O} + O{=}\overset{R}{\overset{|}{C}}{-}\underset{\underset{R^{II}}{|}}{\overset{R^{I}}{\overset{|}{C}}}{}^{\ominus}$$

The foregoing description obviously does not apply to those condensations, included as Michael reactions in the larger sense, in which the acceptor is an unsaturated hydrocarbon of permanent polar character. Here the product C must be formulated exclusively as a carbanion, and the over-all reaction has the appearance of 1,2 addition of the donor RH (as R— and —H) to the polarized double bond.

The Nature of the Anion of the Adduct

Where R^{II} is hydrogen, the carbanion C may undergo a proton shift. It must be supposed that the anion readily assumes the form C′ if this

$$\underset{\mathbf{C}}{O{=}\overset{R}{\overset{|}{C}}{-}\underset{\underset{H}{|}}{\overset{R^{I}}{\overset{|}{C}}}{-}\underset{\underset{R^{IV}}{|}}{\overset{R^{III}}{\overset{|}{C}}}{-}\underset{\ominus}{\overset{R^{V}}{\overset{|}{C}}}{-}\overset{R^{VI}}{\overset{|}{C}}{=}O} \rightleftarrows \underset{\mathbf{C'}}{O{=}\overset{R}{\overset{|}{C}}{-}\underset{\ominus}{\overset{R^{I}}{\overset{|}{C}}}{-}\underset{\underset{R^{IV}}{|}}{\overset{R^{III}}{\overset{|}{C}}}{-}\underset{\underset{H}{|}}{\overset{R^{V}}{\overset{|}{C}}}{-}\overset{R^{VI}}{\overset{|}{C}}{=}O}$$

is more stable than C, as may be the case if the substituent R^{I} makes the proton of the group $R^{I}CH$ more highly acidic than that of $R^{V}CH$.

Although on direct isolation the same product is obtained from C and from C′, the reactions carried out on the anion may disclose when the change has taken place, as in the following example.[23] The Michael product from ethyl cyanoacetate and ethyl methacrylate (with a full equivalent of base) can be methylated in alcoholic solution with methyl iodide. Upon hydrolysis and decarboxylation, α,α′-dimethylglutaric

[23] Thorpe and Young, *J. Chem. Soc.*, **77**, 940 (1900).

acid (IV) is obtained. This must be derived from III, and the anion is then better represented as II than I, which would be the primary result of the addition outlined in the foregoing.

$$^{\ominus}CH(CN)CO_2C_2H_5 + CH_2{=}C(CH_3)CO_2C_2H_5 \rightarrow \underset{\text{I}}{\begin{array}{l} CH(CN)CO_2C_2H_5 \\ | \quad \ominus \\ CH_2C(CH_3)CO_2C_2H_5 \end{array}} \rightarrow$$

$$\underset{\text{II}}{\begin{array}{l} \overset{\ominus}{C}(CN)CO_2C_2H_5 \\ | \\ CH_2CH(CH_3)CO_2C_2H_5 \end{array}} \xrightarrow{CH_3I} \underset{\text{III}}{\begin{array}{l} CH_3C(CN)CO_2C_2H_5 \\ | \\ CH_2CH(CH_3)CO_2C_2H_5 \end{array}} \xrightarrow[-CO_2]{\text{Hydrolysis}} \underset{\text{IV}}{\begin{array}{l} CH_3CHCO_2H \\ | \\ CH_2CH(CH_3)CO_2H \end{array}}$$

Many similar observations of this rearrangement, which is not in itself part of the Michael reaction, have been made in the course of efforts to establish Michael mechanisms.[24]

From one particular example, it appears that the rearrangement may be impeded in non-hydroxylic solvents.[25,26] Ethyl phenylpropiolate (V) with diethyl sodiomalonate in *inert solvents* gives a yellow sodium salt and in *ethanol solution* a colorless isomer. The formulas VI (before rearrangement) and VII (after rearrangement), respectively, have been assigned to these salts. Diethyl sodio*methyl*malonate in benzene also gives a yellow compound VIII with ethyl phenylpropiolate, but no colorless isomer; this is attributed to the lack of an α-hydrogen atom in VIII that would permit shift to the form analogous to VII. It should

$$\underset{\text{V}}{C_6H_5C{\equiv}CCO_2C_2H_5} \qquad \underset{\text{VI}}{\begin{array}{l} C_6H_5C{=}C{=}C(OC_2H_5)ONa \\ | \\ CH(CO_2C_2H_5)_2 \end{array}}$$

$$\underset{\text{VII}}{\begin{array}{l} C_6H_5C{=}CHCO_2C_2H_5 \\ | \\ C_2H_5O_2CC{=}C(OC_2H_5)ONa \end{array}} \qquad \underset{\text{VIII}}{\begin{array}{l} C_6H_5C{=}C{=}C(OC_2H_5)ONa \\ | \\ CH_3C(CO_2C_2H_5)_2 \end{array}}$$

be noted that the structures indicated for VI and VIII do not fully explain their yellow color.

[24] Ingold and Powell, *J. Chem. Soc.*, **119**, 1976 (1921).

[25] Gidvani and Kon, *J. Chem. Soc.*, **1932**, 2443.

[26] Gidvani, Kon, and Wright, *J. Chem. Soc.*, **1932**, 1027.

A Competitive Side Reaction

Compounds of the type formulated above as acceptors tend to undergo addition reactions with anions in general, e.g., with alkoxide anions, which are frequently used as catalysts in the Michael reaction. In such cases, the catalyst competes with the donor for the acceptor molecule.

$$\left.\begin{array}{l} \mathrm{O{=}C(R){-}C^{\ominus}(R^{I})(R^{II})} \\ \text{and} \\ \mathrm{R^{VII}O^{\ominus}} \end{array}\right. + \mathrm{C(R^{III})(R^{IV}){=}C(R^{V}){-}C(R^{VI}){=}O} \rightarrow \left\{\begin{array}{c} \mathrm{O{=}C(R){-}C(R^{I})(R^{II}){-}C(R^{III})(R^{IV}){-}C(R^{V}){=}C(R^{VI}){-}O^{\ominus}} \\ \text{and} \\ \mathrm{R^{VII}{-}O{-}C(R^{III})(R^{IV}){-}C(R^{V}){=}C(R^{VI}){-}O^{\ominus}} \end{array}\right\}$$

Although this possibility should always be borne in mind, it seems that only acceptors in which $R^{III} = R^{IV} = H$ (acrylates, acrylonitrile) add alkoxide anions avidly enough to interfere with the Michael reaction. It is preferable with these acceptors to carry out the condensation without solvent or in non-hydroxylic media.[27]

The Reverse or Retrograde Reaction

The Michael reaction is a reversible process: adducts D can be split into precursors A and B by the same catalysts that effect the condensation.[28] A tendency toward such retrogression can be combatted to a degree by using an excess of one of the reactants; this appears to be a case of mass action affecting an equilibrium. Although few quantitative data are available on the position of the equilibrium, it appears that low temperature favors condensation and elevated temperature retrogression.[29] Furthermore, retrogression is more likely to occur when the condensation is slow; one of the factors causing slow condensation is the presence of a large number of substituents (R^{III}, R^{IV}, R^{V}) at the α,β double bond of the acceptor molecule (see p. 247). These two effects are exemplified in

[27] Koelsch, *J. Am. Chem. Soc.*, **65,** 437 (1943).

[28] Grob and Baumann, *Helv. Chim. Acta,* **38,** 594 (1955).

[29] Dornow and Boberg, *Ann.*, **578,** 101 (1952).

the following table in which the yields of condensation product obtained possibly represent the equilibria attained.

Reaction between Diethyl Malonate and	Yield of Adduct at 100°	25°
Ethyl crotonate	65	?
Ethyl cinnamate	35	?
Ethyl β,β-dimethylacrylate	30	70
Ethyl α,β,β-trimethylacrylate	Trace?	?

Whenever at least one of the substituents R^I and R^{II} in the donor is hydrogen, the general formulation of the condensation product acquires

$$O{=}C(R)-C(R^I)(H)-C(R^{III})(R^{IV})-C(R^V)(H)-C(R^{VI}){=}O \rightarrow O{=}C(R)-C(R^I){=}C(R^{III})(R^{IV}) + H_2C(R^V)-C(R^{VI}){=}O$$

the symmetry of a 1,5-diketopentane with hydrogen atoms in the 2 and 4 positions. With such a structure, retrogression can occur to give fragments different from the starting materials. In this process, the bond broken is the one that was originally α,β in the acceptor; the remainder of this end of the molecule is then isolated as a fragment having O═C—CH ("donor") structure. At the same time, the original donor reappears with C═C—C═O ("acceptor") structure. The combination of condensation and retrogression in such cases has the net effect of transferring an alkylidene substituent from the α-carbon of the original acceptor to the α-carbon of the original donor. Thus, the Michael condensation between phenylacetone and α-nitrostilbene gives, inter alia, 3,4-diphenyl-3-buten-2-one (IX),[29] and the condensation of isopropyl

$$p\text{-}CH_3OC_6H_4CH{=}CHCOCH(CH_3)_2 + CH_2(CO_2C_2H_5)_2 \longrightarrow$$

$$p\text{-}CH_3OC_6H_4CH(CH(CO_2C_2H_5)_2) \vdots CH_2COCH(CH_3)_2 \longrightarrow CH_3COCH(CH_3)_2 +$$

$$p\text{-}CH_3OC_6H_4CH{=}C(CO_2C_2H_5)_2 \xrightarrow{\text{Hydrolysis}} p\text{-}CH_3OC_6H_4CH{=}CHCO_2H$$

p-methoxybenzylidenemethyl ketone with diethyl malonate, when carried out in ethanol as solvent, gives p-methoxycinnamic acid.[30] (See equations at top of p. 189.)

Cleavage formally identical with this can occur in molecules of suitable structure, even though they were not formed by a Michael reaction. The

[30] Vorlaender and Knoetzsch, *Ann.*, **294,** 317 (1897), especially p. 334.

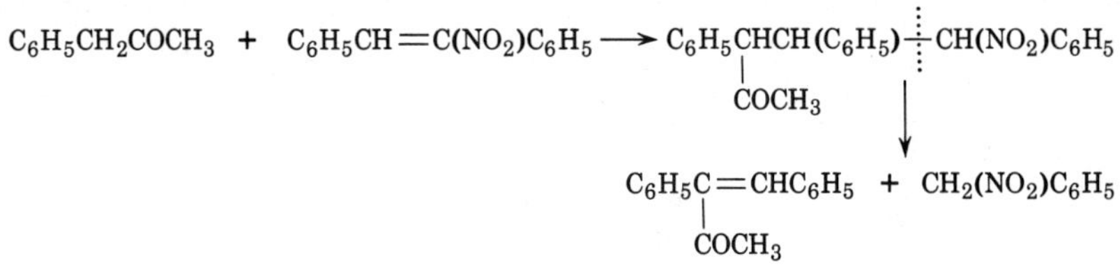

$$C_6H_5CH_2COCH_3 + C_6H_5CH{=}C(NO_2)C_6H_5 \longrightarrow C_6H_5CH(COCH_3)CH(C_6H_5) \vdots CH(NO_2)C_6H_5$$

$$\downarrow$$

$$C_6H_5C(COCH_3){=}CHC_6H_5 + CH_2(NO_2)C_6H_5$$

IX

following examples from the chemistry of natural products illustrate cleavages that may be designated retrograde Michael reactions in a formal sense.

1. Dimethyl caryophyllenate (X) is converted by successive treatments with sodium amide in xylene at 130° and with dilute hydrochloric acid into 4,4-dimethyl-2-cyclohexenone (XI).[31]

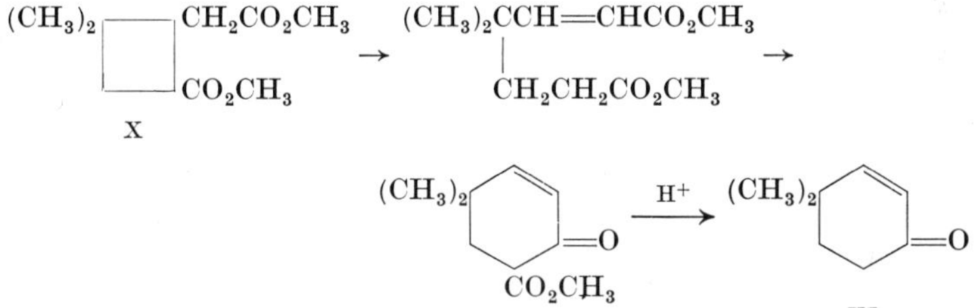

$(CH_3)_2$ [cyclobutane] $CH_2CO_2CH_3$, CO_2CH_3 (X) $\rightarrow$ $(CH_3)_2C(CH_2CH_2CO_2CH_3)CH{=}CHCO_2CH_3$ $\rightarrow$

$(CH_3)_2$ [cyclohexenone] $=O$, CO_2CH_3 $\xrightarrow{H^+}$ $(CH_3)_2$ [cyclohexenone] $=O$ (XI)

2. Dimethyl α-tanacetonedicarboxylate (XII) is analogously converted into tanacetophorone (XIII).[32]

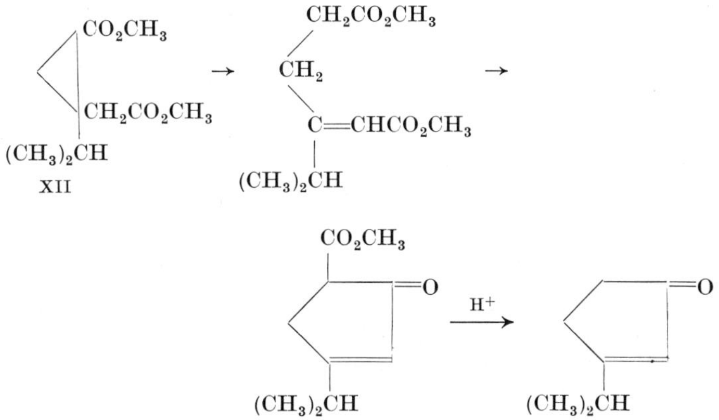

[cyclopropane] CO_2CH_3, $CH_2CO_2CH_3$, $(CH_3)_2CH$ (XII) $\rightarrow$ $CH_2CO_2CH_3$—CH_2—$C(CH(CH_3)_2){=}CHCO_2CH_3$ $\rightarrow$

CO_2CH_3 [cyclopentenone] $=O$, $(CH_3)_2CH$ $\xrightarrow{H^+}$ [cyclopentenone] $=O$, $(CH_3)_2CH$ (XIII)

[31] Eschenmoser and Fuerst, *Experientia*, **7**, 290 (1951).
[32] Wallach, *Ann.*, **388**, 49 (1912).

3. The conversion of santoric acid (XIV) into santoronic acid (heptane-2,3,6-tricarboxylic acid, XV) has been formulated as follows.[33]

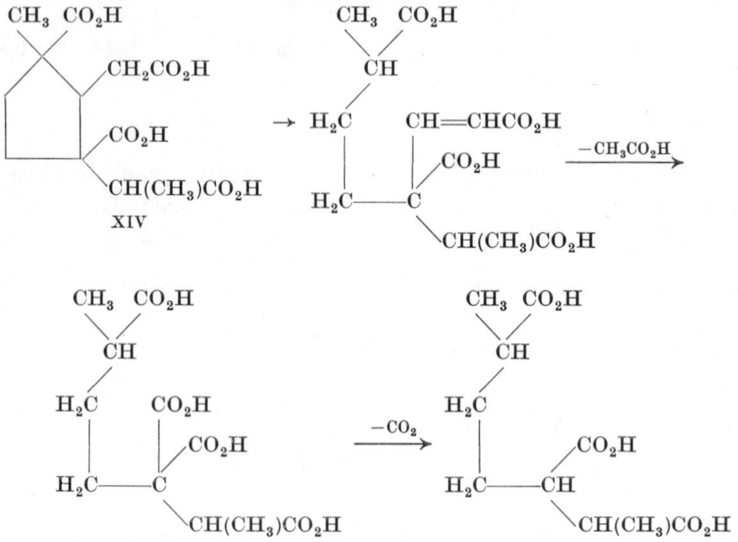

CH_3 CO_2H ... CH_2CO_2H, CO_2H, $CH(CH_3)CO_2H$ XIV → CH_3 CO_2H CH, H_2C, $CH{=}CHCO_2H$, CO_2H, H_2C—C, $CH(CH_3)CO_2H$ $\xrightarrow{-CH_3CO_2H}$

CH_3 CO_2H CH, H_2C, CO_2H, CO_2H, H_2C—C, $CH(CH_3)CO_2H$ $\xrightarrow{-CO_2}$ CH_3 CO_2H CH, H_2C, CO_2H, H_2C—CH, $CH(CH_3)CO_2H$ XV

4. The phenyl ketone XVII, obtained from 4-cholesten-3-one (XVI), is converted (in its intramolecular aldol form) by heating with alkali at 200–240° to XVIII and vinyl phenyl ketone, which decomposes further into formaldehyde and acetophenone.[34]

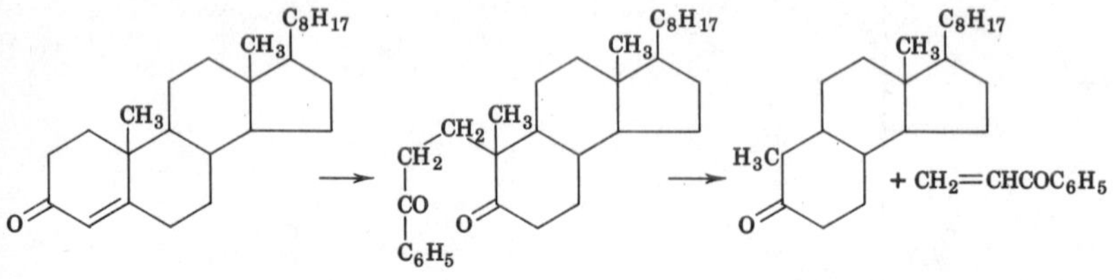

XVI → XVII ($CH_2CH_2COC_6H_5$) → XVIII + $CH_2{=}CHCOC_6H_5$

5. Pyrolysis of the keto aldehyde XIX gives XX and 2-dodecenal.[35,36]

6. Similarly, XXI is converted to 2-methylcyclohexanone and XXII.[37]

[33] Woodward, Brutschy, and Baer, *J. Am. Chem. Soc.*, **70**, 4216 (1948).

[34] Julia, Eschenmoser, Heusser, and Tarköy, *Helv. Chim. Acta*, **36**, 1885 (1953).

[35] Achtermann, *Hoppe-Seyler's Z. physiol. Chem.*, **225**, 141 (1934).

[36] Laucht, *Hoppe-Seyler's Z. physiol. Chem.*, **237**, 236 (1935).

[37] Cornforth, Hunter, and Popják, *Biochem. J.*, **54**, 590 (1953).

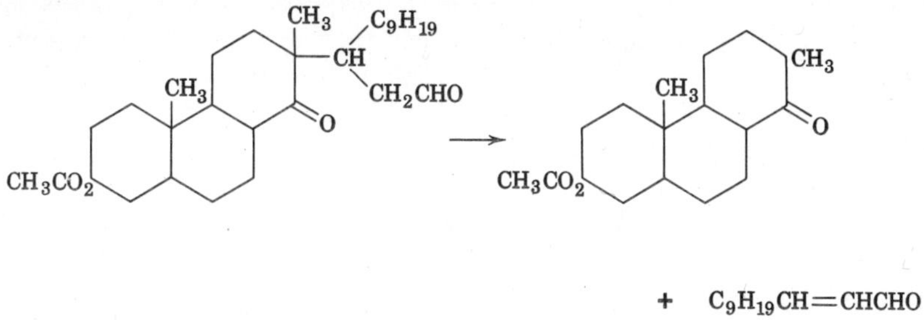

CH_3 C_9H_{19} CH CH_2CHO CH_3 O CH_3CO_2 → CH_3 CH_3 O CH_3CO_2

XIX + $C_9H_{19}CH{=}CHCHO$ XX

C_8H_{17} CH_3 CH_3 CHO O → CH_3 O + C_8H_{17} CH_3 CHO

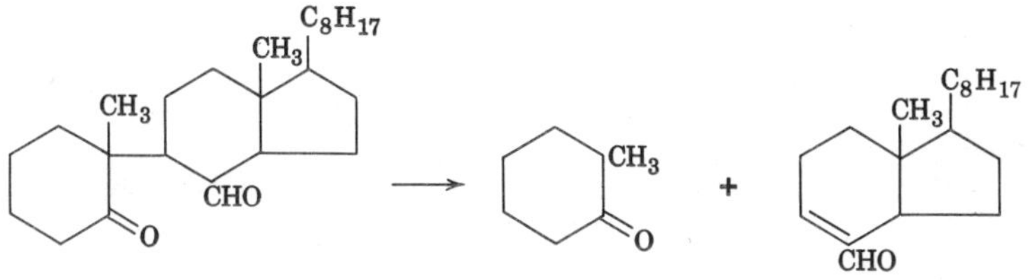

XXI XXII

Other retrogressions of this type may take place by heating or under base catalysis.[38–47]

The "Abnormal" Michael Condensation

When the Michael condensation product from ethyl β,β-dimethylacrylate and ethyl α-cyanopropionate is methylated (with sodium ethoxide and methyl iodide), the product upon hydrolysis and partial decarboxylation is $\alpha,\alpha',\beta,\beta$-tetramethylglutaric acid (XXVI).[23] This carbon skeleton shows that the methylation product before hydrolysis is XXV. In turn, XXV probably can only arise by methylation of XXIV, where the hydrogen atom replaced is doubly activated (enolizable), because it is generally assumed that (singly activated) α-hydrogen atoms like those in XXIII (the alternative possible precursor of XXV) cannot be methylated

[38] Hill, *J. Chem. Soc.*, **1928**, 256.

[39] Leonard, Simon, and Felley, *J. Am. Chem. Soc.*, **73**, 857 (1951).

[40] Vorlaender, *Ber.*, **33**, 3185 (1900).

[41] Vorlaender and Koethner, *Ann.*, **345**, 158 (1906).

[42] Meerwein, *Ber.*, **53**, 1829 (1920).

[43] Smith and Engelhardt, *J. Amer. Chem. Soc.*, **71**, 2676 (1949).

[44] Cornelson and Kostanecki, *Ber.*, **29**, 240 (1896).

[45] Kostanecki and Rossbach, *Ber.*, **29**, 1488 (1896).

[46] Meerwein, *J. prakt. Chem.*, [2], **97**, 225 (1918).

[47] Arigoni, Viterbo, Duennenberger, Jeger, and Ruzicka, *Helv. Chim. Acta*, **37**, 2306 (1954).

by sodium ethoxide plus methyl iodide.* (Hydrolysis of the primary adduct gives α,β,β-trimethylglutaric acid,[49] which does not permit differentiation between XXIII and XXIV.) The initial condensation product must therefore be not the expected ("normal") XXIII but the ester XXIV, which is formally the result of adding the donor molecule as the fragments CH_3— and —$CH(CN)CO_2C_2H_5$. This is called the "abnormal" Michael reaction; in this and similar cases studied by

$$(CH_3)_2C{=}CHCO_2C_2H_5 + CH_3CH(CN)CO_2C_2H_5 \not\rightarrow \underset{\text{XXIII}}{(CH_3)_2CCH_2CO_2C_2H_5 \atop | \atop CH_3C(CN)CO_2C_2H_5}$$

$$\downarrow$$

$$\underset{\text{XXIV}}{(CH_3)_2CCH(CH_3)CO_2C_2H_5 \atop | \atop CH(CN)CO_2C_2H_5} \xrightarrow[CH_3I]{NaOC_2H_5} \underset{\text{XXV}}{(CH_3)_2CCH(CH_3)CO_2C_2H_5 \atop | \atop CH_3C(CN)CO_2C_2H_5} \rightarrow \underset{\text{XXVI}}{(CH_3)_2CCH(CH_3)CO_2H \atop | \atop CH_3CHCO_2H}$$

Thorpe and co-workers, the products formed were attributed to literal addition of a methyl group as one portion of the donor. "Abnormal" addition of diethyl methylmalonate involves the apparent adding of the fragments C_2H_5OCO— and —$CH(CH_3)CO_2C_2H_5$.

In some systems, it is observed that the course of the reaction can be varied at will by the amount of condensing agent employed. For example,[50] diethyl malonate and ethyl crotonate give the normal adduct, triethyl 2-methylpropane-1,1,3-tricarboxylate (XXVII), which, having an enolizable hydrogen atom, can be methylated to triethyl 3-methylbutane-2,2,4-tricarboxylate (XXVIII). The adduct XXVIII is also obtained from ethyl crotonate and diethyl *methyl*malonate in the presence of one-sixth equivalent of sodium ethoxide. If a *full* equivalent of the condensing agent is employed, however, an isomer of XXVIII is formed; this must have the "abnormal" structure XXIX, for it contains an

* There are occasional observations to the contrary.[48]

[48] Schlenk, Hillemann, and Rodloff, *Ann.*, **487**, 135 (1931).

[49] Cf. Michael and Ross, *J. Am. Chem. Soc.*, **53**, 1150 (1931).

[50] Michael and Ross, *J. Am. Chem. Soc.*, **52**, 4598 (1930).

enolizable hydrogen atom and can be methylated by sodium ethoxide and methyl iodide to yield XXX. Furthermore, the isomer XXIX can be obtained by the Michael condensation of ethyl tiglate and diethyl malonate, though this synthesis provides valid evidence only if the condensation takes the "normal" course. In contrast to the behavior of

$$CH_3CH{=}CHCO_2C_2H_5 + CH_2(CO_2C_2H_5)_2 \rightarrow \underset{\text{XXVII}}{CH_3CH(CH_2CO_2C_2H_5)CH(CO_2C_2H_5)_2} \xrightarrow{CH_3I} \underset{\text{XXVIII}}{CH_3CH(CH_2CO_2C_2H_5)C(CH_3)(CO_2C_2H_5)_2}$$

$$CH_3CH{=}CHCO_2C_2H_5 + CH_3CH(CO_2C_2H_5)_2 \xrightarrow[\text{1/6 mole}]{NaOC_2H_5} \text{XXVIII}$$

$$CH_3CH{=}CHCO_2C_2H_5 + CH_3CH(CO_2C_2H_5)_2 \xrightarrow[\text{1 mole}]{NaOC_2H_5} \underset{\text{XXIX}}{CH_3CH(CH(CH_3)CO_2C_2H_5)CH(CO_2C_2H_5)_2}$$

$$CH_3CH{=}C(CH_3)CO_2C_2H_5 + CH_2(CO_2C_2H_5)_2 \rightarrow \text{XXIX}$$

$$\text{XXIX} \xrightarrow{CH_3I} \underset{\text{XXX}}{CH_3CH(CH(CH_3)CO_2C_2H_5)C(CH_3)(CO_2C_2H_5)_2}$$

XXIX, when XXVIII is treated again with sodium ethoxide and subsequently methyl iodide, retrogression takes place to ethyl crotonate and diethyl methylmalonate, the latter being further methylated to diethyl dimethylmalonate.

The most widely accepted explanation for the "abnormal" reaction is that of Holden and Lapworth.[51] The primary product of the Michael condensation always has the normal formula (e.g., XXVIII from ethyl crotonate and diethyl methylmalonate); however, it is stable only when small quantities of catalyst are employed. In the presence of larger quantities of catalyst, a Dieckmann condensation is assumed to occur (XXVIII→XXXI). This cyclization may be facilitated by the presence of a relatively large number of substituents, which could cause a change

[51] Holden and Lapworth, *J. Chem. Soc.*, **1931**, 2368.

in the valence angles, as proposed by Ingold in other cases.[52,53] The cyclobutanone derivative XXXI in turn is also unstable, particularly as a consequence of the β-keto ester structure; accordingly, it is alcoholyzed to XXIX, which is the product actually obtained.

$$
\begin{array}{l}
CH_3CHCH_2CO_2C_2H_5 \\
\quad | \\
CH_3C(CO_2C_2H_5)_2 \\
\quad \text{XXVIII}
\end{array}
\xrightarrow{C_2H_5OH}
\begin{array}{l}
CH_3CH\text{—}CHCO_2C_2H_5 \\
\quad\;\; | \quad \vdots \quad | \\
CH_3C\text{—}\vdots\text{—}CO \\
\quad\;\; | \\
\quad CO_2C_2H_5 \\
\quad \text{XXXI}
\end{array}
\xrightarrow{C_2H_5OH}
\begin{array}{l}
CH_3CHCH(CO_2C_2H_5)_2 \\
\quad | \\
CH_3CHCO_2C_2H_5 \\
\quad \text{XXIX}
\end{array}
$$

A variation of the Holden-Lapworth mechanism proposed later[54] is based on the assumption that the intermediary product is not a cyclobutanone derivative but the anion of a hemiacetal. This yields, for the reaction of ethyl crotonate with diethyl methylmalonate, the following reaction sequence.

$$
\begin{array}{l}
\qquad\quad CO_2R \\
\qquad\qquad | \\
CH_3CH\text{—}CH_2 \\
\quad | \\
CH_3C\text{——}C\text{=}O \\
\quad | \qquad\quad | \\
CO_2R \; OR
\end{array}
\xrightarrow{-H^+}
\begin{array}{l}
\qquad\quad CO_2R \\
\qquad\qquad | \\
CH_3CH\text{—}CH \\
\quad | \qquad\quad \downarrow \\
CH_3C\text{——}C\text{—}O^{\ominus} \\
\quad | \qquad\quad | \\
CO_2R \; OR
\end{array}
\rightarrow
$$

$$
\begin{array}{l}
\qquad\quad CO_2R \\
\qquad\qquad | \\
CH_3CH\text{—}CH \\
\quad | \qquad\quad | \\
CH_3C^{\ominus} \quad C\text{=}O \\
\quad | \qquad\quad | \\
CO_2R \; OR
\end{array}
\xrightarrow{+H^+}
\begin{array}{l}
\qquad\quad CO_2R \\
\qquad\qquad | \\
CH_3CH\text{—}CH \\
\quad | \qquad\quad | \\
CH_3CH \quad C\text{=}O \\
\quad | \qquad\quad | \\
CO_2R \; OR
\end{array}
$$

It was emphasized that the C—C linkage connecting the hemiacetal carbon with the $CHCO_2R$ group is "highly polarized" (symbolized $\downarrow$), but the significance of this statement is not clear. An analogous mechanism was suggested for the abnormal Michael reaction between diethyl methylmalonate and ethyl tetrolate.

A possible means of distinguishing between the mechanisms of Thorpe and of Holden and Lapworth should be to use an acyl group in the acceptor in place of the carbalkoxy group, i.e., to use an unsaturated ketone rather than an ester. However, an attempt to make the distinction in this way was confounded by instability of the condensation

[52] Ingold, *J. Chem. Soc.*, **119**, 305 (1921).

[53] Ingold, *J. Chem. Soc.*, **119**, 951 (1921).

[54] Henecka, *Fortschr. chem. Forsch.*, **1**, 685 (1950).

product. Benzylideneacetophenone and diethyl methylmalonate should give XXXII according to Thorpe, and XXXIII according to Holden and Lapworth. In fact, neither of the two compounds was obtained, but instead a mixture of retrogression products, ethyl α-methylcinnamate and ethyl benzoylacetate. These appear to be compatible only with

$$C_6H_5CH{=}CHCOC_6H_5 + CH_3CH(CO_2C_2H_5)_2 \nearrow \underset{\text{XXXII}}{\begin{array}{l} C_6H_5CHCH(CH_3)COC_6H_5 \\ \quad | \\ \quad CH(CO_2C_2H_5)_2 \end{array}} \rightarrow C_6H_5CH{=}C(CO_2C_2H_5)_2 + CH_3CH_2COC_6H_5$$

$$C_6H_5CH{=}CHCOC_6H_5 + CH_3CH(CO_2C_2H_5)_2 \searrow \underset{\text{XXXIII}}{\begin{array}{l} C_6H_5CHCH(CO_2C_2H_5)COC_6H_5 \\ \quad | \\ CH_3CHCO_2C_2H_5 \end{array}} \rightarrow C_6H_5CH{=}C(CH_3)CO_2C_2H_5 + C_6H_5COCH_2CO_2C_2H_5$$

formula XXXIII, as indicated in the reaction scheme, because if XXXII were formed it would decompose into diethyl benzylidenemalonate and propiophenone.*

Additional evidence on mechanism was sought, with only limited success, by investigations of the condensation of diethyl benzylmalonate with diethyl fumarate,[56,57] of diethyl benzylmalonate with *trans*-dibenzoylethylene and α-chlorodibenzoylethylene,[58] of diethyl methylmalonate with ethyl cyclohexene-1-carboxylate and ethyl α-ethylcrotonate,[59] and of diethyl ethylmalonate with ethyl tiglate.[60] Though no direct proof was obtained, this work tended to support the Holden-Lapworth view.[59,61]

* An effort by Michael and Ross[55] to invalidate this conclusion, on the basis that the observed retrogression products could be derived from an adduct of two molecules of benzylideneacetophenone and one molecule of diethyl methylmalonate (see p. 308), foundered on their inability to prepare such a product from diethyl *methyl*malonate, in spite of its ready preparation from diethyl malonate.

[55] Michael and Ross, *J. Am. Chem. Soc.*, **55**, 1632 (1933).

[56] Duff and Ingold, *J. Chem. Soc.*, **1934**, 87.

[57] Rydon, *J. Chem. Soc.*, **1935**, 420.

[58] Gardner and Rydon, *J. Chem. Soc.*, **1938**, 45.

[59] Gardner and Rydon, *J. Chem. Soc.*, **1938**, 48.

[60] Gardner and Rydon, *J. Chem. Soc.*, **1938**, 42.

[61] Cf. Ingold and Rydon, *J. Chem. Soc.*, **1935**, 857.

Attention has recently been called[62] to the fact that higher yields of "abnormal" Michael products are often obtained from the usual starting materials than by subjecting the "normal" product (synthesized independently) to Michael reaction conditions. This appears to mean that the "normal" product is not necessarily an intermediate in the "abnormal" reaction. Consideration of the experimental results obtained in the condensation of ethyl crotonate and diethyl methylmalonate led to the following suggested pathway of reaction:[63] The full equivalent of base required for the abnormal reaction permits the assumption of initial bond formation between the reactants by a kind of Claisen condensation involving an anion (XXXIV) formed from the base and the acceptor.

$$C_2H_5O^{\ominus} + CH_3CH{=}CHCO_2C_2H_5 \rightleftarrows CH_3CH(OC_2H_5)\overset{\ominus}{C}HCO_2C_2H_5 \quad \text{(XXXIV)}$$

$$\text{XXXIV} + CH_3CH(CO_2C_2H_5)_2 \rightleftarrows CH_3CH(OC_2H_5)CH(CO_2C_2H_5){-}C(OC_2H_5)(O^{\ominus})CH(CH_3)CO_2C_2H_5 \xrightarrow{-C_2H_5O^{\ominus}}$$

$$CH_3CH(OC_2H_5)CH(CO_2C_2H_5)COCH(CH_3)CO_2C_2H_5 \quad \text{(XXXV)}$$

Base-catalyzed loss of ethanol from intermediate XXXV would give the ester XXXVI. This ester may undergo an intramolecular Michael reaction with formation of the cyclobutanone intermediate XXXI postulated by Holden and Lapworth. Alternatively, it was suggested[63] that the cyclic intermediate may not have significant independent existence, but that the ester XXXVI can change directly to the observed abnormal product XXXVII by concerted alcoholysis and addition (see equations on p. 197).

A recent kinetic study[64] of the abnormal reaction between diethyl fumarate and diethyl ethylmalonate showed that the donor anion and diethyl fumarate combine rapidly to form the anion of the normal product

[62] P. R. Shafer, Ph. D. Thesis, University of Wisconsin, 1951.

[63] Shafer, Loeb, and Johnson, *J. Am. Chem. Soc.*, **75**, 5963 (1953).

[64] Tsuruta, Yasuhara, and Furukawa, *J. Org. Chem.*, **18**, 1246 (1953).

(distinguished from the abnormal product by specific gravity measurements). Isomerization of this anion to that of the abnormal product was observed to follow as a slow step. It was also observed that excess free diethyl ethylmalonate suppressed the abnormal reaction even when sodium ethoxide equivalent to the diethyl fumarate was present. This led to the deduction that the first-formed anion can be stabilized by the abstraction of hydrogen ion from free diethyl ethylmalonate in a fast reaction competitive with the isomerization.

$$\text{XXXV} \xrightarrow{-C_2H_5OH} CH_3CH{=}C(CO_2C_2H_5)CO \vdots CH(CH_3)CO_2C_2H_5 \longrightarrow$$

XXXVI

$$\begin{array}{l} CH_3CHCH(CO_2C_2H_5)_2 \\ \quad | \\ CH_3CHCO_2C_2H_5 \\ \quad | \\ \quad CH_3 \end{array}$$

XXXVII

Definitive evidence that the "abnormal" reaction involves migration of a carboxyl group (in some form or other) has at last been obtained by isotopic tracer experiments. When ethyl crotonate containing C^{14} in the carbethoxyl group was condensed with diethyl methylmalonate, the product was found to result from migration of the labeled carbon atom.[65] Enrichment of carbethoxyl groups with O^{18} in ethyl crotonate, ethyl cinnamate, and diethyl methylmalonate provided further evidence that the condensation of either of the first two with the last (using one equivalent of base as catalyst to favor "abnormal" reaction) proceeds by carbethoxyl migration.[66–68]

With this evidence in hand, it can be firmly concluded that the Holden-Lapworth mechanism is basically correct, though the modifications suggested by Johnson[63] provide the most plausible view of the detailed reaction course.

The Question of Para-Bridged Intermediates

The condensation of 3-methyl-2-cyclohexenone (XXXVIII) and diethyl malonate presents features that have been rationalized[69,70] in a fashion

[65] Simamura, Inamoto, and Suehiro, *Bull. Chem. Soc. Japan*, **27**, 221 (1954) [*C.A.*, **49**, 7494 (1955)].
[66] Swan, *J. Chem. Soc.*, **1955**, 1039.
[67] Samuel and Ginsburg, *J. Chem. Soc.*, **1955**, 1288.
[68] Cf. Baker and Rothstein, *Chemistry & Industry*, **1955**, 776.
[69] Farmer and Ross, *J. Chem. Soc.*, **127**, 2358 (1925).
[70] Farmer and Ross, *J. Chem. Soc.*, **1926**, 3233.

consistent with and tending to support the Holden-Lapworth cyclobutanone intermediate. Carried out at room temperature and with one equivalent of sodium ethoxide, the reaction leads to only one identified product, the diethyl ester XXXIX. At the temperature of boiling ethanol, this compound is accompanied by a product of ethanolysis, the open-chain triethyl ester XL.

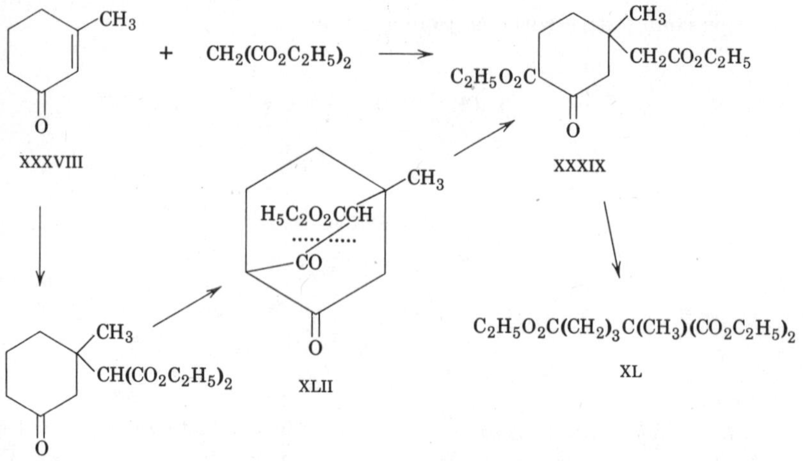

CH_3 + $CH_2(CO_2C_2H_5)_2$ ⟶ CH_3, $CH_2CO_2C_2H_5$, $C_2H_5O_2C$

XXXVIII XXXIX

CH_3, $H_5C_2O_2CCH$, CO

CH_3, $CH(CO_2C_2H_5)_2$ XLII $C_2H_5O_2C(CH_2)_3C(CH_3)(CO_2C_2H_5)_2$

XLI XL

In this condensation, the "abnormal" position in which the carbethoxy portion of the donor molecule appears is para rather than ortho on the alicyclic ring. By way of explanation, it has been postulated that the primary product would be XLI, from the normal condensation; this was believed to be converted by a Dieckmann reaction into the bicyclic diketone XLII. Ethanolysis of the diketone in the manner indicated by the broken line was believed to lead to XXXIX.

This mechanism was advanced as a parallel to the Holden-Lapworth formulation, but with a cyclohexanone rather than a cyclobutanone intermediate because formation of a para bridge where possible (as in this instance) is more favorable than the alternative XLIII.

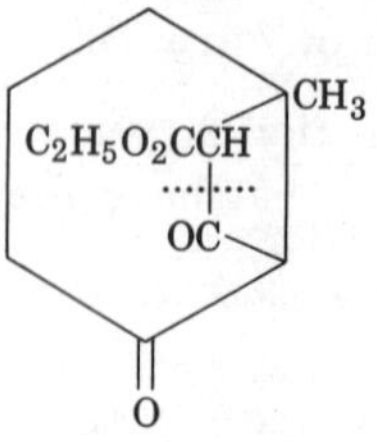

CH_3, $C_2H_5O_2CCH$, OC

XLIII

However, the suggestion has recently been made[63] that a para-bridged intermediate may not be formed in such instances. Instead the expected product of the abnormal Michael reaction, XLIV, may be first produced, and this may undergo ethanolysis (reverse Dieckmann) to give the *open-chain* triester XLV, which then cyclizes (in a known reaction) to XXXIX.

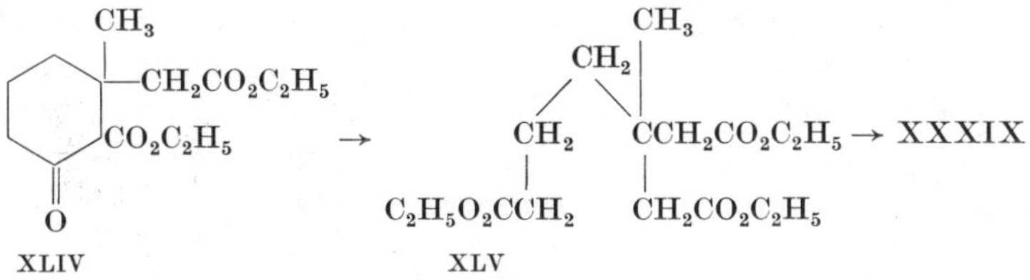

CH_3 $CH_2CO_2C_2H_5$ $CO_2C_2H_5$ O → CH_3 CH_2 CH_2 $CCH_2CO_2C_2H_5$ → XXXIX $C_2H_5O_2CCH_2$ $CH_2CO_2C_2H_5$

XLIV XLV

In any case, it has been shown that the normal adduct XLI is not the precursor of XXXIX, since the latter is produced in higher yield from 3-methyl-2-cyclohexenone and diethyl malonate than from XLI.[63] It is suggested,[63] as in the case mentioned above, that the first step is an ester condensation, either at position 6 (which would involve subsequent para bridging) or more probably at position 2 via the anion XLVI.

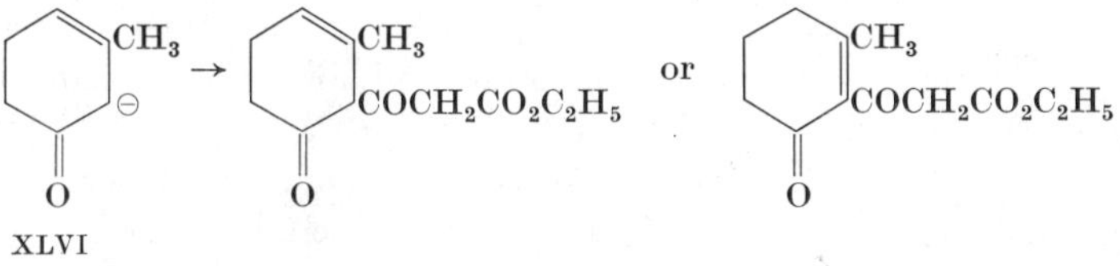

CH_3 ⊖ O → CH_3 $COCH_2CO_2C_2H_5$ O or CH_3 $COCH_2CO_2C_2H_5$ O

XLVI

This explanation is based on a parallel with the mechanism for the reaction of 3-methyl-2-cyclohexenone with ethyl cyanoacetate, which was outlined on the basis of detailed evidence as involving the following succession of intermediates:

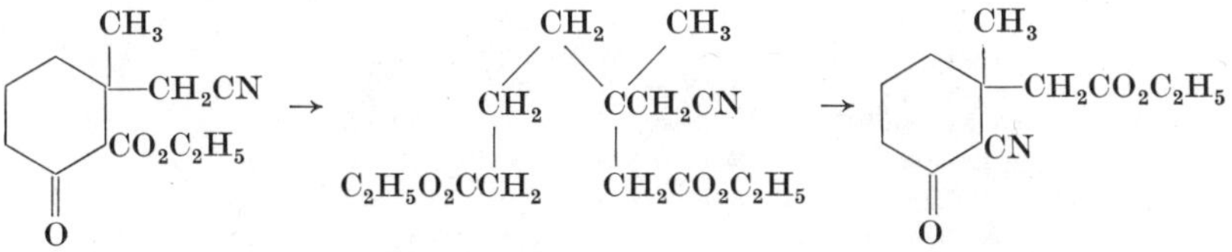

CH_3 CH_2CN $CO_2C_2H_5$ O → CH_2 CH_3 CH_2 CCH_2CN $C_2H_5O_2CCH_2$ $CH_2CO_2C_2H_5$ → CH_3 $CH_2CO_2C_2H_5$ CN O

Stereochemistry of the Michael Condensation

Little is known about the steric course of the Michael condensation, although the formation of asymmetric carbon atoms in open-chain products and the possibility of *cis-trans* isomerism in alicyclic adducts raise a number of stereochemical problems. The formation of diastereomeric adducts has often been noted, e.g., with the following reactants: benzylideneacetone and dimethyl malonate;[71] benzylideneacetophenone and benzyl cyanide,[72] diethyl succinate,[73] and *p*-tolyl benzyl sulfone;[74] α-benzylidenepropiophenone and dimethyl malonate;[75,76] ethyl cinnamate and diethyl methylmalonate;[50,77] ethyl β-isopropylacrylate and ethyl cyanoacetate;[78] ethyl cinnamate and ethyl cyanoacetate;[79,80] ethyl phenylacetate,[81,82] or benzyl cyanide;[27,83,84] cinnamonitrile and *m*-aminobenzyl cyanide;[27] 2-nitro-2-butene and benzyl cyanide,[85] 2-nitro-1-phenyl-1-propene and diethyl malonate;[86] α-nitrostilbene and diethyl malonate;[86] and 3-cyano-1,2,5,6-tetrahydropyridine and diethyl malonate.[87]

In the condensation of ethylideneacetone with 7-chloro-4,6-dimethoxycoumaran-3-one, two possible isomers are formed simultaneously;[88] a similar result was obtained in the condensation with the chlorine-free analog. The reaction between 4-methylcyclohexanone and methyl isopropenyl ketone also leads to two stereoisomeric forms of 3,6-dimethyl-9-hydroxy-2-decalone.[89]

The reaction pairs benzylideneacetophenone-benzyl cyanide[72] and α-benzylidenepropiophenone-dimethyl malonate[75,76] represent two different ways in which asymmetric carbon atoms can be formed as a result of a Michael condensation. In the adduct XLVII the α- and β-carbon atoms of the acceptor become asymmetric; in the adduct XLVIII the β-carbon atom of the acceptor and the carbon atom of the donor molecule that is linked to the acceptor become the centers of asymmetry. In view of the undoubted ability of the alkaline condensing agent to invert configuration around carbon atoms substituted as in —$CH(CH_3)COC_6H_5$

[71] Qudrat-I-Khuda, *J. Indian Chem. Soc.*, **8,** 215 (1931) [*C.A.*, **26,** 123 (1932)].

[72] Kohler and Allen, *J. Am. Chem. Soc.*, **46,** 1522 (1924).

[73] Stobbe, *Ann.*, **314,** 111 (1901).

[74] Connor, Fleming, and Clayton, *J. Am. Chem. Soc.*, **58,** 1386 (1936).

[75] Kohler, *Am. Chem. J.*, **46,** 474 (1911).

[76] Kohler and Davis, *J. Am. Chem. Soc.*, **41,** 992 (1919).

[77] Michael and Ross, *J. Am. Chem. Soc.*, **53,** 1150 (1931).

[78] Howles, Thorpe, and Udall, *J. Chem. Soc.*, **77,** 942 (1900).

[79] Carter and Lawrence, *Proc. Chem. Soc.*, **16,** 178 (1900).

[80] Avery and McGrew, *J. Am. Chem. Soc.*, **57,** 208 (1935).

[81] Badger, Campbell, and Cook, *J. Chem. Soc.*, **1949,** 1084.

[82] Borsche, *Ber.*, **42,** 4496 (1909).

[83] Avery, *J. Am. Chem. Soc.*, **50,** 2512 (1928).

[84] Avery and McDole, *J. Am. Chem. Soc.*, **30,** 1423 (1908).

[85] Buckley, Hunt, and Lowe, *J. Chem. Soc.*, **1947,** 1504.

[86] Boberg and Schultze, *Chem. Ber.*, **88,** 74 (1955).

[87] Wohl and Losanitsch, *Ber.*, **40,** 4698 (1907).

[88] MacMillan, Mulholland, Dawkins, and Ward, *J. Chem. Soc.*, **1954,** 429.

[89] Colonge, Dreux, and Kehlstadt, *Compt. rend.*, **238,** 693 (1954).

and —$CH(CN)C_6H_5$, the product isolated must be an equilibrium mixture of all possible forms. The isolation of diastereomerides from product mixtures is then evidence that the forms involved are approximately equal energetically.

$$C_6H_5CH{=}C(CH_3)COC_6H_5 + CH_2(CO_2CH_3)_2 \rightarrow C_6H_5CH(CH(CO_2CH_3)_2)CH(CH_3)COC_6H_5$$

XLVII

$$C_6H_5CH{=}CHCOC_6H_5 + C_6H_5CH_2CN \rightarrow C_6H_5CH(C_6H_5CHCN)CH_2COC_6H_5$$

XLVIII

Both *cis* and *trans* forms arise in the condensation of 1-nitrocyclohexene with *p*-bromobenzyl cyanide to XLIX,[85] whereas only one isomer (L) is formed from *cis*-2-hydrindylideneacetonitrile and cyanoacetamide.[90]

H NO2 H CH(CN)C6H4Br-*p*

XLIX

H O NH O H CN

L

One unsaturated Michael adduct LI appears in *cis* and *trans* isomeric forms; this is the product of the reaction between acetylacetone and 2 moles of 1-cyanobutadiene.[91]

$$(CH_3CO)_2C(CH_2CH{=}CHCH_2CN)_2$$

LI

When only one adduct is formed, the determination of its configuration is usually difficult due to the lack of reference compounds of established configuration. However, it has been proved that the dicyclic compounds formed from acyl- or carbalkoxy-cyclohexenes frequently, if not generally, have the *trans* configuration. This applies to the following cases: ethyl cyclopentenecarboxylate with ethyl cyanoacetate or diethyl malonate

[90] Kandiah, *J. Chem. Soc.*, **1931,** 922.

[91] Charlish, Davies, and Rose, *J. Chem. Soc.*, **1948,** 232.

(*trans* only);[92] acetylcyclohexene and ethyl acetoacetate (*trans* only);[93] acetylcyclohexene and diethyl malonate (*cis* and *trans*);[94–96] 2-methyl-1-butyrylcyclohexene and diethyl malonate (*trans* only);[96] 2,6-dimethylbutyrylcyclohexene and diethyl malonate (*trans* only);[96] vinyl cyclohexenyl ketone and diethyl malonate (*trans* only);[100] 4-methoxy- and 3,4-methylenedioxy-benzalacetophenone and 3-methylcyclohexanone (*cis* and *trans*);[100a] methyl isopropenyl ketone and 3- and 4-methylcyclohexanone (*cis* and *trans*);[101] and (+)-dihydrocarvone and 1-diethylamino-3-pentanone methiodide (*cis* and *trans*).[102]

Isomers have also been formed in the self-condensation of 1-acetyl-1-cyclohexene[97,98] and in the condensation of 1-acetyl-1-cyclohexene with 1-tetralone.[99]

In the total synthesis of santonin,[103] use was made of the fact that the Michael condensation of diethyl methylmalonate and 1,10-dimethyl-2-oxo-2,3,4,5,6,10-hexahydronaphthalene introduces the side chain so that

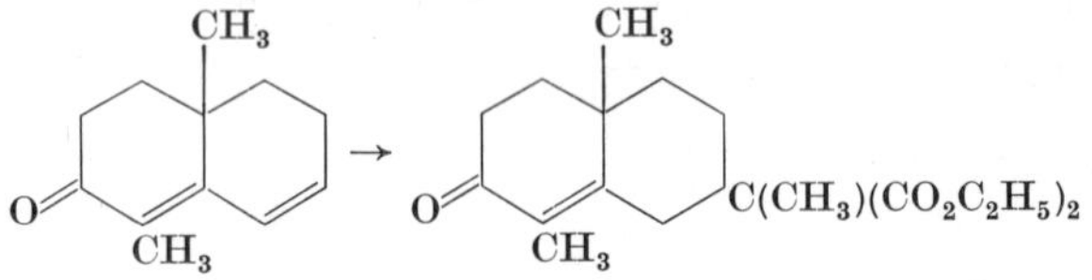

CH_3 CH_3
O CH_3 → O CH_3 $C(CH_3)(CO_2C_2H_5)_2$

it is *cis* to the methyl group at C_{10}.[104] An analogous observation has been made for 3,5-cholestadien-7-one.

Cis addition is observed in the addition of diethyl malonate, diethyl methylmalonate, and ethyl acetoacetate to methyl bicyclo[2.2.1]hepta-2,5-diene-2-carboxylate[104a] and in the addition of diethyl malonate to ethyl 1-cyclohexene-1-carboxylate.[104b]

[92] Cook and Linstead, *J. Chem. Soc.*, **1934,** 956.
[93] Barrett, Cook, and Linstead, *J. Chem. Soc.*, **1935,** 1065.
[94] Chuang and Tien, *Ber.*, **69,** 25 (1936).
[95] Kon and Qudrat-I-Khuda, *J. Chem. Soc.*, **1926,** 3071.
[96] Ruzicka, Koolhaas, and Wind, *Helv. Chim. Acta*, **14,** 1151 (1931).
[97] Jones and Koch, *J. Chem. Soc.*, **1942,** 393.
[98] Rapson and Robinson, *J. Chem. Soc.*, **1935,** 1285; Hawthorne and Robinson, *ibid.* **1936,** 763.
[99] Peak and Robinson, *J. Chem. Soc.*, **1936,** 759.
[100] Downes, Gill, and Lions, *J. Am. Chem. Soc.*, **72,** 3464 (1950); *Australian J. Sci.*, **10,** 147 (1948).
[100a] Kohler, Graustein, and Merrill, *J. Am. Chem. Soc.*, **44,** 2536 (1922).
[101] Colonge, Dreux, and Kehlstadt, *Bull. soc. chim. France*, **1954,** 1404.
[102] Howe and McQuillin, *J. Chem. Soc.*, **1955,** 2423.
[103] Abe, Harukawa, Ishikawa, Miki, and Sami, *Proc. Japan Acad.*, **30,** 116, 119 (1954) [*C.A.*, **49,** 14715 (1955)].
[104] Corey, *J. Am. Chem. Soc.*, **77,** 1044 (1955).
[104a] Alder and Wirtz, *Ann.*, **601,** 138 (1956).
[104b] Helfer, *Helv. Chim. Acta*, **9,** 814 (1926). Other interesting observations of this type are reported by Johnson, *Chem. & Ind.* (*London*), **1956,** 167, and by Wettstein, Heusler, Ueberwasser, and Wieland, *Helv. Chim. Acta*, **40,** 323 (1957).

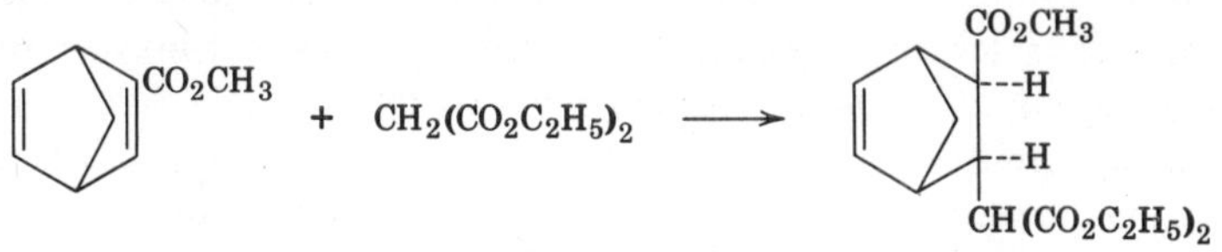

CO_2CH_3 + $CH_2(CO_2C_2H_5)_2$ ⟶ CO_2CH_3, --H, --H, $CH(CO_2C_2H_5)_2$

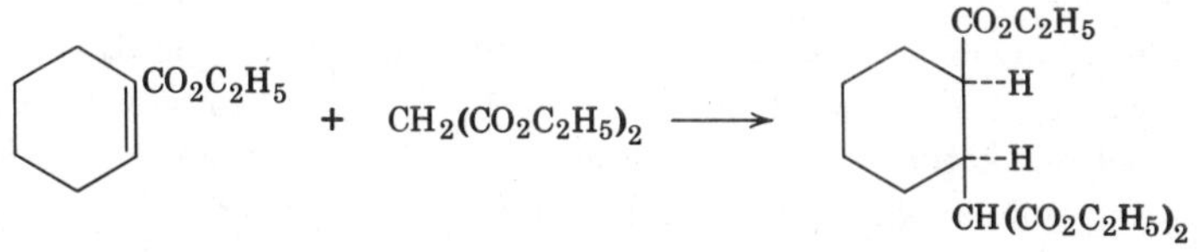

$CO_2C_2H_5$ + $CH_2(CO_2C_2H_5)_2$ ⟶ $CO_2C_2H_5$, --H, --H, $CH(CO_2C_2H_5)_2$

A tendency for *trans* addition is evident in the Michael condensation of 2-aryl-2-cyclohexen-1-ones. Here it has been shown with diethyl malonate that a *trans* compound is obtained, for the product could be related to the known *trans*-2-phenylcyclohexylacetic acid (LII).[105,106]

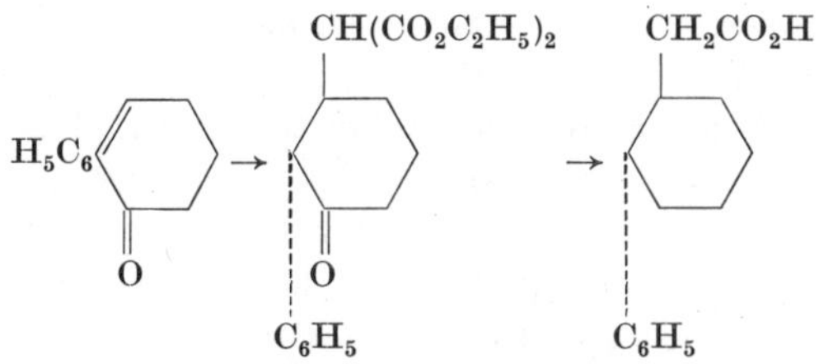

H_5C_6, O → $CH(CO_2C_2H_5)_2$, O, C_6H_5 → CH_2CO_2H, C_6H_5

LII

It has further been demonstrated that the addition of dibenzyl malonate to 4-phenyl- or 5-phenyl-2-cyclohexenone[107] and of methyl nitroacetate to 2-phenyl-2-cyclohexenone takes the same steric course.[108]

SCOPE AND LIMITATIONS

Donors

All of the donor molecules appearing in Tables I–XXI are collected in Table XXII. In the almost complete absence of kinetic studies of the Michael condensation, an exact comparison of the compounds acting as donors in the condensation is impossible. However, in some cases in which the donor contains two active hydrogen atoms, the efficacy of the

105 Bachmann and Fornefeld, *J. Am. Chem. Soc.*, **72**, 5529 (1950).

106 Ginsburg and Pappo, *J. Chem. Soc.*, **1951**, 938.

107 Bergmann and Szmuszkovicz, *J. Am. Chem. Soc.*, **75**, 3226 (1953).

108 Ginsburg and Pappo, *J. Chem. Soc.*, **1953**, 1524.

activating groups can be compared directly. For example, two carbethoxy groups activate hydrogen more than one carbethoxy[109] or one aldehyde group,[110] but one carbonyl group is more effective than one carbethoxy group.[111] The groups $CH(CH_3)$ and $CH(C_6H_5)$ have greater activating power than a methylene group,[112–115] and a nitro group is a more powerful activator than a carbethoxy[116] or an alkylsulfonyl group.[117] It also appears to be generally true that unsaturated ketones are more reactive than nitriles and nitriles more than esters, and that α,β-unsaturated sulfones are least reactive.[118–122] The behavior of methyl β-cyanoethyl ketone in Michael additions[123] confirmed the stronger activating influence of a carbonyl group as opposed to a nitrile group. Recent work[124] has shown that the phosphonate group $—PO(OR)_2$ also activates hydrogen atoms on the adjoining carbon atom. Like the nitro and sulfoxide functions, it also activates neighboring double bonds to act as acceptors (see Table XXI).

Though one would expect the reactivity of a donor to be related to the degree of enolization in the reaction environment, no simple relationship was found between reactivity and the tendency of the donor to enolize in the pure state.[125] Likewise, the reactivity of a methylene or methine group toward a Grignard reagent (Zerewitinoff test) does not appear to parallel its activity as a donor in the Michael reaction.[126]

Generally speaking, one would expect that the degree to which the Michael reaction takes place, as well as its rate, should be importantly influenced by the acidity of the donor and the polarity of the carbon-carbon double bond in the acceptor. As to the former, the acidity of the hydrogen atom in the group $R\overset{/}{\underset{\backslash}{C}}H$ decreases in the following sequence:

[109] Friedmann, *J. prakt. Chem.*, [2], **146,** 79 (1936).
[110] Moe, Warner, and Buckley, *J. Am. Chem. Soc.*, **73,** 1062 (1951).
[111] Hill, *Am. Chem. J.*, **24,** 1 (1900).
[112] Bachmann and Wick, *J. Am. Chem. Soc.*, **72,** 3388 (1950).
[113] Boekelheide, *J. Am. Chem. Soc.*, **69,** 790 (1947).
[114] Frank and Pierle, *J. Am. Chem. Soc.*, **73,** 724 (1951).
[115] Wilds, Ralls, Wildman, and McCaleb, *J. Am. Chem. Soc.*, **72,** 5794 (1950).
[116] Leonard, Felley, and Nicolaides, *J. Am. Chem. Soc.*, **74,** 1700 (1952).
[117] Buckley, Elliott, Hunt, and Lowe, *J. Chem. Soc.*, **1947,** 1505.
[118] Truce and Wellisch, *J. Am. Chem. Soc.*, **74,** 2881 (1952).
[119] Henecka, *Chem. Ber.*, **81,** 197 (1948).
[120] Henecka, *Chem. Ber.*, **82,** 41 (1949).
[121] Henecka, *Chem. Ber.*, **82,** 104 (1949).
[122] Henecka, *Chem. Ber.*, **82,** 112 (1949).
[123] Chem. Werke Huels, Ger. pat. 811,231 [*C.A.*, **47,** 11234 (1953)].
[124] Pudovik and Lebedeva, *Zhur. Obshchei Khim.*, **22,** 2128 (1952) [*C.A.*, **48,** 564 1954)].
[125] Connor and Andrews, *J. Am. Chem. Soc.*, **56,** 2713 (1934).
[126] McAlpine and Ongley, *Anal. Chem.*, **27,** 55 (1955).

R = $NO_2 > SO_3R > CN > CO_2R > CHO > COR$.[127] As to the latter, the electromeric effects of the activating groups which produce polarity in the double bond diminish in the sequence $CHO > COR > CN > CO_2R > NO_2$. Through possession of appropriate combinations of these groups, certain substances, e.g., β-diketones, β-keto esters or ethyl β-aminocrotonate, can act either as donors or acceptors.

Donors	Acceptors
$CH_3CO\underline{CH_2}COCH_3$	$\begin{array}{l} CH_3C{=}CHCOCH_3 \\ \quad\ \vert \\ \quad OH \end{array}$
$CH_3CO\underline{CH_2}CO_2C_2H_5$	$\begin{array}{l} CH_3C{=}CHCO_2C_2H_5 \\ \quad\ \vert \\ \quad OH \end{array}$
$\begin{array}{l} CH_3C\underline{CH_2}CO_2C_2H_5 \\ \quad\ \Vert \\ \quad NH \end{array}$	$\begin{array}{l} CH_3C{=}CHCO_2C_2H_5 \\ \quad\ \vert \\ \quad NH_2 \end{array}$

Reactions with Cyclopropane Derivatives

A few cyclopropane derivatives have been observed to participate in the Michael condensation. In the reaction of ethyl 1-cyanocyclopropane-1-carboxylate (LIII) with both ethyl cyanoacetate[128] and diethyl malonate,[129] ring scission occurs.[129–133] The intermediates LIV and LV cyclize to the corresponding cyclopentanoneimide derivatives LVI and LVII; subsequent elimination of the cyano and the second carbethoxy group, respectively, leads to diethyl cyclopentanone-2,5-dicarboxylate (LVIII). In the analogous reaction between diethyl malonate and diethyl cyclopropane-1,1-dicarboxylate, the same cyclopentanone derivative, LVIII, formed via tetraethyl butane-1,1,4,4-tetracarboxylate can be isolated.[130,134] The similarity between a double bond and the cyclopropane ring illustrated by this reaction is supported by other

[127] Arndt, Scholz, and Frobel, *Ann.*, **521,** 111 (1936).
[128] Thorpe, *J. Chem. Soc.*, **95,** 1901 (1909).
[129] Mitchell and Thorpe, *J. Chem. Soc.*, **97,** 997 (1910).
[130] Bone and Perkin, Jr., *J. Chem. Soc.*, **67,** 108 (1895).
[131] Cf. Fittig and Roeder, *Ann.*, **227,** 13 (1885).
[132] Cf. Best and Thorpe, *J. Chem. Soc.*, **95,** 697, 699 (1909).
[133] Radulescu, *Ber.*, **44,** 1018 (1911).
[134] Kierstead, Linstead, and Weedon, *J. Chem. Soc.*, **1952,** 3616.

evidence,[135–144] particularly by the recent experiments showing that the enolate of diethyl malonate undergoes a Michael reaction with diethyl 2-vinylcyclopropane-1,1-dicarboxylate (LIX);[134] this partly follows the

CN

$CO_2C_2H_5$

LIII

$CH(CN)CO_2C_2H_5$

CH_2

$CH_2CH(CN)CO_2C_2H_5$

LIV

$CH(CO_2C_2H_5)_2$

CH_2

$CH_2CH(CN)CO_2C_2H_5$

LV

NC

$C_2H_5O_2C$

$CO_2C_2H_5$

H

NH

LVI

$C_2H_5O_2C$

$C_2H_5O_2C$

$CO_2C_2H_5$

H

NH

LVII

$C_2H_5O_2C$

$CO_2C_2H_5$

O

LVIII

$CH_2{=}CH$

$CO_2C_2H_5$

LIX

$CO_2C_2H_5$ →

$CO_2C_2H_5$

$CH_2{=}CH$

=O

$CO_2C_2H_5$

↘

$(C_2H_5O_2C)_2CHCH_2CH{=}CHCH_2CH(CO_2C_2H_5)_2$

[135] Cf. Klotz, *J. Am. Chem. Soc.*, **66,** 88 (1944); Roberts and Green, *ibid.*, **68,** 214 (1946); Rogers, *ibid.*, **69,** 2544 (1947); cf. ref. 137.

[136] Kierstead, Linstead, and Weedon, *J. Chem. Soc.*, **1952,** 3610.

[137] Mariella, Peterson, and Ferris, *J. Am. Chem. Soc.*, **70,** 1494 (1948).

[138] Smith and Rogier, *J. Am. Chem. Soc.*, **73,** 3831 (1951).

[139] Smith and Rogier, *J. Am. Chem. Soc.*, **73,** 3840 (1951).

[140] Mariella and Raube, *J. Org. Chem.*, **18,** 282 (1953).

[141] Greenfield, Friedel, and Orchin, *J. Am. Chem. Soc.*, **76,** 1258 (1954).

[142] Perold, *J. S. African Chem. Inst.*, **6,** 22 (1953) [*C.A.*, **48,** 4314 (1954)].

[143] Eastman, *J. Am. Chem. Soc.*, **76,** 4115 (1954).

[144] Eastman and Selover, *J. Am. Chem. Soc.*, **76,** 4118 (1954).

above scheme, but partly takes place at the ends of the "conjugated" system. Both reactions occur also in $\alpha,\beta,\gamma,\delta$ doubly unsaturated carboxylic acid derivatives (see p. 237).

A similar study has been made[145] of the reaction of ethyl cyanoacetate with ethyl 1-cyano-2-vinylcyclopropane-1-carboxylate, synthesized *in situ* from *trans*-1,4-dibromo-2-butene and ethyl cyanoacetate. The product, obtained in 30% yield, was a mixture of the two cyclopentane derivatives LX and LXI.

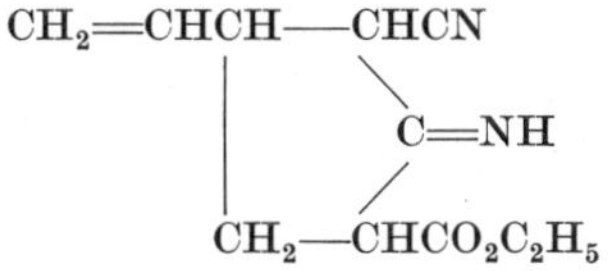

```
CH2=CHCH——CHCN                      CH2——CHCN
     |        \                       |       \
     |        C=NH                    |       C=NH
     |        /                       |       /
    CH2——CHCO2C2H5          CH2=CHCH——CHCO2C2H5
      LX                             LXI
```

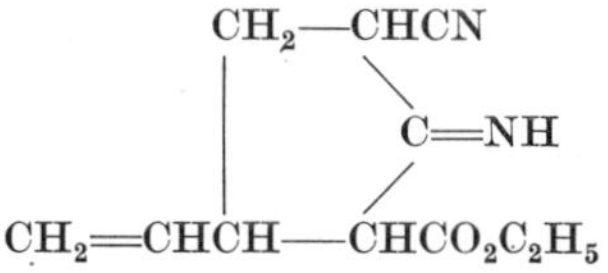

The System C=C—C=N

The system C=C—C=N behaves like the system C=C—C=O in the Michael reaction. The most extensive studies, on the addition of reactive methylene compounds to quinone imides, have been summarized:[145a] selected examples are given in Table IX.

2-Vinylpyridine and 4-vinylpyridine are suitable acceptors for the Michael reaction (Table XXI). Analogously, phenanthridine-9-carboxaldehyde reacts with 9-methylphenanthridine (LXII) to give 1,2,3-tri-(9-phenanthridyl)propane (LXIII),[146] undoubtedly as shown on page 208. The formation of diethyl 4-methyl-5-acetylpyridine-2,6-dicarboxylate (LXVIII) from ethyl acetylpyruvate (LXIV) and ammonia[147] appears to result from reaction of part of the ester with ammonia to give the imine of its enolic form and a subsequent Michael condensation between the latter and the keto form of the original ester or its imine.

In this connection, it should be mentioned that Schiff bases of the benzylideneaniline type (but not ketone anils) add, for example, ethyl acetoacetate,[148–150] ethyl oxaloacetate,[148,151] diethyl malonate,[152] ethyl

[145] Kierstead, Linstead, and Weedon, *J. Chem. Soc.*, **1953,** 1799.
[145a] Adams and Reifschneider, *Bull. soc. chim. France*, **1958,** 23.
[146] Caldwell, *J. Chem. Soc.*, **1952,** 2035.
[147] Mumm and Bergell, *Ber.*, **45,** 3040 (1912).
[148] Schiff and Bertini, *Ber.*, **30,** 601 (1897).
[149] Schiff, *Ber.*, **31,** 205 (1898).
[150] Schiff, *Ber.*, **31,** 601 (1898).
[151] Philpott and Jones, *J. Chem. Soc.*, **1938,** 337.
[152] Betti, *Gazz. chim. ital.*, **30,** II, 301 (1900).

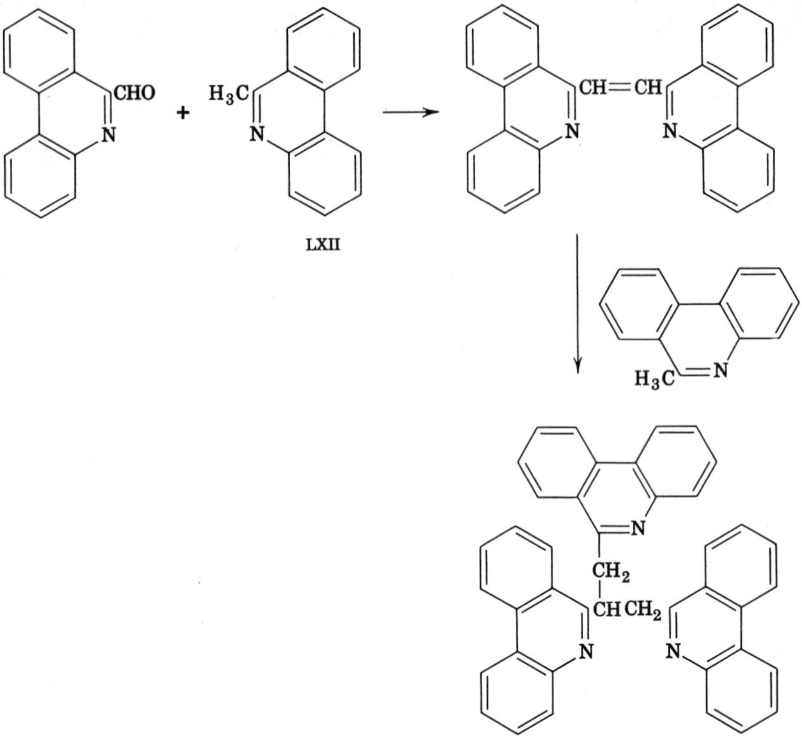

CHO + H_3C N → CH=CH N N

LXII

H_3C N

N CH_2 CH CH_2 N N

LXIII

$$CH_3COCH_2COCO_2C_2H_5 + NH_3 \rightarrow$$

LXIV

$$\underset{\text{LXV}}{CH_3COCH_2\underset{\underset{NH}{\|}}{C}CO_2C_2H_5} \rightleftarrows \underset{\text{LXVI}}{CH_3\underset{\underset{OH}{|}}{C}{=}CH\underset{\underset{NH}{\|}}{C}CO_2C_2H_5}$$

CH_3 OH C CH $C_2H_5O_2CC$ NH + CH_2COCH_3 $COCO_2C_2H_5$ → CH_3 OH C CH_2 $CHCOCH_3$ $C_2H_5O_2CC$ NH $COCO_2C_2H_5$ →

LXVII

CH_3 $COCH_3$ $C_2H_5O_2C$ N $CO_2C_2H_5$

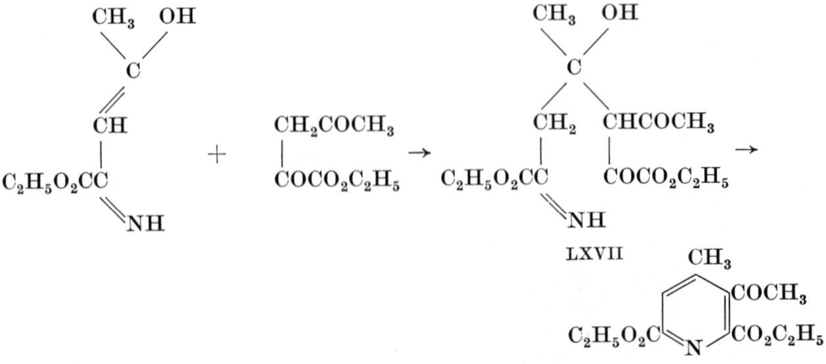

LXVIII

cyclopentanone-2-carboxylate,[151] ethyl cyanoacetate, malonamide, cyanoacetamide,[153] and ethyl nitroacetate,[154] according to the following scheme.

$$C_6H_5CH{=}NC_6H_5 + CH_3COCH_2CO_2C_2H_5 \rightarrow \begin{array}{c} C_6H_5CHNHC_6H_5 \\ | \\ CH_3COCHCO_2C_2H_5 \end{array}$$

The C=N group in Schiff bases and azines appears to behave as a carbonyl group, for these compounds can serve as donors. Examples are furnished by the Schiff bases of aliphatic aldehydes and ketones and of cycloalkanones which can be cyanoethylated in the α position to the carbon atom of the azomethine group.[154a] The reaction can be illustrated with cyclohexanone azine and methyl acrylate.[154b]

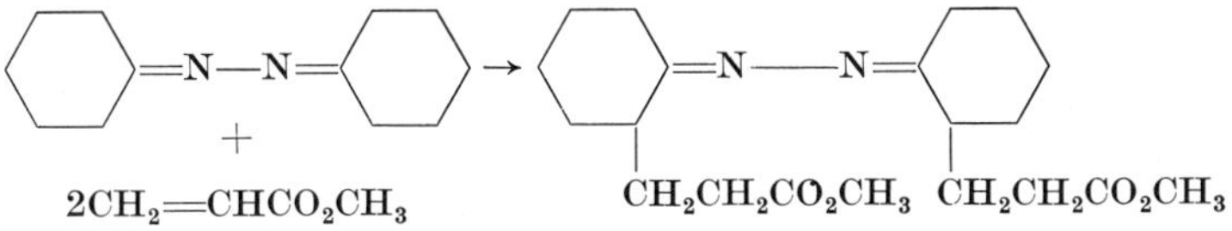

$$\text{C}_6\text{H}_{10}{=}N{-}N{=}\text{C}_6\text{H}_{10} + 2CH_2{=}CHCO_2CH_3 \rightarrow (CH_3O_2CCH_2CH_2)\text{C}_6\text{H}_9{=}N{-}N{=}\text{C}_6\text{H}_9(CH_2CH_2CO_2CH_3)$$

Also, one can at least formally explain the reaction of the 3-hydrogen atom of indole (LXIX) with 1-ethylthiomethyl-2-naphthol[155] by the formulation of indole as the tautomeride LXX. An analogous reaction

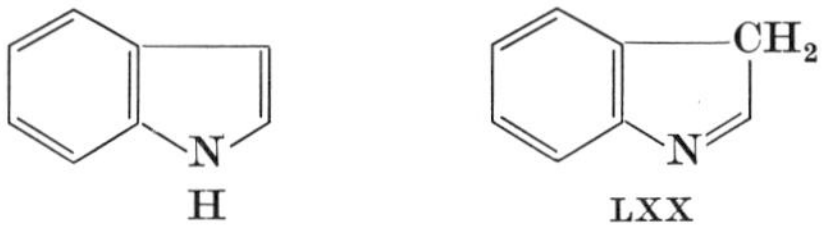

LXIX LXX

is that between indolylmagnesium bromide and compounds of the ω-nitrostyrene type.[156]

Acceptors

α,β-Ethylenic Aldehydes (Table I). The condensation of α,β-ethylenic aldehydes (acrolein, crotonaldehyde, cinnamaldehyde) with suitable acid derivatives[110,157–162] (malonates, cyanoacetates, ethyl

[153] Lazzareschi, *Gazz. chim. ital.*, **67,** 371 (1937).
[154] Dornow and Frese, *Ann.*, **578,** 122 (1952).
[154a] Krimm, U.S. pat. 2,768,962 [*C.A.*, **51,** 6684 (1957)].
[154b] Häring and Wagner-Juareg, *Helv. Chim. Acta*, **40,** 852 (1957).
[155] Poppelsdorf and Holt, *J. Chem. Soc.*, **1954,** 4094.
[156] Noland, Christensen, Sauer, and Dutton, *J. Am. Chem. Soc.*, **77,** 456 (1955).
[157] Farmer and Mehta, *J. Chem. Soc.*, **1931,** 2561.
[158] Staudinger and Ruzicka, *Helv. Chim. Acta*, **7,** 442 (1924).
[159] Warner and Moe, *J. Am. Chem. Soc.*, **70,** 3470 (1948).
[160] Warner and Moe, *J. Am. Chem. Soc.*, **71,** 2586 (1949); U.S. pat. 2,468,352 [*C.A.*, **43,** 7505 (1949)].
[161] Warner and Moe, U.S. pat. 2,506,050 [*C.A.*, **44,** 8946 (1950)].
[162] Cope and Synerholm, *J. Am. Chem. Soc.*, **72,** 5228 (1950).

cyclohexanone-2-carboxylate) leads to derivatives of δ-aldehydo acids. Alkyl substitution in the α position does not appear to influence adversely the ability of the aldehydes to undergo Michael condensation; β substitution, on the other hand, alters the course of the reaction.[157,158] (For further synthetic uses of the condensation products see p. 249.)

There are very few examples of condensations between α,β-ethylenic aldehydes and ketones or aldehydes. In the aldehyde–α,β-ethylenic aldehyde condensations secondary reactions regularly accompany the condensation.[163–165] For example, the product to be expected from the interaction between cinnamaldehyde and phenylacetaldehyde, the dialdehyde LXXI, undergoes an intramolecular Cannizzaro reaction to yield δ-hydroxy-β,γ-diphenylvaleric acid, isolated as its lactone LXXII.

$$C_6H_5CH{=}CHCHO + C_6H_5CH_2CHO \rightarrow \underset{\text{LXXI}}{\begin{array}{l} C_6H_5CHCH_2CHO \\ \quad | \\ C_6H_5CHCHO \end{array}} \qquad \underset{\text{LXXII}}{\text{(lactone ring: } H_5C_6\text{, } H_5C_6\text{, O, C=O)}}$$

The "dimerization" of α,β-unsaturated aldehydes such as 2-ethyl-2-hexenal which takes place under the influence of aqueous-alcoholic alkali has been explained as a Michael reaction followed by intramolecular aldolization to yield a cyclic product.[165a]

$$C_2H_5CH_2CH{=}C(C_2H_5)CHO + n\text{-}C_3H_7CH{=}C(C_2H_5)CHO \rightarrow \begin{array}{c} C_2H_5 \\ | \\ CH \\ \diagup \quad \diagdown \\ CH \qquad CHC_3H_7\text{-}n \\ \| \qquad\quad | \\ C_2H_5C \qquad CH(C_2H_5)CHO \\ \diagdown \\ CHO \end{array} \rightarrow \begin{array}{c} C_2H_5 \\ | \\ CH \\ \diagup \quad \diagdown \\ CH \qquad CHC_3H_7\text{-}n \\ \| \qquad\quad | \\ H_5C_2C \qquad C(C_2H_5)CHO \\ \diagdown \quad \diagup \\ CHOH \end{array}$$

Table I includes some acceptors having a hydroxy (or alkoxy or amino) group attached to the double bond, i.e., they are the enolic forms of compounds that can also function as donors in the Michael reaction (see p. 205). All primary condensation products from donors that contain a C=NH group in the immediate vicinity of the reactive methylene group spontaneously cyclize with elimination of the hydroxy (alkoxy, amino) groups to yield pyridine derivatives.[166]

[163] Meerwein, *J. prakt. Chem.*, [2], **97**, 225 (1918).

[164] Haeusermann, *Helv. Chim. Acta*, **34**, 1482 (1951).

[165] Meerwein, *Ber.*, **53**, 1829 (1920).

[165a] Nielsen, *J. Am. Chem. Soc.*, **79**, 2518, 2524 (1957).

[166] Dornow, *Ber.*, **72**, 1548 (1939). Compare, Baumgarten and Dornow, *Ber.*, **72**, 563 (1939).

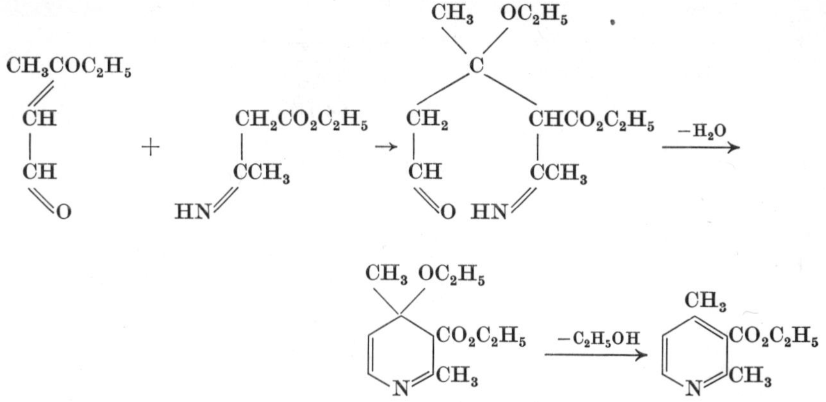

$$CH_3COC_2H_5{=}CH{-}CH{=}O + CH_2CO_2C_2H_5{-}C(CH_3){=}NH \rightarrow \text{(CH}_3\text{)(OC}_2\text{H}_5\text{)C[CH}_2\text{CH=O][CH(CO}_2\text{C}_2\text{H}_5\text{)C(CH}_3\text{)=NH]} \xrightarrow{-H_2O}$$

$$\text{4-methyl-4-ethoxy-3-carbethoxy-2-methyl-dihydropyridine} \xrightarrow{-C_2H_5OH} \text{ethyl 2,4-dimethylpyridine-3-carboxylate}$$

However, the course of cyclization can sometimes vary. From benzoylacetaldehyde and ethyl β-aminocrotonate one does not obtain the expected ethyl 2-methyl-4-phenylpyridine-3-carboxylate, but the 6-phenyl isomer LXXIV.[167] This probably results from the reaction of benzoylacetaldehyde as β-hydroxycinnamic aldehyde (LXXIII) or as hydroxymethyleneacetophenone.

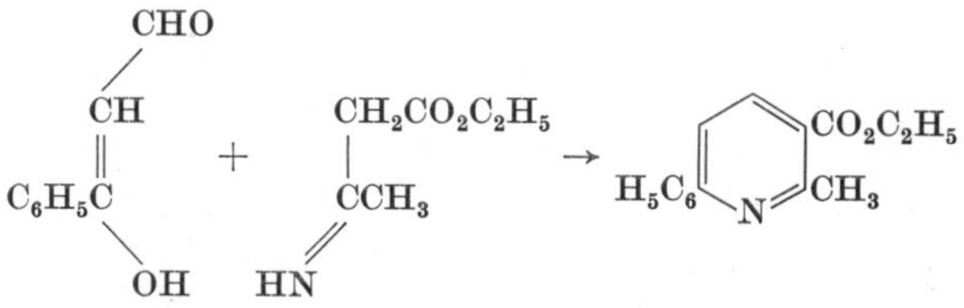

$$C_6H_5C(OH){=}CH{-}CHO + CH_2CO_2C_2H_5{-}C(CH_3){=}NH \rightarrow \text{LXXIV}$$

LXXIII (CHO, CH, C_6H_5C, OH) + $CH_2CO_2C_2H_5$, CCH_3, HN → LXXIV (H_5C_6, N, $CO_2C_2H_5$, CH_3)

Aliphatic α,β-Ethylenic Ketones (Table II). The Michael condensation of aliphatic α,β-ethylenic ketones proceeds normally; the yields reported are often very high. The ease with which the ethylenic ketones undergo the condensation is exemplified by the fact that substances such as β-naphthol[168] or ethyl 3-hydroxy-4,5-benzofuran-2-carboxylate[119] react with methyl vinyl ketone in their ketonic forms. The same is true for the reactions of 4-hydroxycoumarin with ethylideneacetone and mesityl oxide, respectively.[169] Compare also the reaction of kojic acid with acrylonitrile.[170]

[167] Spaeth and Burger, *Monatsh.*, **49**, 265 (1928).

[168] Miller and Robinson, *J. Chem. Soc.*, **1934**, 1535.

[169] Ikawa, Stahmann, and Link, *J. Am. Chem. Soc.*, **66**, 902 (1944).

[170] Woods, *J. Am. Chem. Soc.*, **74**, 3959 (1952).

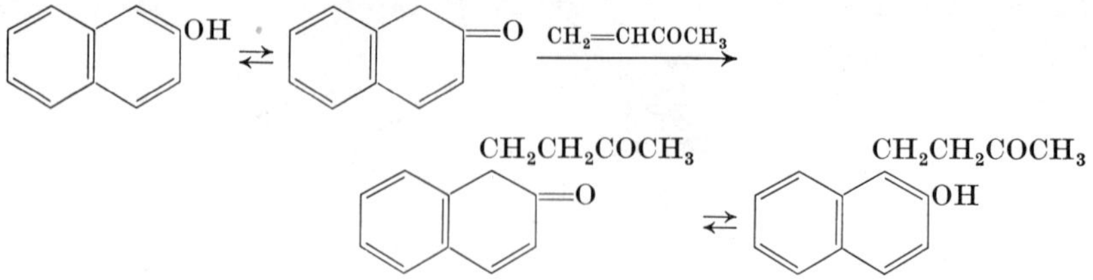

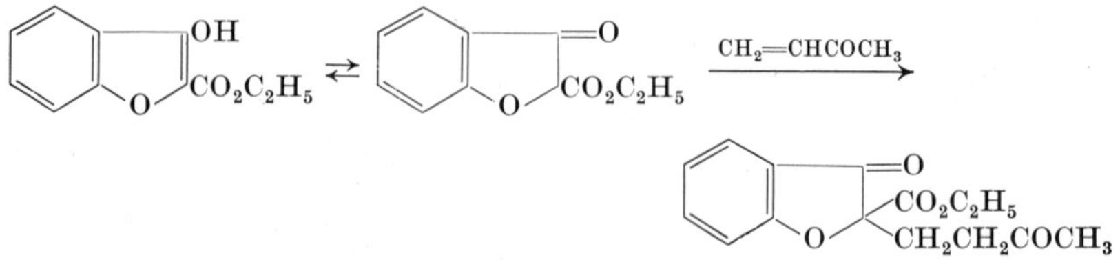

OH ⇄ =O CH_2=CHCOCH$_3$ →

$CH_2CH_2COCH_3$ =O ⇄ $CH_2CH_2COCH_3$ OH

OH $CO_2C_2H_5$ ⇄ =O $CO_2C_2H_5$ CH_2=CHCOCH$_3$ →

=O $CO_2C_2H_5$ $CH_2CH_2COCH_3$

An example of the reaction of hydroxymethylene ketones is seen in the condensation of the methyl ethyl ketone derivative LXXV with cyanoacetamide (under the catalytic influence of pyridine or piperidine).[171,172] The primary product cyclizes spontaneously and, dependent on the operating conditions, 2-keto-3-cyano-4-hydroxy-5,6-dimethyl-1,2,3,4-tetrahydropyridine (LXXVI) or its dehydration product, 2-hydroxy-3-cyano-5,6-dimethylpyridine (LXXVII), is obtained.

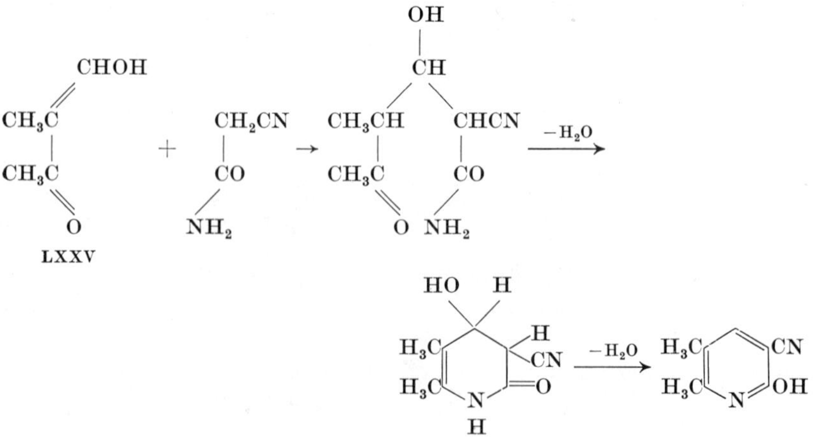

CHOH, CH_3C, CH_3C, O (LXXV) + CH_2CN, CO, NH_2 → OH, CH, CH_3CH, CHCN, CH_3C, CO, O, NH_2 $\xrightarrow{-H_2O}$

HO H, H_3C, H_3C, H, CN, =O, N, H (LXXVI) $\xrightarrow{-H_2O}$ H_3C, H_3C, CN, OH, N (LXXVII)

Mention should finally be made of the behavior of doubly unsaturated ketones. Of this group, two types have been somewhat cursorily investigated. Crotylideneacetone (LXXVIII) yields with diethyl malonate

[171] Tracy and Elderfield, *J. Org. Chem.*, **6**, 63 (1941).

[172] Joshi, Kaushal, and Deshapande, *J. Indian Chem. Soc.*, **18**, 479 (1941) [*C.A.*, **36**, 4482 (1942)].

in the presence of sodium methoxide a mixture of two substances, of which the predominant one, LXXIX, results from 1,6 addition, the isomer LXXX from 1,4 addition.[173] 5-Methyl-1,4-hexadien-3-one (LXXXI) reacts, under the influence of sodium methoxide, both with diethyl

$$CH_3CH{=}CHCH{=}CHCOCH_3 \text{ (LXXVIII)} + CH_2(CO_2C_2H_5)_2 \longrightarrow CH_3CHCH{=}CHCH_2COCH_3 \text{ with } CH(CO_2C_2H_5)_2 \text{ on C-2 (LXXIX, 66\%)} + CH_3CH{=}CHCHCH_2COCH_3 \text{ with } CH(CO_2C_2H_5)_2 \text{ on C-4 (LXXX, 29\%)}$$

malonate and acetylacetone at the less-substituted end of the molecule only, giving LXXXII and LXXXIII, respectively.[174] Phorone (LXXXIV) does not react analogously to LXXXI with diethyl malonate in alcoholic solution. Instead the product obtained, LXXXV,[175] is identical with that obtained from mesityl oxide.[176–179] Apparently

$$(CH_3)_2C{=}CHCOCH{=}CH_2 \text{ (LXXXI)} \longrightarrow (CH_3)_2C{=}CHCOCH_2CH_2CH(CO_2C_2H_5)_2 \text{ (LXXXII, 75\%)}$$

$$(CH_3)_2C{=}CHCOCH{=}CH_2 \text{ (LXXXI)} \longrightarrow (CH_3)_2C{=}CHCOCH_2CH_2CH(COCH_3)_2 \text{ (LXXXIII, 65–70\%)}$$

$$(CH_3)_2C{=}CHCOCH{=}C(CH_3)_2 \text{ (LXXXIV)}$$

LXXXV: 5,5-dimethylcyclohexane-1,3-dione (ring with H_3C and CH_3 on one carbon, two $C{=}O$ groups)

phorone reverts to mesityl oxide more quickly than it reacts with the malonate, or the adduct formed suffers retrogression.

α,β-Acetylenic Ketones. Acetylenic ketones that contain the triple bond in the α,β position would be expected to give α,β-olefinic ketones in

[173] Farmer and Mehta, *J. Chem. Soc.*, **1931,** 1904.

[174] Nazarov and Terekhova, *Bull. acad. sci. U.R.S.S. Classe sci. chim.*, **1946,** 201 [*C.A.*, **42,** 7729 (1948)].

[175] Vorlaender and Gaertner, *Ann.*, **304,** 1 (1899).

[176] Komppa, *Ber.*, **32,** 1421 (1899).

[177] Shriner and Todd, *Org. Syntheses Coll. Vol.* **2,** 200 (1950).

[178] Vorlaender, *Ann.*, **294,** 273 (1897).

[179] Vorlaender and Erig, *Ann.*, **294,** 302 (1897).

the Michael condensation, as shown in the formulation. In the cases investigated (acetyl-n-butylacetylene,[180] propionylphenylacetylene,[181]

$$RC{\equiv}CCOR' + CH_2(CO_2C_2H_5)_2 \rightarrow \underset{\displaystyle |\atop CH(CO_2C_2H_5)_2}{RC{=}CHCOR'}$$

benzoylphenylacetylene,[182] benzoyl-o-chlorophenylacetylene[183]), the primary products from malonic esters and the corresponding sodium alkoxides as catalysts proved too reactive to be isolated; cyclization products were isolated instead. From acetyl-n-butylacetylene, the α-pyrone derivative LXXXVI, which could be converted to 5-n-butylresorcinol, was obtained. The phenylacetylene derivatives also cyclized

$$n\text{-}C_4H_9C{\equiv}CCOCH_3 + CH_2(CO_2R)_2 \xrightarrow{NaOR} n\text{-}C_4H_9C(=CH{-}COCH_3)CH(CO_2R)_2 \rightarrow$$

$$\text{LXXXVI } (n\text{-}H_9C_4,\ CH_3,\ RO_2C\text{-substituted } \alpha\text{-pyrone}) \xrightarrow[-CO_2]{\text{Hydrolysis}} n\text{-}H_9C_4C_6H_3(OH)_2$$

LXXXVI

$$C_6H_5C(=CH{-}COR')CH(CO_2R)_2 \qquad \text{LXXXVII } (H_5C_6,\ R',\ RO_2C\text{-substituted } \alpha\text{-pyrone})$$

LXXXVII

to yield α-pyrones, LXXXVII.[181,182] Analogously, the reaction between cyanoacetamide and propionylphenylacetylene[181] or benzoylphenylacetylene[184] leads to the substituted 2-pyridols, LXXXVIII. From

$$C_6H_5C(=CH{-}COR)CH(CN)CONH_2 \rightarrow (H_5C_6,\ NC,\ R,\ OH,\ NH,\ C{=}O \text{ ring}) \rightarrow (H_5C_6,\ NC,\ R,\ N,\ OH \text{ pyridine})$$

LXXXVIII

[180] Anker and Cook, *J. Chem. Soc.*, **1945,** 311.
[181] Bardhan, *J. Chem. Soc.*, **1929,** 2223.
[182] Kohler, *J. Am. Chem. Soc.*, **44,** 379 (1922).
[183] Bickel, *J. Am. Chem. Soc.*, **72,** 1022 (1950).
[184] Barat, *J. Indian Chem. Soc.*, **7,** 851 (1930) [*C.A.*, **25,** 2145 (1931)].

5-methyl-3-hexyn-2-one and diethyl malonate in the presence of a small quantity of sodium ethoxide 3-carbethoxy-4-isopropyl-6-methyl-α-pyrone (LXXXIX) was obtained in 59% yield.[185]

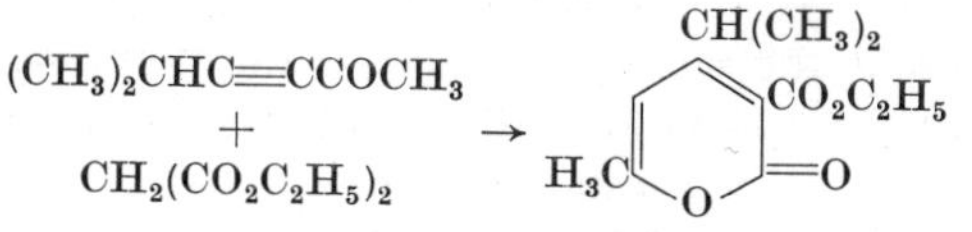

$$(CH_3)_2CHC{\equiv}CCOCH_3 + CH_2(CO_2C_2H_5)_2 \rightarrow$$

CH(CH3)2, CO2C2H5, H3C, O, =O

LXXXIX

Cyclization also takes place in the reaction between methyl ethynyl ketone and 2-methylcyclohexanone. Under the influence of sodium hydride, 2-keto-10-methyl-2,5,6,7,8,10-hexahydronaphthalene is formed.[186]

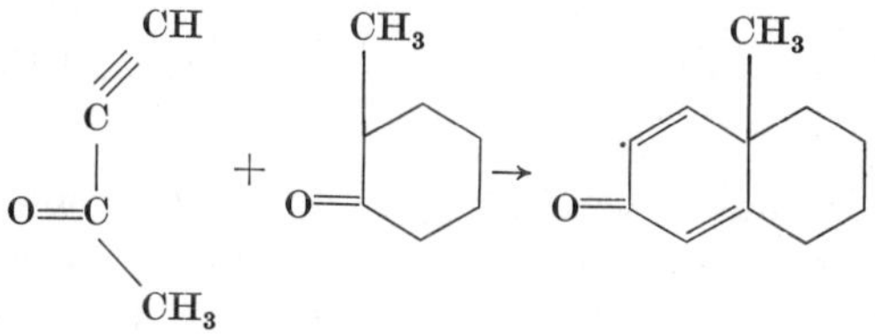

CH≡C–C(=O)–CH3 + 2-methylcyclohexanone (CH3, O=) → (CH3, O=)

In the Michael condensation between ethyl ethynyl ketone and the cyclohexanone derivative XC under the influence of sodium triphenylmethide, very low yields of XCI were obtained;[187] cf. refs. 188 and 189. As similar unsatisfactory results had been recorded in analogous

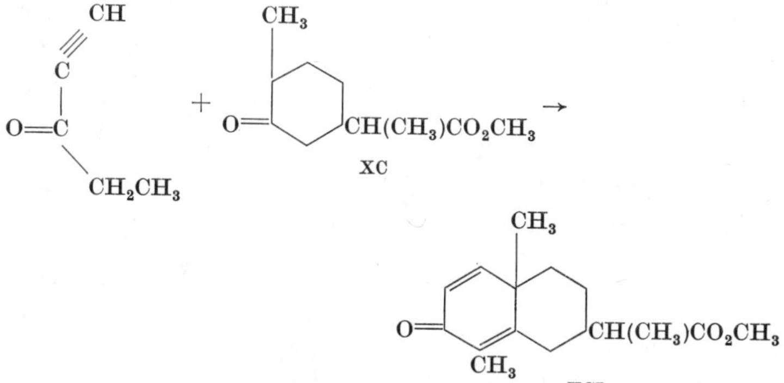

CH≡C–C(=O)–CH2CH3 + (CH3, O=, CH(CH3)CO2CH3) XC →

(CH3, O=, CH3, CH(CH3)CO2CH3) XCI

[185] Smith and Kelly, *J. Am. Chem. Soc.*, **74**, 3305 (1952).

[186] Woodward and Singh, *J. Am. Chem. Soc.*, **72**, 494 (1950).

[187] Clemo and McQuillin, *J. Chem. Soc.*, **1952**, 3839.

[188] Gunstone and Tulloch, *J. Appl. Chem. London*, **4**, 291 (1954).

[189] Abe, Harukawa, Ishikawa, Miki, Sumi, and Toga, *Proc. Japan. Acad.*, **28**, 425 (1952) [*C.A.*, **48**, 1317 (1954)].

reactions,[190,191] a systematic study of the reaction between 2-methylcyclohexanone (in the form of its metal enolates) and ethyl ethynyl ketone, formed in situ, was undertaken. However, β-chlorovinyl ethyl ketone, β-ethoxyvinyl ethyl ketone, and β-propionylvinylpyridinium chloride gave about the same yields as ethyl ethynyl ketone itself; and β-dimethylaminovinyl ethyl ketone did not react at all with the sodium enolate. Moreover, in addition to the expected 1,10-dimethyl-2-keto-2,5,6,7,8,10-hexahydronaphthalene (XCII), the open-chain product 2-methyl-2-(β-propionylvinyl)cyclohexanone (XCIII) was formed. A

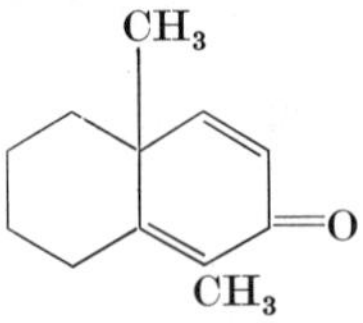

XCII 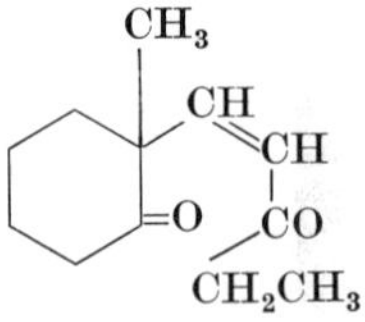 XCIII

considerable advantage was noted in use of the calcium or the lithium enolate of 2-methylcyclohexanone with β-chlorovinyl ethyl ketone; these gave yields of 12–14 and 20%, respectively, whereas the sodium enolate gave only 3–4%.

Aromatic α,β-Ethylenic Ketones (Tables III, IV). The introduction of aromatic radicals into the terminal positions of the system C=C—C=O appears to increase its polar character and therefore its tendency to undergo the Michael condensation. Perhaps it is for this reason that a very large number of such reactions has been carried out. Those in which the ketone is unsaturated on only one side are summarized in Table III, in which the following order is observed: vinyl phenyl ketones, methyl styryl ketones, phenyl styryl ketones.

The unsaturated ketone dypnone (XCIV) undergoes self-condensation when treated with alkali. The product "dypnopinacol" has been given the formula XCV.[191–193] Although XCVI has been assumed to be an intermediate,[191,192] it seems quite unlikely that the methyl group has a

$C_6H_5COCH{=}C(CH_3)C_6H_5$

XCIV

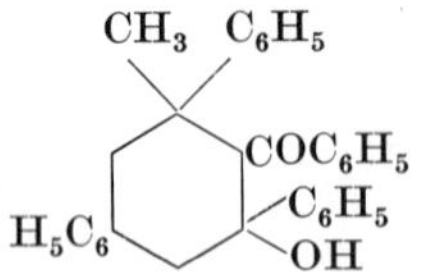

XCV

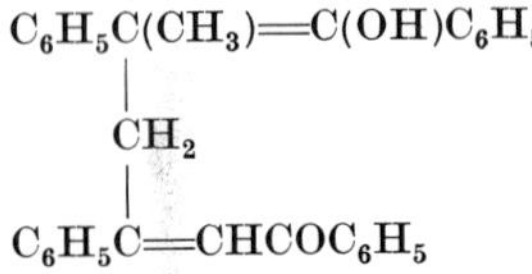

$C_6H_5C(CH_3){=}C(OH)C_6H_5$
$|$
CH_2
$|$
$C_6H_5C{=}CHCOC_6H_5$

XCVI

[190] Gunstone and Heggie, *J. Chem. Soc.*, **1952,** 1437.

[191] Iwanow and Iwanow, *Ber.*, **76,** 988 (1943).

[192] Iwanow and Iwanow, *Ber.*, **76,** 1148 (1943).

[193] Meerwein, *Ber.*, **77,** 229 (1944).

sufficiently reactive hydrogen to act as a donor. It is suggested by the authors that some of the dypnone is hydrolyzed to acetophenone by analogy with the known hydrolysis of mesityl oxide. Acetophenone then gives the diketone XCVII by Michael condensation; the diketone condenses with another molecule of acetophenone to yield the aldol XCVIII, which cyclizes normally to dypnopinacol.

$C_6H_5COCH_2C(CH_3)C_6H_5$
|
$CH_2COC_6H_5$

XCVII

$C_6H_5COCH_2C(CH_3)C_6H_5$
|
$C_6H_5(CH_3)CCHCOC_6H_5$
|
OH

XCVIII

Few doubly unsaturated ketones of the type $C_6H_5CH{=}CHCH{=}CHCOR$ appear to have been studied. When cinnamylideneacetone (XCIX) is treated with diethyl malonate and sodium ethoxide, 1,4 addition takes place. The primary product C cyclizes spontaneously, leading to

$C_6H_5CH{=}CHCH{=}CHCOCH_3$ (XCIX) + $CH_2(CO_2C_2H_5)_2$ → $C_6H_5CH{=}CHCH(CH_2COCH_3)(CHCO_2C_2H_5 \text{—} CO_2C_2H_5)$ (C) →

$C_6H_5CH{=}CH$–[cyclohexane-1,3-dione ring, =O, =O]–$CO_2C_2H_5$

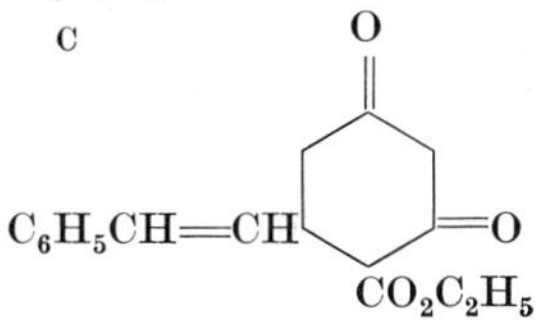

I*

4-carbethoxy-5-styrylcyclohexane-1,3-dione (I).[178,194,195] Cinnamylideneacetophenone also gives the 1,4 addition products II and III, respectively, with diethyl malonate and sodium ethoxide,[196] and with acetophenone

$C_6H_5CH{=}CHCHCH_2COC_6H_5$
|
$CH(CO_2C_2H_5)_2$

II

$C_6H_5CH{=}CHCHCH_2COC_6H_5$
|
$CH_2COC_6H_5$

III

* Enumeration of formulas begins with I again after C to reduce the complexity of the numbers.

[194] Vorlaender, *Ber.*, **36,** 2339 (1903).

[195] Vorlaender and Groebel, *Ann.*, **345,** 155 (1906), especially p. 206.

[196] Vorlaender and Staudinger, *Ann.*, **345,** 155 (1906), especially p. 217.

and potassium hydroxide in ethanol.[197] This is in contradiction to the behavior of diethyl cinnamylidenemalonate (see p. 501), which undergoes 1,6 condensation. The adduct III from cinnamylideneacetophenone and acetophenone is accompanied by a product whose formation involves two moles of acetophenone. Condensation of cinnamylideneacetophenone with ethyl acetoacetate gave a substance $C_{28}H_{22}O_3$ of unelucidated structure.[196]

Considerable attention has been paid to Michael condensations with doubly unsaturated ketones of the type RCH=CHCOCH=CHR, e.g., dibenzylideneacetone (IV)[198–200] and dicinnamylidenacetone (V).[198] The experimental material available, summarized in Table IV, shows that the two double bonds in dibenzylideneacetone undergo Michael condensation

$$C_6H_5CH{=}CHCOCH{=}CHC_6H_5$$
IV

$$C_6H_5CH{=}CHCH{=}CHCOCH{=}CHCH{=}CHC_6H_5$$
V

independently of each other. If the donor contains two enolizable hydrogen atoms, there is often a secondary intramolecular step leading to a six-membered ring (VI).[198] Substances of the dicinnamylideneacetone type appear to undergo the Michael condensation by 1,4 (not 1,6) addition.[198]

$$C_6H_5CH{=}CH{-}CO{-}CH{=}CHC_6H_5 \xrightarrow{CH_2(CO_2C_2H_5)_2} C_6H_5CH(CH(CO_2C_2H_5)_2){-}CH_2{-}CO{-}CH{=}CHC_6H_5 \rightarrow$$

(VI: cyclohexanone ring bearing H_5C_6 and C_6H_5 on the carbons flanking a quaternary carbon carrying $C_2H_5O_2C$ and $CO_2C_2H_5$)

VI

[197] Wittig and Kosack, *Ann.*, **529**, 167 (1937).
[198] Kohler and Dewey, *J. Am. Chem. Soc.*, **46**, 1267 (1924).
[199] Kohler and Helmkamp, *J. Am. Chem. Soc.*, **46**, 1018 (1924).
[200] Marvel and Moore, *J. Am. Chem. Soc.*, **71**, 28 (1949).

It is of interest to compare the reactivity of the double bonds in unsymmetrically substituted dibenzylidene-acetones. In dibenzylidene-acetone, chlorine in the 2, 3, or 4 position[201] or a methoxyl group in the 4 position[198] deactivates the neighboring double bond so that Michael reaction occurs only on the side of the unsubstituted benzene ring. The chlorine atom in α-(3- or 4-chlorobenzylidene)-β-(4′-methoxybenzylidene)-acetone causes the reaction to take place on the double bond adjacent to the chlorinated nucleus. On the other hand, a hydroxyl group in the 2 or 4 position of the benzene nucleus has a stronger activating influence than a 2-methoxy group or a chlorine atom in the 3 or 4 position.[202–204]

It is noteworthy as well as surprising that ethyl acetoacetate condenses with α-(4-dimethylaminobenzylidene)-β-(2-hydroxybenzylidene)acetone, in the presence of *potassium* hydroxide as catalyst on the dimethylamino group side, whereas ethyl cyanoacetate with *sodium* hydroxide as catalyst adds to the side of the 2-hydroxyphenyl radical.[205] The same difference is evident in two other cases listed in Table IV.

Heterocyclic α,β-Ethylenic Ketones (Tables V, VI). In view of the aromatic character of the furan system, α,β-ethylenic ketones containing the furyl group should behave like their phenyl analogs.[121,206–210] This expectation is borne out by the examples in Table V. A characteristic difference, however, is the fact that almost no secondary cyclization or isomerization reactions take place. Table V also includes a few heterocyclic compounds not derived from furan.

Table VI lists a number of other heterocyclic α,β-ethylenic ketones, mostly of the acylcoumarin type.[211–213] Several reactions carried out with 2-(*p*-methoxybenzylidene)-4,5-benzo-2,3-dihydrofuran-3-one[214,214a] and γ-pyrone are included.[215] The reaction of γ-pyrone and diethyl malonate is somewhat complicated, but it can be assumed that the first step is a Michael condensation to VII, which is followed by ring opening and

[201] Heilbron and Hill, *J. Chem. Soc.*, **1928,** 2863.
[202] Heilbron and Forster, *J. Chem. Soc.*, **125,** 2064 (1924).
[203] Heilbron and Hill, *J. Chem. Soc.*, **1927,** 918.
[204] Jennings and McGookin, *J. Chem. Soc.*, **1934,** 1741.
[205] Heilbron, Forster, and Whitworth, *J. Chem. Soc.*, **127,** 2159 (1925).
[206] Peak and Robinson, *J. Chem. Soc.*, **1937,** 1581.
[207] Andrews and Connor, *J. Am. Chem. Soc.*, **57,** 895 (1935).
[208] Drake and Gilbert, *J. Am. Chem. Soc.*, **52,** 4965 (1930).
[209] Kloetzel, *J. Am. Chem. Soc.*, **69,** 2271 (1947).
[210] Turner, *J. Am. Chem. Soc.*, **73,** 1284 (1951).
[211] Koelsch and Sundet, *J. Am. Chem. Soc.*, **72,** 1681 (1950).
[212] Koelsch and Sundet, *J. Am. Chem. Soc.*, **72,** 1844 (1950).
[213] Sastri and Seshadri, *Proc. Indian Acad. Sci.*, **16A,** 29 (1942) [*C.A.*, **37,** 880 (1943)].
[214] Panse, Shah, and Wheeler, *J. Indian Chem. Soc.*, **18,** 453 (1941) [*C.A.*, **36,** 4507 (1942)].
[214a] Panse, Shah, and Wheeler, *J. Univ. Bombay*, **10,** Part 3, 83 (1941) [*C.A.*, **36,** 4507 (1942)].
[215] R. B. Woodward, private communication.

recyclization. Elimination of one of the carbethoxyl groups makes possible the aromatization to form VIII.

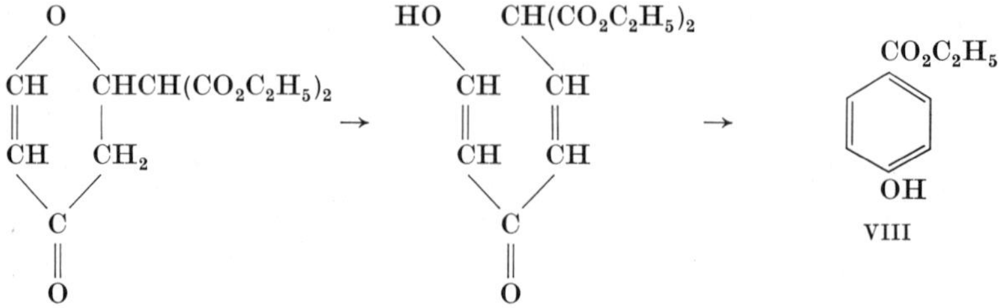

$$\text{VII} \rightarrow \text{HO–CH=CH–C(=O)–CH=CH–CH(CO}_2\text{C}_2\text{H}_5)_2 \rightarrow \text{VIII}$$

VII

VIII

Table VI also includes the Michael condensation between rhodanine and alkylidenerhodanines. In this reaction, α,α-bis-(2-thio-4-ketotetrahydro-5-thiazolyl)alkanes are formed from rhodanine and aliphatic aldehydes.[216]

Cycloalkenones and Acyl Cycloalkenes (Table VII). The Michael condensations of cycloalkenones and 1-acylcycloalkenes have been listed in a separate table (Table VII) in view of the importance of the products in the synthesis of hydroaromatic polycyclic substances related to the steroids and steroidal alkaloids.

The adducts obtained from acetylcycloalkenes[83–99,216–218] undergo intramolecular condensation to polycyclic ring systems, as exemplified in the accompanying reactions of 1-acetylcyclohexene (IX).[93,98]

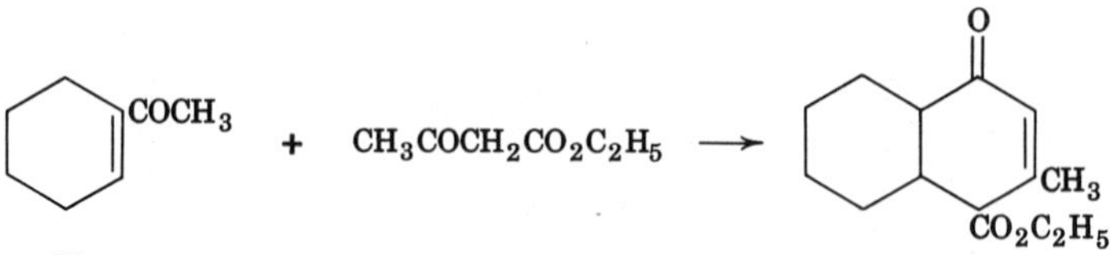

$$\text{IX (1-acetylcyclohexene, COCH}_3) + \text{CH}_3\text{COCH}_2\text{CO}_2\text{C}_2\text{H}_5 \longrightarrow \text{(bicyclic enone with CH}_3\text{, CO}_2\text{C}_2\text{H}_5)$$

IX

$$\text{IX (COCH}_3) + \text{cyclohexanone} \longrightarrow \text{(tricyclic enone)}$$

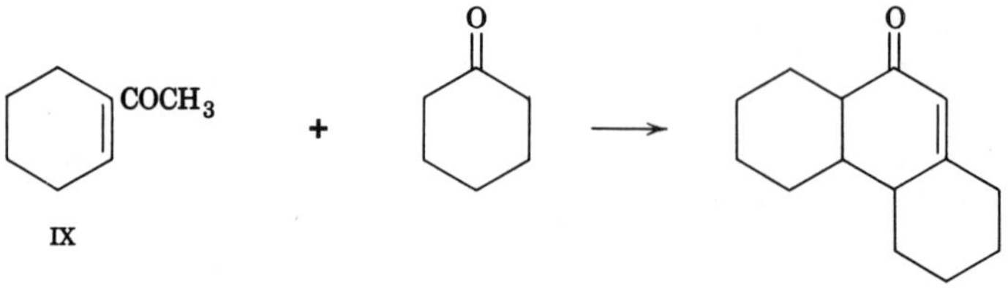

IX

[216] Bradsher, Brown, and Grantham, *J. Am. Chem. Soc.*, **73**, 5377 (1951).

[217] Hawthorne and Robinson, *J. Chem. Soc.*, **1936**, 763.

[218] Hewett, *J. Chem. Soc.*, **1936**, 50.

Table VII further includes some cases in which cycloalkylideneacetones have been subjected to the Michael condensation.[219–223] Here, too, cyclization of the primary adduct is spontaneous as shown by the formation of X.[221] As in many other reactions, the remaining carbethoxyl group is often eliminated in the process.

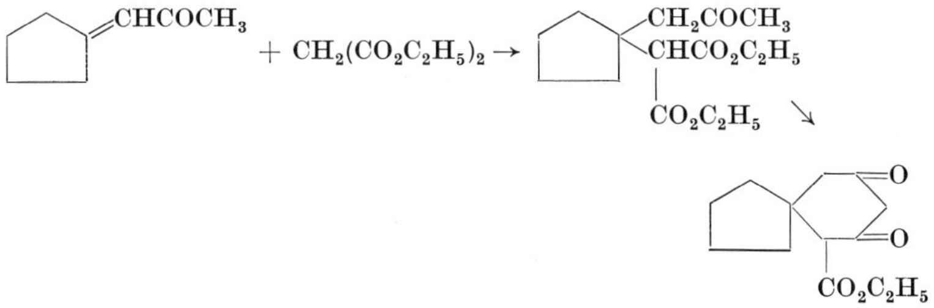

$$\text{C}_5\text{H}_8{=}\text{CHCOCH}_3 + CH_2(CO_2C_2H_5)_2 \rightarrow \text{C}_5\text{H}_8(CH_2COCH_3)(CH(CO_2C_2H_5)CO_2C_2H_5) \rightarrow \text{X}$$

X ($CO_2C_2H_5$)

Michael condensations with hydroxymethylene- or alkoxymethylene-cycloalkanones lead to interesting cyclic products. The product, e.g., from 2-hydroxymethylenecyclohexanone and cyanoacetamide (in the presence of piperidine or diethylamine),[224] eliminates water between the amide group and the carbonyl group of the cyclohexanone. The hydroxyl of the hydroxymethylene group is also eliminated as water, yielding XI ($R = H, CH_3$).

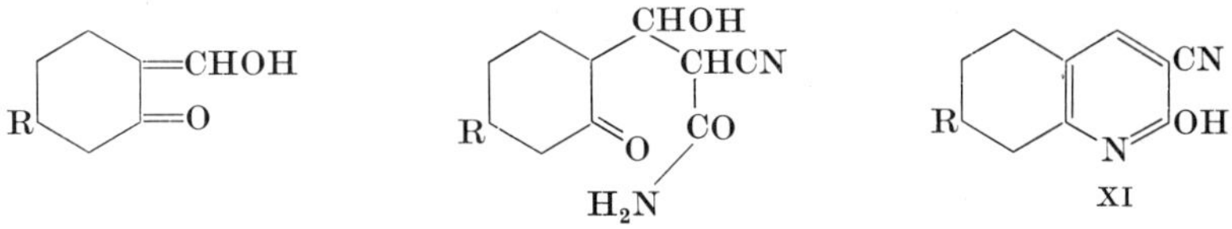

R, =CHOH, =O; CHOH, CHCN, CO, O, H_2N, R; R, CN, OH, N, XI

The dimerization of piperitone[225] (XII) appears to be a special case of Michael condensation. The methyl group of one molecule provides the hydrogen for the saturation of the second; the first molecule behaves, therefore, as a vinylog of a methyl ketone and does not utilize the existing hydrogen in the ortho position, perhaps due to steric inhibition by the isopropyl group. Two stereoisomers are formed. The structure of the dimeride of piperitone, which is stabilized by hydrogen bond formation

[219] Kandiah, *J. Chem. Soc.*, **1931,** 952.

[220] Kon and Thakur, *J. Chem. Soc.*, **1930,** 2217.

[221] Norris and Thorpe, *J. Chem. Soc.*, **119,** 1199 (1921).

[222] Thakur, *J. Chem. Soc.*, **1932,** 2147.

[223] Thakur, *J. Chem. Soc.*, **1932,** 2157.

[224] Sen-Gupta, *J. Chem. Soc.*, **107,** 1347 (1915).

[225] Taylor, *Chemistry & Industry*, **1954,** 252. Cf. Cole, *ibid.*, **1954,** 661.

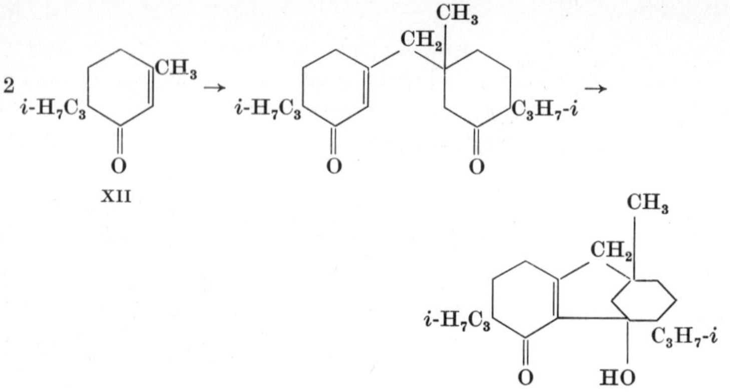

XII

between the carbonyl and the hydroxyl groups,[226] has been indicated by analogy with evidence obtained by degradation of the dimeride of 3,5-dimethyl-2-cyclohexen-1-one.[227]

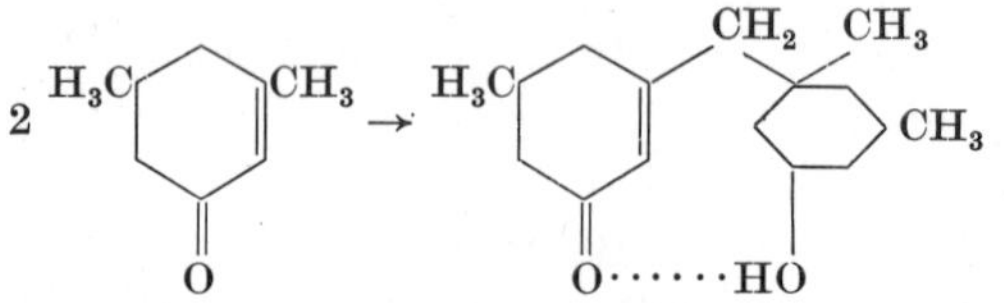

Robinson's Modification of the Michael Condensation (Table VIII). The use of a masked form of the α,β-ethylenic carbonyl compound, which produces the latter *in situ*, is of practical importance with sensitive ketones and in condensations requiring stringent experimental conditions. Although saturated β-chloroketones had had some use as precursors of the corresponding α,β-ethylenic ketones,[228] Robinson and his co-workers[98,229–231] introduced the use of β-dialkylaminoketones or their quaternary salts; these decompose gradually into a dialkylamine or trialkylammonium salt and the desired α,β-ethylenic ketone. These starting materials are readily accessible by appropriate Mannich reactions[232] of saturated ketones and, if necessary, subsequent quaternization as shown in the accompanying reaction sequence.

$$CH_3COCH_3 \rightarrow CH_3COCH_2CH_2N(CH_3)_2 \rightarrow$$
$$CH_3COCH_2CH_2N(CH_3)_3I \rightarrow CH_3COCH{=}CH_2 + (CH_3)_3NHI$$

[226] Briggs and Colebrook, *Chemistry & Industry*, **1955,** 200.
[227] Ayer and Taylor, *J. Chem. Soc.*, **1955,** 2227.
[228] Allen and Bell, *Can. J. Research*, **11,** 40 (1934) [*C.A.*, **29,** 150 (1935)].
[229] du Feu, McQuillin, and Robinson, *J. Chem. Soc.*, **1937,** 53.
[230] McQuillin and Robinson, *J. Chem. Soc.*, **1938,** 1097.
[231] McQuillin and Robinson, *J. Chem. Soc.*, **1941,** 586.
[232] Blicke, in Adams, *Organic Reactions*, Vol. 1, Chapter 10, John Wiley & Sons, 1942.

Although these reactions are included here (Table VIII) among Michael condensations, it has not been certain that they proceed by way of the α,β-ethylenic ketone as an intermediate.[233] A recent study of these reactions has led to the conclusion that the olefinic intermediate, as outlined by Robinson, occurs whenever there is a hydrogen atom on the carbon atom beta to the nitrogen.*

The scope of Robinson's modification of the Michael reaction has been widened by the observation[251] that 1-dialkylamino-2-nitroalkanes (the Mannich bases of nitroalkanes) can replace the corresponding nitroölefins in Michael condensations.

$$R_2NCH_2CH(NO_2)CH_2CH_3 \rightleftharpoons R_2NH + CH_2{=}C(NO_2)CH_2CH_3$$

Another variant is the use of the alkylthio instead of the dialkylamino group. Thus, 1-ethylthiomethyl-2-naphthol reacts as the 1-methylene derivative of the keto form of 2-naphthol.[155]

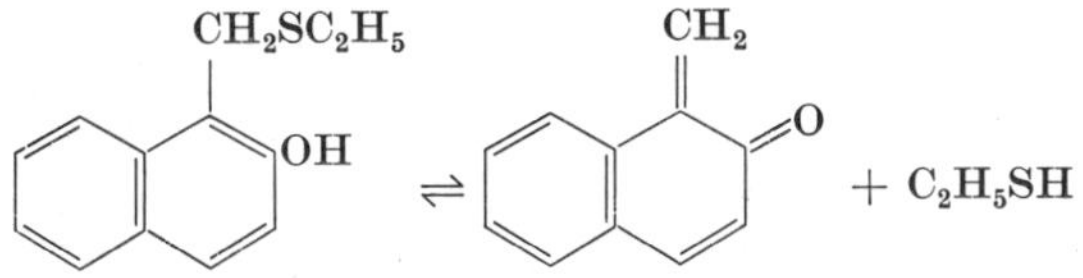

$$\text{1-}(CH_2SC_2H_5)\text{-2-naphthol (OH)} \rightleftharpoons \text{1-methylene-2(1H)-naphthalenone } (=CH_2, =O) + C_2H_5SH$$

[233] Brewster and Eliel, in Adams, *Organic Reactions,* Vol. 7, Chapter 3, John Wiley & Sons, 1953.

* Note, however, that Bradford and co-workers[234] have observed differences of reaction in cyanoethylation with β-diethylaminoethyl cyanide methiodide as compared with cyanoethylation with acrylonitrile, and have assumed that the positive ion $NCCH_2CH_2^{\oplus}$ is the intermediate. This explanation suggests the relation of the Michael condensation to reactions of typical Michael donors with gramine (β-diethylaminoethylindole) and its derivatives.[235–250]

[234] Bradford, Meek, Turnbull, and Wilson, *Chemistry & Industry,* **1951,** 839.

[235] Eliel and Murphy, *J. Am. Chem. Soc.,* **75,** 3589 (1953).

[236] Dornow and Theis, *Ann.,* **581,** 219 (1953).

[237] Holland and Nayler, *J. Chem. Soc.,* **1953,** 280.

[238] Gray, *J. Am. Chem. Soc.,* **75,** 1252 (1953).

[239] Kissman and Witkop, *J. Am. Chem. Soc.,* **75,** 1967 (1953).

[240] Atkinson, Poppelsdorf, and Williams, *J. Chem. Soc.,* **1953,** 580.

[241] Jones and Kornfeld, U.S. pat. 2,621,187 [*C.A.,* **47,** 10557 (1953)].

[242] Kutscher and Klamerth, *Chem. Ber.,* **86,** 352 (1953).

[243] Brewster and Eliel, in Adams, *Organic Reactions,* Vol. 7, p. 99, John Wiley & Sons, 1953.

[244] Thesing, *Chem. Ber.,* **87,** 692 (1954).

[245] Atkinson, *J. Chem. Soc.,* **1954,** 1329.

[245a] Hellmann, Hallmann, and Lingens, *Chem. Ber.,* **86,** 1346 (1953).

[246] Hardegger and Corrodi, *Helv. Chim. Acta,* **38,** 468 (1955).

[247] Albertson, Archer, and Suter, *J. Am. Chem. Soc.,* **66,** 500 (1944).

[248] Snyder and Smith, *J. Am. Chem. Soc.,* **66,** 350 (1944).

[249] Lyttle and Weisblat, *J. Am. Chem. Soc.,* **69,** 2118 (1947).

[250] Hegedüs, *Helv. Chim. Acta,* **29,** 1499 (1946).

[251] Shoemaker and Keown, *J. Am. Chem. Soc.,* **76,** 6374 (1954).

***p*-Quinones and Derivatives (Table IX).** As in many other reactions, e.g., the Diels-Alder synthesis, *p*-quinones behave in the Michael condensation as α,β-ethylenic ketones. However, although the enols formed in the Michael condensation of most α,β-ethylenic ketones ketonize spontaneously, the enols formed from quinones are hydroquinones and are stable.

Certain of the hydroquinone products are dehydrogenated *in situ* by an excess of the original quinone, so that the newly formed quinone can undergo a second Michael condensation.[252]

p-Benzoquinone + $NCCH_2CO_2C_2H_5$ → 2-($CHCO_2C_2H_5$, CN)-hydroquinone (XIII)

XIII + p-benzoquinone → 2-($CHCO_2C_2H_5$, CN)-p-benzoquinone (XIV) + hydroquinone

XIV + $NCCH_2CO_2C_2H_5$ → 2,5-bis($CH(CN)CO_2C_2H_5$)-hydroquinone

2,6-Dimethyl-3-methyl-p-benzoquinone (H_3C, CH_3, CH_3) + $CH_2(CO_2C_2H_5)_2$ → adduct with $CH(CO_2C_2H_5)_2$ (CH_3, H) →

XV (benzofuranone: H_3C, HO, CH_3, CH_3, =O, $CO_2C_2H_5$)

[252] Wood, Colburn, Jr., Cox, and Garland, *J. Am. Chem. Soc.*, **66**, 1540 (1944).

Other hydroquinones undergo cyclization involving the hydroxyl group of the hydroquinone and leading to condensed heterocyclic ring systems. As example is the formation of the lactone XV shown on p. 224.[253]

In other cases not only isocoumarones are formed, but also coumarin derivatives such as XVI.[254] When zinc chloride is used to catalyze the

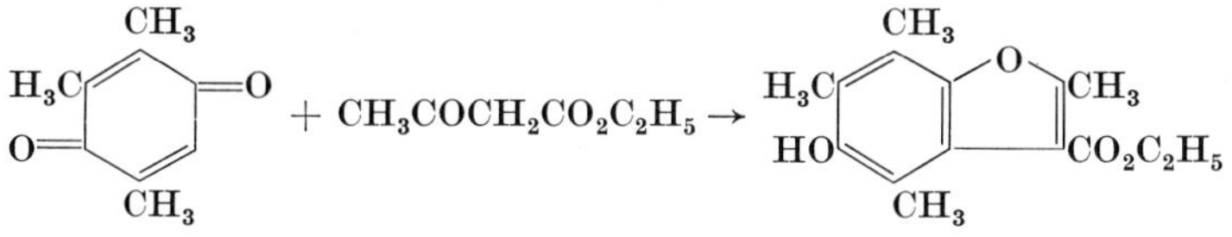

$$\text{2,5-dimethyl-}p\text{-benzoquinone} + CH_3COCH_2CO_2C_2H_5 \rightarrow \text{XVI}$$

XVI

reaction of *p*-benzoquinone and ethyl acetoacetate, either a mono (XVII) or bis derivative (XVIII) can be formed.[255–257] Cyclization also takes place

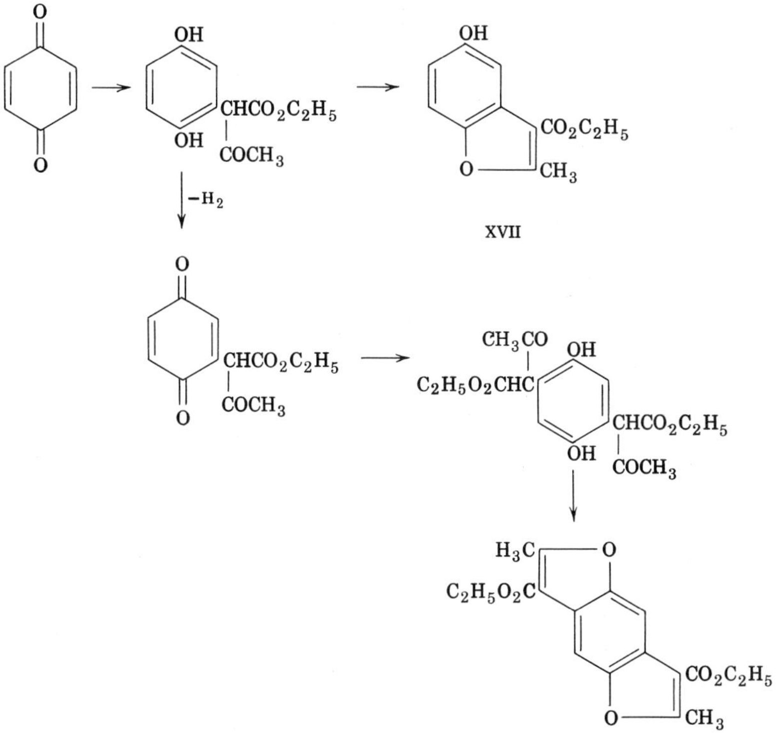

XVII

XVIII

[253] Smith and Prichard, *J. Org. Chem.*, **4**, 342 (1939).
[254] Smith and Boyack, *J. Am. Chem. Soc.*, **70**, 2690 (1948).
[255] Pechmann, *Ber.*, **21**, 3005 (1888).
[256] Ikuta, *J. prakt. Chem.*, [2], **45**, 78 (1892).
[257] Graebe and Levy, *Ann.*, **283**, 245 (1894).

when benzoquinone reacts with the imine of ethyl acetoacetate (ethyl β-aminocrotonate). In acetone or anhydrous ethanol as solvent, 2-methyl-3-carbethoxy-5-hydroxyindole (XIX) is formed.[258] In the same way,

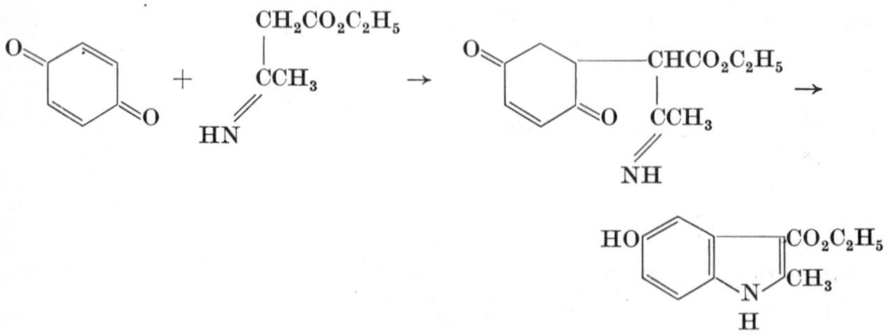

$CH_2CO_2C_2H_5$ — CCH_3 — HN → $CHCO_2C_2H_5$ — CCH_3 — NH →

HO — $CO_2C_2H_5$ — CH_3 — N — H

XIX

N-phenyl-2-methyl-3-carbethoxy-5-hydroxyindole was obtained with ethyl β-anilinocrotonate, and the corresponding N-carbethoxymethyl compound from ethyl β-(carbethoxymethylamino)crotonate.

Ordinarily only an unsubstituted carbon atom of the quinone ring is attacked by a donor anion, possibly for steric reasons. Thus, trisubstituted quinones undergo only mono condensation.[254,259,260] However, it

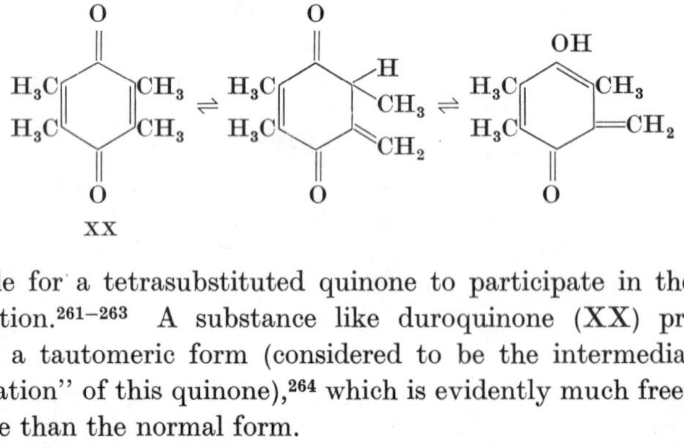

H_3C, CH_3, H_3C, CH_3 ⇌ H_3C, H, CH_3, H_3C, CH_2 ⇌ OH, H_3C, CH_3, H_3C, $=CH_2$

XX

is possible for a tetrasubstituted quinone to participate in the Michael condensation.[261–263] A substance like duroquinone (XX) presumably reacts in a tautomeric form (considered to be the intermediate in the "dimerization" of this quinone),[264] which is evidently much freer of steric hindrance than the normal form.

In one instance, a methylene quinone (1-methylene-1,2-naphthoquinone, XXI) has been shown to undergo the Michael reaction with diethyl

[258] Nenitzescu, *Bul. Soc. Chim. România*, **11**, 37 (1929) [*C.A.*, **24**, 110 (1930)].

[259] Smith and Kaiser, *J. Am. Chem. Soc.*, **62**, 133 (1940).

[260] Smith and King, *J. Am. Chem. Soc.*, **65**, 441 (1943).

[261] Smith and Dobrovolny, *J. Am. Chem. Soc.*, **48**, 1693 (1926).

[262] Smith and Kaiser, *J. Am. Chem. Soc.*, **62**, 138 (1940).

[263] Smith and Tenenbaum, *J. Am. Chem. Soc.*, **59**, 667 (1937).

[264] Smith, Tess, and Ullyot, *J. Am. Chem. Soc.*, **66**, 1320 (1944).

malonate, though in small yield. In this case, too, cyclization occurred and ethyl 5,6-benzo-3,4-dihydrocoumarin-3-carboxylate (XXII) was formed.[265]

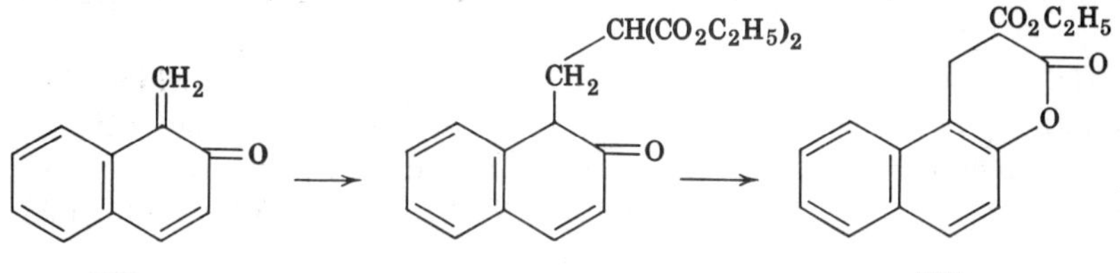

CH_2 $CH(CO_2C_2H_5)_2$ CH_2 $CO_2C_2H_5$

XXI XXII

A complicated modification of the Michael reaction of *p*-quinones has been observed to result from condensation of 1,4-naphthoquinone (cf. ref. 261) with ethyl acetoacetate in the presence of pyridine and pyridinium hydrochloride;[266] cf. ref. 267. The final product had lost the acetyl group of the acetoacetate molecule; the same product (1-carbethoxy-2,3-phthaloylpyrrocoline, XXIII) was therefore obtained when ethyl benzoylacetate was employed. The reaction has been formulated as shown.

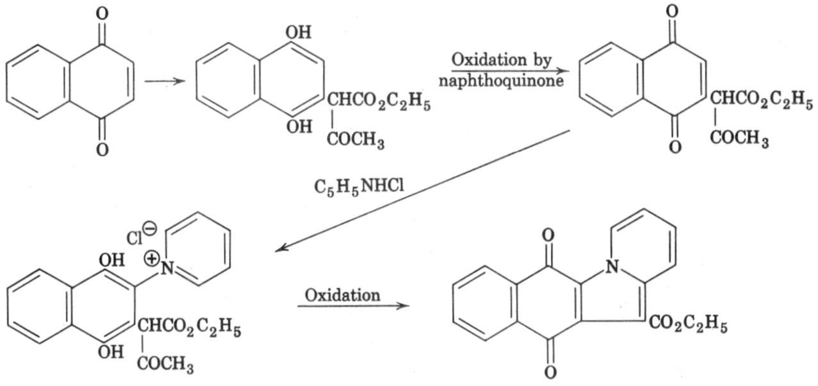

Oxidation by naphthoquinone

$CHCO_2C_2H_5$ $COCH_3$

C_5H_5NHCl

Oxidation

$CO_2C_2H_5$

XXIII

The complexity of this sequence explains the low yield (14%) as well as the fact that also 2-bromo- and 2,3-dichloro-naphthoquinone and 1,4-naphthoquinone-2-sulfonate give the same product, with loss of the polar

[265] Smith and Horner, Jr., *J. Am. Chem. Soc.*, **60**, 676 (1938).

[266] Pratt, Luckenbaugh, and Erickson, *J. Org. Chem.*, **19**, 176 (1954).

[267] Pratt and Boehme, *J. Am. Chem. Soc.*, **73**, 444 (1951). Isoquinoline shows a reactivity comparable with that of pyridine. Quinoline, however, is relatively unreactive and the products described in ref. 266 as derived from quinoline have been shown to have been formed from isoquinoline present in the quinoline used. Pratt, Rice, and Luckenbaugh, *J. Am. Chem. Soc.*, **79**, 1212 (1957).

substituents.[268] According to Suryanarayana and Tilak,[269] 2,3-dichloronaphthoquinone also yields the same compound (XXIII) when condensed with diethyl malonate or ethyl benzoylacetate. The Indian authors assigned to it, originally, the formula XXIV, but withdrew it later in favor of XXIII.[270–273]

They further observed, in the condensation of 2,3-dichloro-1,4-naphthoquinone with acetoacetanilide in pyridine, that the ultimate partial degradation of the side chain involved *either* the acetyl *or* the anilide group, thus leading both to XXV and XXVI. Compound

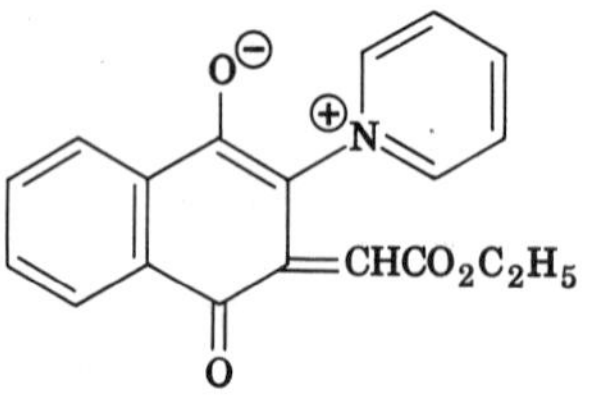

$=CHCO_2C_2H_5$

XXIV

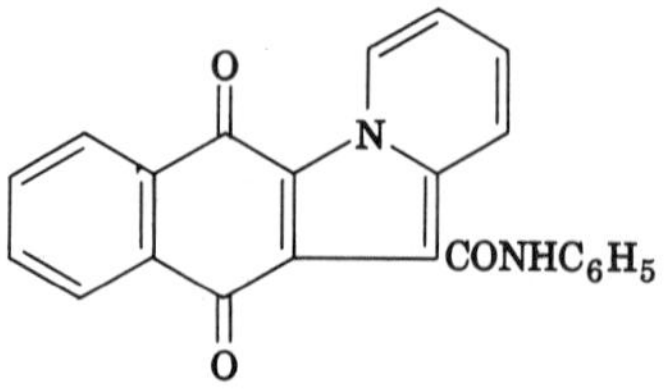

$CONHC_6H_5$

XXV

$COCH_3$

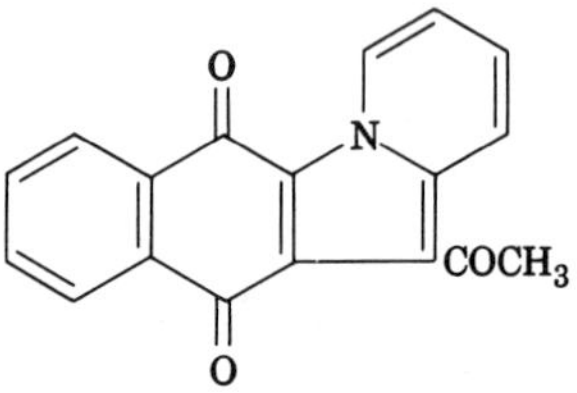

XXVI

XXVI is also obtained when acetoaceto-*o*-chloroanilide, -*o*-toluide, or 2-(acetoacetamido)-6-ethoxybenzothiazole is employed instead of the unsubstituted anilide.

An analogous reaction was observed when ethyl acetoacetate in pyridine solution was condensed with chloranil or 2,6-dichloroquinone, leading to a mixture of XXVIIA and XXVIIB. The structure of XXVIIA was proved by its synthesis from tetraethyl 2,5-dichloroquinone-3,6-dimalonate and ethyl acetoacetate in pyridine solution.

[268] Michel, *Ber.*, **33,** 2402 (1900).

[269] Suryanarayana and Tilak, *Proc. Indian Acad. Sci.*, **39A,** 185 (1954) [*C.A.*, **49,** 12411 (1955)].

[270] Suryanarayana and Tilak, *Proc. Indian Acad. Sci.*, **38A,** 534 (1953) [*C.A.*, **49,** 2396 (1955)].

[271] Suryanarayana and Tilak, *Current Sci. India*, **22,** 171 (1953) [*C.A.*, **48,** 14212 (1954)].

[272] Acharya, Tilak, and Venkiteswaran, *J. Sci. Ind. Research India*, **14B,** 250 (1955) [*C.A.*, **50,** 15531 (1956)].

[273] Acharya, Suryanarayana, and Tilak, *J. Sci. Ind. Research India*, **14B**, 394 (1955) [*C.A.*, **50,** 12971 (1956)].

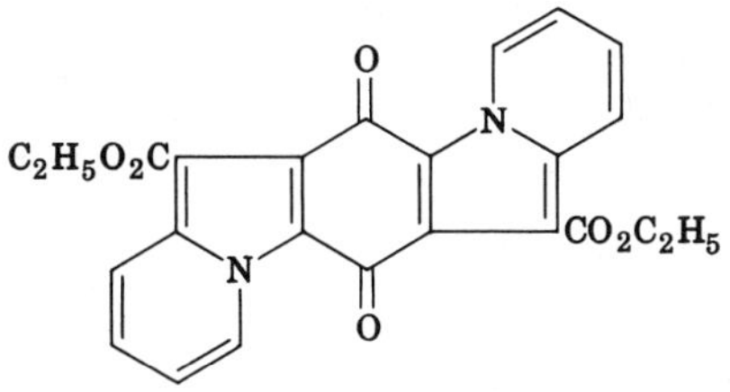

XXVIIA

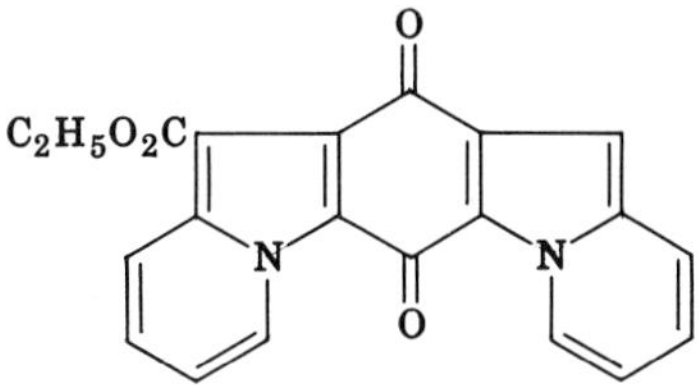

XXVIIB

Chloranil enters also into Michael reactions with β-naphthol or 2-hydroxy-3-naphthanilide. These donors react in their tautomeric keto forms, as in several other instances (see p. 211), and cause the loss of the halogen atoms, leading to compounds of the following type.

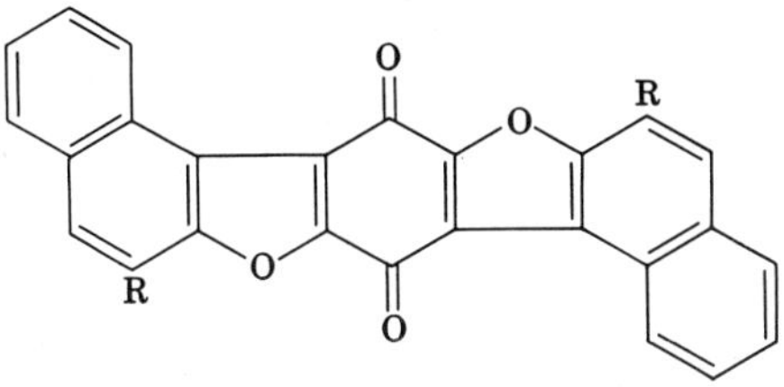

($R = H, CONHC_6H_5$)

Acrylonitrile, Other α,β-Unsaturated Nitriles, and Their Amides (Tables X, XI, and XIA). Acrylonitrile has been used as an acceptor in Michael synthesis more widely than any other derivative of α,β-ethylenic acids. The reaction with acrylonitrile has not only been used for preparative purposes, but it has become a tool for testing organic molecules for enolizable hydrogen atoms. The literature is summarized in Table X, which also brings up to date an earlier review of the cyanoethylation reaction.[274]

Some interesting generalizations emerge from Table X. In aliphatic methyl ketones, a methine group adjacent to the carbonyl is more reactive than a methylene group, and a methylene group is more reactive than a methyl group.[275–277] In cyclohexanone and 2-substituted cyclohexanones, hydrogen in the 2 position reacts first with acrylonitrile;[114,275,278,279] when no more labile hydrogen remains at the 2 position, the 6 position is

[274] Bruson, in Adams, *Organic Reactions*, Vol. 5, p. 79, John Wiley & Sons, 1949. See also U.S. pat. 2,386,736 [*C.A.*, **40**, 7234 (1946)].

[275] Barkley and Levine, *J. Am. Chem. Soc.*, **72**, 3699 (1950).

[276] Campbell, Carter, and Slater, *J. Chem. Soc.*, **1948**, 1741.

[277] Zellars and Levine, *J. Org. Chem.*, **13**, 911 (1948).

[278] Bruson and Niederhauser, U.S. pat. 2,437,906 [*C.A.*, **42**, 4196 (1948)].

[279] Bruson and Riener, *J. Am. Chem. Soc.*, **70**, 214 (1948).

attacked by the nitrile.[275,279] In aryl methyl ketones, all three hydrogen atoms of the methyl group react successively with acrylonitrile.[277]

Nitromethane and nitroethane are reported to give varying yields in the reaction with acrylonitrile.[117,280–282] Dinitromethane, on the other hand, readily gives bis(cyanoethyl)dinitromethane, which loses one nitro group, and the scission product reacts with a third molecule of acrylonitrile to yield tris(cyanoethyl)nitromethane.[809]

$$CH_2(NO_2)_2 \rightarrow (NCCH_2CH_2)_2C(NO_2)_2 \xrightarrow{\text{Hydrolysis}} \underset{\text{XXVIII}}{(NCCH_2CH_2)_2CHNO_2} \rightarrow (NCCH_2CH_2)_3CNO_2$$

In some α,β-ethylenic carbonyl and carboxyl compounds, the inherent possibility of tautomerization to the β,γ-unsaturated forms is enhanced by the reaction with acrylonitrile. From mesityl oxide, for example, a mono and a bis adduct are obtained;[283,284] cf. ref. 764. For the latter, the formula XXIX has been established by degradation. For the former, Bruson and Riener have proposed the α,β-unsaturated structure XXX because of the formation of XXXI by hydrolysis. The evidence does

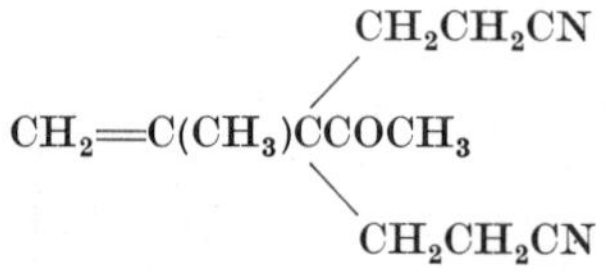

$$CH_2{=}C(CH_3)C(CH_2CH_2CN)_2COCH_3 \quad \text{XXIX}$$

$$(CH_3)_2C{=}C(CH_2CH_2CN)COCH_3 \quad \text{XXX}$$

$$(CH_3)_2C{=}C(CH_2CH_2CO_2H)COCH_3 \quad \text{XXXI}$$

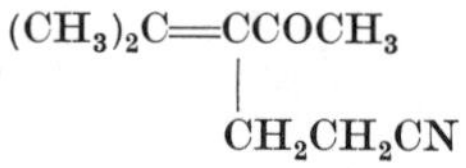

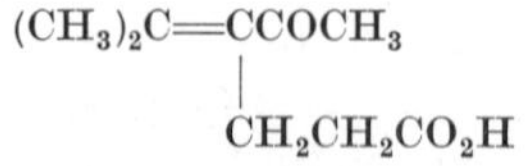

$$CH_2{=}C(CH_3)CH(CH_2CH_2CN)COCH_3 \quad \text{XXXII}$$

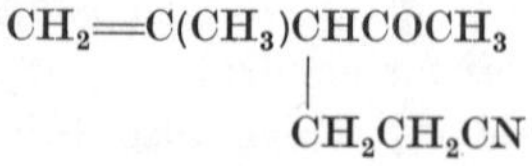

not exclude the possibility, however, that during hydrolysis the double bond shifts into the α,β position and that the correct structure is the one shown in XXXII. In any event, XXXII undoubtedly represents the structure of the primary product of the interaction between acrylonitrile and mesityl oxide.

Revising a previous statement[283] on the reaction of isophorone with acrylonitrile, Bruson and Riener have obtained mono-, bis-, and

[280] Thurston, Can. pat. 443,713 [*C.A.*, **42,** 205 (1948)].

[281] Wulff, Hopff, and Wiest, Ger. pat. 728,531 [*C.A.*, **38,** 376 (1944)].

[282] Bruson and Riener, *J. Am. Chem. Soc.*, **65,** 23 (1943).

[283] Bruson and Riener, *J. Am. Chem. Soc.*, **64,** 2850 (1942).

[284] Bruson and Riener, *J. Am. Chem. Soc.*, **66,** 56 (1944).

tris-cyanoethyl derivatives (XXXIII to XXXV) of isophorone, to which they assigned the following structures (R = CH_2CH_2CN).[285]

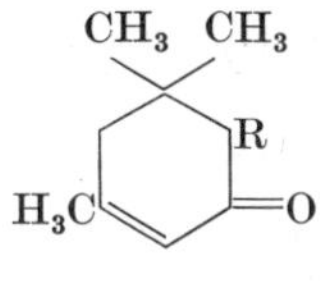

XXXIII 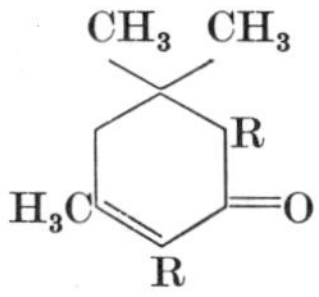 XXIV 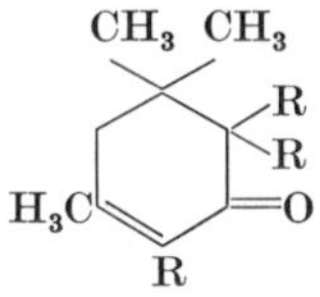 XXXV

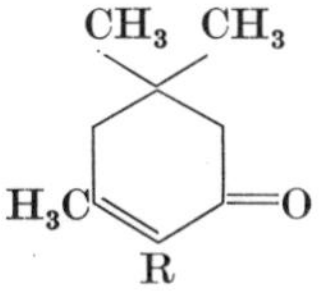

XXXVI 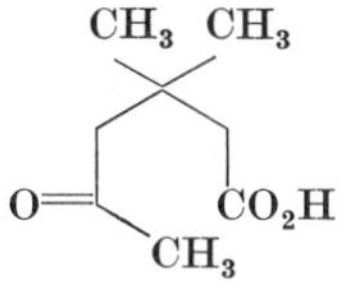 XXXVII 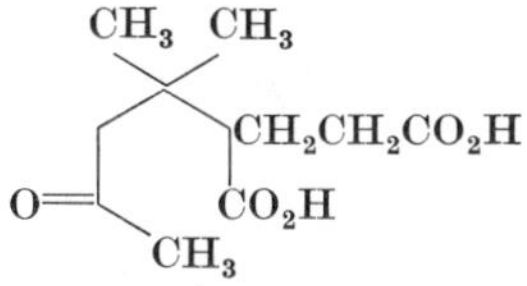 XXXVIII

However, it has been shown[286] that the mono derivative is XXXVI, as it could be ozonized to yield 3,3-dimethyl-5-ketohexanoic acid (XXXVII) (after hydrolysis of the nitrile group), whereas XXXIII should have given XXXVIII. As in the case of mesityl oxide (p. 230), the tautomeric

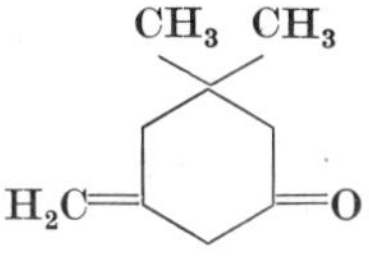

XXXIX 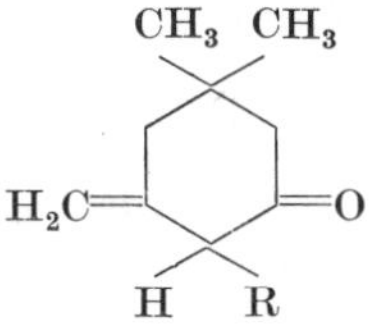 XL

form (XXXIX) of isophorone undergoes reaction; the primary product XL then isomerizes to an α,β-unsaturated ketone. The infrared spectra of the bis and tris products reported by Bruson and Riener[285] suggest the following structures for the mono-, di-, and tri-cyanoethylated products, respectively.

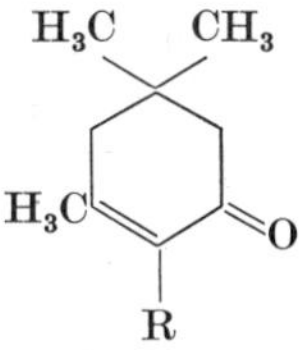

$\lambda = 6.05$ 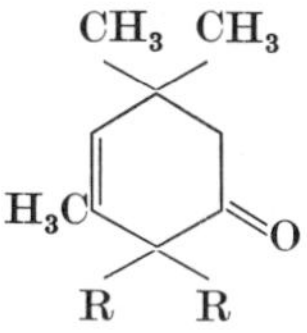 $\lambda = 5.90$ 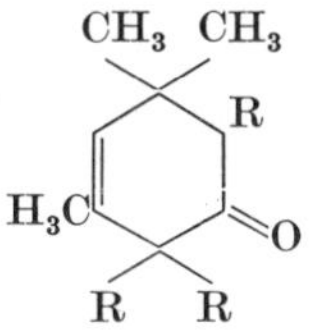 $\lambda = 5.90$

The alkylation of isophorone takes place in an analogous manner.[287]

[285] Bruson and Riener, *J. Am. Chem. Soc.*, **75**, 3585 (1953).
[286] Julia, *Compt. rend.*, **237**, 913 (1953).
[287] Conia, *Bull. soc. chim. France*, **1954**, 690.

2-Ethyl-2-hexenal (XLI) also reacts in the β,γ-isomeric form with crotononitrile and β,β-dimethylacrylonitrile.

$$\underset{\text{XLI}}{CH_3CH_2CH_2CH{=}C(C_2H_5)CHO} \rightleftharpoons CH_3CH_2CH{=}CHCH(C_2H_5)CHO$$

An interesting point emerges from the behavior of compounds such as indene (XLII),[288] which gives a tris(cyanoethyl) derivative. One has to assume that the primary products rearrange to give a new reactive methylene group. In a similar fashion, cyclopentadiene gives a hexacyanoethyl derivative.

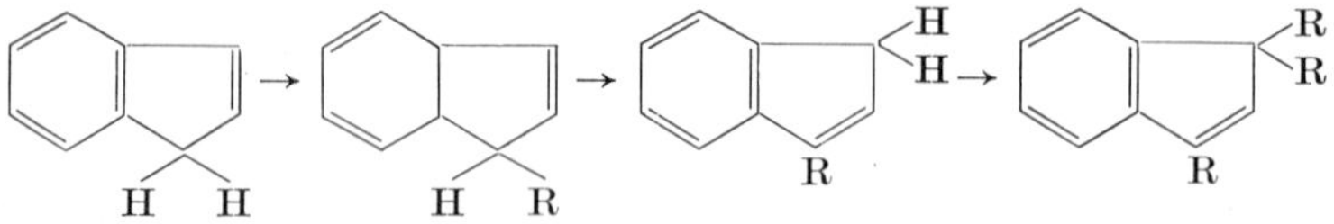

XLII

R = $—CH_2CH_2CN$

In the reaction of dimethylbenzofulvene (XLIII), which gives a mono derivative XLIV, it has been supposed that an isomerization precedes the reaction.

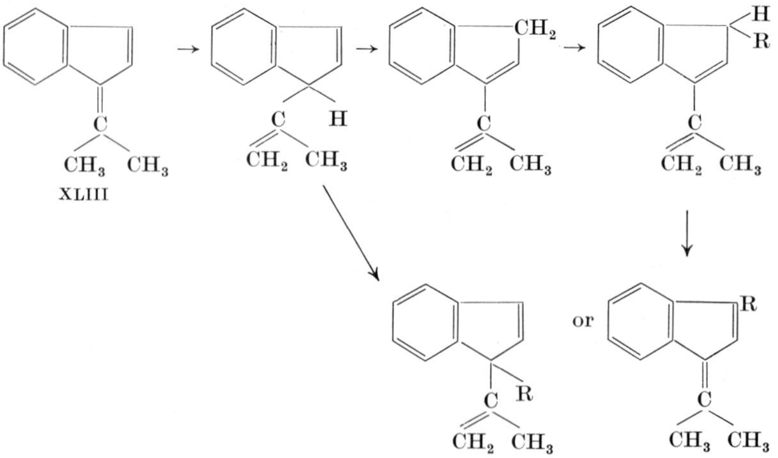

XLIII

XLIV

Kojic acid (XLV) provides an instance in which an enolic hydroxyl group reacts in the tautomeric keto form;[170] after hydrolysis the product is a 6-propionic acid derivative (XLVI) of kojic acid:

[288] Bruson, *J. Am. Chem. Soc.*, **64**, 2457 (1942).

HOH_2C, O, OH, O (XLV) ⇄ HOH_2C, O, =O, O → HOH_2C, O, CH_2CH_2CN, =O, O →

HOH_2C, O, CH_2CH_2CN, OH, O → HOH_2C, O, $CH_2CH_2CO_2H$, OH, O (XLVI)

XLV

XLVI

Considerably less work has been done on the Michael condensation with other unsaturated nitriles. The available data, collected in Table XI, deal mainly with cinnamonitrile,[27,289,290] and allyl cyanide,[27,77,117,291] isomerized to crotononitrile by the alkaline reagents that catalyze the Michael condensation. Table XI also includes some data on 1-cyanobutadiene.[91,292,293] In contradistinction to $\alpha,\beta,\gamma,\delta$-diethylenic ketones (see p. 217), the Michael condensation of 1-cyanobutadiene with nitroalkanes takes place in the 1,6 positions, yielding β,γ-unsaturated nitriles.[293]

α,β-Unsaturated amides could be expected to react in the same manner as the nitriles. Acrylamide adds, in the presence of benzyltrimethylammonium hydroxide, one molecule of 2-nitropropane,[294] and cinnamamide condenses with diethyl sodiomalonate to give the normal 1:1 adduct which cylizes to yield ethyl 2,6-diketo-4-phenylpiperidine-3-carboxylate (XLVII).[294a] However, in the reactions studied (Table XI*A*) acrylamide appears to offer no particular advantage for synthesis.[295]

$$C_6H_5CH{=}CHCONH_2 + CH_2(CO_2C_2H_5)_2 \rightarrow$$

(piperidine ring: C_6H_5, $CO_2C_2H_5$, O=, =O, N, H)

XLVII

[289] Campbell and Fairfull, *J. Chem. Soc.*, **1949,** 1239.

[290] Koelsch, *J. Am. Chem. Soc.*, **65,** 2459 (1943).

[291] Tucker, *J. Chem. Soc.*, **1949,** 2182.

[292] Bruson, U.S. pat. 2,484,683 [*C.A.*, **44,** 5904 (1950)].

[293] Charlish, Davies, and Rose, *J. Chem. Soc.*, **1948,** 227.

[294] Bruson, U.S. pat. 2,370,142 [*C.A.*, **39,** 3544 (1945)].

[294a] Herrmann and Vorlaender, *Chem. Zentr.*, **1899, I,** 730.

[295] Elad and Ginsburg, *J. Chem. Soc.*, **1953,** 4137.

α,β-Ethylenic Aliphatic Esters (Tables XII, XIII, XIV). The Michael condensations that have been carried out with α,β-ethylenic aliphatic esters (Table XII) show that activation by a carbalkoxy group is less strong than that effected by a nitro group.

A number of saturated α- and β-hydroxy esters react with ethyl cyanoacetate as if they were first dehydrated to α,β-ethylenic esters, which then undergo the Michael condensation;[296] the same applies to certain cyanohydrins.[297] In view of the uncertainty of the mechanism, these reactions have not been listed in Table XII. Likewise, the dimerization of methyl acrylate and ethyl acrylate[5,298–300] can be considered formally as involving a Michael reaction, but it probably proceeds by a different mechanism.

The self-condensation of diethyl glutaconate (XLVIII) under the influence of sodium ethoxide is, by contrast, a typical Michael condensation. It can be formulated as involving an intermediary shift of the double bond. Part of the product aromatizes, by elimination of ethyl acetate, to give diethyl 4-hydroxyisophthalate (XLIX).[301] One molecule

$$\underset{\text{XLVIII}}{2C_2H_5O_2CCH_2CH{=}CHCO_2C_2H_5} \rightarrow \begin{array}{c} C_2H_5O_2CCH_2CHCH_2CO_2C_2H_5 \\ | \\ C_2H_5O_2CCHCH{=}CHCO_2C_2H_5 \end{array} \rightarrow$$

$$\begin{array}{c} C_2H_5O_2CCH_2CHCH_2CO_2C_2H_5 \\ | \\ C_2H_5O_2CC{=}CHCH_2CO_2C_2H_5 \end{array} \rightarrow O{=}\text{(ring)}\ [CH_2CO_2C_2H_5,\ CO_2C_2H_5,\ CO_2C_2H_5] \rightarrow$$

$$HO\text{(ring)}\ [CH_2CO_2C_2H_5,\ CO_2C_2H_5,\ CO_2C_2H_5] \rightarrow \underset{\text{XLIX}}{HO\text{(benzene ring)}\ [CO_2C_2H_5,\ CO_2C_2H_5]}$$

of glutaconate, therefore, acts as a donor, and a second one as acceptor. (Under the influence of metallic sodium, a Claisen condensation takes place.)[302] The same interpretation applies to the self-condensation of trimethyl propylene-2,3,3-tricarboxylate, which involvės two successive

[296] Ingold, *J. Chem. Soc.*, **119**, 329 (1921).

[297] See, e.g., Higson and Thorpe, *J. Chem. Soc.*, **89**, 1455 (1906).

[298] Pechmann, *Ber.*, **33**, 3323 (1900).

[299] Pechmann and Roehm, *Ber.*, **34**, 427 (1901).

[300] Bergmann, *Chem. Revs.*, **29**, 529 (1941).

[301] Pechmann, Bauer, and Obermiller, *Ber.*, **37**, 2113 (1904).

[302] Blaise, *Compt. rend.*, **136**, 692 (1903); *Bull. soc. chim. France*, [3], **29**, 1028 (1903).

Michael condensations. The first yields the open-chain ester L, whereas the second is intramolecular and yields the cyclic product LI.[303]

$$\begin{array}{l} H_2C{=}C(CO_2CH_3)CH(CO_2CH_3)_2 \\ \qquad\qquad + \qquad\qquad\qquad \rightarrow \\ (CH_3O_2C)_2CHC(CO_2CH_3){=}CH_2 \end{array}$$

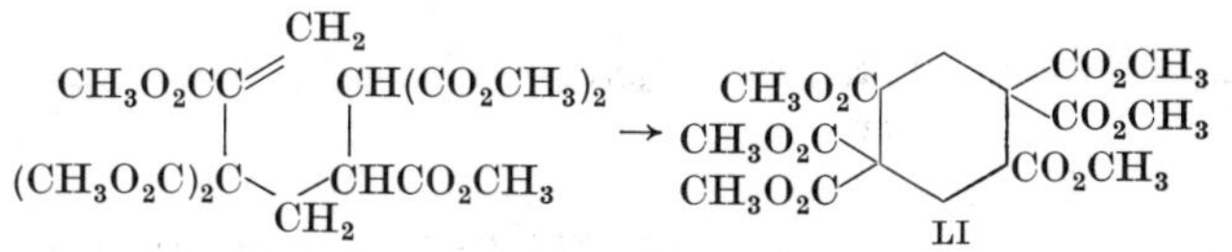

$$\begin{array}{ccc} & CH_2 & \\ CH_3O_2CC\!\!\diagup\!\!\!\!\!\!= & & CH(CO_2CH_3)_2 \\ | & & | \\ (CH_3O_2C)_2C\diagdown & & \diagup CHCO_2CH_3 \\ & CH_2 & \\ & \text{L} & \end{array} \rightarrow \begin{array}{l} CH_3O_2C,\ CH_3O_2C,\ CH_3O_2C \text{ (cyclohexane ring)},\ CO_2CH_3,\ CO_2CH_3,\ CO_2CH_3 \\ \qquad\qquad \text{LI} \end{array}$$

The addition of ethyl 5-methylcyclopentanone-2-carboxylate to ethyl crotonate involves the α-hydrogen atom in the 2 position, and not in the 5 position as erroneously stated in the abstract literature.[304,305]

The Michael reaction is not involved in the condensation of ethyl acetoacetate and diethyl acetone-1,3-dicarboxylate to diethyl 3,5-dihydroxytoluene-2,4-dicarboxylate.[306]

Table XIII is devoted to reactions of β-hydroxy-, β-ethoxy-, and β-amino-α,β-ethylenic esters. These reactions are generally accompanied by the elimination of the β substituent (as water, alcohol, or ammonia, respectively). For example, when ethyl β-ethoxyacrylate is condensed with diethyl methylmalonate under the catalytic influence of benzyltrimethylammonium ethoxide, the expected triester LII not only undergoes ethanolysis to diethyl carbonate and the diester LIII but the diester decomposes further to give ethanol and the unsaturated ester LIV.[307]

$$\begin{array}{ccc} CH_2CO_2C_2H_5 & CH_2CO_2C_2H_5 & CHCO_2C_2H_5 \\ | & | & \| \\ CHOC_2H_5 & CHOC_2H_5 & CH \\ | & | & | \\ CH_3C(CO_2C_2H_5)_2 & CH_3CHCO_2C_2H_5 & CH_3CHCO_2C_2H_5 \\ \text{LII} & \text{LIII} & \text{LIV} \end{array}$$

The behavior of diethyl 2-ethoxyethylene-1,1-dicarboxylate LV is very similar.[308–310] With nitromethane and secondary bases the ester LV

[303] Baker, *J. Chem. Soc.*, **1935,** 188.

[304] Sen-Gupta, Chakraborti, and Bhattacharayya, *J. Indian Chem. Soc.*, **24,** 249 (1947) [*C.A.*, **43,** 2584 (1949)].

[305] Private communication from Dr. B. K. Bhattacharayya.

[306] Koller and Krakauer, *Monatsh.*, **53-54,** 931 (1929).

[307] Croxall and Fegley, *J. Am. Chem. Soc.*, **72,** 970 (1950).

[308] Menon, *J. Chem. Soc.*, **1935,** 1061.

[309] Menon, *J. Chem. Soc.*, **1936,** 1775.

[310] Simonsen, *J. Chem. Soc.*, **93,** 1022 (1908).

undergoes a curious reaction, which has been represented as a Michael reaction followed by scission of the product according to the accompanying scheme.[311] By this reaction, 2-piperidino- and 2-morpholino-1-nitroethylene were obtained in 40 and 34% yield, respectively. Analogously, diethyl 2-ethoxypropylene-1,1-dicarboxylate gave 2-piperidino- and 2-morpholino-1-nitropropene in 21 and 40% yield, respectively.[311]

$$\underset{\text{LV}}{C_2H_5OCH{=}C(CO_2C_2H_5)_2} + CH_3NO_2 \rightarrow C_2H_5O\underset{\displaystyle CH_2NO_2}{\underset{|}{C}}HCH(CO_2C_2H_5)_2 \xrightarrow{R_2NH}$$

$$R_2NCH{=}CHNO_2 + CH_2(CO_2C_2H_5)_2 + C_2H_5OH$$

A β-amino group is not always eliminated. Ethyl β-aminocrotonate[312,313] and ethyl α-methyl-β-aminocrotonate[314] react with diethyl malonate in presence of sodium ethoxide to give the pyridine derivatives LVI. These, however, are not Michael reactions.

$C_2H_5O_2CCH_2$—OC—OC_2H_5 + C_2H_5OCO—$CR{=}CCH_3$—H_2N → ($C_2H_5O_2C$, O=, R, CH_3, NH ring, C=O) → ($C_2H_5O_2C$, OH, R, HO, N, CH_3 pyridine) LVI

R = H, CH_3

It is interesting that dry sodium ethoxide or sodium metal causes a direct condensation of diethyl citraconate (LVII), whereas alcoholic ethoxide solution leads first to isomerization to diethyl itaconate (LVIII) and then to Michael condensation.[315] It is equally worthy of note that,

$$\underset{\text{LVII}}{C_2H_5O_2CC(CH_3){=}CHCO_2C_2H_5} \qquad \underset{\text{LVIII}}{C_2H_5O_2CC({=}CH_2)CH_2CO_2C_2H_5}$$

in the addition of ethyl acetoacetate, ethyl methylacetoacetate, or ethyl cyanoacetate to diethyl citraconate, the α-hydrogen atom of the donor adds to the non-methylated side of the unsaturated ester[316] whereas the addition of diethyl malonate to the unsaturated ester involves the methylated side. Diethyl malonate adds in the same direction to diethyl

[311] Hurd and Sherwood, Jr., *J. Org. Chem.*, **13**, 471 (1948).
[312] Knoevenagel and Fries, *Ber.*, **31**, 767 (1898).
[313] Kooyman and Wibaut, *Rec. trav. chim.*, **65**, 10 (1946).
[314] Wibaut and Kooyman, *Rec. trav. chim.*, **63**, 231 (1944).
[315] Crossley, *J. Chem. Soc.*, **79**, 138 (1901); *Proc. Chem. Soc.*, **16**, 90 (1900).
[316] Mitter and Roy, *J. Indian Chem. Soc.*, **5**, 33 (1928) [*C.A.*, **22**, 3882 (1928)].

mesaconate; this is the only example of the use of this *trans* compound as an acceptor in the Michael condensation.[317]

In the Michael condensation of esters of polycarboxylic acids, two tendencies are apparent. First, the highly substituted reaction products tend to dissociate into simpler substances by elimination of some smaller molecules, such as ethanol or diethyl malonate, with formation of a double bond.[315,318–321] Second, those adducts containing both an enolizable hydrogen atom and a suitable acceptor structure undergo an intramolecular Michael condensation with the formation of a six-membered ring. Tetraethyl propylene-1,1,3,3-tetracarboxylate is reported to lead, under the influence of piperidine or sodium ethoxide, to the cyclobutane derivative LIX,[321–323] and piperidine converts diethyl

$$\begin{array}{ccc} (C_2H_5O_2C)_2CH\,CH & - & C(CO_2C_2H_5)_2 \\ | & & | \\ (C_2H_5O_2C)_2C & - & CHCH(CO_2C_2H_5)_2 \end{array}$$

LIX

$$\begin{array}{ccc} C_2H_5O_2C(CN)C & - & CHCH_2CO_2C_2H_5 \\ | & & | \\ C_2H_5O_2CCH_2CH & - & C(CN)CO_2C_2H_5 \end{array}$$

LX

$$\begin{array}{ccc} C_2H_5O_2C(CN)C & - & CHCH(CH_3)CO_2C_2H_5 \\ | & & | \\ C_2H_5O_2C(CH_3)HCCH & - & C(CN)CO_2C_2H_5 \end{array}$$

LXI

3-cyanopropylene-1,3-dicarboxylate and diethyl 4-cyanobutylene-2,4-dicarboxylate into the cyclobutanes LX and LXI, respectively.[322,323] However, reaction of diethyl acetylenedicarboxylate with tetraethyl ethane-1,1,2,2-tetracarboxylate has been recently shown[324,325] to give not a cyclobutane derivative but hexaethyl butene-1,1,2,2,3,4-hexacarboxylate.

Table XIV summarizes our knowledge of the behavior of aliphatic dienic esters and one trienic ester in the Michael condensation. With the dienic esters, 1,6 addition predominates over 1,4 addition; with the trienic ester, 1,8 addition predominates. This, however, applies only to esters in which the polar groups are unsymmetrically distributed about the double bond; dialkyl muconates, $RO_2CCH{=}CHCH{=}CHCO_2R$, undergo 1,4 addition exclusively, giving $RO_2CCH{=}CHCHR'CH_2CO_2R$.[326]

317 Hope, *J. Chem. Soc.*, **101,** 892 (1912).

318 Cornforth and Robinson, *J. Chem. Soc.*, **1949,** 1855.

319 Cox and McElvain, *J. Am. Chem. Soc.*, **56,** 2459 (1934).

320 Cox, Kroeker, and McElvain, *J. Am. Chem. Soc.*, **56,** 1173 (1934).

321 Guthzeit, *Ber.*, **34,** 675 (1901).

322 Ingold, Perren, and Thorpe, *J. Chem. Soc.*, **121,** 1765 (1922), especially p. 1788.

323 Verkade, *Verslag. Akad. Wetenschappen Amsterdam*, **27,** 1130 (1919) [*C.A.*, **13,** 3149 (1919)].

324 Overberger and Kabasakalian, *J. Am. Chem. Soc.*, **75,** 6058 (1953).

325 Reid, *Chemistry & Industry*, **1953,** 846.

326 Farmer, *J. Chem. Soc.*, **121,** 2015 (1922).

Alicyclic and Aromatic α,β-Ethylenic Esters (Tables XV and XVI). In the alicyclic series, a small number of Michael condensations have been carried out (Table XV). These proceed normally, and the only point of interest is that the reactions of ethyl cyclopentenecarboxylate with ethyl acetoacetate and diethyl malonate, respectively, give exclusively the *trans* form of the reaction products.[92] As pointed out on p. 199, relatively little is known of the stereochemistry of the Michael reaction.

In the aromatic series, even fewer reactions have been studied (Table XVI). Acetophenone gives a Michael condensation with methyl and ethyl cinnamate; it is in competition, however, with a Claisen condensation between the reactants under the influence of sodium amide or sodium. Acetone undergoes with alkyl cinnamates the Claisen reaction exclusively.[327,328]

The three dienic esters that have been studied do not give a consistent picture. In two of them 1,6 and in one 1,4 addition takes place, without any obvious difference either in the structure of the unsaturated ester or in the operating conditions.[56,194,195,329]

Ortho-substituted aromatic α,β-ethylenic esters provide ideal structures for internal Michael condensation. If one introduces in the ortho position to the unsaturated ester group a substituent that contains an enolizable hydrogen atom at a suitable distance from the ring, a bicyclic system can be formed easily. This possibility has been utilized with substances of the general formula LXII for the synthesis of bicyclic systems such as LXIII, where X = O, S, or N-alkyl. The pertinent data form the second part of Table XVI, in which an analogous case from the alicyclic series is also included.

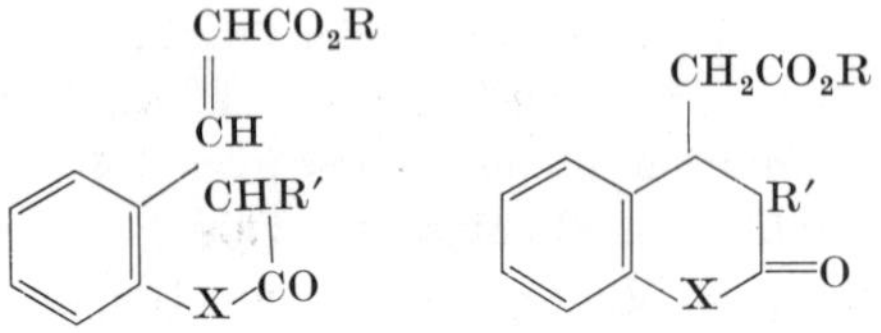

$CHCO_2R$ ‖ CH, CHR′, X, CO

LXII

CH_2CO_2R, R′, X, =O

LXIII

Unsaturated Keto Esters (Table XVII). Table XVII contains the scanty material pertaining to the Michael condensation of unsaturated keto esters, in which the double bond is activated both by a keto and an ester group.[8,120,310,330,331] It is interesting to note that in esters of the type $RCOCH{=}CHCO_2R'$, the keto group gives a more stable carbanion

327 Hauser, Yost, and Ringler, *J. Org. Chem.*, **14**, 261 (1949).

328 Ryan and Dunlea, *Proc. Roy. Irish Acad.*, **32B**, 1 (1913) [*Chem. Zentr.*, **1913, II**, 2039].

329 Kohler and Engelbrecht, *J. Am. Chem. Soc.*, **41**, 764 (1919).

330 Errera, *Ber.*, **33**, 2969, 3469 (1900).

331 Palit, *J. Indian Chem. Soc.*, **14**, 354 (1937) [*C.A.*, **32**, 561 (1938)].

than the ester group: the Michael condensation with a donor R″H leads to a product of the structure $RCOCH_2CHR''CO_2R'$.

Theoretically, it should be possible to effect internal Michael condensations with *o*-acetyl derivatives of cinnamic acid. It has, indeed, been found that methyl *o*-acetylcinnamate reacts with sodium methoxide, but the expected product LXIV could not be isolated in pure form.[332]

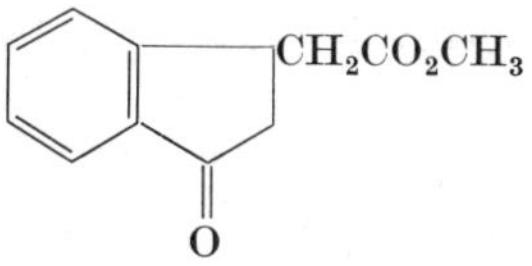

$CH_2CO_2CH_3$

O

LXIV

Aromatic α,β-Acetylenic Esters (Table XVIII). In the aromatic series, as in the aliphatic, an acetylenic bond in conjunction with an ester group behaves in the Michael condensation like a double bond (Table XVIII). In certain cases, the correct formulation of the anion of the primary product of the condensation appears uncertain. It has been observed, for example, that the condensation of ethyl phenylpropiolate with diethyl malonate, using ethanolic sodium ethoxide and using sodium in benzene, lead to different anions, formulated as LXV and LXVI.[25,26,333,334] This problem is discussed on p. 186.

$$[C_2H_5O_2CCH{=}C(C_6H_5)\overset{\ominus}{C}(CO_2C_2H_5)_2]Na^{\oplus}$$

LXV

$$[C_2H_5O_2C\overset{\ominus}{C}{=}C(C_6H_5)CH(CO_2C_2H_5)_2]Na^{\oplus}$$

LXVI

It is often thought that the reaction between acetylenic esters and substances like 2-picoline or quinaldine is a specific case of the Michael condensation, although the components react in a 2:1 ratio. Diethyl acetylenedicarboxylate and 2-picoline yield the conjugated diene LXVII;

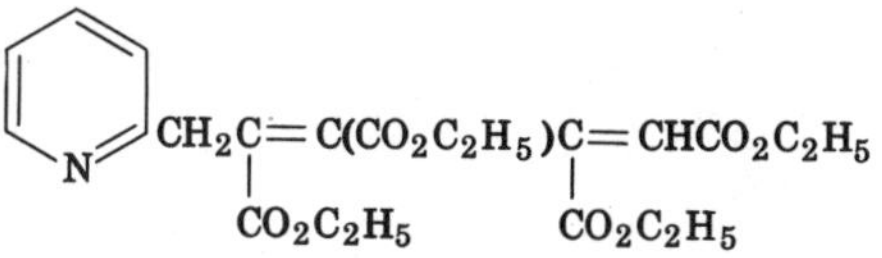

$$\text{(2-pyridyl)}CH_2C(CO_2C_2H_5){=}C(CO_2C_2H_5)C(CO_2C_2H_5){=}CHCO_2C_2H_5$$

LXVII

CH_3O_2C ... N ... =O, CO_2CH_3, CO_2CH_3

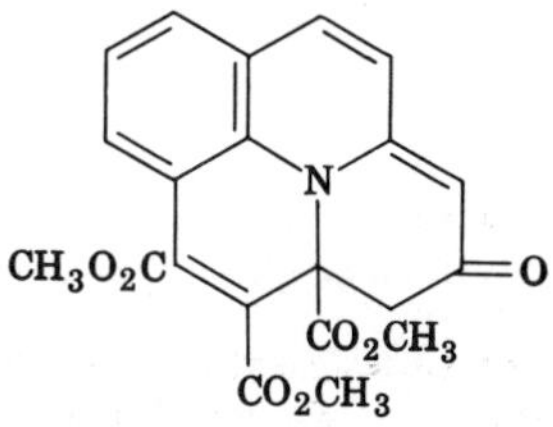

LXVIII

[332] Koelsch and Stephens, Jr., *J. Am. Chem. Soc.*, **72,** 2209 (1950).
[333] Farmer, Ghosal, and Kon, *J. Chem. Soc.*, **1936,** 1804.
[334] Michael, *J. Org. Chem.*, **2,** 303 (1938).

the acetylenic dimethyl ester with 2-quinaldine gives the analogous, but more complex, product LXVIII.[335–337]

It is known that similar dimeric forms of acetylenic compounds often occur in the Diels-Alder reaction at least as formal intermediary products.[338]

Olefins with Substituents Based on Hetero Atoms (N, S, P; Tables XIX, XX, XXI). A nitro group activates a double bond to which it is attached as it activates adjacent hydrogen atoms. Table XIX summarizes the Michael condensations involving α,β-ethylenic nitro compounds. Data pertaining to hydroxymethylenenitroacetaldehyde (the enolic form of nitromalondialdehyde, LXIX) are included. This

$$O_2NC(=CHOH)CHO\ (\text{LXIX}) + CH_2CH_3COCH_3 \rightarrow O_2NCH(CHO)-CHOH-CHCH_3(COCH_3) \rightarrow$$

$$O_2NCH(-CHOH-CHCH_3-CO-CH=CH-) \rightarrow O_2N\text{-}C_6H_3(CH_3)(OH)$$

compound reacts with many donor molecules, including even aliphatic ketones, to give derivatives of 4-nitrophenol.[111,339–343] The reaction with methyl ethyl ketone is illustrative. The activating power of the nitro group is so great that *o*- and *p*-nitrostyrene can also act as acceptors in

$$C_6H_4(NO_2)CH{=}CH_2 + CH_3COCH_2CO_2C_2H_5 \rightarrow C_6H_4(NO_2)CH_2CH_2CH(COCH_3)CO_2C_2H_5$$

[335] Diels, Alder, et al., *Ann.*, **498,** 16 (1932).

[336] Diels and Kech, *Ann.*, **519,** 140 (1935).

[337] Diels and Pistor, *Ann.*, **530,** 87 (1937).

[338] Diels and Alder, *Ann.*, **498,** 16 (1932); *ibid.*, **505,** 103 (1933); *ibid.*, **510,** 87 (1934); Diels and Kock, *ibid.*, **556,** 38 (1944).

[339] Hill and Torrey, Jr., *Am. Chem. J.*, **22,** 89 (1899).

[340] Hill and Hale, *Am. Chem. J.*, **33,** 1 (1905).

[341] Hill, *Ber.*, **33,** 1241 (1900).

[342] Prelog and Wiesner, *Helv. Chim. Acta*, **30,** 1465 (1947).

[343] Prelog, Wiesner, Ingold, and Haefliger, *Helv. Chim. Acta*, **31,** 1325 (1948).

the Michael reactions. Formally, the addition of the donor takes place in the γ,δ and ε,ζ positions of the activated unsaturated system, respectively.[344]

It appears that the S=O bond in sulfoxides and sulfones (Table XX) has sufficient double bond character to conjugate with and activate neighboring ethylenic double bonds.[345–354] In this respect, it is recalled that 1,2-bis(arylsulfonyl)ethenes are highly active dienophiles,[355] and that vinyl sulfones add aromatic hydrocarbons in the presence of aluminum chloride in the same manner as do α,β-unsaturated ketones.[356] Organomagnesium and organolithium compounds also add 1,4 to α,β-unsaturated sulfones.[357]

Table XX also includes the Michael reactions of N,N-diethylvinylsulfonanilide[358] and the interesting condensations of vinyldimethylsulfonium bromide with ethyl acetoacetate and diethyl malonate.[22]

Reactions involving diethyl vinylphosphonate, $CH_2{=}CHPO(OC_2H_5)_2$, a newly discovered type of acceptor in the Michael reaction, are listed in Table XXI. It has already been pointed out (p. 204) that compounds containing phosphono groups have sufficiently active hydrogen atoms to serve as donors in the Michael condensation. The reaction referred to here leads to the supposition that the P=O bond, like the S=O bond, is able to form a conjugated system with an adjacent ethylenic linkage.

2- and 4-Vinylpyridines (Table XXI). Although practically no work appears to have been done on the ability of the open-chain system C=C—C=N to undergo Michael condensations (see p. 207), the behavior of 2- and 4-vinylpyridine shows that, at least under certain conditions, this system gives typical Michael products. The reactions investigated appear in Table XXI.[359]

[344] Dale and Strobel, *J. Am. Chem. Soc.*, **76**, 6172 (1954).

[345] Samuel, *J. Chem. Physics*, **12**, 380 (1944); *ibid.*, **13**, 572 (1945); Bergmann and Tschudnowsky, *Ber.*, **65**, 457 (1932); Lister and Sutton, *Trans. Faraday Soc.*, **35**, 495 (1939). See, however, Arndt and Eistert, *Ber.*, **74**, 423 (1941).

[346] Koch, *J. Chem. Soc.*, **1950**, 2892.

[347] Karrer, Antia, and Schwyzer, *Helv. Chim. Acta*, **34**, 1392 (1951).

[348] Varsanyi and Ladik, *Acta Chim. Acad. Sci. Hung.*, **3**, 243 (1953) [*C.A.*, **47**, 11000 (1953)].

[349] Kloosterziel and Backer, *Rec. trav. chim.*, **72**, 185 (1953).

[350] Zollinger, Buechler, and Wittwer, *Helv. Chim. Acta*, **36**, 1711 (1953).

[351] Bordwell and Andersen, *J. Am. Chem. Soc.*, **75**, 6019 (1953).

[352] Jaffé, *J. Phys. Chem.*, **58**, 185 (1954).

[353] Price and Morita, *J. Am. Chem. Soc.*, **75**, 4747 (1953).

[354] Price and Gillis, *J. Am. Chem. Soc.*, **75**, 4750 (1953).

[355] Truce and McManimie, *J. Am. Chem. Soc.*, **75**, 1672 (1953).

[356] Truce, Simms, and Hill, *J. Am. Chem. Soc.*, **75**, 5411 (1953).

[357] Potter, *J. Am. Chem. Soc.*, **76**, 5472 (1954).

[358] Buess and Jones, *J. Am. Chem. Soc.*, **76**, 5558 (1954).

[359] For the addition of enolizable hydrogen compounds to the C=N double bond itself, see Lazzareschi[153] and Philpott and Jones.[151]

Fulvenes. Calculations as well as physical and chemical evidence have shown that the fulvenes, represented by the formula LXX, possess a polar double bond.[360,361] It is, therefore, not surprising that fulvenes are

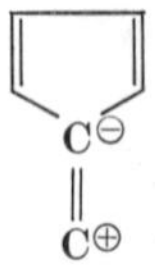

LXX

also acceptors in the Michael condensation. The experimental material on the subject is scanty,[362,363] and the only donors that have been tested so far are fluorenes. Thus dibiphenyleneëthylene (LXXI) adds fluorene under the catalytic influence of sodium hydroxide, to give an 82% yield

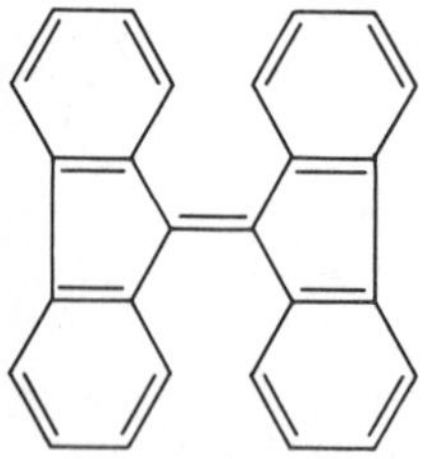

LXXI

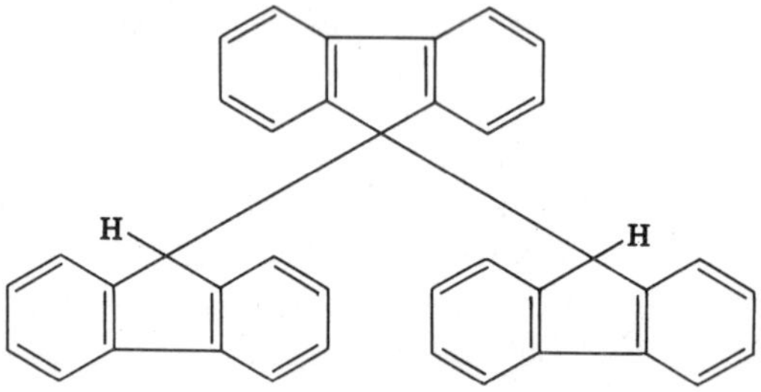

LXXII

of tribiphenylenepropane (LXXII). The same reaction can be effected between 2,7-dibromofluorene and 2,7,2′,7′-tetrabromodibiphenylene-ethylene.

It is to be expected that these highly substituted systems will show a considerable tendency to dissociate (in the way that decaphenylbutane dissociates into pentaphenylethyl).[364] Thus one can explain the observation that 9-aminofluorene (LXXIII) reacts with dibiphenyleneëthylene (LXXIV) in the presence of ammonia to give dibiphenyleneëthane (LXXV) and fluorenone imide (LXXVI) by the accompanying equation. 9-Fluorenol behaves analogously. The observation that 2,7,2′,7′-tetra-bromodibiphenyleneëthylene and fluorene yield the dibromo derivative

[360] Pullman, Berthier, and Pullman, *Bull. soc. chim. France*, **1950**, 1097.

[361] Bergmann and Fischer, *Bull. soc. chim. France*, **1950**, 1084.

[362] Pinck and Hilbert, *J. Am. Chem. Soc.*, **68**, 2014 (1946).

[363] Pinck and Hilbert, *J. Am. Chem. Soc.*, **68**, 2739 (1946).

[364] Schlenk and Mark, *Ber.*, **55**, 2296 (1922).

(LXXVII) and 2,7-dibromofluorene can be understood on the basis of a sequence of condensation and disproportionation steps.

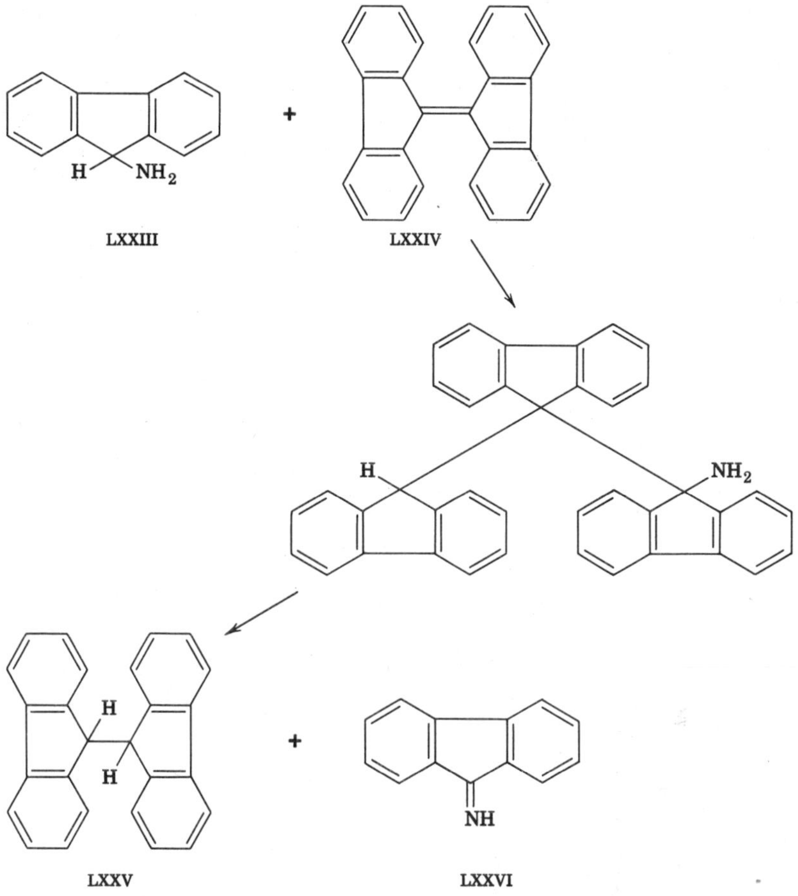

LXXIII + LXXIV

LXXV + LXXVI

2,7-Dibromofluorene and dibiphenyleneëthylene give with sodium ethoxide as catalyst a 58% yield of α-(2,7-dibromobiphenylene)-β,γ-dibiphenylenepropane (LXXVII), whereas, in the presence of potassium hydroxide and pyridine, α,β-bis-(2,7-dibromobiphenylene)-γ-biphenylene-propane (LXXVIII) is formed. Thermal decomposition of these two compounds gives, inter alia, 2,7-dibromodibiphenyleneëthylene, 2,7-dibromodibiphenyleëthane, 2,7,2′,7′-tetrabromodibiphenyleneëthylene, and 2,7,2′,7′-tetrabromodibiphenyleneëthane (formulas on p. 244).

The second fulvene derivative that has been employed as an acceptor

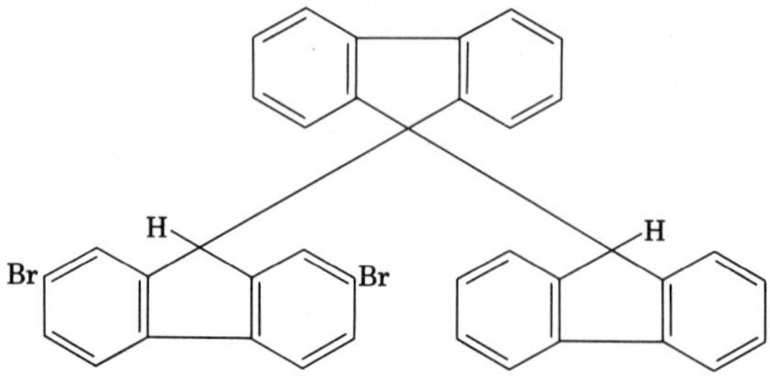

LXXVII

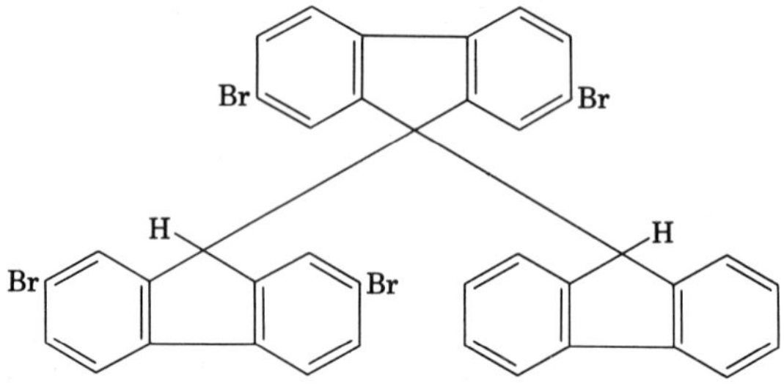

LXXVIII

in the Michael condensation is benzylidenefluorene (LXXIX), which adds fluorene in 70% yield under the influence of a mixture of pyridine and aqueous sodium hydroxide. In accordance with the direction of the dipole moment in the semicyclic double bond of the fulvenes, the product is α,γ-dibiphenylene-β-phenylpropane (LXXX).[365]

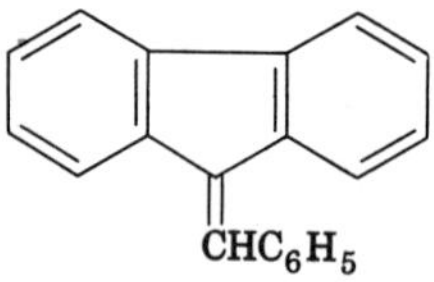

CHC_6H_5
LXXIX

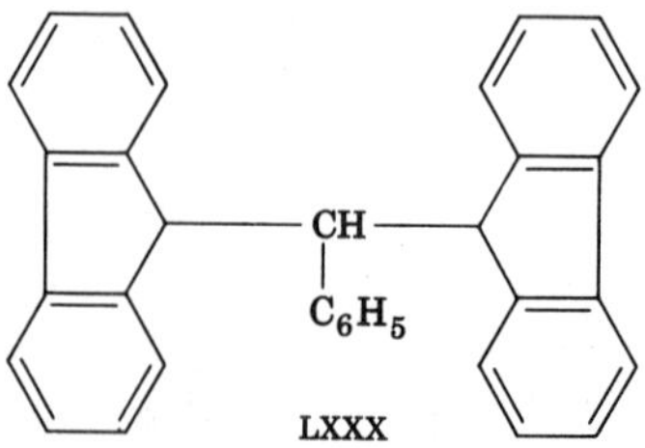

CH
C_6H_5
LXXX

It is not surprising that formylfluorene, i.e., 9-hydroxymethylene-fluorene, is also capable of undergoing the Michael condensation (see pp. 221, 235). Formylfluorene has been converted by reaction with malonic

[365] Bergmann and Lavie, *J. Am. Chem. Soc.*, **74**, 3173 (1952).

acid (with loss of water and carbon dioxide) to β-(9-fluorenylidene)-propionic acid (LXXXI) in 11% yield.[366]

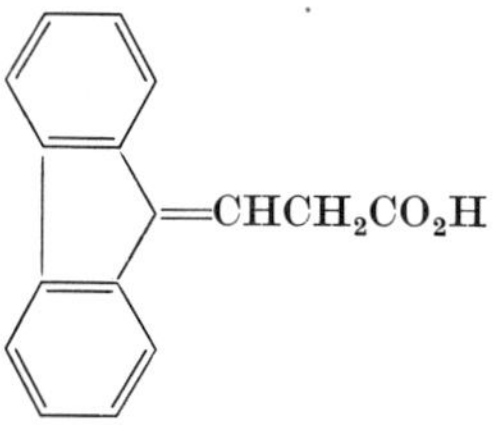

$$=CHCH_2CO_2H$$

LXXXI

Systems That Did Not Undergo Condensation

The following is a list of reactant systems that have not given Michael condensation products. The listing is in order of increasing number of carbon atoms in the acceptor.

Acrylonitrile and diethyl acetosuccinate.[367]

Methyl vinyl sulfone and ethyl phenylacetate, acetophenone, or benzyl *p*-tolyl sulfone.[118]

Methyl vinyl ketone and "Inhoffen's ketone."[368]

Methyl isopropenyl ketone and cyclopentanone.[369]

Acetylacetone and chloroacetamide, phenylacetamide, benzyl cyanide,[370] or α-cyanopropionamide.[371]

Ethyl acrylate and 3-acetyloxindole or 1-methyl-3-acetyloxindole.[372]

Methyl crotonate and nitropropane in the presence of diethylamine.[373]

Mesityl oxide and 2-quinaldine.[374]

Crotonaldehyde with N-(1,3-dimethylbutylidene)-1,3-dimethylbutylamine.[375]

Ethyl crotonate and 2,7-dibromofluorene.[376]

p-Benzoquinone and ethyl N-acetyl-β-aminocrotonate or diethyl aminomethylenemalonate.[377]

[366] Borsche and Niemann, *Ber.*, **69**, 1993(1936).
[367] Blood and Linstead, *J. Chem. Soc.*, **1952**, 2255.
[368] Pinder and Robinson, *J. Chem. Soc.*, **1952**, 1224.
[369] Colonge and Dreux, *Bull. soc. chim. France*, **1952**, 47.
[370] Basu, *J. Indian Chem. Soc.*, **7**, 815 (1930) [*C.A.*, **25**, 1528 (1931)].
[371] Bardhan, *J. Chem. Soc.*, **1929**, 2223.
[372] Julian and Printy, *J. Am. Chem. Soc.*, **75**, 5301 (1953).
[373] Kloetzel, *J. Am. Chem. Soc.*, **70**, 3571 (1948).
[374] Weiss and Hauser, *J. Am. Chem. Soc.*, **71**, 2026 (1949).
[375] Smith, Norton, and Ballard, *J. Am. Chem. Soc.*, **75**, 3316 (1953).
[376] Taylor and Connor, *J. Org. Chem.*, **6**, 696 (1941).
[377] Beer, Davenport, and Robertson, *J. Chem. Soc.*, **1953**, 1262.

3-Methyl-2-cyclopentenone and ethyl acetoacetate.[378]

Ethyl α-acetamidoacrylate and oxindole.[379]

1-Acetylcyclohexene and 6-methoxy-9-methyl-1-keto-1,4,5,6,7,8,9,10-octahydronaphthalene.[380]

Methyl 5-methyl-2-hexenoate or δ-methylsorbate with dimethyl malonate or methyl cyanoacetate.[381]

1-Acetyl-2-methylcyclohexene with various reagents.[382–387]

Trimethylquinone and biacetyl or its half-acetal.[388]

Methyl α-cyano-β-methylsorbate and methyl cyanoacetate.[381]

Ethyl β-diethylaminovinyl ketone and 2-methylcyclohexanone.[389]

Trimethylquinone monomethylimine and 3,3-dimethoxy-2-butanone.[388]

Methyl 2-hydroxystyryl ketone and ethyl oxaloacetate, ethyl cyanoacetate, or diethyl malonate.[38]

Methyl α-cyclohexylideneëthyl ketone with diethyl malonate.[390]

4-Phenyl-2-methylamino-2-buten-4-one and ethyl cyanoacetate.[391]

Diethyl 1-pentene-1,3-dicarboxylate and ethyl cyanoacetate.[392]

Ethyl cinnamate or diethyl benzylidenemalonate and fluorene or 2,7-dibromofluorene.[376]

Diethyl 2-acetyl-2-hexene-1,6-dioate and 1-tetralone or 6-methoxy-1-tetralone.[206,393]

2-Dimethylamino- or 2-morpholino-benzosuberone or their methiodides with biacetyl or its monoxime.[394]

3-Phenyl-5,5-dimethyl-2-cyclohexenone and diethyl malonate, ethyl cyanoacetate, or nitromethane.[395]

3-Benzylidene-6-formylcyclohexanone and 5-diethylaminopentane-2,3-dione-3-monoxime or its methiodide.[394]

[378] Acheson, *J. Chem. Soc.*, **1952,** 3415.

[379] Julian, Printy, Ketcham, and Doone, *J. Am. Chem. Soc.*, **75,** 5305 (1953).

[380] Nazarov and Zav'yalov, *Izvest. Akad. Nauk S.S.S.R. Otdel. Khim. Nauk*, **1952,** 437 [*C.A.*, **47,** 5365 (1953)].

[381] Reid and Sause, *J. Chem. Soc.*, **1954,** 516.

[382] Bagchi and Banerjee, *J. Indian Chem. Soc.*, **23,** 397 (1946) [*C.A.*, **42,** 1601 (1948)].

[383] Dimroth, *Angew. Chem.*, **59,** 215 (1947).

[384] Huber, *Ber.*, **71,** 725 (1938).

[385] Johnson, Szmuszkovicz, and Miller, *J. Am. Chem. Soc.*, **72,** 3726 (1950).

[386] Ludevitz, Dissertation, Goettingen, 1944.

[387] Turner and Voitle, *J. Am. Chem. Soc.*, **72,** 4166 (1950).

[388] Smith and Dale, *J. Org. Chem.*, **15,** 832 (1950).

[389] Hills and McQuillin, *J. Chem. Soc.*, **1953,** 4060.

[390] Kon, *J. Chem. Soc.*, **1926,** 1792.

[391] Basu, *J. Indian Chem. Soc.*, **12,** 299 (1935) [*C.A.*, **29,** 6878 (1935)].

[392] Thorpe and Wood, *J. Chem. Soc.*, **103,** 1579 (1913).

[393] Peak, Robinson, and Walker, *J. Chem. Soc.*, **1936,** 752.

[394] Tarbell, Wilson, and Ott, *J. Am. Chem. Soc.*, **74,** 6263 (1952).

[395] Woods, *J. Am. Chem. Soc.*, **69,** 2549 (1947).

Benzylideneacetophenone and diethyl cyanomalonate,[125] diethyl ethylmalonate,[396] diethyl butylmalonate[125] or diethyl phenylmalonate.[125]

m- or *p*-Nitrobenzylideneacetophenone and fluorene.[376]

α-Cyanostilbene and ethyl phenylacetate.[82]

Diethyl cinnamylidenemalonate and methyl cyanoacetate.[397]

cis-Dibenzoylethylene and diethyl benzylmalonate.[58]

2-Acetyl-1,3-diphenyl-2-propen-1-al and ethyl tetrahydroanthranilate.[398]

Ethyl 2,4-diphenylbutadiene-1-carboxylate and ethyl cyanoacetate.[397]

2-(Trimethylquinonyl)methylene-3,5,6-trimethyl-2-acetoxy- (or methoxy-)3,5-cyclohexadienone with diethyl malonate or ethyl cyanoacetate.[399]

Unsaturated carbonyl-bridged system such as

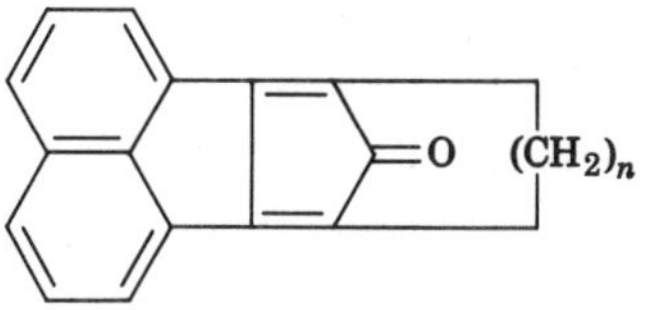

=O $(CH_2)_n$

with diethyl malonate or cyanoacetamide.[400]

Diethyl benzylidenemalonate and nitroethane.[86]

2,3-Dichloro-1,4-naphthoquinone and acetone.[273]

Mesityl oxide and cyclohexanone.[401]

Acrylonitrile and diethyl trimethylsuccinate, which appears to give an O-substituted derivative of the enol form.[402]

3-Methyl-4-amino-3-penten-2-one and cyanoacetamide.[398]

2-Methylcycloheptylideneacetonitrile and cyanoacetamide.[402a]

Examination of these examples does not lead to definite conclusions as to the factors responsible for the failure of the condensation. However, the qualitative impression gained is that many substituents about the reacting centers tend to prevent the reaction. In the donors, this can be ascribed to lowering acidity, but steric factors undoubtedly also play a part in interfering with the condensation. As a case in point, the failure of diethyl phenylmalonate to undergo any Michael reaction[403] may be cited.

[396] de Benneville, Clagett, and Connor, *J. Org. Chem.*, **6**, 690 (1941).

[397] Bloom and Ingold, *J. Chem. Soc.*, **1931**, 2765.

[398] Basu, *J. Indian Chem. Soc.*, **8**, 319 (1931) [*C.A.*, **26**, 458 (1932)].

[399] Smith, Davis, Jr., and Sogn, *J. Am. Chem. Soc.*, **72**, 3651 (1950).

[400] Allen and Van Allan, *J. Org. Chem.*, **18**, 882 (1953).

[401] Braude and Wheeler, *J. Chem. Soc.*, **1955**, 329.

[402] Talukdar and Bagchi, *J. Org. Chem.*, **20**, 13 (1955).

[402a] Kandiah and Linstead, *J. Chem. Soc.*, **1929**, 2139.

[403] Connor, *J. Am. Chem. Soc.*, **55**, 4597 (1933).

SYNTHETIC APPLICATIONS

Certain products of the Michael condensation may be used for the preparation of amino acids; others may undergo spontaneous cyclization or cycloisomerization reactions and thus open routes to a variety of ring compounds. In particular, the Robinson modification of the Michael reaction has been utilized for the synthesis of alicyclic ring systems (Table VIII). It seems, therefore, desirable to give a systematic picture of these synthetic possibilities.

Synthesis of Cyclic Systems

Cyclopropane Rings. Compounds that serve as intermediates for the formation of products containing the cyclopropane ring can be obtained by Michael condensation. For example, the product of the Michael reaction between benzylideneacetophenone and dimethyl malonate can be brominated and dehydrobrominated to yield a cyclopropane

$$\underset{\displaystyle |\atop \displaystyle CH(CO_2CH_3)_2}{C_6H_5CHCH_2COC_6H_5} \xrightarrow{Br_2} \underset{\displaystyle |\atop \displaystyle CH(CO_2CH_3)_2}{C_6H_5CHCHBrCOC_6H_5} \xrightarrow{Mg(OCH_3)_2}$$

H₅C₆ — COC₆H₅ / CH₃O₂C CO₂CH₃ (cyclopropane)

LXXXII

derivative (LXXXII), as shown in the formulation.[404] Many highly substituted cyclopropane derivatives can be prepared by this route.

Cyclobutane Rings. It has been reported that cyclobutane derivatives were formed by intramolecular Michael condensation of esters of certain polycarboxylic acids.[322,323,405] Recent investigations[324,325] have shown, however, that reaction of diethyl acetylenedicarboxylate with, for example, tetraethyl ethane-1,1,2,2-tetracarboxylate does not give hexaethyl cyclobutane-1,2,3,3,4,4-hexacarboxylate but hexaethyl butene-1,1,2,2,3,4-hexacarboxylate.

Cyclopentane Rings. Cyclopentanone derivatives are formed *in situ* by Dieckmann condensation of the primary adducts of the Michael condensation between ethyl citraconate (or itaconate) and malonates or

[404] Kohler and Conant, *J. Am. Chem. Soc.*, **39**, 1404 (1917).

[405] Guthzeit, Weiss, and Shaefer, *J. prakt. Chem.*, [2], **80**, 393 (1909).

substituted malonates.[6,145,406] (Compare also the analogous formation of cyclopentanones from cyclopropane derivatives; see pp. 205–207).

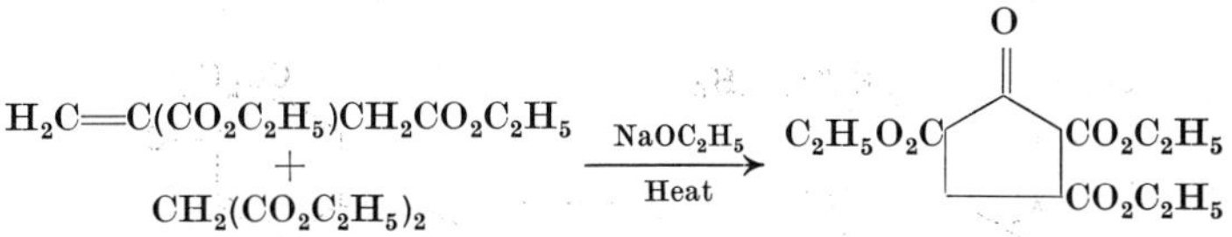

$$H_2C{=}C(CO_2C_2H_5)CH_2CO_2C_2H_5 + CH_2(CO_2C_2H_5)_2 \xrightarrow[\text{Heat}]{NaOC_2H_5} \text{2-oxocyclopentane-1,3,3-tricarboxylate } (C_2H_5O_2C, CO_2C_2H_5, CO_2C_2H_5)$$

Cyclohexane and Condensed Alicyclic Ring Systems. Divinyl ketones of the dibenzylideneacetone type react with donors that contain an active methylene group according to the accompanying general equation, yielding substituted cyclohexanones (LXXXIII).[198–200]

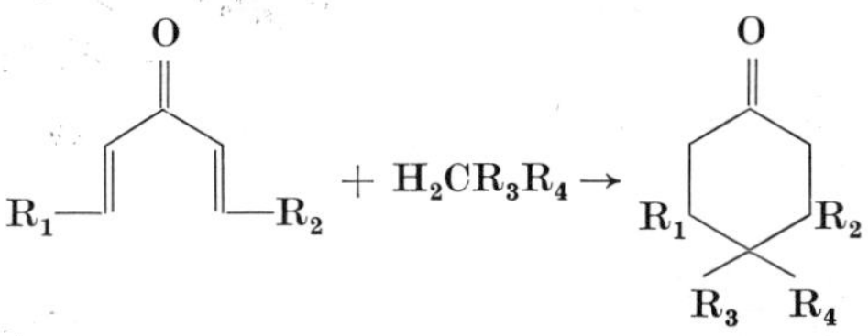

$$R_1CH{=}CH{-}CO{-}CH{=}CHR_2 + H_2CR_3R_4 \rightarrow \text{cyclohexanone with } R_1, R_2 \text{ at 3,5 and } R_3, R_4 \text{ at 4}$$

LXXXIII

In general, Michael adducts of unsaturated aldehydes and ketones with ethyl acetoacetate easily undergo a secondary condensation between the terminal methyl group of the adduct and the carbonyl group of the original acceptor molecule. In a fair number of cases, this cyclization reaction is accompanied by the elimination of the carbethoxy group. This reaction is illustrated by the synthesis of the keto esters LXXXIV,[229] LXXXV,[15,16,17] and LXXXVI.[407] In the last example, the reaction stops at the intermediary aldol stage, without the additional dehydration step[408] (see equations on p. 250).

Obviously, the same reaction will take place whenever 1,5-diketones of the above type are formed, e.g., in the condensation product of ethyl cyclohexanone-2-carboxylate and ethylideneacetone or benzylideneacetone, yielding LXXXVII (R = CH_3 or C_6H_5).[409] A similar cyclization takes place with the adduct of 1-tetralone and ethylideneacetoacetate or

[406] Toivonen, John, Sainio, and Kuusinen, *Suomen Kemistilehti*, **8B**, 46 (1935) [*C.A.*, **30**, 2185 (1936)].

[407] Mannich, Koch, and Borkowsky, *Ber.*, **70**, 355 (1937).

[408] In this and the following formulations, the dotted lines indicate the components from which the starting materials of the cyclization reaction are formed.

[409] Rapson, *J. Chem. Soc.*, **1936**, 1626.

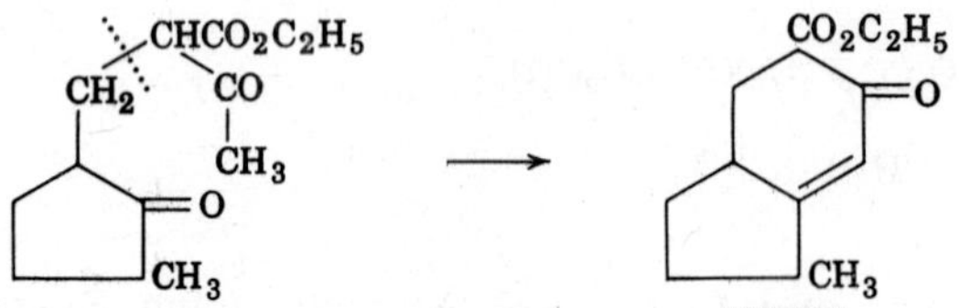

CH_2 $CHCO_2C_2H_5$ CO CH_3 O CH_3 → $CO_2C_2H_5$ O CH_3

LXXXIV

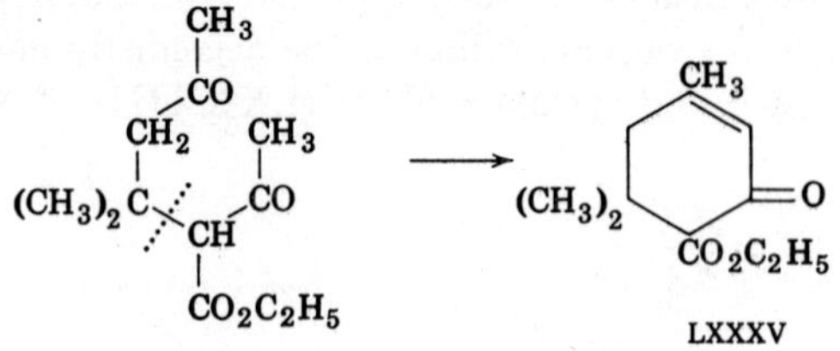

CH_3 CO CH_2 CH_3 CO $(CH_3)_2C$ CH $CO_2C_2H_5$ → CH_3 O $(CH_3)_2$ $CO_2C_2H_5$

LXXXV

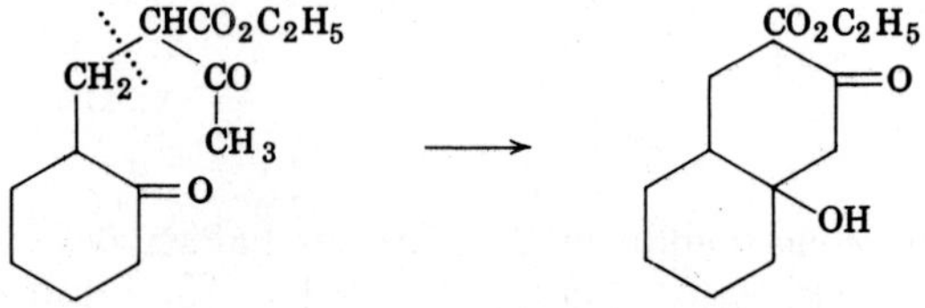

CH_2 $CHCO_2C_2H_5$ CO CH_3 O → $CO_2C_2H_5$ O OH

LXXXVI

O H_3C C CH_2 O CHR $CO_2C_2H_5$ → O R $CO_2C_2H_5$

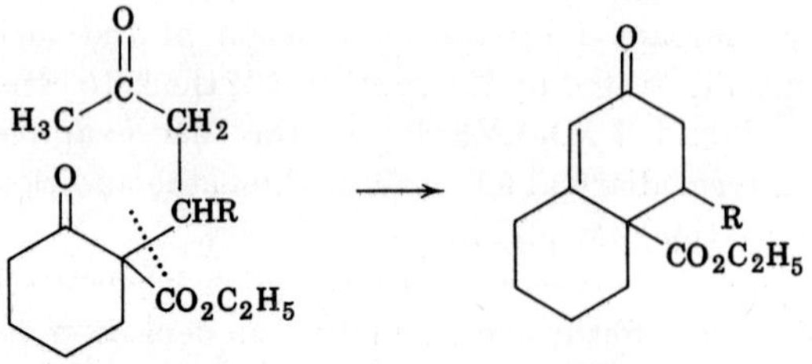

LXXXVII

acetylcyclopentene, yielding the tricyclic keto ester LXXXVIII[206] and (via LXXXIX) the tetracyclic ketone XC,[98] respectively.

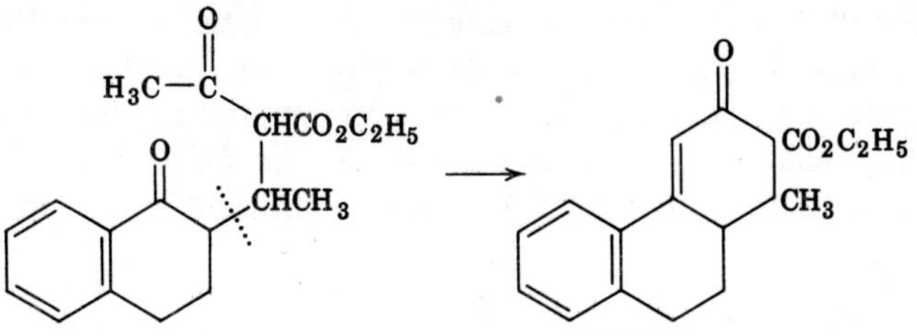

LXXXVIII

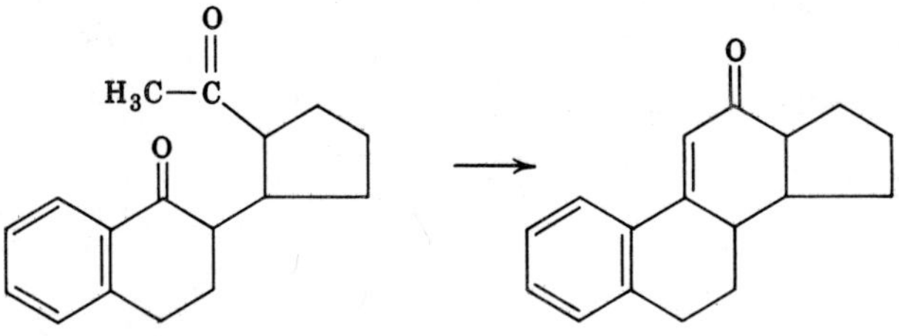

LXXXIX XC

A related reaction is the cyclization of diethyl alkylidenebisacetoacetates. Diethyl methylenebisacetoacetate (XCI), for example, forms XCII: this then loses water and one carbethoxyl group to give the "Hagemann ester" XCIII. In other instances, both carboethoxy groups

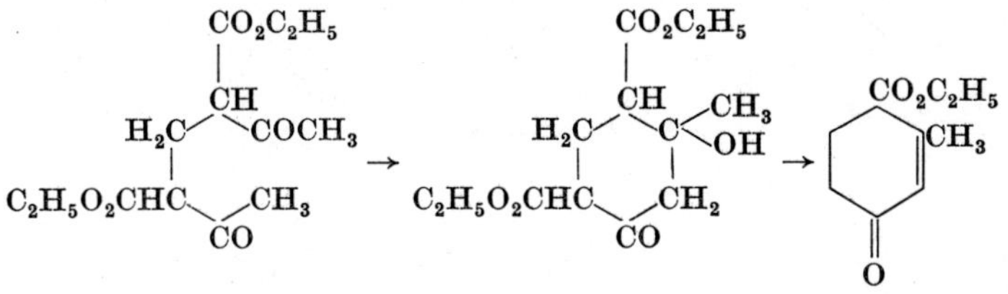

XCI XCII XCIII

are split off and 1-methyl-5-alkyl-1-cyclohexen-3-ones are formed. The reaction of ethyl sodioacetoacetate and ethyl ethoxymethyleneacetoacetate is more complicated.[410–413] Other examples are the condensation products of mesityl oxide and ethyl benzoylacetate,[414] acetylacetone,[415]

410 Claisen, *Ann.*, **297**, 1 (1897), especially p. 49.

411 Liebermann, *Ber.*, **39**, 2071 (1906), and previous papers.

412 Feist, Delfs, and Langenkamp, *Ber.*, **59**, 2958 (1926).

413 Feist, Janssen, and Chen, *Ber.*, **60**, 199 (1927).

414 Beringer and Kuntz, *J. Am. Chem. Soc.*, **73**, 364 (1951).

415 Scheiber and Meisel, *Ber.*, **48**, 238 (1915).

or deoxybenzoin;[416] the 1:2 adducts of diethyl malonate or its monosubstitution products with acrolein and methacrolein;[110,417] and the condensation products of methyl vinyl ketone with 2-methylcyclopentanone,[229,230] 2-methylcyclohexanone,[229] or aliphatic ketones.[418,419]

There are a few cases in which the methyl of an acetyl group other than that of the ethyl acetoacetate component supplies the hydrogen for the water molecule to be eliminated, e.g., in the formation of the cyclohexenones XCIV[420] and XCV.[93] This cyclization is also possible with

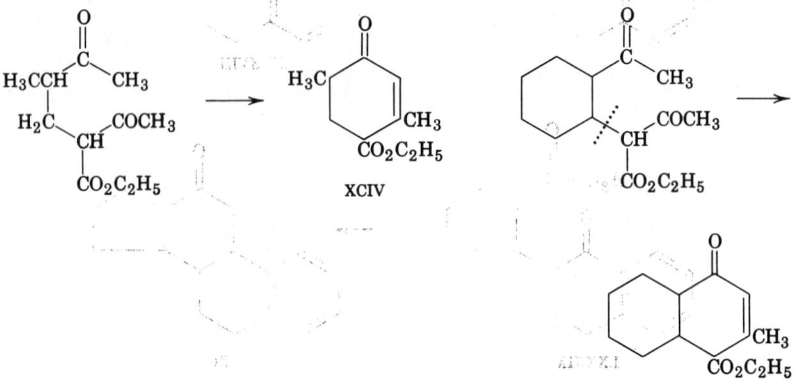

XCIV

XCV

unsaturated 1,5-diketones. Obviously, the configuration of the double bond must be *cis* for cyclization to take place. The product XCVI from acetylacetylene and 2-methylcyclohexanone gives the dienone XCVII.

XCVI XCVII

A meta ring is alleged[421] to be formed from carvone and ethyl acetoacetate.

The addition products of diethyl malonate and α,β-ethylenic nonaromatic ketones are δ-keto esters, which can cyclize by elimination of

[416] Ionescu and Popescu, *Bull. soc. chim. France*, **51**, 1215 (1932).

[417] Warner and Moe, U.S. pat. 2,575,376 [*C.A.*, **46**, 5082 (1952)].

[418] Colonge and Dreux, *Compt. rend.*, **231**, 1504 (1950).

[419] Ebel and Pesta, Ger. pat. 714,314 [*C.A.*, **38**, 1754 (1944)].

[420] Décombe, *Compt. rend.*, **205**, 680 (1937).

[421] Rabe and Weilinger, *Ber.*, **36**, 227 (1903).

an ethoxy group and a hydrogen atom in the ε position. Cyclic 1,3-diones, such as XCVIII,[422] XCIX,[423] C,[424] and I,[424,*] are formed. Analogous

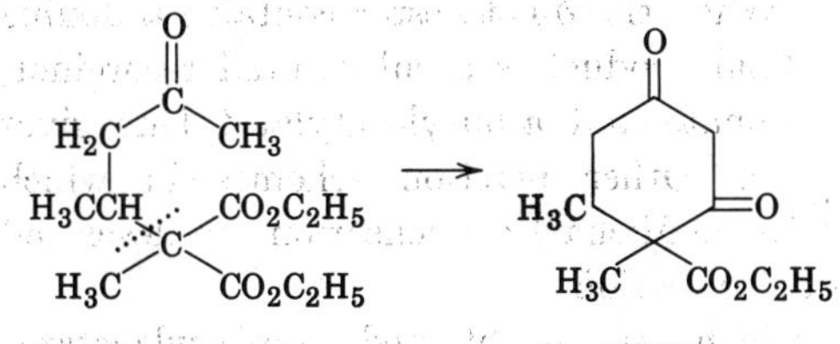

XCVIII

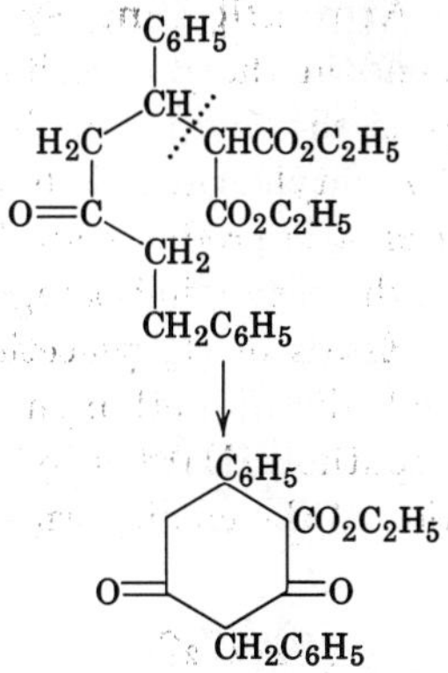

XCIX

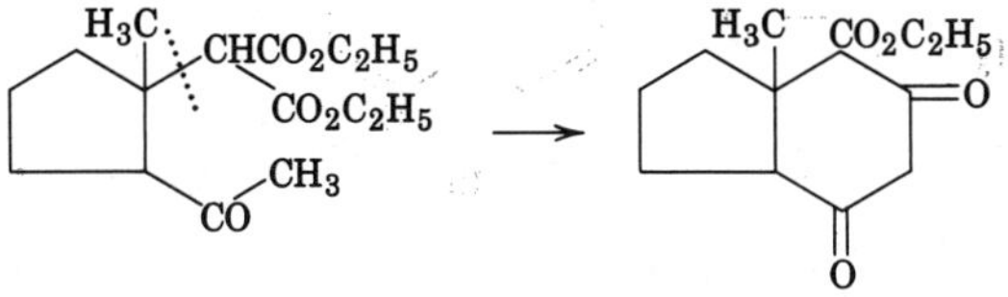

C

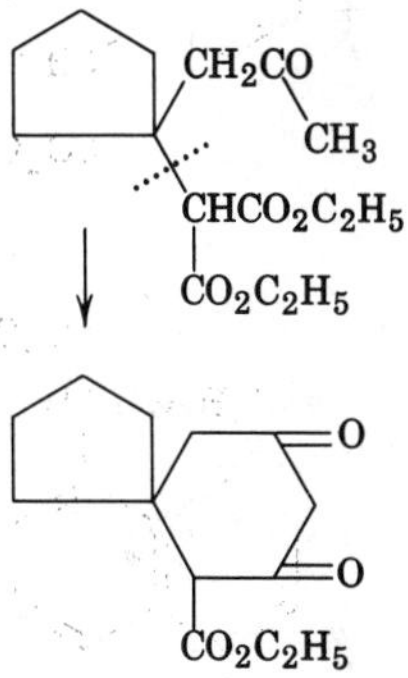

I

adducts derived from ethyl cyanoacetate (instead of malonate) give the same final products, e.g., the cyclohexanedione II.[425]

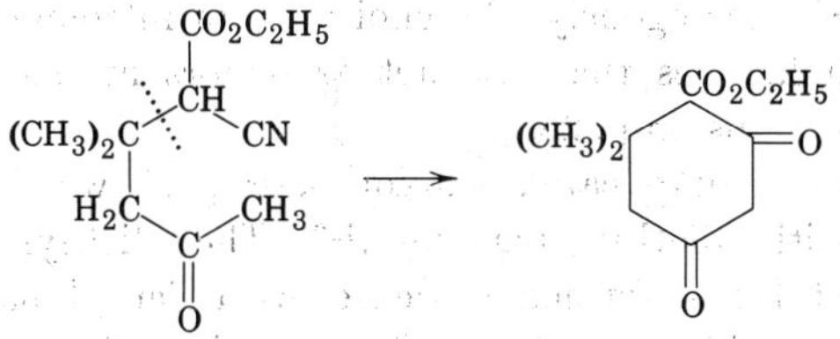

II

[422] Hinkel, Ayling, Dippy, and Angel, *J. Chem. Soc.*, **1931,** 814.

[423] Mattar, Hastings, and Walker, *J. Chem. Soc.*, **1930,** 2455.

[424] Chuang, Ma, and Tien, *Ber.*, **68,** 1946 (1935).

* Enumeration of formulas begins with I again after C to reduce the complexity of the numbers.

[425] Vorlaender, *Ann.*, **294,** 253 (1897).

Analogous behavior has, of course, been observed with the δ-keto esters formed, for example, from β-keto esters and α,β-ethylenic esters.[426]

Aromatic Ring Systems. When the δ-keto ester contains a double bond in the β,γ position, the final product is a substituted resorcinol; thus the adduct of diethyl malonate and *n*-butylacetylacetylene gives 5-*n*-butylresorcinol (see p. 214). Other reaction schemes in which aromatic products are formed in the Michael condensation are described in the remaining paragraphs of this section.

Esters of styrylacetic acid, which can be obtained from arylacetates and diethyl ethoxymethylenemalonate, cyclize to derivatives of α-naphthol (III)[308] or hydroxyphenanthrene IV.[309] Similarly, the condensation of the enolic forms of β-keto aldehydes and β-diketones with diethyl

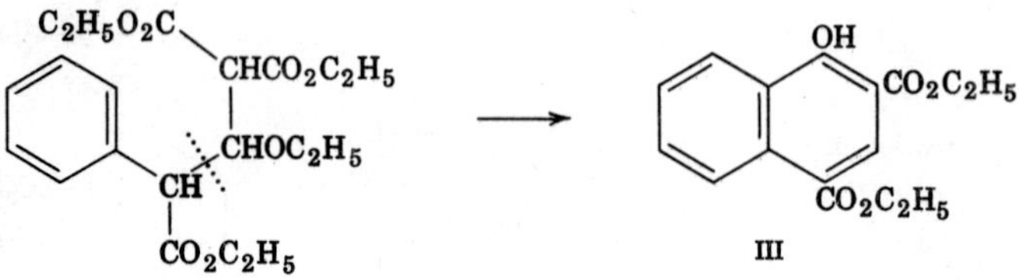

$C_2H_5O_2C$ — $CHCO_2C_2H_5$ — $CHOC_2H_5$ — CH — $CO_2C_2H_5$ → OH, $CO_2C_2H_5$, $CO_2C_2H_5$

III

$CHOC_2H_5$, $C_2H_5O_2CCH$, $CHCO_2C_2H_5$, $CO_2C_2H_5$ → $C_2H_5O_2C$, $CO_2C_2H_5$, OH

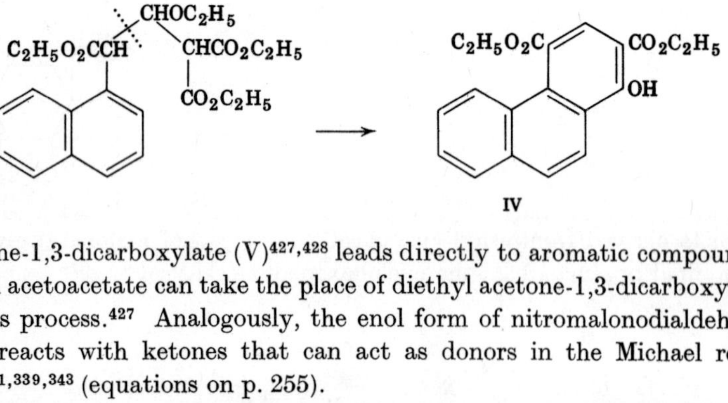

IV

acetone-1,3-dicarboxylate (V)[427,428] leads directly to aromatic compounds. Ethyl acetoacetate can take the place of diethyl acetone-1,3-dicarboxylate in this process.[427] Analogously, the enol form of nitromalonodialdehyde (VI) reacts with ketones that can act as donors in the Michael reaction[111,339,343] (equations on p. 255).

A somewhat more complicated reaction takes place when formaldehyde is condensed with diethyl malonate.[429] The diethyl ethylene-1,1-dicarboxylate (VIII) first formed condenses with diethyl malonate to give tetraethyl methylenebismalonate (VII), and this with another molecule

[426] Papadakis and Scigliano, *J. Am. Chem. Soc.*, **73**, 5483 (1951).

[427] Prelog, Metzler, and Jeger, *Helv. Chim. Acta*, **30**, 675 (1947).

[428] Prelog, Ruzicka, and Metzler, *Helv. Chim. Acta*, **30**, 1883 (1947).

[429] Meerwein and Schuermann, *Ann.*, **398**, 196 (1913), especially p. 223; Meerwein and co-workers, *J. prakt. Chem.*, [2], **104**, 161 (1922).

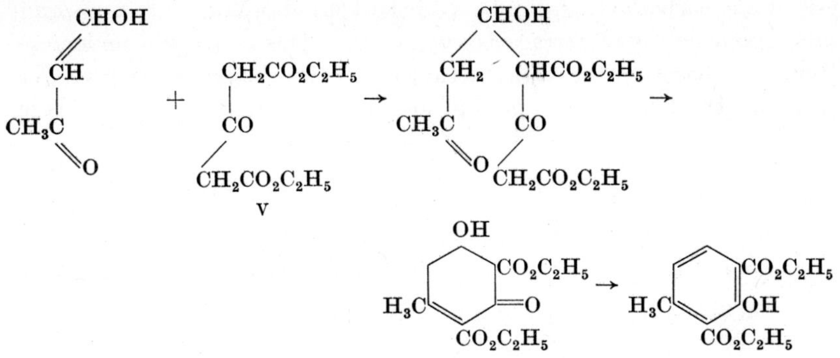

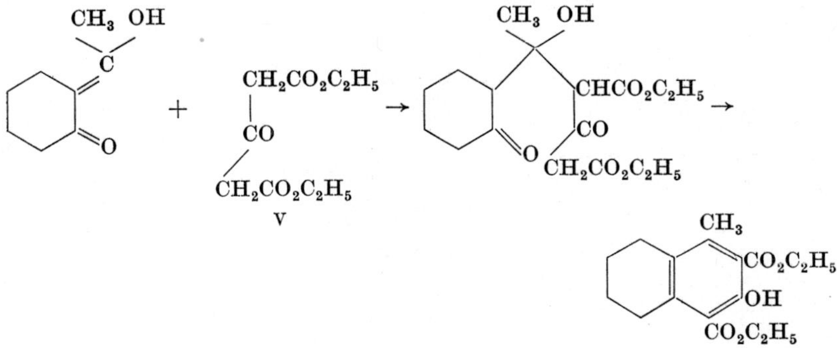

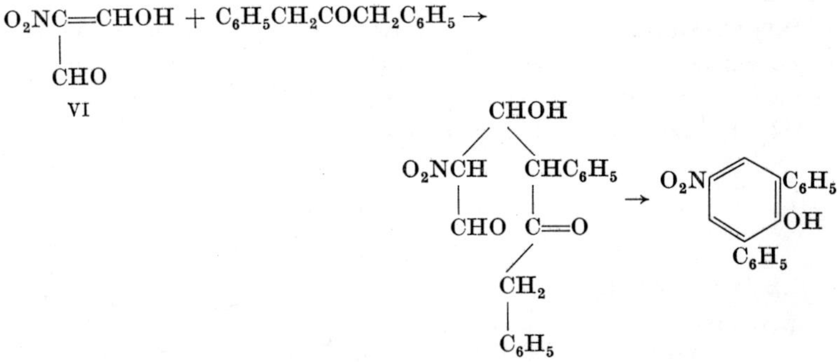

$$CH_3C(=O)CH=CHOH + CH_2(CO_2C_2H_5)COCH_2CO_2C_2H_5 \ (\text{V}) \rightarrow CH_3C(=O)CH_2CH(OH)CH(CO_2C_2H_5)COCH_2CO_2C_2H_5 \rightarrow$$

$$\text{(cyclohexenone: OH, } CO_2C_2H_5\text{, } H_3C\text{, } =O\text{, } CO_2C_2H_5) \rightarrow H_3C\text{-}C_6H(CO_2C_2H_5)(OH)(CO_2C_2H_5)$$

$$\text{2-(CH}_3\text{)(OH)C=cyclohexanone} + CH_2(CO_2C_2H_5)COCH_2CO_2C_2H_5 \ (\text{V}) \rightarrow \text{cyclohexanone-C(CH}_3\text{)(OH)-CHCO}_2C_2H_5\text{-CO-CH}_2CO_2C_2H_5 \rightarrow$$

$$\text{tetrahydronaphthalene: } CH_3\text{, } CO_2C_2H_5\text{, OH, } CO_2C_2H_5$$

$$O_2NC(CHO){=}CHOH \ (\text{VI}) + C_6H_5CH_2COCH_2C_6H_5 \rightarrow$$

$$O_2NCH(CHO)\text{-}CHOH\text{-}CH(C_6H_5)C(=O)CH_2C_6H_5 \rightarrow O_2N\text{-}C_6H(C_6H_5)(OH)(C_6H_5)$$

of diethyl ethylene-1,1-dicarboxylate yields hexaethyl pentane-1,1,3,3,5,5-hexacarboxylate (IX). Cyclization of IX, by a Dieckmann reaction and

$$\underset{\text{VII}}{(C_2H_5O_2C)_2CHCH_2CH(CO_2C_2H_5)_2} + \underset{\text{VIII}}{H_2C{=}C(CO_2C_2H_5)_2} \rightarrow$$

$$\underset{\text{IX}}{(C_2H_5O_2C)_2CHCH_2C(CO_2C_2H_5)_2CH_2CH(CO_2C_2H_5)_2}$$

loss of one carbethoxy group beta to the keto group, leads to tetraethyl cyclohexanone-2,4,4,6-tetracarboxylate (X). This can again undergo a Michael reaction with diethyl ethylene-1,1-dicarboxylate to give XI. Renewed Dieckmann reaction and loss of a carbethoxy group yields as

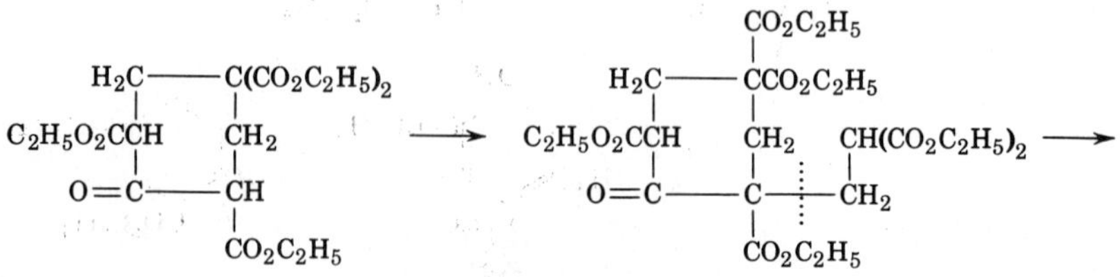

```
                                                        CO2C2H5
                                                        |
      H2C——————C(CO2C2H5)2                    H2C——————CCO2C2H5
      |        |                              |        |
C2H5O2CCH      CH2           ——→     C2H5O2CCH         CH2    CH(CO2C2H5)2  ——→
      |        |                              |        |  :   |
    O=C————————CH                           O=C————————C——:———CH2
               |                                       |
               CO2C2H5                                 CO2C2H5
          X                                                XI

                         CO2C2H5
                         |
              H2C————————C————————C=O
              |          |        |
      C2H5O2CCH          CH2      CHCO2C2H5
              |          |        |
            O=C——————————C————————CH2
                         |
                         CO2C2H5
                           XII
```

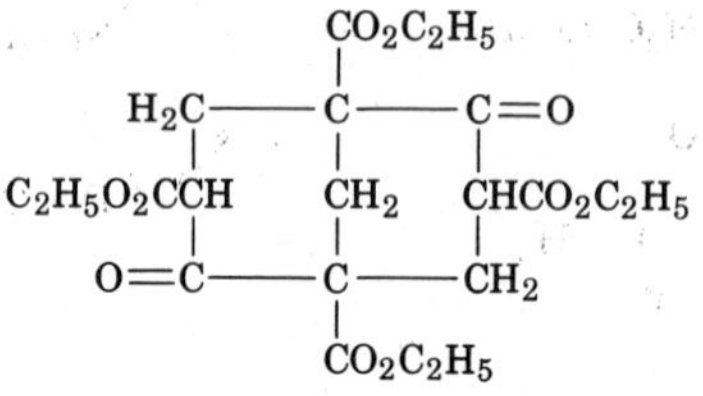

the final product tetraethyl bicyclo[3.3.1]nonane-2,6-dione-1,3,5,7-tetracarboxylate (XII).

Oxygen-Containing Rings. δ-Keto esters containing a double bond in the α,β position cyclize by an entirely different course from their β,γ analogs. Thus, although the β,γ compounds form 5-alkylresorcinols (see p. 214), the adducts of diethyl malonate and hydroxymethylene ketone

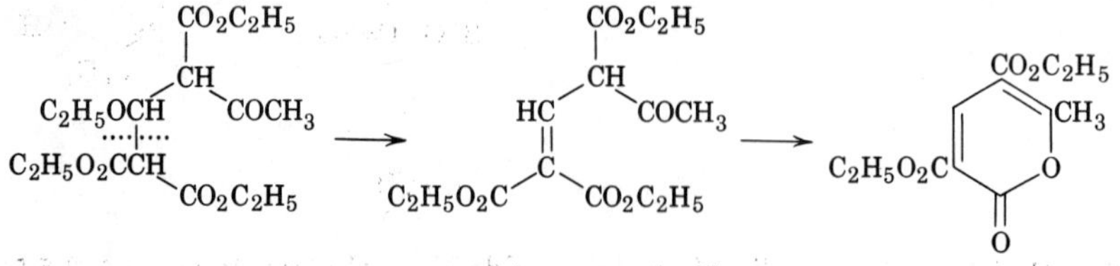

```
        CO2C2H5                      CO2C2H5
        |                            |                          CO2C2H5
        CH                           CH                     ___/
       /  \                         /  \                   |    \CH3
C2H5OCH    COCH3             HC      COCH3         ——→      |     |
  ....|....                ——→ ||                   C2H5O2C\      O
C2H5O2CCH                        C                          \ __ /
         \CO2C2H5        C2H5O2C/ \CO2C2H5                    ||
                                                              O
                                                           XIII
```

derivatives lose water or ethanol in the course of condensation, and α-pyrone derivatives such as XIII are formed. Another example is the adduct of ethyl acetoacetate and diethyl ethoxymethylene-malonate or -cyanoacetate.[310] The condensation products of ethyl phenylpropiolate with ethyl acetoacetate[430,431] and acetylacetone[432,433] behave analogously, giving XIV (R = OC_2H_5 and CH_3, respectively).

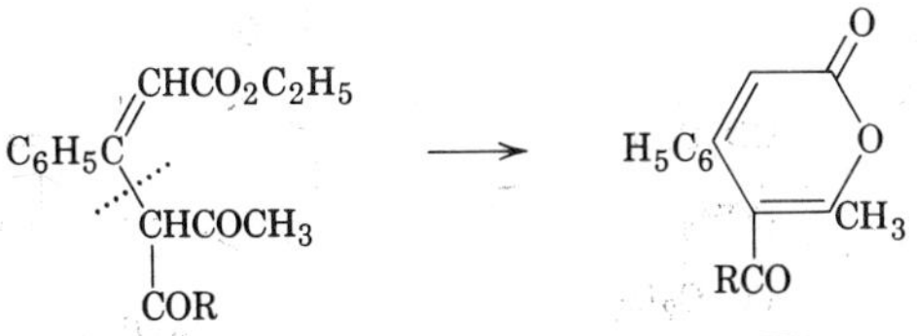

XIV

An additional case, in which a saturated δ-keto ester is cyclized by enolization of the carbonyl group, is represented by the adduct of cyclohexanone and diethyl benzylidenemalonate. Here, the ε-methylene group is sterically prevented from participation in a potential ring system and the enol lactone XV is formed.

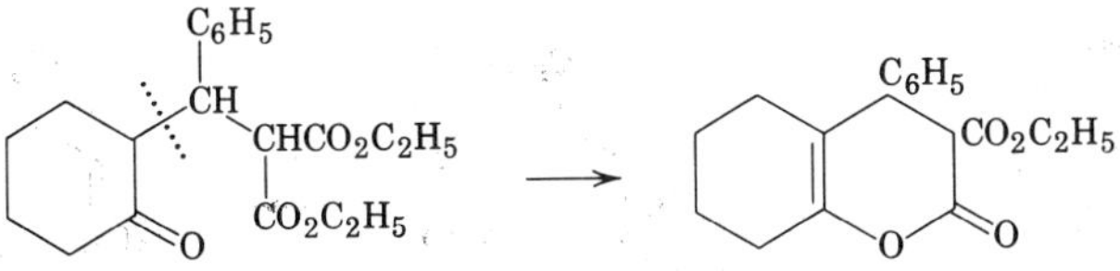

XV

γ-(o-Hydroxyphenyl)ketones are converted to 2,3-benzo-1,4-dihydropyran derivatives (XVI, R = CH_3, C_6H_5) under the conditions of the

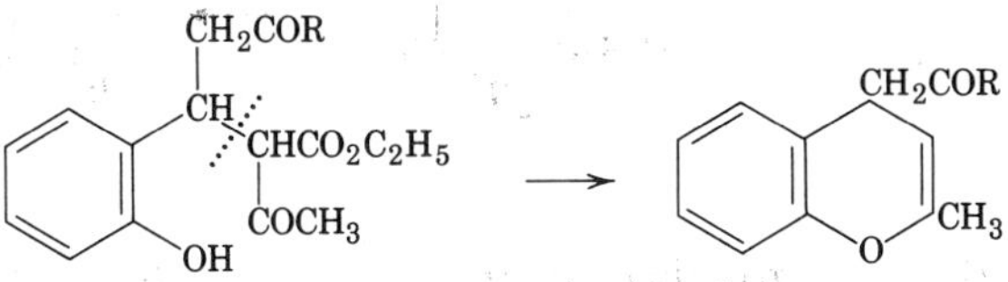

XVI

Michael condensation.[203,434] Similar ring closures have been treated in an earlier chapter of *Organic Reactions*.[435] The adduct from 3-chloro-2-cyclohexen-1-one and diethyl methylmalonate loses hydrogen chloride

[430] Feist and Pomme, *Ann.*, **370**, 72 (1909).

[431] Ruhemann, *J. Chem. Soc.*, **75**, 245 (1899).

[432] Ruhemann, *J. Chem. Soc.*, **75**, 411 (1899).

[433] Ruhemann and Cunnington, *J. Chem. Soc.*, **75**, 778 (1899).

[434] Forster and Heilbron, *J. Chem. Soc.*, **125**, 340 (1924).

[435] Hauser, Swamer, and Adams, in Adams, *Organic Reactions*, Vol. 8, Chapter 3, John Wiley & Sons, 1954. See especially pp. 90–95 and Tables XVI and XVII.

and cyclizes to the saturated lactone XVII.[436] Dovey and Robinson[437] have suggested that the formation of 2,4,6-triphenylpyrylium fluoroborate

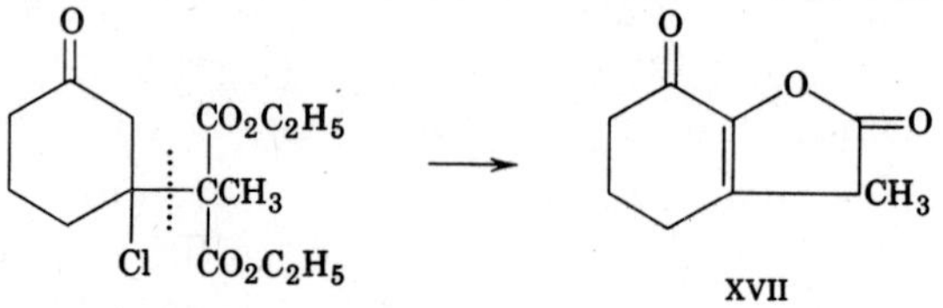

XVII

from acetophenone and boron trifluoride takes place by a Michael reaction. However, it has recently been proved that this is not the case.[438]

Piperidines and Pyridines. δ-Ketonic amides formed by Michael condensations from cyanoacetamide and α,β-ethylenic ketones undergo cyclization to unsaturated cyano-substituted 2-ketopiperidines (XVIII).

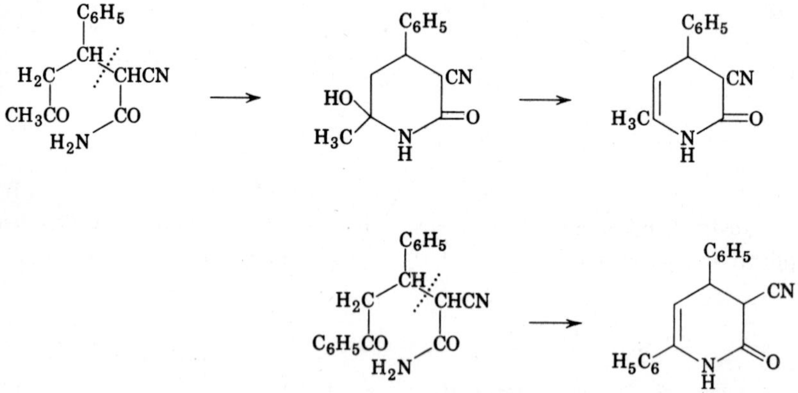

XVIII

The first of the accompanying examples shows a hydroxylated intermediate, such as has been isolated in a number of reactions.[439]

A slightly different scheme applies to the condensation products of cyanoacetamide and α-hydroxymethylene ketones, in which, by the loss of water, a second double bond is introduced into the ring and thus the enolization to 2-hydroxypyridines (XIX and XX) is facilitated.[171,224] Aminomethylene ketones behave analogously,[398] and cyanoacetamide can

[436] Paranjpe, Phalnikar, Bhide, and Nargund, *Current Sci. India*, **12**, 150 (1943) [*C.A.*, **37**, 6671 (1943)].

[437] Dovey and Robinson, *J. Chem. Soc.*, **1935**, 1389.

[438] Elderfield and King, *J. Am. Chem. Soc.*, **76**, 5437 (1954).

[439] Barat, *J. Indian Chem. Soc.*, **7**, 321 (1930) [*C.A.*, **24**, 4786 (1930)].

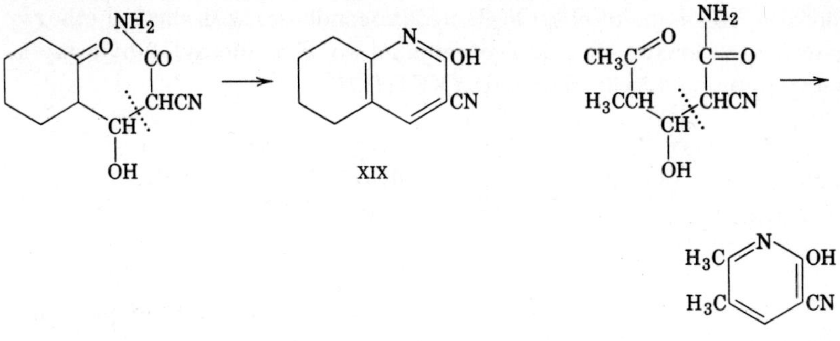

XIX

XX

be replaced by malonamide.[370] The same result is obtained with the adducts from cyanoacetamide and acetylenic ketones. Compounds having the general structure XXI (R = C_2H_5 or C_6H_5) are formed.[181,184]

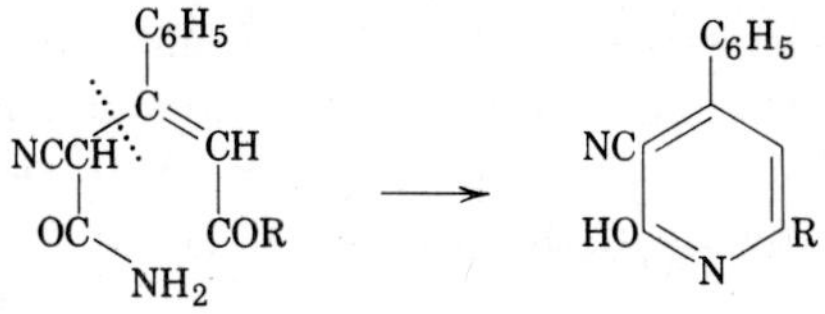

XXI

If the precursor of XXI is shown in the tautomeric form XXIA, it is evident that compounds of type XXIB will be capable of a similar

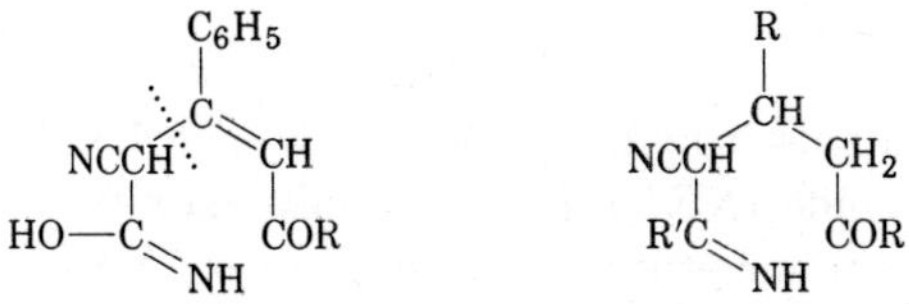

XXIA

XXIB

transformation into pyridine derivatives. Thus "diacetonitrile" and benzylideneacetone give, after spontaneous loss of hydrogen from the primary product, 3-cyano-4-phenyl-2,6-dimethylpyridine (XXII).[440]

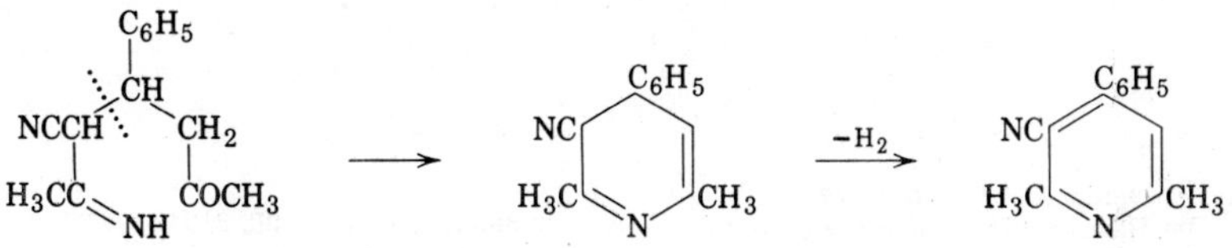

XXII

[440] Chatterjee, *J. Indian Chem. Soc.*, **29**, 323 (1952) [*C.A.*, **47**, 9972 (1953)].

Likewise, the imine of ethyl acetoacetate condenses with diethyl ethoxymethylenemalonate with loss of ethanol to give diethyl 2-hydroxy-6-methylpyridine-3,5-dicarboxylate (XXIII).[441]

$C_2H_5O_2CCH(CHOC_2H_5)\ldots CHCO_2C_2H_5$, $C_2H_5O_2C$, $HN{=}CCH_3$ → $C_2H_5O_2CCH(CHOC_2H_5)CHCO_2C_2H_5$, $O{=}C{-}N{=}CCH_3$ →

$C_2H_5O_2C$, $CO_2C_2H_5$, HO, CH_3, N

XXIII

Generally speaking, the imines of β-keto esters and β-diketones react in this manner with hydroxymethylene, alkoxymethylene, and aminomethylene ketones and esters.[442–444] Thus, from 2-hydroxymethylenecyclopentanone and ethyl iminoacetoacetate, ethyl 5-methyl-4-azaindene-6-carboxylate (XXIV) becomes available.[445] Also ethyl tetrahydroanthranilate (XXV) reacts in the manner of an aminomethylene ester

$CO_2C_2H_5$, CH_3, N — XXIV

NH_2, $CO_2C_2H_5$ — XXV

$CONH_2$, =O, NH, OH — XXVI

giving with malonamide 1-hydroxy-3-keto-2,3,4,5,6,7,8,10-octahydroisoquinoline-4-carboxamide (XXVI).[381] The only exception to this rule is the reaction of 2-aminomethylenecyclohexanone (XXVII) with ethyl cyanoacetate, which is claimed[446] to yield 3-keto-4-cyano-2,3,5,6,7,8-hexahydroisoquinoline (XXVIII). In this connection Berson and

CH, NH_2, O (XXVII) + OC_2H_5–CO–CH_2–CN → NH, C=O, CN (XXVIII)

XXVII XXVIII

[441] Ochiai and Ito, *Ber.*, **74**, 1111 (1941).
[442] Basu and Banerjee, *J. Indian Chem. Soc.*, **12**, 665 (1935) [*C.A.*, **30**, 2194 (1936)].
[443] Basu, *Ann.*, **512**, 131 (1934).
[444] Dornow and Machens, *Chem. Ber.*, **80**, 502 (1947).
[445] Basu, *Science and Culture India*, **2**, 466 (1937) [*C.A.*, **31**, 3919 (1937)].
[446] Basu and Banerjee, *Ann.*, **516**, 243 (1935).

Brown[447] consider that Hantzsch's synthesis of 1,4-dihydropyridines involves a Michael reaction. These authors assume that, e.g., in the condensation of formaldehyde, ammonia, and ethyl acetoacetate, ethyl β-aminocrotonate and ethyl methyleneacetoacetate are formed and then react in the following way.

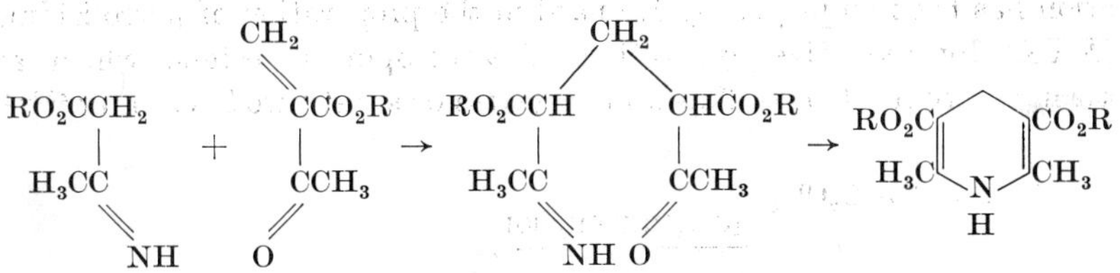

$$RO_2CCH_2-C(CH_3)=NH + CH_2=C(CO_2R)-C(CH_3)=O \rightarrow RO_2CCH(C(CH_3)=NH)-CH_2-CH(CO_2R)C(CH_3)=O \rightarrow$$

(1,4-dihydropyridine ring: RO_2C, CO_2R, H_3C, CH_3, N–H)

Another route to the pyridine series is possible in all Michael condensations that lead to 1,5-diketones capable of being cyclized by treatment with ammonia; in these reactions ammonia can be used as the catalyst for the Michael condensation. A special example of this general possibility is provided in the reaction of ethyl aminomethyleneacetoacetate with ethyl acetoacetate or cyclohexanone:[120] ammonia is eliminated from the primary product XXIX in the first step and utilized in the second step of the subsequent process.

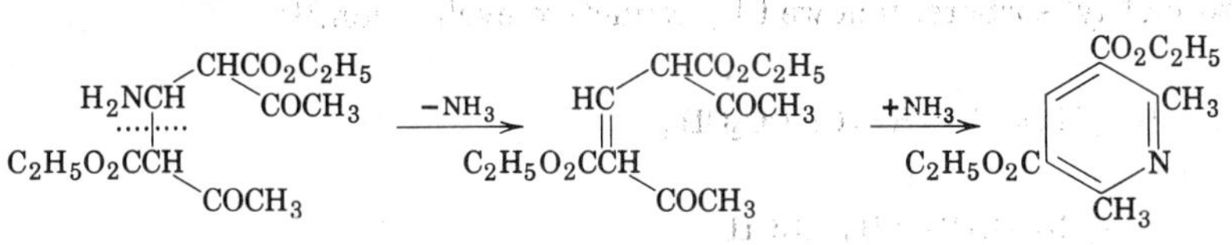

$$\underset{\text{XXIX}}{H_2NCH(CHCO_2C_2H_5COCH_3)\cdots C_2H_5O_2CCH(COCH_3)} \xrightarrow{-NH_3} HC(CHCO_2C_2H_5COCH_3)=C_2H_5O_2CC(COCH_3) \xrightarrow{+NH_3}$$

(pyridine ring: $CO_2C_2H_5$, CH_3, N, CH_3, $C_2H_5O_2C$)

Pyrroles. Clarke and Lapworth[448] have assumed that the pyrrole synthesis discovered by von Miller and Ploechl[449] involves a Michael reaction; thus, one could formulate the synthesis of 1-(p-tolyl)-2,3-diphenylpyrrole from α-toluidinobenzyl cyanide and cinnamaldehyde in the presence of potassium hydroxide as follows. (Compare ref. 450.)

$$C_6H_5CH{=}CHCHO + C_6H_5CH(CN)NHC_6H_4CH_3\text{-}p \rightarrow$$

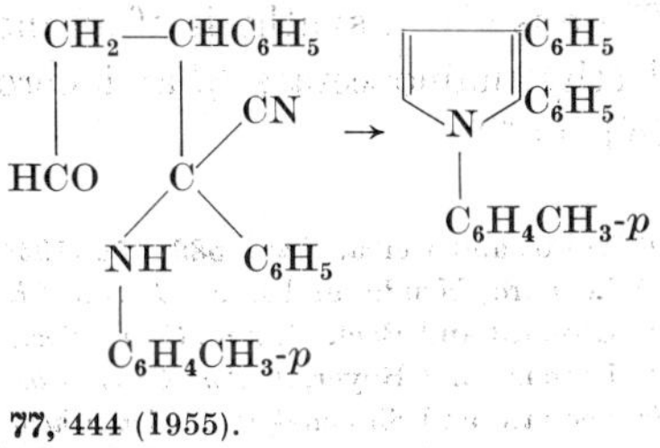

$$HCO-CH_2-CHC_6H_5-C(CN)(C_6H_5)-NH-C_6H_4CH_3\text{-}p \rightarrow$$

(pyrrole ring: C_6H_5, C_6H_5, N–$C_6H_4CH_3$-p)

[447] Berson and Brown, *J. Am. Chem. Soc.*, **77**, 444 (1955).
[448] Clarke and Lapworth, *J. Chem. Soc.*, **91**, 694 (1907).
[449] Miller and Ploechl, *Ber.*, **31**, 2718 (1898).
[450] Bodforss, *Ber.*, **64**, 1111 (1931).

Treibs and Derra,[451] however, have suggested that the synthesis proceeds through a hemiacetal of the unsaturated aldehyde (formed by interaction with the solvent, e.g., methanol) and is, therefore, not a Michael reaction.

Pyrrolizidines and Related Ring Systems. The Michael condensation has been employed by Leonard in the preparation of pyrrolizidines (XXX) by reductive cyclization of γ-nitropimelic esters, which are available from nitroparaffins and acrylates or substituted acrylates.[452–457]

$$2CH_2{=}CHCO_2CH_3 + CH_3NO_2 \xrightarrow{[C_6H_5CH_2N(CH_3)_3]OH} CH_3O_2CCH_2CH_2CH(NO_2)CH_2CH_2CO_2CH_3 \xrightarrow[(PtO_2)]{H_2} \text{XXX}$$

Similarly, the reaction has been extended to the synthesis of 6-methyl-azabicyclo[5.3.0]decane (XXXI) by 1,6-addition of methyl γ-nitrobutyrate to methyl sorbate, followed by reductive cyclization.[116]

$$CH_3CH{=}CHCH{=}CHCO_2CH_3 + O_2NCH_2CH_2CH_2CO_2CH_3 \rightarrow CH_3O_2CCH_2CH_2CH(NO_2)CH(CH_3)CH{=}CHCH_2CO_2CH_3 \rightarrow \text{XXXI}$$

There is also a synthesis of an indole derivative XXXII from quinone and ethyl iminoacetate (β-aminocrotonate),[288] which can be formulated as follows.[258]

[451] Treibs and Derra, *Ann.*, **589,** 176 (1954).
[452] Leonard, Hruda, and Long, *J. Am. Chem. Soc.*, **69,** 690 (1947).
[453] Leonard and Beck, *J. Am. Chem. Soc.*, **70,** 2504 (1948).
[454] Leonard and Boyer, *J. Am. Chem. Soc.*, **72,** 4818 (1950).
[455] Leonard and Shoemaker, *J. Am. Chem. Soc.*, **71,** 1762 (1949).
[456] Leonard and Felley, *J. Am. Chem. Soc.*, **71,** 1758 (1949).
[457] Leonard and Felley, *J. Am. Chem. Soc.*, **72,** 2537 (1950).

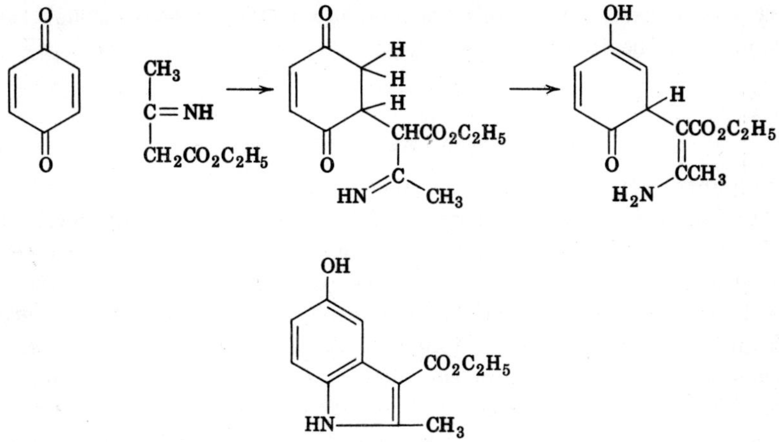

XXXII

Synthesis of Amino Acids

The observation that substances such as ethyl acetamidomalonate and ethyl phthalimido-malonate or -cyanoacetate act as donors in the Michael condensation has opened a useful avenue to the synthesis of amino acids.[161,458–462] The preparation of DL-glutamic acid (XXXIII) illustrates this method.[463] The products derived from α,β-ethylenic aldehydes and N-acylated aminomalonates[160,161,460–462,464] and aminocyanoacetates[160,460] are likewise of considerable interest; they are potential

$$CH_2{=}CHCO_2CH_3 + CH_3CONHCH(CO_2C_2H_5)_2 \xrightarrow{NaOC_2H_5}$$

$$CH_3CONHC(CO_2C_2H_5)_2CH_2CH_2CO_2CH_3 \xrightarrow[-\ CO_2]{Hydrolysis}$$

$$HO_2CCH(NH_2)CH_2CH_2CO_2H$$

XXXIII

intermediates in the construction of the ornithine system and appear to be the key substances in the biogenesis of a number of alkaloids.[465]

[458] Albertson and Archer, *J. Am. Chem. Soc.*, **67**, 2043 (1945).
[459] Galat, *J. Am. Chem. Soc.*, **69**, 965 (1947).
[460] Moe and Warner, *J. Am. Chem. Soc.*, **70**, 2763 (1948).
[461] Rinderknecht and Niemann, *J. Am. Chem. Soc.*, **72**, 2296 (1950).
[462] Van Zyl, van Tamelen, and Zuidema, *J. Am. Chem. Soc.*, **73**, 1765 (1951).
[463] Snyder, Shekleton, and Lewis, *J. Am. Chem. Soc.*, **67**, 310 (1945).
[464] Moe and Warner, U.S. pat. 2,508,927 [*C.A.*, **44**, 8374 (1950)].
[465] Robinson, *Proc. Univ. Durham Phil. Soc.*, **8**, Pt. 1, 14 (1927–1928) [*C.A.*, **23**, 1883 (1929)].

As esters of nitroacetic acid become more generally available, these may also be used in the synthesis of amino acid precursors through the Michael condensation.[106,466]

EXPERIMENTAL CONDITIONS

Solvents. If the products are sensitive to alcoholysis or if there is competition between the alkoxide ion and the donor anion for the acceptor molecule, a non-hydroxylic solvent is chosen or the reaction is carried out without solvent. Compare, however, ref. 278. When such competition is encountered or when the enolate of the donor is prepared with difficulty, sodium or sodium amide in an inert solvent may be used. Solvents used most often in the Michael condensation are methanol, ethanol, *t*-butyl alcohol, ether, benzene, dioxane, and mixtures of these solvents. Ester exchange has been observed in some condensations in which esters were employed as reactants.[183]

Catalysts. The following catalysts have been used: sodium methoxide, sodium ethoxide, potassium methoxide, potassium ethoxide, potassium isopropoxide, potassium *n*-butoxide, potassium *t*-butoxide, potassium α,α-dimethylpropoxide; dry or aqueous sodium or potassium hydroxide, methanolic or ethanolic sodium or potassium hydroxide, potassium hydroxide in *t*-butanol; metallic sodium or potassium; ammonia, alcoholic ammonia, ammonia in conjunction with ammonium chloride, sodium amide as such or in liquid ammonia; diethylamine, diisopropylamine, piperidine, pyridine, triethylamine, tributylamine, and other trialkylamines; methyltriethylammonium hydroxide, benzyltrimethylammonium hydroxide (Triton B), and its methoxide or butoxide.

Calcium and sodium hydride have been used very rarely;[186,466a,467] the same applies to potassium carbonate[206] and sodium triphenylmethide,[468] which was used as condensing agent for Michael reactions with the ethyl esters of acetic, isobutyric, and phenylacetic acids. The first ester underwent Claisen condensation under these conditions before Michael reaction took place.

Aqueous sodium cyanide was employed as catalyst in the condensations of acrylonitrile with ethyl cyanoacetate or benzyl cyanide.[469]

It is worthy of note that the reaction between cyclohexanone or 2-methylcyclohexanone and acrylonitrile, carried out in the presence of

[466] E. D. Bergmann, unpublished results.

[466a] Fishman and Zuffanti, *J. Am. Chem. Soc.*, **73**, 4466 (1951).

[467] McElvain and Lyle, Jr., *J. Am. Chem. Soc.*, **72**, 384 (1950).

[468] Hauser and Abramovitch, *J. Am. Chem. Soc.*, **62**, 1763 (1940).

[469] Rogers, U.S. pat. 2,460,536 [*C.A.*, **43**, 3446 (1949)].

optically active quartz, coated with sodium, potassium, or lithium ethoxide, has been reported to give slightly optically active products.[470]

Several examples have been reported[155,255,471–473] of Michael-type condensations brought about by acidic catalysts such as boron trifluoride, zinc chloride, or sulfur dioxide. Of practical importance are the condensations of pyrrole derivatives with free α positions which react with α,β-unsaturated aldehydes, ketones, acids, and acid derivatives in the presence of acidic catalysts such as boron trifluoride etherate or hydrobromic acid.[474,475] As in the case of indole (see p. 209), one can assume that the donor is a tautomeric form of the pyrrole, in which the α position is transformed into an (activated) methylene group. This product reacts further to give a dipyrryltrimethine derivative.

RO_2C, CH_3, H_3C, N, H (pyrrole) → [RO_2C, CH_3, H_3C, N, H, H] $\xrightarrow[\text{HBr}]{CH_2{=}CHCOCH_3}$ RO_2C, CH_3, H_3C, N, H, $CH_2CH_2COCH_3$

One or two condensations have been effected without an added catalyst. Thus condensation occurs when ethyl hydroxymethylenephenylacetate is heated with malonic or cyanoacetic acid,[366,476,477] and when methyl vinyl ketone vapor is passed together with acetone or methyl ethyl ketone through a hot tube.[419]

Particular mention should be made of the possibility offered by the recent development of strongly basic exchange resins; they appear to be highly promising condensing agents, especially where either a reactant or a reaction product is sensitive to dissolved alkali. Thus acetone or methyl ethyl ketone reacts easily with acrylonitrile in the presence of quaternized cross-linked polyvinylpyridine resin.[478] More complicated reactions can also be catalyzed in this way.[479,480]

[470] Terent'ev, Klabunovskiĭ, and Budovskiĭ, *Sbornik Stateĭ Obshcheĭ Khim.*, **2,** 1612 (1953) [*C.A.*, **49,** 5263 (1955)].

[471] Hauser, *J. Am. Chem. Soc.*, **60,** 1957 (1938).

[472] Hauser and Breslow, *J. Am. Chem. Soc.*, **62,** 2389 (1940).

[473] Berlin and Sherlin, *J. Gen. Chem. USSR*, **8,** 16 (1938) [*C.A.*, **32,** 5397 (1938)].

[474] Treibs and Michl, *Ann.*, **589,** 163 (1954).

[475] Treibs and Herrmann, *Ann.*, **592,** 1 (1955).

[476] Phalnikar and Nargund, *J. Univ. Bombay*, **4,** 106 (1935) [*C.A.*, **30,** 5186 (1936)].

[477] Harris, Stiller, and Folkers, *J. Am. Chem. Soc.*, **61,** 1242 (1939).

[478] Howk and Langkammerer, U.S. pat. 2,579,580 [*C.A.*, **46,** 7114 (1952)].

[479] E. D. Bergmann and R. Korett, *J. Org. Chem.*, **21,** 107 (1956); **23,** 1507 (1958).

[480] Schmidle and Mansfield, U.S. pat. 2,658,070 [*C.A.*, **48,** 13715 (1954)].

Only qualitative conclusions can be drawn from the available experimental material regarding the catalysts used in the Michael reaction. One is inclined to assume that the efficiency of a particular catalyst in a given reaction is due to its ability to enolize the donor,[468] but a few more factors are important in the selection of a condensing agent. Thus, piperidine seems to cause secondary cyclization reactions less easily than sodium ethoxide, but it also acts relatively slowly. These secondary reactions can also be avoided when less (1/6 to 1/3) than the equivalent amount of the ethoxide is employed or the reaction is carried out at low temperature.[58,481] On the other hand, ethanolic solutions of potassium ethoxide are likely to cause ring scission of cyclopentanone or cyclohexanone derivatives.

Sometimes, when piperidine is not effective, reaction can be achieved by means of sodium ethoxide, e.g., the Michael condensation between ethyl cinnamate and ethyl phenylacetate. Dry potassium hydroxide or a mixture of pyridine and aqueous sodium hydroxide has been employed successfully with fluorene and its derivatives, substances in which the catalyst does not cause enolization but replacement of hydrogen on a carbon atom.[362,482] The use of dry potassium hydroxide, however, is not limited to this particular group of donors. It has been shown that suspensions of finely divided potassium hydroxide in acetals (which perhaps form loose molecular compounds with the base) are excellent catalysts for Michael condensations.[483] Surprisingly, ester groups are not attacked under these conditions, although the hydroxide usually employed contains about 15% water. It is interesting that only potassium and not sodium hydroxide can be used in this way as a catalyst, particularly in view of the occasional observations on differences in behavior of the two alkali hydroxides when used as catalysts in the Michael condensation.[205] It has also been observed that 4-picoline condenses with 4-vinylpyridine to give 1,3-di-(4-pyridyl)propane in the presence of metallic potassium, but not under the influence of metallic sodium.[484]

Temperature. Higher temperatures usually favor rearrangement and retrogression (see p. 187) as well as secondary cyclization reactions, both of which, of course, reduce the yield of normal adduct. With alkoxide catalysts, reaction times of twenty to one hundred fifty hours at room temperature have been used with good results. When employing secondary amines as catalysts, it is usually necessary to reflux the mixture for twenty to forty-eight hours in order to obtain a fair yield of product.

[481] Wachs and Hedenburg, *J. Am. Chem. Soc.*, **70**, 2695 (1948).

[482] Kloetzel and Mertel, *J. Am. Chem. Soc.*, **72**, 4786 (1950).

[483] Weizmann, Bergmann, and Sulzbacher, *J. Org. Chem.*, **15**, 918 (1950).

[484] Jampolsky, Baum, Kaiser, Sternbach, and Goldberg, *J. Am. Chem. Soc.*, **74**, 5222 (1952).

EXPERIMENTAL PROCEDURES

γ-Acetamido-γ-carbethoxy-γ-cyanobutyraldehyde.[460] A solution of 50 mg. of sodium in 60 ml. of absolute ethanol is mixed with 17 g. of ethyl acetamidocyanoacetate, and the resulting suspension is cooled in a water bath while 7.5 ml. of acrolein is added dropwise. After the addition is complete, the mixture is stirred for two hours and neutralized with glacial acetic acid. The mixture is filtered, and the filtrate, after refrigeration for twenty-four hours, deposits the crystalline product. Filtration yields 15 g. (66%) of material melting at 106–109°. Crystallization from 95% ethanol raises the melting point to 113.5–114.5°.

5-Nitro-4,4-dimethylpentan-2-one.[209] A mixture of 1 mole of mesityl oxide, 10 moles of nitromethane, and 1 mole of diethylamine is allowed to stand at 30° for thirty days. Unreacted material is removed by distillation up to 55°/20 mm., and the residue is fractionated. After a forerun of 4-diethylamino-4-methylpentan-2-one (10%), the product distils as an oil, b.p. 112–113.5°/14 mm. (65%). The product may be completely freed of basic impurities by shaking with 10% hydrochloric acid. After two distillations, a pure product, boiling at 128–129°/22 mm., can be obtained in 58% yield.

The same product may be obtained in 55–60% yield by heating the reaction mixture under reflux for forty-eight hours and treating subsequently as above.

7-Keto-1-methoxy-13-methyl-5,6,7,9,10,13-hexahydrophenanthrene (Robinson's modification).[318] While 15.05 g. of diethylaminobutanone[485] is swirled gently in a 1-l. flask and cooled in ice, 15.0 g. of methyl iodide is added portionwise during thirty minutes. The swirling is regulated so as to obtain the crystalline methiodide as an even coating on the walls of the flask. When no more liquid remains, the flask is kept in ice for thirty minutes and then under the tap for forty-five minutes. A solution of 20.0 g. of 5-methoxy-1-methyl-2-tetralone in 100 ml. of dry thiophene-free benzene is added, air is expelled by dry nitrogen, and a solution of 6.5 g. of potassium in 100 ml. of dry ethanol is added with cooling during five minutes.

Swirling is continued until the methiodide dissolves (about thirty minutes) and is replaced by a precipitate of potassium iodide. The mixture is kept in ice for an additional hour, and then boiled gently for twenty-five minutes. An excess of 2 *N* sulfuric acid is added, followed by enough water to dissolve the potassium sulfate. The benzene layer is separated and the aqueous layer extracted twice with ether. The ether and benzene layers are combined, washed with water, and clarified with

[485] Wilds and Shunk, *J. Am. Chem. Soc.*, **65**, 469 (1943).

magnesium sulfate, and the solvents are evaporated. The residue is distilled and 23.2 g. of product is collected up to 180°/0.1 mm. Crystallization from ether yields 17 g. of product, m.p. 115–117°. An additional gram of material is obtained by distillation of the mother liquors, making a total yield of 18 g. (71%).

This procedure is a general one, in which sodium methoxide or sodium ethoxide may be used effectively as a catalyst.

***trans*-3-Keto-2-phenylcyclohexaneacetic Acid.**[108] A mixture of 50 g. of 2-phenyl-2-cyclohexen-1-one, 150 g. of dibenzyl malonate, and a solution of potassium *t*-butoxide, prepared from 1.3 g. of potassium and 20 ml. of *t*-butyl alcohol, is kept at 60° for three hours, and then left overnight at room temperature. The mixture is acidified with 2.5 ml. of acetic acid and diluted to a volume of 250 ml. with ethyl acetate. Thirteen grams of 10% palladium-charcoal is added, and the mixture is hydrogenated for an hour at room temperature at an initial pressure of 4 atm. The catalyst is filtered, the solvent evaporated, and the residue is heated for 10 minutes at 170–180° to effect decarboxylation of the malonic acid. The residue is taken up in ether, the solution extracted several times with 10% sodium carbonate solution, and the alkaline extract acidified. The product is obtained as a solid, m.p. 125° (55 g., 82%).

Dibenzyl malonate is preferred to diethyl malonate as a donor if further hydrolysis of the Michael condensation adduct is desired.

Methyl 3-Keto-2-phenylcyclohexyl-α-nitroacetate.[106,108] A mixture of 17.2 g. of 2-phenyl-2-cyclohexen-1-one, 23.0 g. of methyl nitroacetate,[486] and 0.025 mole of 30% methanolic solution of benzyltrimethylammonium methoxide[487] is allowed to stand at 60° for twelve hours. The mixture is acidified with acetic acid and extracted with ether, and the extract is washed with water and with sodium bicarbonate solution to remove most of the unchanged ester. After removal of the rest of the unreacted materials by distillation in high vacuum, 26.2 g. of product (90% yield) is obtained as an oil.

Triethyl α-Acetyltricarballylate.[483] To 20 g. of technical potassium hydroxide in 150 ml. of acetaldehyde dipropyl acetal are added 51.6 g. of diethyl maleate and 52 g. of ethyl acetoacetate, the temperature being maintained at 20° during the addition. The temperature then rises spontaneously to 27°, and the mixture is heated at 90° for one hour. After acidification with dilute sulfuric acid, the acetal layer is separated, the solvent is removed, and the residue distilled in vacuum. Some ethyl acetoacetate is recovered, and 65 g. of product is obtained as an oil,

[486] Feuer, Hass, and Warren, *J. Am. Chem. Soc.*, **71**, 3078 (1949).

[487] Croxall and Schneider, *J. Am. Chem. Soc.*, **71**, 1257 (1949). Cf. Meisenheimer, *Ann.*, **397**, 295 (1913).

b.p. 189°/12 mm. The yield based on material that entered the reaction is 72%.

Diethyl 6-Keto-4-methyl-2-heptene-1,5-dicarboxylate.[488] To a solution of 2.5 g. of potassium in 150 ml. of absolute *t*-butyl alcohol are added 98 g. of ethyl acetoacetate and 53 g. of ethyl sorbate. The mixture is heated under reflux in an oil bath at 110–120° for twelve hours. The cooled solution is poured into dilute sulfuric acid and the precipitated oil taken up in benzene. After removal of the benzene and unreacted material by distillation, 78 g. of product (75% yield) is obtained as an almost colorless oil, b.p. 120°/0.5 mm.

Hexaethyl 3-Butene-1,1,2,2,3,4-hexacarboxylate.[324,325,489] Under anhydrous conditions and with stirring, a mixture of 34 g. of diethyl acetylenedicarboxylate, 66 g. of tetraethyl ethane-1,1,2,2-tetracarboxylate, and 10 ml. of absolute ethanol is heated to 45° to obtain a clear solution. A solution of 1.5 g. of sodium dissolved in 24 ml. of absolute ethanol is added dropwise with rapid stirring. After addition of about 10 drops of ethoxide solution, the temperature of the reaction mixture suddenly rises to 92° and then slowly falls as the rest of the catalyst is added. As the temperature rises, the color of the solution changes to dark brown. The mixture is poured into 100 ml. of *N* hydrochloric acid and is exhaustively extracted with ether. Evaporation of the ether leaves a mixture of solid and oil. The solid is collected and crystallized from 80% ethanol. The product, obtained in several crops, weighs 48.5 g. (48%) and melts at 78°.

Diethyl α,β-Diphenylglutarate.[81,82] One hundred grams of ethyl cinnamate and 100 g. of ethyl phenylacetate are mixed with a solution of 4 g. of sodium in 60 ml. of ethanol and heated under reflux for two and one-half hours. The mixture is neutralized with the calculated amount of dilute hydrochloric acid, and enough water is added to produce turbidity. When the solution is cooled, the product crystallizes in quantitative yield as a mixture of isomers. After several crystallizations from dilute ethanol, the product melts at 92–93°.

Dimethyl (α-Phenyl-β-nitroethyl)malonate.[329] To an ice-cold solution of 26 g. of dimethyl malonate and 1 g. of sodium in 30 ml. of dry methanol, 5 g. of finely powdered ω-nitrostyrene is added. The mixture is shaken until all the solid dissolves. The clear solution is acidified with glacial acetic acid, cooled in ice, and saturated with hydrogen chloride. When the solution is colorless, it is poured into a suspension of ice in sodium carbonate. The colorless oil that precipitates crystallizes upon scratching. The product is washed with water and crystallized from methanol to furnish 8.7 g. (92%) of the ester, m.p. 57°.

488 Ames and Bowman, *J. Chem. Soc.*, **1950,** 329.

489 Reid and Sack, *J. Am. Chem. Soc.*, **73,** 1985 (1951).

Ethyl α-Benzoyl-γ-(2-pyridyl)butyrate.[490] To a mixture of 246 g. of freshly distilled ethyl benzoylacetate and 66 g. of freshly distilled 2-vinylpyridine, 1 g. of sodium is added, and the mixture is boiled for five hours. The solution is cooled, acidified, and extracted with ether to remove neutral material. The aqueous layer is made alkaline, the oil that separates is taken up in ether, and the extract is dried over anhydrous calcium sulfate. The ether and 2-vinylpyridine are evaporated under reduced pressure, and the residue is distilled to furnish 135 g. (70%) of the product as a pale orange oil, b.p. 170–175°/0.3 mm.

TABULAR SURVEY OF THE MICHAEL CONDENSATIONS

The following tables summarize the data in the literature through October 1955. Tables I–XXI classify the material according to the unsaturated acceptors. Table XXII lists most of the important donors that have been used in the Michael condensation.

The acceptors in Tables I–XXI have been arranged according to increasing number of carbon atoms unless otherwise stated. Alkyl esters are listed (independent of the number of the carbon atoms in the alkyl group) under the lowest member of the series employed. With each acceptor, the donors have been listed according to the following scheme:

Esters and other acid derivatives (except nitriles)
Keto esters
Cyano compounds
Aldehydes and ketones
Nitro compounds
Sulfones
Miscellaneous donors

Commas between items in the catalyst column separate the components of a catalyst combination; semicolons are used to separate different catalyst combinations.

When yields are cited, the first references cited are those to the articles containing the information on yields.

[490] Boekelheide and Agnello, *J. Am. Chem. Soc.*, **72**, 5005 (1950).

TABLE I

MICHAEL CONDENSATIONS WITH α,β-ETHYLENIC ALDEHYDES

Reactants	Catalyst	Product (Yield, %)	References
Acrolein and		A = $-CH_2CH_2CHO$	
Diethyl malonate	$NaOC_2H_5$	$ACH(CO_2C_2H_5)_2$ (50)	159, 417, 491
	$(n\text{-}C_4H_9)_3N$	$A_2C(CO_2C_2H_5)_2$	492
Diethyl ethylmalonate	$NaOC_2H_5$	$AC(C_2H_5)(CO_2C_2H_5)_2$ (40)	159, 161, 491
Diethyl *n*-hexylmalonate	$NaOC_2H_5$	$AC(C_6H_{13}\text{-}n)(CO_2C_2H_5)_2$	159, 161, 491
Diethyl *n*-decylmalonate	$NaOC_2H_5$	$AC(C_{10}H_{21}\text{-}n)(CO_2C_2H_5)_2$	159, 161, 491
Diethyl *n*-hexadecylmalonate	$NaOC_2H_5$	$AC(C_{16}H_{33}\text{-}n)(CO_2C_2H_5)_2$	491
Diethyl bromomalonate	$(n\text{-}C_4H_9)_3N$; $NaOC_2H_5$	$ACBr(CO_2C_2H_5)_2$*	159, 493
Diethyl chloromalonate	$(n\text{-}C_4H_9)_3N$	$ACCl(CO_2C_2H_5)_2$* (76)	493
Diethyl formamidomalonate	$NaOC_2H_5$	$AC(NHCHO)(CO_2C_2H_5)_2$	494
Diethyl acetamidomalonate	Na	$AC(NHCOCH_3)(CO_2C_2H_5)_2$ (87)	460
	$NaOCH_3$	$AC(NHCOCH_3)(CO_2C_2H_5)_2$ (61)	461
	$NaOC_2H_5$	$AC(NHCOCH_3)(CO_2C_2H_5)_2$ (56)	462, 494, 495
	Exchange resin (HO^- or CN^- form)	$AC(NHCOCH_3)CO_2C_2H_5)_2$ (62)†	496
Diethyl phthalimidomalonate	$NaOC_2H_5$	$o\text{-}C_6H_4(CO)_2NC(A)(CO_2C_2H_5)_2$	460, 494

Note: References 491–1045 are on pp. 545–555.

* When sodium ethoxide was used as the catalyst, dehydrohalogenation took place.

† The product was isolated as the phenylhydrazone.

TABLE I—*Continued*

MICHAEL CONDENSATIONS WITH α,β-ETHYLENIC ALDEHYDES

Reactants	Catalyst	Product (Yield, %)	References
Acrolein (Cont.) and		$A = -CH_2CH_2CHO$	
Diethyl acetoxymalonate	$NaOC_2H_5$	$CH_3CO_2C(A)(CO_2C_2H_5)_2$	159, 497
$CH(CO_2C_2H_5)_2$ | CH_2CH_2CHO	$NaOC_2H_5$	$A_2C(CO_2C_2H_5)_2$; 5,5-dicarbethoxy-1-cyclohexene-1-carboxaldehyde	110, 417
Ethyl acetoacetate	$NaOC_2H_5$	$CH_3COCH(A)CO_2C_2H_5$ (40, 39); 2-cyclohexen-1-one (20, 23)	498, 499
	$NaOC_2H_5$	$CH_3COCH(A)CO_2C_2H_5$	500
	Not indicated	2-Cyclohexen-1-one	501
Ethyl methylacetoacetate	$NaOC_2H_5$	6-Methyl-2-cyclohexen-1-one (20)	499
Ethyl cyclohexanone-2-carboxylate	$NaOC_2H_5$	[structure: cyclohexanone with A and $CO_2C_2H_5$ on C-2]	162
Ethyl cyanoacetate	$NaOC_2H_5$	$ACH(CN)CO_2C_2H_5$ (12); 5-carbethoxy-5-cyano-1-cyclohexene-1-carboxaldehyde	159, 417, 502, 503
Ethyl acetamidocyanoacetate	$NaOC_2H_5$	$AC(NHCOCH_3)(CN)CO_2C_2H_5$ (82, 60)	460, 494, 504
$CH(CN)CO_2C_2H_5$ | CH_2CH_2CHO	$NaOC_2H_5$	$A_2C(CN)CO_2C_2H_5$ (18)	110, 417
Cyclohexanecarboxaldehyde	SO_2	[structure: cyclohexane with A and CHO on the same carbon] (23)	472

3-Cyclohexene-1-carboxaldehyde	SO_2	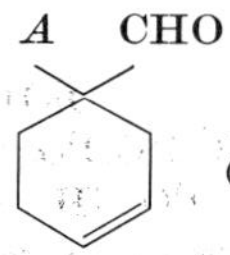 A CHO (27)	472
Deoxybenzoin	$NaOC_2H_5$	$C_6H_5CH(A)COC_6H_5$ (100)	163
Acetylacetone	Pyridine	$CH_3COCH(A)COCH_3$ (27); 6-Acetyl-2-cyclohexen-1-one (13); compound $C_{13}H_{18}O_4$ (27); 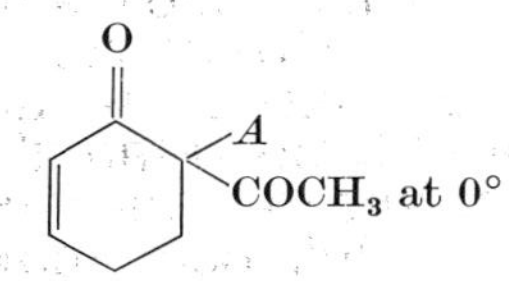 O, A, $COCH_3$ at 0°	505
Nitromethane	$[C_6H_5CH_2N(CH_3)_3]OH$; $NaOCH_3$	ACH_2NO_2 (41)	506
Nitroethane	$[C_6H_5CH_2N(CH_3)_3]OH$; $NaOCH_3$	$CH_3CH(A)NO_2$ (51)	506
1-Nitropropane	$NaOC_2H_5$	$CH_3CH_2CH(A)NO_2$ (30)	507
2-Nitropropane	$[C_6H_5CH_2N(CH_3)_3]OH$	$(CH_3)_2C(A)NO_2$ (49)	506
	$NaOCH_3$	$(CH_3)_2C(A)NO_2$ (33)	506
	$NaOC_2H_5$	$(CH_3)_2C(A)NO_2$	507
	K_2CO_3	$(CH_3)_2C(A)NO_2$ (35)	508
Ethyl nitroacetate	$NaOC_2H_5$	$ACH(NO_2)CO_2C_2H_5$	509
Diethyl nitromalonate	$NaOC_2H_5$	$AC(NO_2)(CO_2C_2H_5)_2$	510
	Exchange resin (HO^- or CN^--form)	$AC(NO_2)(CO_2C_2H_5)_2$ (94)	496
$(CH_3)_2CHCH_2C(CH_3)=NCH(CH_3)CH_2CH(CH_3)_2$	None	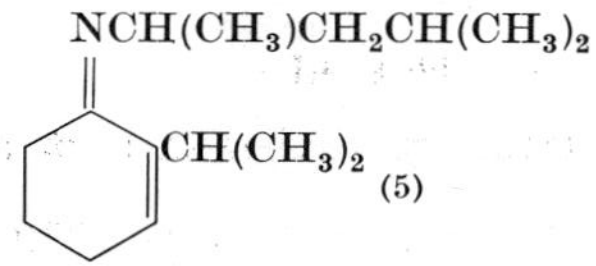 $NCH(CH_3)CH_2CH(CH_3)_2$, $CH(CH_3)_2$ (5)	375

Note: References 491–1045 are on pp. 545–555.

TABLE I—*Continued*

MICHAEL CONDENSATIONS WITH α,β-ETHYLENIC ALDEHYDES

Reactants	Catalyst	Product (Yield, %)	References
Crotonaldehyde and		$A = CH_3\overset{\vert}{C}HCH_2CHO$	
Diethyl malonate	$(C_2H_5)_2NH$	$CH(CO_2C_2H_5)_2CH(CH_3)CH{=}CHCH(CO_2C_2H_5)_2$	158
	$NaOC_2H_5$	3-Carbethoxymethyl-5-methylcyclohexanone	157
	$NaOC_2H_5$	$ACH(CO_2C_2H_5)_2$ (12)	160, 491
	$NaOC_2H_5$	$A_2C(CO_2C_2H_5)_2$	492
Diethyl ethylmalonate	$NaOC_2H_5$	$AC(C_2H_5)(CO_2C_2H_5)_2$ (38)	160, 491
Diethyl *n*-hexadecylmalonate	$NaOC_2H_5$	$AC(C_{16}H_{33}\text{-}n)(CO_2C_2H_5)_2$	491
Diethyl chloromalonate	$(n\text{-}C_4H_9)_3N$	$ACCl(CO_2C_2H_5)_2$*	493, 511
Diethyl acetamidomalonate	$NaOC_2H_5$	$AC(NHCOCH_3)(CO_2C_2H_5)_2$	160, 494
Diethyl acetoxymalonate	$NaOC_2H_5$	$AC(OCOCH_3)(CO_2C_2H_5)_2$	497
Ethyl acetoacetate	$NaOC_2H_5$	6-Carbethoxy-5-methyl-2-cyclohexen-1-one	512
	$NaOC_2H_5$	5-Methyl-2-cyclohexen-1-one (15–20, 35)	498, 499
Ethyl cyanoacetate	$NaOC_2H_5$	$ACH(CN)CO_2C_2H_5$	502
Ethyl acetamidocyanoacetate	$NaOC_2H_5$	$AC(NHCOCH_3)(CN)CO_2C_2H_5$	160, 494
Deoxybenzoin	$NaOCH_3$	$C_6H_5CH(A)COC_6H_5$ (100)	163
1-Nitropropane	$NaOC_2H_5$	$CH_3CH_2CH(A)NO_2$ (15)	507
2-Nitropropane	$NaOC_2H_5$	$(CH_3)_2C(A)NO_2$ (34)	507
Ethyl nitroacetate	$NaOC_2H_5$	$ACH(NO_2)CO_2C_2H_5$	509
Diethyl nitromalonate	$NaOC_2H_5$	$AC(NO_2)(CO_2C_2H_5)_2$	510
Methacrolein and		$A = \text{—}CH_2CH(CH_3)CHO$	
Diethyl malonate	$NaOC_2H_5$	$ACH(CO_2C_2H_5)_2$ (42)	160, 491
	$NaOC_2H_5$	$A_2C(CO_2C_2H_5)_2$	492
Diethyl ethylmalonate	$NaOC_2H_5$	$AC(C_2H_5)(CO_2C_2H_5)_2$ (25)	160, 491

Diethyl chloromalonate	$(n\text{-}C_4H_9)_3N$	$A\text{CCl}(CO_2C_2H_5)_2$	493
Diethyl acetamidomalonate	$NaOC_2H_5$	$A\text{C}(NHCOCH_3)(CO_2C_2H_5)_2$ (quant.)	160, 494
Diethyl acetoxymalonate	$NaOC_2H_5$	$A\text{C}(OCOCH_3)(CO_2C_2H_5)_2$	497
Ethyl acetoacetate	Not indicated	4-Methyl-2-cyclohexen-1-one (15–20)	498
	$NaOC_2H_5$	4-Methyl-2-cyclohexen-1-one (35)	499
$CH_3CH(CHO)CH_2CH(CO_2C_2H_5)_2$	$NaOC_2H_5$	Cyclohexene ring: CH_3; H_3C, OHC; $CO_2C_2H_5$, $CO_2C_2H_5$	110
Ethyl cyanoacetate	$NaOC_2H_5$	$A\text{CH}(CN)CO_2C_2H_5$	503
Ethyl acetamidocyanoacetate	$NaOC_2H_5$	$A\text{C}(NHCOCH_3)(CN)CO_2C_2H_5$	160, 494
β-Methoxyisobutyraldehyde‡	NaOH	2-Methoxymethyl-2,4-dimethylpentanedial (59)	513
β-Ethoxyisobutyraldehyde‡	NaOH	2-Ethoxymethyl-2,4-dimethylpentanedial (34)	513
β-Allyloxyisobutyraldehyde‡	NaOH	2-Allyloxymethyl-2,4-dimethylpentanedial (16)	513
β-*n*-Butoxyisobutyraldehyde‡	NaOH	2-*n*-Butoxymethyl-2,4-dimethylpentanedial (23)	513
1-Nitropropane	$NaOC_2H_5$	$CH_3CH_2CH(A)NO_2$ (31)	507
2-Nitropropane	$NaOC_2H_5$	$(CH_3)_2C(A)NO_2$ (20)	507
	K_2CO_3	$(CH_3)_2C(A)NO_2$ (85)	503
Ethyl nitroacetate	$NaOC_2H_5$	$A\text{CH}(NO_2)CO_2C_2H_5$	509
Diethyl nitromalonate	$NaOC_2H_5$	$A\text{C}(NO_2)(CO_2C_2H_5)_2$	510
$(CH_3)_2CHCH_2C(CH_3){=}NCH(CH_3)CH_2CH(CH_3)_2$	None	Cyclohexene ring: $=NCH(CH_3)CH_2CH(CH_3)_2$§; $CH(CH_3)_2$; CH_3 (5)	375

Note: References 491–1045 are on pp. 545–555.

* When sodium ethoxide was used as the catalyst, dehydrohalogenation took place.

‡ The alkoxy aldehyde was formed in situ from methacrolein and the appropriate alcohol.

§ The position of the nuclear double bond has not been established.

TABLE I—*Continued*

MICHAEL CONDENSATIONS WITH α,β-ETHYLENIC ALDEHYDES

Reactants	Catalyst	Product (Yield, %)	References
β-Hydroxycrotonaldehyde and			
$H_2NC({=}NH)CH_2CO_2C_2H_5$‖	None	Ethyl 2-amino-6-methylpyridine-3-carboxylate (13)	514
β,β-Dimethylacrolein and			
β,β-Dimethylacrolein	$NaNH_2$	4,6,6-Trimethyl-1,3-cyclohexadiene-4-carboxaldehyde	516
β-Ethoxyacrolein¶ *and*			
$H_2NC({=}NH)CH_2CO_2C_2H_5$‖	None	Ethyl 2-aminopyridine-3-carboxylate (18)	514
$CH_3C({=}NH)CH_2CO_2C_2H_5$	None	Ethyl 2-methylpyridine-3-carboxylate (30)	515
$CH_3C({=}NH)CH_2CN$	None	3-Cyano-2-methylpyridine (4)	515
$CH_3({=}NH)CH_2COCH_3$	None	3-Acetyl-2-methylpyridine (25)	515
$CH_3C({=}NH)CH_2COC_6H_5$	None	3-Benzoyl-2-methylpyridine (5)	515
β-Ethoxycrotonaldehyde¶ *and*			
$H_2NC({=}NH)CH_2CO_2C_2H_5$‖	None	Ethyl 2-amino-6-methylpyridine-3-carboxylate	514
$CH_3C({=}NH)CH_2CO_2C_2H_5$	None	Ethyl 2,6-dimethylpyridine-3-carboxylate (40)	166
$CH_3C({=}NH)CH_2CN$	None	3-Cyano-2,6-dimethylpyridine (40)	166
$CH_3C({=}NH)CH_2COCH_3$	None	3-Acetyl-2,6-dimethylpyridine (40)	166
$CH_3C({=}NH)CH_2COC_6H_5$	None	3-Benzoyl-2,6-dimethylpyridine (35)	166
α-Methyl-β-ethylacrolein and			
Isobutyraldehyde	$KOCH_3$, aq. NaOH, 130–180°	$CH_3CH_2CHCH(CH_3)C{=}O$ (42, 15) | | $(CH_3)_2C{-}CH_2{-}O$	165, 164
Deoxybenzoin	$NaOCH_3$	$CH_3CH_2CHCH(CH_3)CHO$ | $C_6H_5CHCOC_6H_5$	163

Reactants	Catalyst	Product (Yield, %)	Refs.
α-Ethyl-β-n-propylacrolein and			
Ethyl acetoacetate	KOH, acetal	n-$C_3H_7CHCH(C_2H_5)CHO$ (61) $CH_3COCHCO_2C_2H_5$	483, 517, 518
Butyraldehyde**	Aq. NaOH, 200°	n-$C_3H_7CHCH(C_2H_5)C{=}O$ C_2H_5CH —CH_2—O	164
Cinnamaldehyde and		$A = C_6H_5CHCH_2CHO$	
Diethyl ethylmalonate	$NaOCH_3$	$AC(C_2H_5)(CO_2C_2H_5)_2$	519
Diethyl acetamidomalonate	$NaOC_2H_5$	$AC(NHCOCH_3)(CO_2C_2H_5)_2$	464
Ethyl acetoacetate	$NaOC_2H_5$	6-Carbethoxy-5-phenyl-2-cyclohexen-1-one	512
Ethyl *n*-butylcyanoacetate	$NaOCH_3$	$AC(C_4H_9\text{-}n)(CN)(CO_2C_2H_5)$	519
Ethyl formamidocyanoacetate	$NaOC_2H_5$	$AC(NHCHO)(CN)CO_2C_2H_5$	464
Phenylacetaldehyde	$NaOCH_3$	β,γ-Diphenylvalerolactone (18)	163
Deoxybenzoin	$NaOCH_3$	$C_6H_5CH(A)COC_6H_5$ (quant.)	163
1-Nitropropane	$NaOC_2H_5$	$CH_3CH_2CH(A)NO_2$	520
2-Nitropropane	$NaOC_2H_5$	$(CH_3)_2C(A)NO_2$	520
β-Hydroxycinnamaldehyde and			
$H_2NC(=NH)CH_2CO_2C_2H_5$ ‖	None	Ethyl 2-amino-6-phenylpyridine-3-carboxylate (31)	521
2-*Heptylideneheptanal*†† *and*			
Heptanal	Aq. NaOH, 200°	3-*n*-Hexyl-2,4-di-*n*-pentylvalerolactone (9)	167

Note: References 491–1045 are on pp. 545–555.

‖ Malonic acid ethyl ester imino ether was employed; it reacted as the amidine.

¶ The aldehyde was introduced in the form of its acetal.

** The butyraldehyde was formed in situ by scission of α-ethyl-β-*n*-propylacrolein.

†† The unsaturated aldehyde was formed *in situ* from heptanal.

TABLE II

Michael Condensations with Aliphatic α,β-Ethylenic Ketones

Reactants	Catalyst	Product (Yield, %)	References
Methyl Vinyl Ketone and		$A = CH_3COCH_2CH_2$—	
Diethyl malonate	$[C_6H_5CH_2N(CH_3)_3]OH$	$A_2C(CO_2C_2H_5)_2$ (85)	522, cf. 523
Diethyl ethylmalonate	$NaOC_2H_5$	$AC(C_2H_5)(CO_2C_2H_5)_2$ (42)	524
α-Methyl-β-oxo-γ-butyrolactone	$NaOCH_3$	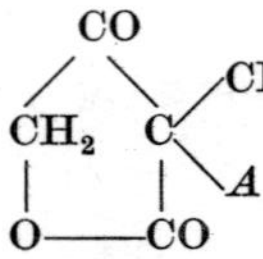 CO; CH_2 C(CH_3)(*A*); O—CO (56)	525
	$NaOCH_3$*	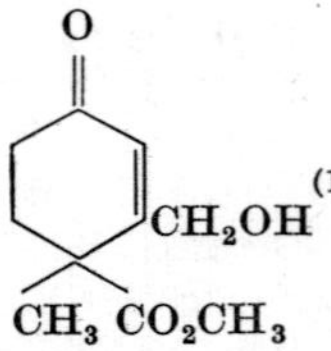 O; CH_2OH; CH_3 CO_2CH_3 (14) 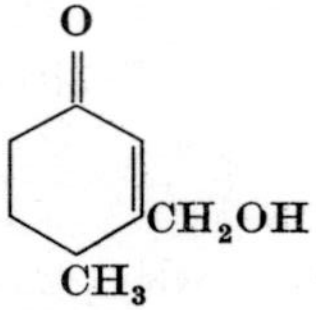 O; CH_2OH; CH_3 (4)	525
Ethyl acetoacetate	$NaOC_2H_5$	$CH_3COC(A)_2CO_2C_2H_5$ (92)	119
Ethyl ethylacetoacetate	Na	4-Ethyl-3-methyl-2-cyclohexen-1-one	420
Ethyl α-(methylthiomethyl)-acetoacetate	$NaOC_2H_5$	$CH_3COC(CH_2SCH_3)(A)CO_2C_2H_5$ (47)	526
Ethyl isopropylacetoacetate†	$NaOC_2H_5$	6-Carbethoxy-6-isopropyl-3-methyl-2-cyclohexen-1-one (32)†††	527
		$CH_3COC(A)(C_3H_7\text{-}i)CO_2C_2H_5$ (74)	119
Ethyl 2-oxocyclohexane-1-carboxylate‡	NaOH	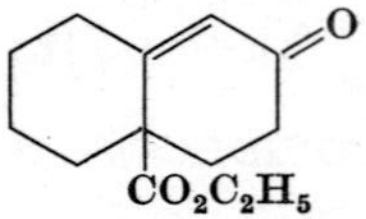 O; $CO_2C_2H_5$ (small)	528

Reactant	Catalyst	Product (Yield, %)	Ref.
	Not indicated	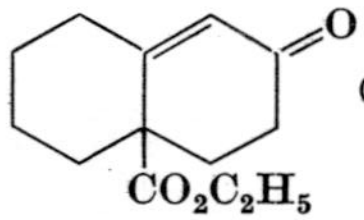 $CO_2C_2H_5$ (73)	529
	$[C_6H_5CH_2N(CH_3)_3]OH$	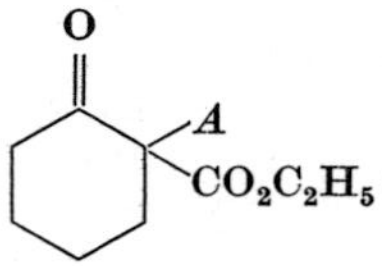 O, A, $CO_2C_2H_5$ (91)	530
Ethyl 4-methyl-2-oxo-3-cyclohexene-1-carboxylate	$NaOCH_3$	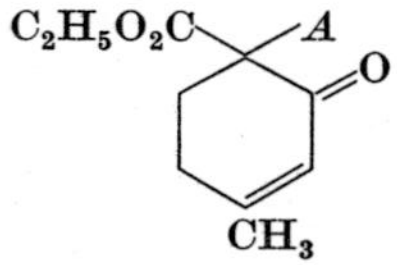 $C_2H_5O_2C$, A, O, CH_3 (84)	122
Ethyl benzoylacetate	$[C_6H_5CH_2N(CH_3)_3]OH$	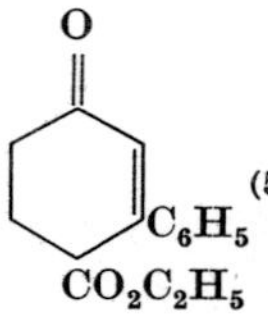 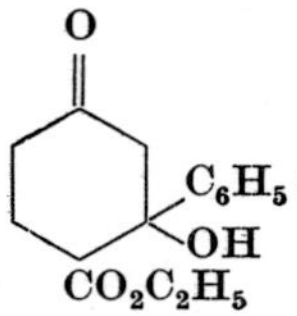 O, C_6H_5, $CO_2C_2H_5$ (55); O, C_6H_5, OH, $CO_2C_2H_5$ (21)	536
Ethyl (α-furoyl)acetate	Not indicated	4-Carbethoxy-3-(α-furyl)-3-hydroxycyclohexan-1-one	531

Note: References 491–1045 are on pp. 545–555.

* In this condensation the amount of catalyst was twice that used in the preceding condensation.

† Methyl chloroethyl ketone was employed.

‡ In this experiment the actual reagents used were the ester, acetone, and formaldehyde.

††† When the adduct was hydrolyzed, a 26% over-all yield of (±)-piperitone was obtained.

TABLE II—*Continued*

MICHAEL CONDENSATIONS WITH ALIPHATIC α,β-ETHYLENIC KETONES

Reactants	Catalyst	Product (Yield, %)	References
Methyl Vinyl Ketone (*Cont.*) *and*		$A = CH_3COCH_2CH_2$—	
Methyl 1-oxo-1,2,3,4-tetrahydro-phenanthrene-2-carboxylate	$NaOCH_3$	(93)	532
Methyl 4-oxo-1,2,3,4-tetrahydro-phenanthrene-3-carboxylate	$NaOCH_3$	(96)	533
Ethyl phenylpyruvate	Not indicated	3-Carbethoxy-3-hydroxy-2-methyl-4-phenyl-cyclobexanone	531
Malononitrile	$NaOCH_3$	$(A)_2C(CN)_2$ (74)	119, 122
Benzyl cyanide	Na	$C_6H_5CH(A)CN$	121
Ethyl phenylcyanoacetate	Na	$C_6H_5C(A)(CN)CO_2C_2H_5$ (90)	121
Methyl β-cyanoethyl ketone	KCN		123

Acetone	—§	3-Methyl-2-cyclohexen-1-one (3)	419
Isobutyraldehyde	$KOCH_3$	4,4-Dimethyl-2-cyclohexen-1-one‖ (40)	534
Methyl ethyl ketone	—§	3,6-Dimethyl-2-cyclohexen-1-one (3)	419
Diethylacetaldehyde	$KOCH_3$	4,4-Diethyl-2-cyclohexen-1-one	534
2-Ethylhexanal	$KOCH_3$	4-*n*-Butyl-4-ethyl-2-cyclohexen-1-one	534
Cyclohexanone	Enamine from cyclohexanone	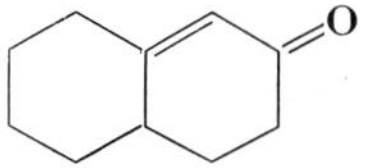 O (30–40)	535, 531
Phenylacetone	$[C_6H_5CH_2N(CH_3)_3]OH$	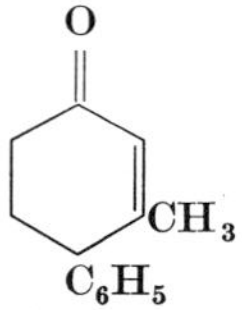 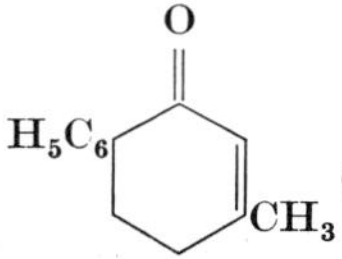 O, CH_3, C_6H_5 and O, H_5C_6, CH_3 (40)	536
Cyclohexane-1,3-dione	$NaOCH_3$	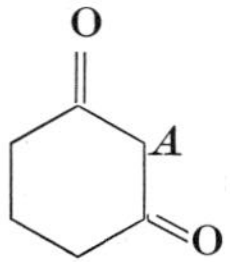 O, *A*, O	532
	KOH, CH_3OH	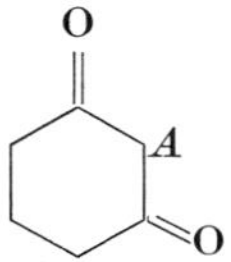 O, *A*, O (38) 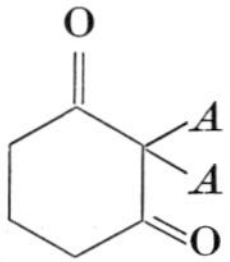 O, *A*, *A*, O (36)	538

Note: References 491–1045 are on pp. 545–555.

§ This experiment was run in the vapor phase, in the presence of oxides of group II to IV of the periodic system.

‖ This was reported as the probable structure of the product.

TABLE II—*Continued*

MICHAEL CONDENSATIONS WITH ALIPHATIC α,β-ETHYLENIC KETONES

Reactants	Catalyst	Product (Yield, %)	References
Methyl Vinyl Ketone (Cont.) and		$A = CH_3COCH_2CH_2$—	
2-Methylcyclohexane-1,3-dione	$NaOCH_3$; $(C_2H_5)_3N$	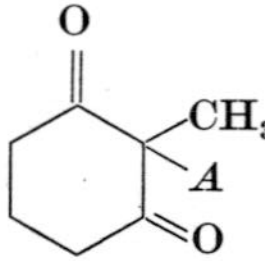 2-CH_3-2-A-cyclohexane-1,3-dione (64)	525, 539
5,5-Dimethylcyclohexane-1,3-dione	KOH, CH_3OH	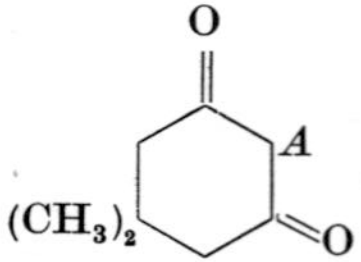 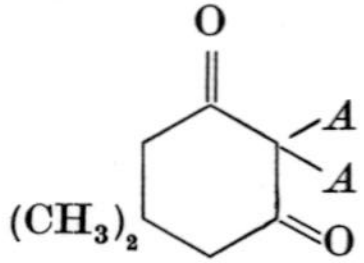 2-A-5,5-$(CH_3)_2$-cyclohexane-1,3-dione (52); 2,2-di-A-5,5-$(CH_3)_2$-cyclohexane-1,3-dione (43)	538
5-Methyloctahydronaphthalene-1,6-dione	$NaOCH_3$	5-Methyl-5-(γ-ketobutyl)-$\Delta^{4a,5a}$-octahydronaphthalene-1,6-dione	115
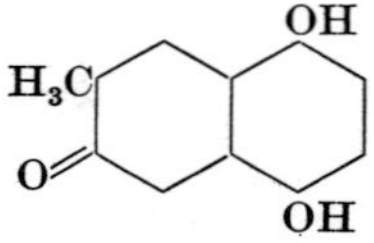 (H_3C, O, OH, OH — structure)	$[C_6H_5CH_2N(CH_3)_3]OH$	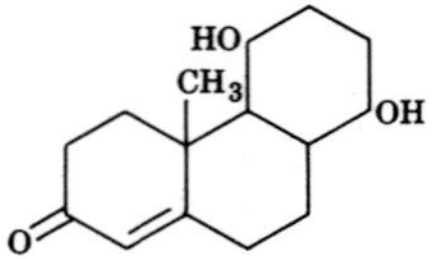 (HO, CH_3, OH, O — structure) (39)	540, 541
6-Methoxy-1-methyl-2-tetralone	Not indicated	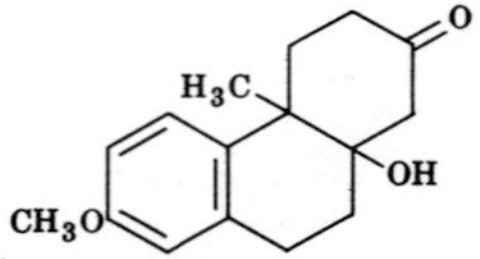 (H_3C, O, OH, CH_3O — structure)	531

3-Hydroxymethylene-4-keto-1,2,3,4-tetrahydrophenanthrene	$NaOCH_3$	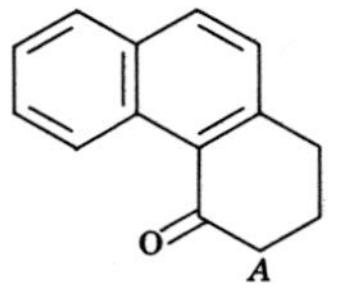 and the 3-formyl derivative	533
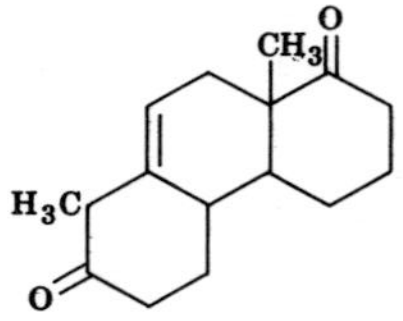	$NaOC_2H_5$; *t*-amines	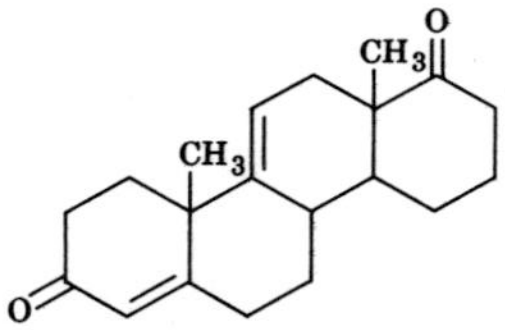	542
Nitromethane	$[C_6H_5CH_2N(CH_3)_3]OH$; $NaOCH_3$	ACH_2NO_2 (51)	506, 523
Nitroethane	$NaOCH_3$	$CH_3CH(A)NO_2$ (49)	506
2-Nitropropane	$NaOCH_3$	$(CH_3)_2C(A)NO_2$ (69)	506, 543
Methyl fluorene-9-carboxylate	KOH	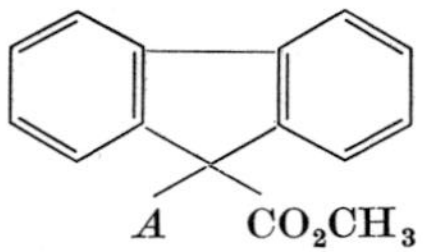 (71)	544
2-Naphthol	KOC_2H_5	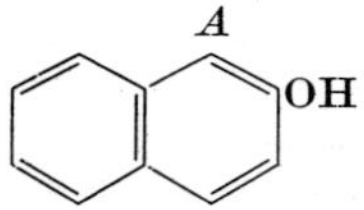 (24)	168

Note: References 491–1045 are on pp. 545–555.

TABLE II—*Continued*

MICHAEL CONDENSATIONS WITH ALIPHATIC α,β-ETHYLENIC KETONES

Reactants	Catalyst	Product (Yield, %)	References
Methyl Vinyl Ketone (Cont.) and		$A = CH_3COCH_2CH_2$—	
Ethyl 3-hydroxybenzofuran-2-carboxylate	$NaOC_2H_5$	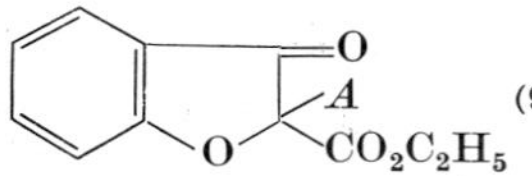 =O, A, O, $CO_2C_2H_5$ (90)	119
2′-Hydroxymethylene-1′-oxo-1′,2′,3′,4′-tetrahydro-1,2-benz-3,4-aceperinaphthane	$NaOCH_3$	1′-Oxo-2′-(γ-oxobutyl)-1′,2′,3′,4′-tetrahydro-1,2-benz-3,4-aceperinaphthane (70)	545
	KOC_4H_9-*t*	1′-Oxo-2′-(γ-oxobutyl)-1′,2′,3′,4′-tetrahydro-1,2-benz-3,4-aceperinaphthane (26)	545
Hydroxymethyleneacetone and			
Ethyl acetoacetate	$NaOC_2H_5$	2-Hydroxy-4-methylbenzoic acid (55)	427
Diethyl acetone-1,3-dicarboxylate	$NaOC_2H_5$	Diethyl 2-hydroxy-4-methylisophthalate (49)	427
Nitromethane	$CH_3COCH{=}CHONa$	$CH_3COCH_2CHOHCH_2NO_2$ (4)	546
Ethyl malonamate¶	None	Ethyl 2-amino-6-methylnicotinate (32)	521
Cyanoacetamide	Piperidine acetate	3-Cyano-2-hydroxy-6-methylpyridine (55–62)	547
Ethylideneacetone and		$A = CH_3CHCH_2COCH_3$ (with a vertical bond line below the CH)	
Diethyl methylmalonate	$NaOC_2H_5$	2,3-Dimethylcyclohexane-1,5-dione (10)	422
Ethyl 2-oxocyclohexane-1-carboxylate	KOC_2H_5	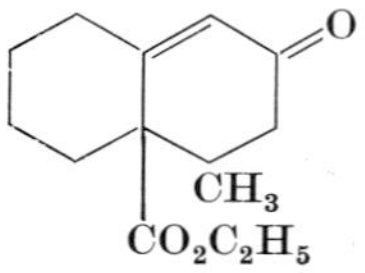 O, CH_3, $CO_2C_2H_5$	409

Reactant	Catalyst	Product (Yield, %)	Refs.
Methyl 1-oxo-1,2,3,4-tetrahydro-phenanthrene-2-carboxylate	$NaOCH_3$	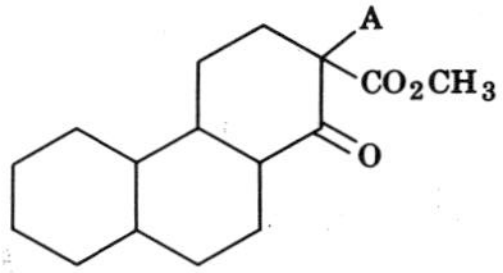 (83 crude, 59 pure)	548
4-Hydroxycoumarin	Pyridine	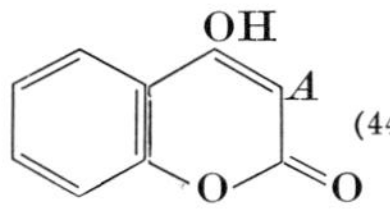 (44)	169
7-Chloro-4,6-dimethoxycoumaran-3-one	$NaOC_2H_5$	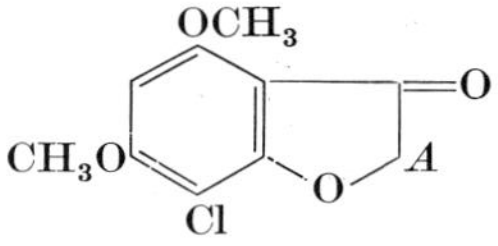 (Two isomers)	88
4,6-Dimethoxycoumaran-3-one	$NaOC_2H_5$	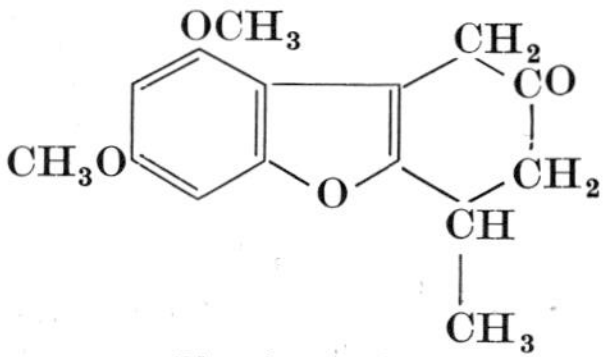 (Two isomers)	88
2-Carbethoxy-4,6-dimethoxy-coumaran-3-one	$NaOC_2H_5$	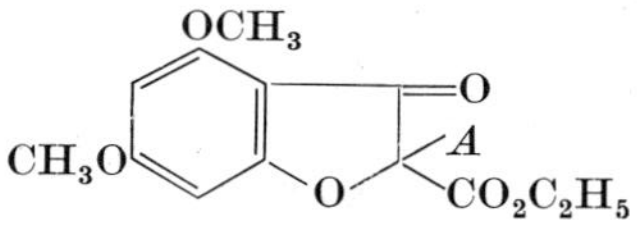 see structure	88

Note: References 491–1045 are on pp. 545–555.

¶ The ester imino ether was used.

TABLE II—*Continued*

MICHAEL CONDENSATIONS WITH ALIPHATIC α,β-ETHYLENIC KETONES

Reactants	Catalyst	Product (Yield, %)	References
Ethyl Vinyl Ketone and		$A = CH_3CH_2COCH_2CH_2$—	
Diethyl malonate**	$NaOC_2H_5$	$ACH(CO_2C_2H_5)_2$	549
Ethyl acetoacetate**	$NaOC_2H_5$	$CH_3COCH(A)CO_2C_2H_5$	550
Acetylacetone**	$NaOC_2H_5$	$CH_3COCH(A)COCH_3$	549
Cyclohexane-1,3-dione	Piperidine	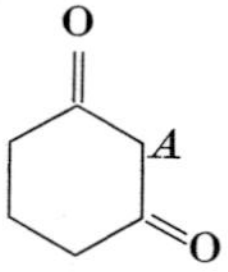 O, A, O	537
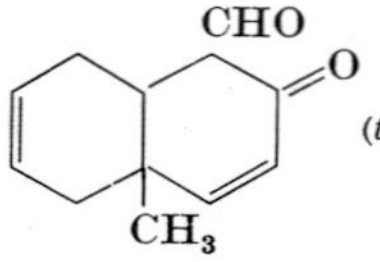 CHO, O, CH_3 (*trans*)	KOC_4H_9-*t*	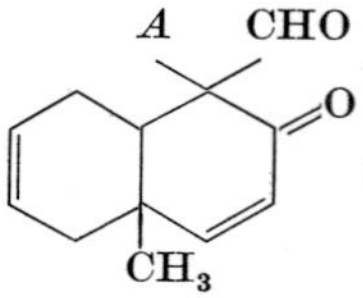 A, CHO, O, CH_3 (45–57)	551
Divinyl Ketone and			
2-Methylcyclohexane-1,3-dione	$NaOCH_3$	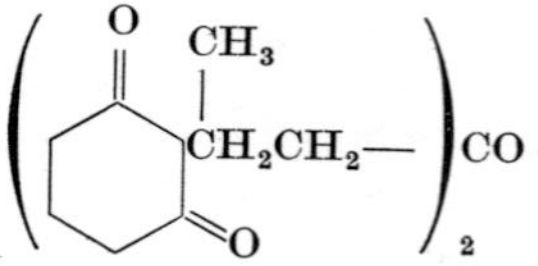 O, CH_3, CH_2CH_2—, O, ( )$_2$CO (18)	538

Methyl Isopropenyl Ketone and		A = $CH_3COCH(CH_3)CH_2$—	
Ethyl acetoacetate	Na	3,4-Dimethyl-2-cyclohexen-1-one	420
Ethyl propionylacetate	Na	3-Ethyl-4-methyl-2-cyclohexen-1-one	420
Ethyl isobutyrylacetate	KOH, C_2H_5OH	$(CH_3)_2CHCOCH(A)CO_2C_2H_5$ (75)	119
Acetone	KOH, CH_3OH	3,6-Dimethyl-2-cyclohexen-1-one (20)	418, 552††
Methyl ethyl ketone	KOH, CH_3OH	3,4,6-Trimethyl-2-cyclohexen-1-one‡‡ (49, 43)	418, 552
Cyclohexanone	KOH, C_2H_5OH	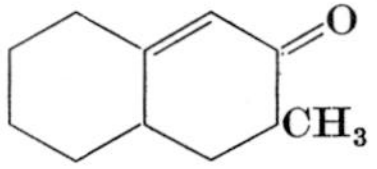 O, CH_3 (80, 90, 25); 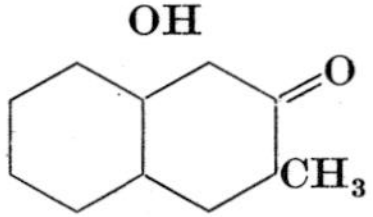 OH, O, CH_3 (32)	369, 101
4-Methylcyclohexanone	KOH, C_2H_5OH	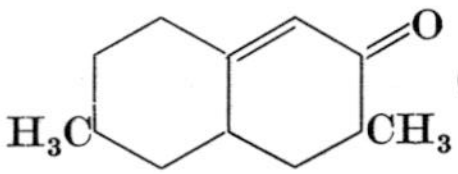 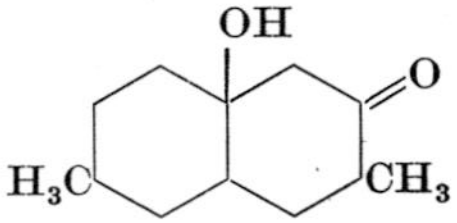 H_3C, O, CH_3 (13); OH, H_3C, O, CH_3 (50) (Two isomers)	101, cf. 8

Note: References 491–1045 are on pp. 545–555.

** β-Chloroethyl ethyl ketone was employed.

†† When 3-hydroxy-3-methylbutan-2-one was used, instead of the unsaturated ketone, the yield was 11%.

‡‡ The same product was obtained from methyl ethyl ketone and formaldehyde (49–52%) and from methyl ethyl ketone and 3-hydroxy-3-methylbutan-2-one (43–49%).

TABLE II—*Continued*

MICHAEL CONDENSATIONS WITH ALIPHATIC α,β-ETHYLENIC KETONES

Reactants	Catalyst	Product (Yield, %)	References
Methyl Isopropenyl Ketone (Cont.) and		A = $CH_3COCH(CH_3)CH_2$—	
3-Methylcyclohexanone	KOH, C_2H_5OH	(18)	101
		(19) (Two isomers)	
2-Methylcyclohexanone	KOH, C_2H_5OH	(28) (1)	101
Tetrahydrocarvone	KOH, C_2H_5OH	(40)	101
4-Hydroxy-3-penten-2-one and			
Diethyl acetone-1,3-dicarboxylate	$NaOC_2H_5$	Diethyl 2-hydroxy-4,6-dimethylisophthalate (92)	427
Malonamide	None	4,6-Dimethyl-2-pyridone-3-carboxamide	370
Malononitrile	None	4,6-Dimethyl-3-cyano-2-pyridone	370

$H_2NC(=NH)CH_2CO_2C_2H_5$¶	None	Ethyl 2-amino-4,6-dimethylpyridine-3-carboxylate (50, 69)	514, 521
Cyanoacetamide	None	4,6-Dimethyl-2-pyridone-3-carboxamide	370
	Piperidine	3-Cyano-4,6-dimethyl-2-pyridone (87, 100)	553, 371, 554
Cyanoacetamide§§	NH_3	3-Cyano-4,6-dimethyl-2-pyridone	555
$NCCH_2CONHCH_3$§§	CH_3NH_2	3-Cyano-1,4,6-trimethyl-2-pyridone	555
$NCCH_2CONHC_2H_5$§§	$C_2H_5NH_2$	3-Cyano-4,6-dimethyl-1-ethyl-2-pyridone	555
$NCCH_2CONHCH_2CH=CH_2$§§	$CH_2=CHCH_2NH_2$	1-Allyl-3-cyano-4,6-dimethyl-2-pyridone	555
$CH_3COCH_2C(=NH)CH_3$§§	None	Methyl 2,4,6-trimethyl-3-pyridyl ketone (>75)	444
4-*Amino*-3-*penten*-2-*one and*			
Ethyl cyanoacetate	None	3-Cyano-4,6-dimethyl-2-pyridone	555
N-Methylcyanoacetamide	None	3-Cyano-1,4,6-trimethyl-2-pyridone	556
Methyl α-Hydroxymethyleneëthyl Ketone and			
Cyanoacetamide	Piperidine	3-Cyano-4-hydroxy-5,6-dimethyl-2,3,4,5-tetrahydro-2-pyridone or 3-cyano-5,6-dimethyl-2-hydroxypyridine (23)	171, 172
$CH_3C(=NH)CH_2CO_2C_2H_5$	None	Ethyl 2,5,6-trimethylpyridine-3-carboxylate	557
3-*Hydroxymethylenepentane*-2,4-*dione and*			
Cyanoacetamide	$NaOC_2H_5$	Compound $C_9H_8N_2O_2$	254
Mesityl Oxide and		$A = CH_3COCH_2C(CH_3)_2$ |	
Dimethyl malonate	$NaOCH_3$	4-Carbomethoxy-5,5-dimethylcyclohexane-1,3-dione (85)	558

Note: References 491–1045 are on pp. 545–555.

¶ The ester imino ether was used.

§§ A mixture of ethyl cyanoacetate and ammonia or the appropriate amine was used in these experiments.

TABLE II—*Continued*

MICHAEL CONDENSATIONS WITH ALIPHATIC α,β-ETHYLENIC KETONES

Reactants	Catalyst	Product (Yield, %)	References
Mesityl Oxide (*Cont.*) *and*		$A = CH_3COCH_2C(CH_3)_2$ (bond to A from the quaternary C)	
Diethyl malonate	$NaOC_2H_5$	5,5-Dimethylcyclohexane-1,3-dione (67–85) or 4-carbethoxy-5,5-dimethylcyclohexane-1,3-dione (95–97)	558, 558*a*
Diethyl methylmalonate	$NaOC_2H_5$	4,5,5-Trimethylcyclohexane-1,3-dione	315
Ethyl phenylacetate	$NaOC_2H_5$	5,5-Dimethyl-4-phenylcyclohexane-1,3-dione	82
Ethyl acetoacetate	$NaOC_2H_5$	3,5,5-Trimethyl-2-cyclohexen-1-one (low)	15, 16, 17, cf. 119
Ethyl benzoylacetate	$NaOC_2H_5$	4-Carbethoxy-5,5-dimethyl-3-phenyl-2-cyclohexen-1-one (44)	414
Methyl cyanoacetate	Na	$NCCH(A)CO_2CH_3$	415
Ethyl cyanoacetate	$NaOC_2H_5$	4-Cyano-5,5-dimethylcyclohexane-1,3-dione (50)	415, 425
Cyanoacetamide	$NaOC_2H_5$	3-Cyano-6-hydroxy-4,4,6-trimethyl-2-piperidone (quant.)	559
Deoxybenzoin	$NaOC_2H_5$	$C_6H_5COCH(A)C_6H_5$ and 5,5-dimethyl-3,4-diphenyl-2-cyclohexen-1-one	414
Acetylacetone	Na	6-Acetyl-3,5,5-trimethyl-2-cyclohexen-1-one	415
Nitromethane	$NaOC_2H_5$	ACH_2NO_2 (63)	560
	$(C_2H_5)_2NH$	ACH_2NO_2 (65)	209
Fluorene	KOH, pyridine	5-(9-Fluorenyl)-4,4-dimethylpentan-2-one (15–20)	561
4-Hydroxycoumarin	Pyridine	4-(4-Hydroxycoumarinyl)-4-methylpentan-2-one (43)	169
3-*Ethyl*-3-*buten*-2-*one and*			
Methyl propyl ketone‖‖	KOH, CH_3OH	4,6-Diethyl-3-methyl-2-cyclohexenone¶¶ (7, 20)	552, 418

3-Methyl-3-penten-2-one and			
Diethyl malonate	$NaOC_2H_5$	4,5-Dimethylcyclohexane-1,3-dione*** (10)	422
2-Methyl-1-penten-3-one and			
Ethyl propionylacetate	Not indicated	2,4-Dimethyl-3-ethyl-2-cyclohexenone	420
Ethyl methylacetoacetate	Not indicated	3-Ethyl-4,6-dimethyl-2-cyclohexenone	420
Ethyl ethylacetoacetate	Not indicated	3,6-Diethyl-4-methyl-2-cyclohexenone	420
4-Hydroxy-3-methyl-3-penten-2-one and			
Cyanoacetamide §§	None	3-Cyano-4,5,6-trimethyl-2-pyridone	555
	Piperidine	3-Cyano-4,5,6-trimethyl-2-pyridone	562, cf. 563
$NCCH_2CONHCH_3$ §§	None	3-Cyano-1,4,5,6-tetramethyl-2-pyridone	555
Ethyl α-Hydroxymethyleneëthyl Ketone and			
Cyanoacetamide	*sec*-Amine	3-Cyano-6-ethyl-2-hydroxy-5-methylpyridine	254
$CH_3C({=}NH)CH_2CO_2C_2H_5$	None	Ethyl 6-ethyl-2,5-dimethylpyridine-3-carboxylate (50)	442
$CH_3C({=}NH)CH_2COCH_3$	None	Methyl 6-ethyl-2,5-dimethyl-3-pyridyl ketone (46)	442
Nitromethane	$CH_3CH_2COC({=}CHONa)CH_3$	5-Hydroxy-4-methyl-6-nitrohexan-3-one (54)	546
Methyl β-Ethoxyvinyl Ketone and			
Cyanoacetamide	Piperidine	3-Cyano-6-methyl-2-pyridone (75)	564

Note: References 491–1045 are on pp. 545–555.

§§ A mixture of ethyl cyanoacetate and ammonia or the appropriate amine was used in these experiments.

‖‖ A mixture of trioxymethylene and the ketone was used.

¶¶ The same product was obtained in 23% yield from the ketone and 3-ethyl-4-hydroxy-2-butanone, and in 20% yield from methyl propyl ketone and formaldehyde.

*** The name used in the reference is erroneous.

TABLE II—*Continued*

MICHAEL CONDENSATIONS WITH ALIPHATIC α,β-ETHYLENIC KETONES

Reactants	Catalyst	Product (Yield, %)	References
β-Methoxyvinyl Ethyl Ketone and			
2-Methylcyclohexanone	Na	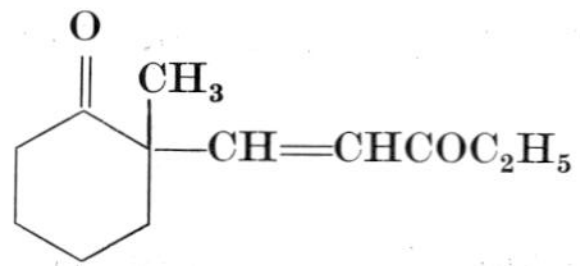 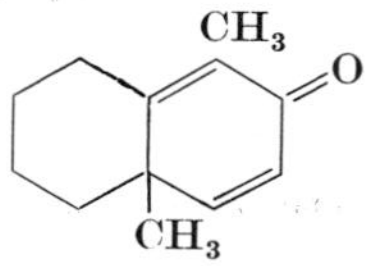 2-Methyl-2-($CH=CHCOC_2H_5$)cyclohexanone; 4a,?-dimethyl-octalinone [structures] (Small)	389
3-Hepten-2-one and			
Diethyl malonate	$NaOC_2H_5$	5-*n*-Propylcyclohexane-1,3-dione (16, 24)	565, 422
4-Methyl-3-hexen-2-one and			
Cyanoacetamide	$NaOC_2H_5$	3-Cyano-4-ethyl-6-hydroxy-4,6-dimethyl-2-piperidone (63)	566
5-Methyl-3-hexen-2-one and			
Diethyl malonate	$NaOC_2H_5$	5-Isopropylcyclohexane-1,3-dione (80)	422, 567, 568
3,4-Dimethyl-3-penten-2-one and			
Diethyl malonate	$NaOC_2H_5$	4,5,5-Trimethylcyclohexane-1,3-dione	569
5-Hydroxy-4-hepten-3-one and			
Cyanoacetamide	None	3-Cyano-4,6-diethyl-2-pyridone	370
4-Hydroxy-5-ethoxy-3-penten-2-one and			
Cyanoacetamide	Piperidine	3-Cyano-4-ethoxymethyl-6-methyl-2-pyridone (81)	477

4-Hydroxy-3-ethyl-3-penten-2-one and			
Cyanoacetamide	None	3-Cyano-5-ethyl-4,6-dimethyl-2-pyridone	371
Methyl β-Isopropoxyvinyl Ketone and			
Diethyl malonate	Na	$CH_3COCH{=}CHCH(CO_2C_2H_5)_2$ and 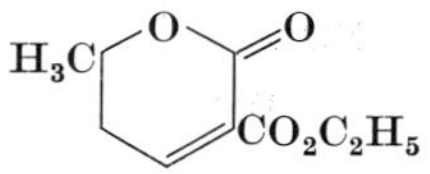	389
Methyl 4-Oxo-5-hexenoate and			
2-Methylcyclohexane-1,3-dione	$NaOCH_3$	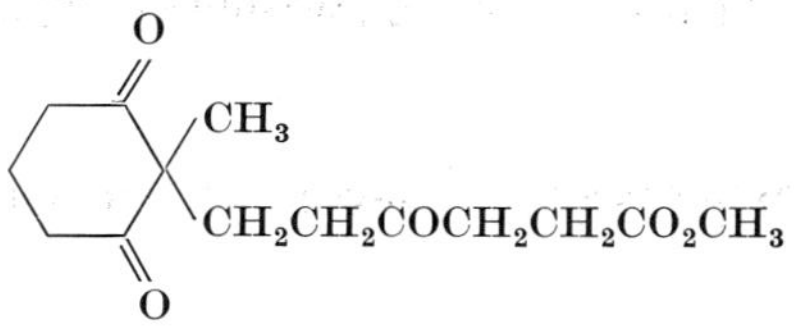	525
6-Methyl-4-hepten-3-one and			
Diethyl malonate	$NaOC_2H_5$	5-Isopropyl-2-methylcyclohexane-1,3-dione (43)	422
4-Ethyl-3-hexen-2-one and			
Diethyl malonate	$NaOC_2H_5$	5,5-Diethylcyclohexane-1,3-dione (50)	570
Cyanoacetamide	$NaOC_2H_5$	3-Cyano-4,4-diethyl-6-hydroxy-6-methyl-2-piperidone (75)	566
n-Propyl β-Ethoxyvinyl Ketone and			
Cyanoacetamide	Piperidine	3-Cyano-6-*n*-propyl-2-pyridone (64)	564

Note: References 491–1045 are on pp. 545–555.

TABLE II—*Continued*

MICHAEL CONDENSATIONS WITH ALIPHATIC α,β-ETHYLENIC KETONES

Reactants	Catalyst	Product (Yield, %)	References
Isopropyl β-Ethoxyvinyl Ketone and			
Cyanoacetamide	Piperidine	3-Cyano-6-isopropyl-2-pyridone (77)	564
3-n-Amyl-3-buten-2-one‖‖ *and*			
Methyl hexyl ketone	KOH, CH_3OH	4,6-Di-(*n*-amyl)-3-methyl-2-cyclohexenone (23, 33)	418, 552
6-Methyl-5-nonen-4-one and			
Diethyl malonate	$NaOC_2H_5$	2-Ethyl-5-methyl-5-*n*-propylcyclohexane-1,3-dione	571
Decane-2,4-dione (enol) and			
Cyanoacetamide§§	None	CH_3, CN, *n*-$H_{13}C_6$, N, H, =O or C_6H_{13}-*n*, CN, H_3C, N, H, =O	555
β-Ethoxyvinyl n-Amyl Ketone and			
Cyanoacetamide	Piperidine	6-*n*-Amyl-3-cyano-2-pyridone (68)	564

8-*Methyl-7-tridecen-6-one and*		$A = n$-$C_5H_{11}COCH_2C(CH_3)C_5H_{11}$-$n$	
Diethyl malonate	$NaOC_2H_5$	5-*n*-Amyl-2-*n*-butyl-5-methylcyclohexane-1,3-dione (60)	572
Cyanoacetamide	$NaOC_2H_5$	$ACH(CN)CONH_2$ (64)	572
1-*Hydroxymethyleneheptadecan-2-one and*			
Diethyl acetone-1,3-dicarboxylate	$NaOC_2H_5$	Diethyl 2-hydroxy-4-*n*-pentadecylisophthalate (52)	427
13-*Methyl-12-tricosen-11-one and*		$A = n$-$C_{10}H_{21}C(CH_3)CH_2COC_{10}H_{21}$-$n$	
Diethyl malonate	$NaOC_2H_5$	5-*n*-Decyl-5-methyl-2-*n*-nonylcyclohexane-1,3-dione (60)	572
Cyanoacetamide	$NaOC_2H_5$	$ACH_2CO_2C_2H_5$‡‡‡	572

Note: References 491–1045 are on pp. 545–555.

§§ A mixture of ethyl cyanoacetate and ammonia or the appropriate amine was used in these experiments.

‖‖ A mixture of trioxymethylene and the ketone was used.

‡‡‡ This product was obtained after acid hydrolysis and esterification.

TABLE III

Michael Condensations with Aromatic α,β-Ethylenic Ketones

Reactants	Catalyst	Product (Yield, %)	References
Vinyl Phenyl Ketone and*		$A = C_6H_5COCH_2CH_2—$	
Dimethyl malonate	$NaOCH_3$	$ACH(CO_2CH_3)_2$ (70), $(A)_2C(CO_2CH_3)_2$ (small)	573
Methyl fluorene-9-carboxylate	KOH	A CO_2CH_3 (56)	544
Ethyl acetoacetate	$NaOC_2H_5$	6-Carbethoxy-3-phenyl-2-cyclohexen-1-one	574
Malononitrile	$NaOCH_3$	$(A)_2C(CN)_2$	228
Methyl cyanoacetate	$NaOCH_3$	$(A)_2C(CN)CO_2CH_3$ (70)	228
Cyanoacetamide	$NaOCH_3$	$(A)_2C(CN)CONH_2$	228
Methyl benzyl ketone	$NaOCH_3$	3,6-Diphenyl-2-cyclohexen-1-one	574
Deoxybenzoin	$NaOCH_3$	$C_6H_5COCH(A)C_6H_5$ (60)	575
Dibenzyl ketone	$NaOC_2H_5$	2,3,6-Triphenyl-2-cyclohexen-1-one	574
Benzyl *p*-biphenylyl ketone	$NaOCH_3$	$C_6H_5CH(A)COC_6H_4C_6H_5$-*p*	575
Nitromethane	$NaOCH_3$	$(A)_3CNO_2$	228
Phenylnitromethane	$NaOCH_3$	$C_6H_5CH(A)NO_2$ (82)	576
Hydroxymethyleneacetophenone and			
Ethyl acetoacetate	$[CH_3COCHCO_2C_2H_5]Na$	Ethyl 3-hydroxybiphenyl-4-carboxylate (42)	577
Diethyl acetone-1,3-dicarboxylate	$NaOC_2H_5$	Diethyl 3-hydroxybiphenyl-2,4-dicarboxylate (59)	427
$CH_3C(=NH)CH_2COCH_3$	None	3-Acetyl-2-methyl-6-phenylpyridine	422
$CH_3C(=NH)CH_2COC_6H_5$	None	3-Benzoyl-2-methyl-6-phenylpyridine	442
Nitromethane	$C_6H_5COCH=CHONa$	β-Hydroxy-γ-nitrobutyrophenone	545
(Methoxymethylene)acetophenone and			
Ethyl acetoacetate	$[CH_3COCHCO_2C_2H_5]Na$	Ethyl 3-hydroxybiphenyl-4-carboxylate (42)	577

		$A = CH_3COCH_2CHC_6H_5$ (with a bond drawn up from CH)	
Benzylideneacetone and			
Dimethyl malonate	$NaOCH_3$	$ACH(CO_2CH_3)_2$	71
Diethyl malonate	Na, $NaOC_2H_5$	5-Phenylcyclohexane-1,3-dione (75)	4, 578
		or its 4-carbethoxy derivative	579
	KOH, acetal	$ACH(CO_2C_2H_5)_2$ (84)	483, 517, 518, 580, 30
Ethyl phenylacetate	$NaOC_2H_5$	4,5-Diphenylcyclohexane-1,3-dione	82
Ethyl cyclopentanone-2-carboxylate	KOC_2H_5	Cyclopentanone with A and $CO_2C_2H_5$ on C-2 (structure)	409
Ethyl cyclohexanone-2-carboxylate	KOC_2H_5	Cyclohexanone with A and $CO_2C_2H_5$ on C-2 (structure)	409
Ethyl cyanoacetate	$NaOC_2H_5$	$ACH(CN)CO_2C_2H_5$ (91)	121
Ethyl α-cyanobutyrate	$NaOC_2H_5$	$CH_3CH_2C(A)(CN)CO_2C_2H_5$ (23)	581
Ethyl α-cyanocaproate	$NaOC_2H_5$	$C_4H_9C(A)(CN)CO_2C_2H_5$ (78)	121
Cyanoacetamide	*sec.* Amine	3-Cyano-6-hydroxy-6-methyl-4-phenyl-2-piperidone	439
	$NaOC_2H_5$	3-Cyano-2-keto-6-methyl-4-phenyl-2,3,4,5-tetrahydropyridine	439, 224
Acetonitrile	KOH, acetal	ACH_2CN (82)	483, 517, 518
$CH_3C(=NH)CH_2CN$	$NaOC_2H_5$	3-Cyano-2,6-dimethyl-4-phenylpyridine (12)	440
Benzyl cyanide	$NaOCH_3$	$C_6H_5CH(A)CN$ (87)	121
Deoxybenzoin	$NaOC_2H_5$	$C_6H_5COCH(A)C_6H_5$	416

Note: References 491–1045 are on pp. 545–555.

* β-Chloropropiophenone was actually used in these condensations.

TABLE III—*Continued*

MICHAEL CONDENSATIONS WITH AROMATIC α,β-ETHYLENIC KETONES

Reactants	Catalyst	Product (Yield, %)	References
Benzylideneacetone (*Cont.*) *and*		$A = CH_3COCH_2CHC_6H_5$	
Cyclohexanone	$NaNH_2$	C_6H_5 (43)	98
2-Methyl-1-tetralone	$NaNH_2$	O, C_6H_5, CH_3	98
Anthrone	Piperidine	O, H, A (66)	582
Nitromethane	$(C_2H_5)_2NH$	ACH_2NO_2 (58)	209
1-Nitropropane	$(C_2H_5)_2NH$	$CH_3CH_2CH(A)NO_2$ (two isomers: total, 90)	209
2-Nitropropane	$(C_2H_5)_2NH$	$(CH_3)_2C(A)NO_2$ (77)	209
Ethyl nitroacetate	$(C_2H_5)_2NH$	$O_2NCH(A)CO_2C_2H_5$ (54)†	154
	$[C_6H_5CH_2N(CH_3)_3]OH$	$O_2NCH(A)CO_2C_2H_5$	

Fluorene	$NaOC_2H_5$	(2)	376
2,7-Dibromofluorene	$NaOC_2H_5$	(11)	376
2-Hydroxy-1,4-naphthoquinone	Pyridine		583
4-Hydroxycoumarin	Piperidine	(67)	169, 584
	NH_3, *t*-amines	(76–90)	585
Triethyl phosphonoacetate	$NaOC_2H_5$	$(C_2H_5O)_2P(O)CH(A)CO_2C_2H_5$ (48)	124

Note: References 491–1045 are on pp. 545–555.
† The product was obtained as a salt of the *aci* form.

TABLE III—*Continued*

MICHAEL CONDENSATIONS WITH AROMATIC α,β-ETHYLENIC KETONES

A. Substituted Benzylideneacetones

Substituent in $C_6H_5CH{=}CHCOCH_3$ (ring positions 2–6)	Addend	Catalyst	Product (Yield, %) $A = \text{ArylCHCH}_2\text{COCH}_3$ (with a bond drawn down from CH)	References
2-Hydroxy	Ethyl acetoacetate	$NaOC_2H_5$	4-Acetonyl-2-methyl-1,4-benzopyran	434
	Ethyl methylacetoacetate	$NaOC_2H_5$	4-Acetonyl-2,3-dimethyl-1,4-benzopyran (52)	38
	Ethyl phenylacetoacetate	$NaOC_2H_5$	4-Acetonyl-2-methyl-3-phenyl-1,4-benzopyran	38
	2-Hydroxybenzylideneacetone	$NaOC_2H_5$	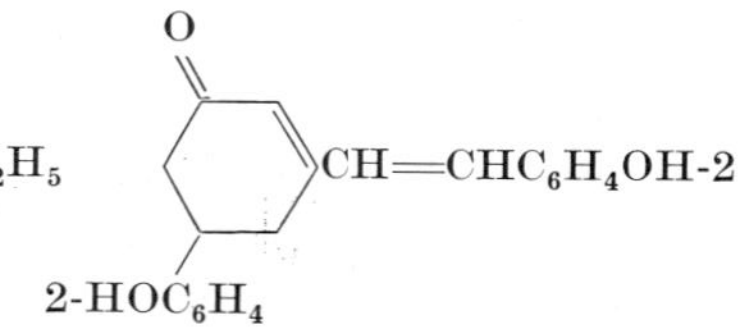 O; $CH{=}CHC_6H_4OH$-2; 2-HOC_6H_4	586
2-Methoxy	Ethyl acetoacetate	Aq. NaOH	2 (or 4)-Carbethoxy-5-(*o*-methoxyphenyl)-3-methyl-2-cyclohexen-1-one	434
	Diethyl malonate	$NaOC_2H_5$	5-(*o*-Methoxyphenyl)cyclohexane-1,3-dione	587
4-Methoxy	Diethyl malonate	$NaOC_2H_5$	5-(*p*-Methoxyphenyl)cyclohexane-1,3-dione (59)	587
	Ethyl acetoacetate	Piperidine	$CH_3COCH(A)CO_2C_2H_5$ (55)	588
	Triethyl ethane-1,2,2-tricarboxylate	$NaOC_2H_5$	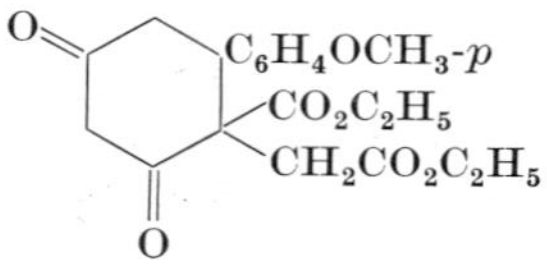 O; $C_6H_4OCH_3$-*p*; $CO_2C_2H_5$; $CH_2CO_2C_2H_5$; O (40)	109

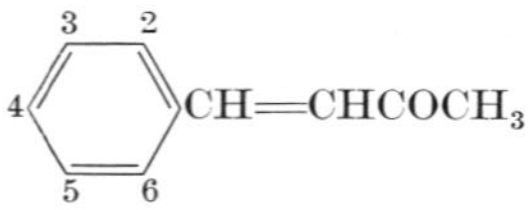

	Ethyl cyclopentanone-2-carboxylate	KOC_2H_5	$CH_3COCH_2CH(C_6H_4OCH_3\text{-}p)CH(CO_2C_2H_5)\text{-}CH_2CH_2CH_2CO_2H$	409
	Ethyl cyclohexanone-2-carboxylate	KOC_2H_5	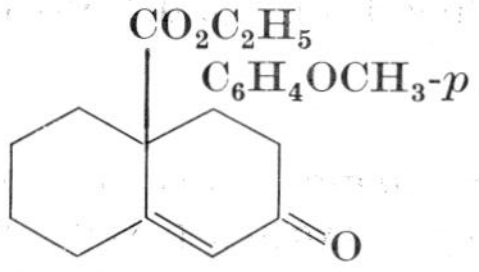 $CO_2C_2H_5$; $C_6H_4OCH_3\text{-}p$; O	409
	Ethyl cyanoacetate	$NaOC_2H_5$	4-Cyano-5-(*p*-methoxyphenyl)cyclohexane-1,3-dione (90)	589, 589
	Deoxybenzoin	$NaOC_2H_5$	$C_6H_5COCH(A)C_6H_5$	416
	4-Hydroxycoumarin	Pyridine	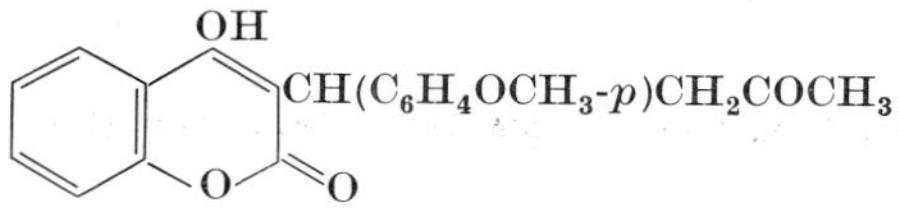 OH; $CH(C_6H_4OCH_3\text{-}p)CH_2COCH_3$; O; O (45)	169
3-Nitro	Diethylmalonate	$NaOC_2H_5$	5-(*m*-Nitrophenyl)cyclohexane-1,3-dione	590
4-Nitro	Diethyl malonate	$NaOC_2H_5$	5-(*p*-Nitrophenyl)cyclohexane-1,3-dione	590
2-Chloro	Diethyl malonate	$NaOC_2H_5$	5-(*o*-Chlorophenyl)cyclohexane-1,3-dione (27)	587
4-Hydroxy-3-methoxy	4-Hydroxycoumarin	Pyridine	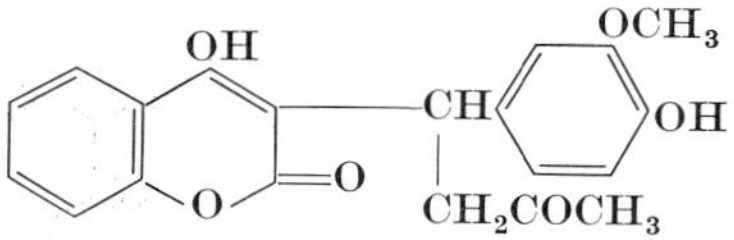 OH; O; O; CH; OCH_3; OH; CH_2COCH_3	169
2,3-Dimethoxy	Ethyl α-cyanobutyrate	$NaOC_2H_5$	$CH_3CH_2C(CN)(A)CO_2C_2H_5$	581
4-Dimethylamino	Ethyl acetoacetate	Aq. NaOH	2-Carbethoxy-3-(*p*-dimethylaminophenyl)-5-hydroxy-5-methylcyclohexan-1-one	285
4-Isopropyl	Diethyl malonate	$NaOC_2H_5$	5-(*p*-Isopropylphenyl)cyclohexane-1,3-dione (60)	578

Note: References 491–1045 are on pp. 545–555.

TABLE III—*Continued*

MICHAEL CONDENSATIONS WITH AROMATIC α,β-ETHYLENIC KETONES

Reactants	Catalyst	Product (Yield, %)	References
Ethylideneacetophenone and			
Cyanoacetamide	$NaOC_2H_5$	CH_3, CN, H_5C_6, N, O	591
Hydroxymethylene-p-methylacetophenone and			
$CH_3C(=NH)CH_2CO_2C_2H_5$	None	Ethyl 2-methyl-6-(*p*-tolyl)pyridine-3-carboxylate	557
$CH_3C(=NH)CH_2COCH_3$	None	3-Acetyl-2-methyl-6-(*p*-tolyl)pyridine	442, 557
$CH_3C(=NH)CH_2COC_6H_5$	None	3-Benzoyl-2-methyl-6-(*p*-tolyl)pyridine	442
α-Hydroxymethyleneëthyl Phenyl Ketone and			
$CH_3C(=NH)CH_2CO_2C_2H_5$	None	Ethyl 2,5-dimethyl-6-phenylpyridine-3-carboxylate	557
Benzoylacetone (Enol) and			
Diethyl acetone-1,3-dicarboxylate	$NaOC_2H_5$	Diethyl 3-hydroxy-5-methylbiphenyl-2,4-dicarboxylate (47)	427
Cyanoacetamide	$(C_2H_5)_2NH$	3-Cyano-6-methyl-4-phenyl-2-pyridone and 3-cyano-4-methyl-6-phenyl-2-pyridone	371, 592
Ethyl cyanoacetate	$(C_2H_5)_2NH$	3-Carbethoxy-4-methyl-6-phenyl-2-pyridone (low)	370
Malononitrile	$(C_2H_5)_2NH$	3-Cyano-4-methyl-6-phenyl-2-pyridone	370
3-Amino-1-phenyl-2-buten-1-one and			
Malonamide	None	2-Hydroxy-4-methyl-6-phenylpyridine-3-carboxamide	391, 398
Ethyl cyanoacetate	$NaOC_2H_5$	3-Cyano-6-methyl-4-phenyl-2-pyridone	391
Cyanoacetamide	None	3-Cyano-4-methyl-6-phenyl-2-pyridone	391

$NCCH_2CONHCH_3$	None	3-Cyano-1,4-dimethyl-6-phenyl-2-pyridone and 3-cyano-4-methyl-6-phenyl-2-pyridone	391
Ethyl Styryl Ketone and			
Diethyl malonate	$NaOC_2H_5$	4-Carbethoxy-2-methyl-5-phenylcyclohexane-1,3-dione (79)	423
		2-Methyl-5-phenyl-cyclohexane-1,3-dione (80)	422
Ethyl phenylacetate	$NaOC_2H_5$	2-Methyl-4,5-diphenylcyclohexane-1,3-dione (21, 32)	423, 422
Ethyl Phenacyl Ketone (Enol) and			
Cyanoacetamide	None	3-Cyano-4-ethyl-6-phenyl-2-pyridone	371
1-*Hydroxy*-5-*phenyl*-1-*penten*-3-*one and*			
Cyanoacetamide	Piperidine	$C_{14}H_{12}N_2O$, 5-cyano-6-hydroxy-2-phenethyl-pyridine (?)	172
1-*Phenyl*-2-*methyl*-2-*buten*-1-*one and*			
Nitromethane	$NaOC_2H_5$	$C_6H_5COCH(CH_3)CH(CH_3)CH_2NO_2$ (63)	560
1-*Phenyl*-3-*methyl*-2-*buten*-1-*one and*			
Nitromethane	$NaOC_2H_5$	$C_6H_5COCH_2C(CH_3)_2CH_2NO_2$ (76)	560
5-*Phenyl*-3-*penten*-2-*one*‡ *and*			
Diethyl malonate	$NaOC_2H_5$	5-Benzylcyclohexane-1,3-dione	593
4-*Phenyl*-4-*methoxy*-3-*buten*-2-*one and*			
Cyanoacetamide	$NaOC_2H_5$; $(C_2H_5)_2NH$	3-Cyano-6-methyl-4-phenyl-2-pyridone (30)	592
1-*Phenyl*-3-*ethoxy*-2-*buten*-1-*one and*			
Cyanoacetamide	$NaOC_2H_5$	3-Cyano-4-methyl-6-phenyl-2-pyridone	592

Note: References 491–1045 are on pp. 545–555.

‡ This ketone was produced *in situ* by isomerization of 5-phenyl-4-penten-2-one.

TABLE III—*Continued*

MICHAEL CONDENSATIONS WITH AROMATIC α,β-ETHYLENIC KETONES

Reactants	Catalyst	Product (Yield, %)	References
p-Methylbenzoylacetone (Enol) and			
Cyanoacetamide	$(C_2H_5)_2NH$	3-Cyano-4-methyl-6-*p*-tolyl-2-pyridone (80) and 3-cyano-6-methyl-4-*p*-tolyl-2-pyridone (in small amount from the isomeric enol)	594
$NCCH_2CONHCH_3$	$(C_2H_5)_2NH$	3-Cyano-1,6-dimethyl-4-*p*-tolyl-2-pyridone	594
1-*Phenyl*-3-*methylamino*-2-*buten*-1-*one and*			
Cyanoacetamide		3-Cyano-4-methyl-6-phenyl-2-pyridone and 3-cyano-1,4-dimethyl-6-phenyl-2-pyridone	391
Ethoxymethyleneacetophenone and			
Diethyl malonate	Na enolate of the ester	Ethyl 6-phenylcoumalin-3-carboxylate (44)	577
n-Propyl Styryl Ketone and			
Diethyl malonate	$NaOC_2H_5$	4-Carbethoxy-2-ethyl-5-phenylcyclohexane-1,3-dione (41)	423
Isopropyl Styryl Ketone and			
Diethyl malonate	$NaOC_2H_5$	$(CH_3)_2CHCOCH_2CH(C_6H_5)CH(CO_2C_2H_5)_2$ (79)	319
Ethyl p-Methoxystyryl Ketone and			
Diethyl malonate	$NaOC_2H_5$	4-Carbethoxy-5-(*p*-methoxyphenyl)-2-methylcyclohexane-1,3-dione (44)	595
Ethyl cyanoacetate	$NaOC_2H_5$	4-Cyano-5-(*p*-methoxyphenyl)cyclohexane-1,3-dione (55)	589

Reactants	Catalyst	Product (Yield, %)	Refs.
Triethyl ethane-1,1,2-tricarboxylate	$NaOC_2H_5$	H_3C, O, O, $C_6H_4OCH_3$-*p*, $C_2H_5O_2C$, $CH_2CO_2C_2H_5$ (20)	109
Cyclopropyl Styryl Ketone and			
Nitromethane	$NaOCH_3$	CH_2—$CHCOCH_2CHC_6H_5$ / CH_2 / CH_2NO_2 (42–52)	138
1-*Phenyl*-3-*cyclopropyl*-2-*propen*-1-*one and*			
Nitromethane	$NaOCH_3$	CH_2—$CHCHCH_2COC_6H_5$ / CH_2 / CH_2NO_2 (71)	138
1-*Acetyl*-3,4-*dihydronaphthalene and*			
Ethyl acetoacetate	$NaOC_2H_5$	O, CH_3, $CO_2C_2H_5$	596
3-*Acetyl*-4-*phenyl*-3-*buten*-2-*one and*			
Phenylnitromethane	$(C_2H_5)_2NH$	3-Acetyl-4,5-diphenyl-5-nitropentan-2-one (84)	29
n-*Butyl Styryl Ketone and*			
Diethyl malonate	$NaOC_2H_5$	4-Carbethoxy-5-phenyl-2-*n*-propylcyclohexane-1,3-dione (35)	423

Note: References 491–1045 are on pp. 545–555.

TABLE III—*Continued*

MICHAEL CONDENSATIONS WITH AROMATIC α,β-ETHYLENIC KETONES

Reactants	Catalyst	Product (Yield, %)	References
Vinyl p-n-Propoxyphenyl Ketone and		$A = p$-n-$C_3H_7OC_6H_4COCH_2CH_2$—	
Nitromethane	NaOH	$(A)_2CHNO_2$ (73)	597
Phenylnitromethane	$NaOCH_3$	$C_6H_5CH(A)NO_2$ (71)	597
Cyanoacetamide	$NaOCH_3$	$NCC(A)_2CONH_2$ (83)	597
Benzalpinacolone and		$A = (CH_3)_3CCOCH_2CHC_6H_5$ (with a bond drawn down from the CH)	
Dimethyl malonate	$NaOCH_3$	$ACH(CO_2CH_3)_2$ (82)	598
Diethyl malonate	$NaOC_2H_5$	$ACH(CO_2C_2H_5)_2$ (97, 70§)	598, 599
Methyl p-nitrophenylacetate	$NaOCH_3$	p-$O_2NC_6H_4CH(A)CO_2CH_3$	600
Ethyl p-nitrophenylacetate	$NaOC_2H_5$	p-$O_2NC_6H_4CH(A)CO_2C_2H_5$	600
Nitromethane	$NaOCH_3$	ACH_2NO_2 (80–90)	601
Isopropyl p-Methoxystyryl Ketone and			
Diethyl malonate	Enolate	$(CH_3)_2CHCOCH_2CH(C_6H_4OCH_3$-$p)CH_2CO_2H$	30
3-*Ethoxy*-1-*p-tolyl*-2-*buten*-1-*one and*			
Cyanoacetamide	$(C_2H_5)_2NH$	3-Cyano-4-methyl-6-p-tolyl-2-pyridone (quant.)	594
2-*Benzylidenecyclohexanone and*			
Diethyl malonate	Enolate	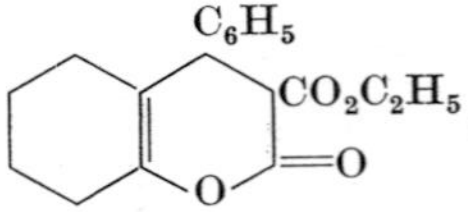 C_6H_5; $CO_2C_2H_5$; O; =O (89)	602
	Enolate	Ethyl β-(2-oxocyclohexyl)hydrocinnamate (70)	603

Reactants	Catalyst	Product (Yield, %)	Refs.
p-Methoxybenzylidenecyclohexanone and			
Diethyl malonate	Na	$C_6H_4OCH_3$-*p*; $CO_2C_2H_5$; O; =O	602
n-Hexyl Styryl Ketone and			
Diethyl malonate	$NaOC_2H_5$	4-Carbethoxy-2-pentyl-5-phenylcyclohexane-1,3-dione (45)	423
1,2-*Diphenyl*-2-*propen*-1-*one and*		$A = C_6H_5COCH(C_6H_5)CH_2$—	
Benzyl *p*-chlorophenyl ketone	KOH, CH_3OH	$C_6H_5CH(A)COC_6H_4Cl$-*p* (88)	604, cf. 605, 606
Benzyl *p*-tolyl ketone	KOH, CH_3OH	$C_6H_5CH(A)COC_6H_4CH_3$-*p* (85)	604
Benzyl *p*-anisyl ketone	KOH, CH_3OH	$C_6H_5CH(A)COC_6H_4OCH_3$-*p* (74)	604
Deoxybenzoin	KOH, CH_3OH	$C_6H_5CH(A)COC_6H_5$ (80)	604
Phenyl *p*-chlorobenzyl ketone	KOH, CH_3OH	*p*-$ClC_6H_4CH(A)COC_6H_5$ (77)	604
Phenyl *p*-methylbenzyl ketone	KOH, CH_3OH	*p*-$CH_3C_6H_4CH(A)COC_6H_5$ (71)	604
Phenyl *p*-dimethylaminobenzyl ketone	KOH, CH_3OH	*p*-$(CH_3)_2NC_6H_4CH(A)COC_6H_5$ (86)	604
Dibenzoylmethane (*Enol*) *and*			
Cyanoacetamide	$NaOC_2H_5$	3-Cyano-4,6-diphenyl-2-pyridone (5–20)	370, 592
	$(C_2H_5)_2NH$	3-Cyano-4,6-diphenyl-2-pyridone (55–70)	370, 592
	Piperidine	3-Cyano-4,6-diphenyl-2-pyridone	370, 592
Vinyl p-Biphenylyl Ketone and			
Deoxybenzoin	$NaOCH_3$	*p*-$C_6H_5C_6H_4COCH_2CH_2CH(C_6H_5)COC_6H_5$	575

Note: References 491–1045 are on pp. 545–555.

§ The acid was isolated in this experiment.

TABLE III—*Continued*

MICHAEL CONDENSATIONS WITH AROMATIC α,β-ETHYLENIC KETONES

Reactants	Catalyst	Product (Yield, %)	References
Chalcone, $C_6H_5CH{=}CHCOC_6H_5$, *and*		$A = C_6H_5CH(-)CH_2COC_6H_5$	
Dimethyl malonate	$NaOCH_3$	$ACH(CO_2CH_3)_2$ (80, 94)	75, 404
	Piperidene	$ACH(CO_2CH_3)_2$ (poor)	71
Diethyl malonate	Piperidine; 0.1 equiv. $NaOC_2H_5$; KOH, acetal	$ACH(CO_2C_2H_5)_2$ (71, 93, 98)	30, 55, 125, 483, 517, 518
	1 equiv. $NaOC_2H_5$	Diethyl 5-benzoyl-2,4,6-triphenyl-4 cyclohexenyl-1,1-dicarboxylate (70)	55
Diethyl methylmalonate	Piperidine, $NaOC_2H_5$	$AC(CH_3)(CO_2C_2H_5)_2$ (80)	55, 125, 51
	Na	Retrogression products	396, 607
Diethyl ethylmalonate	$NaOC_2H_5$	Retrogression products	125
Diethyl phenylmalonate	$NaOC_2H_5$	$AC(C_6H_5)(CO_2C_2H_5)_2$ (94)	403
Diethyl succinate	$NaOC_2H_5$	$ACHCO_2H$ ‖ with CH_2CO_2H (on CH)	73
Methyl phenylacetate	$NaOCH_3$	$C_6H_5CH(A)CO_2CH_3$	163, 608
Ethyl phenylacetate	$NaOC_2H_5$	$C_6H_5CH(A)CO_2C_2H_5$ (92); compound $C_{40}H_{34}O_8$	82, 125
Ethyl α-phenylbutyrate	$NaOC_2H_5$	$C_6H_5C(C_2H_5)(CO_2C_2H_5)A$ (3)	125
p-$O_2NC_6H_4CH_2CO_2CH_3$	$NaOCH_3$	p-$O_2NC_6H_4CH(A)CO_2CH_3$ (95)	600
p-$O_2NC_6H_4CH_2CO_2C_2H_5$	$NaOC_2H_5$	p-$O_2NC_6H_4CH(A)CO_2C_2H_5$	600
p-$O_2NC_6H_4CH_2CO_2C_4H_9$-n	$NaOC_2H_5$	p-$O_2NC_6H_4CH(A)CO_2C_4H_9$-$n$	600
Ethyl acetoacetate	$NaOC_2H_5$; piperidine	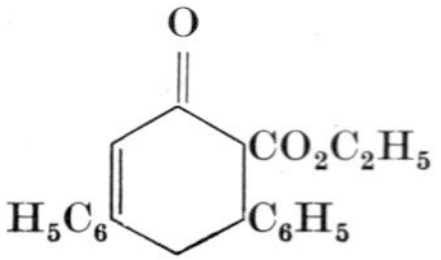 Cyclohexenone ring: C=O; $CO_2C_2H_5$; C_6H_5; H_5C_6 (on ring double bond)	125, cf. 19

$CH_3COCH(C_2H_5)CO_2C_2H_5$	$NaOC_2H_5$	O; $CO_2C_2H_5$; C_2H_5; H_5C_6; C_6H_5 (9)	125
Ethyl benzoylacetate	Piperidine, $NaOC_2H_5$	$C_6H_5COCH(A)CO_2C_2H_5$ (94)	125
$C_6H_5COCH_2CH(C_6H_5)CH(C_6H_5)$-$CO_2C_2H_5$	Na in C_6H_5	Compound $C_{40}H_{34}O_8$	403
Methyl cyanoacetate	$NaOCH_3$	$ACH(CN)CO_2CH_3$ and $(A)_2C(CN)CO_2CH_3$ (83)	609
Ethyl cyanoacetate	$NaOC_2H_5$	$(A)_2C(CN)CO_2C_2H_5$ (91)	121
Ethyl *n*-butylcyanoacetate	$NaOC_2H_5$	$AC(C_4H_9\text{-}n)(CN)CO_2C_2H_5$ (78)	121
Cyanoacetamide	$NaOCH_3$	$ACH(CN)CONH_2$ (72)	610
	Piperidine or $(C_2H_5)_2NH$	3-Cyano-6-hydroxy-4,6-diphenyl-2-piperidone (75)	439
	1 equiv. $NaOC_2H_5$	3-Cyano-4,6-diphenyl-3,4-dihydro-2-pyridone (87)	439
$CH_3C(=NH)CH_2CN$	$NaOC_2H_5$	5-Cyano-6-methyl-2,4-diphenylpyridine and its 1,4-dihydro derivative	440
Malononitrile	$NaOCH_3$	$ACH(CN)_2$	610
Benzyl cyanide	$NaOCH_3$	$C_6H_5CH(A)CN$ (two isomers: 87; 40 and 30)	72, 611
	$NaOCH_3$	$C_6H_5C(A)_2CN$ (94)	612
Phenylacetaldehyde	$NaOCH_3$	$C_6H_5CHOHCH_2CH(C_6H_5)CH(C_6H_5)CO_2H$ (30)	163
Diethyl ketone	$NaOC_2H_5$	$CH_3CH(A)COC_2H_5$ and $CH_3C(A)_2COC_2H_5$ (90–100)	207
Pinacolone	$NaOC_2H_5$	$(CH_3)_3CCOCH(A)_2$ (69)	207
Acetophenone	$NaOC_2H_5$	$C_6H_5COCH(A)_2$ (27) and $C_6H_5COC(A)_3$ (25)	125
Propiophenone	$NaOC_2H_5$	$CH_3CH(A)COC_6H_5$ (54) and $CH_3C(A)_2COC_6H_5$ (27)	207
n-Butyrophenone	$NaOC_2H_5$	$CH_3CH_2CH(A)COC_6H_5$ (19) and $CH_3CH_2C(A)_2COC_6H_5$ (58)	207
Isobutyrophenone	$NaOC_2H_5$	$(CH_3)_2C(COC_6H_5)CH(C_6H_5)CH(A)COC_6H_5$ (30)	207
Deoxybenzoin	$NaOC_2H_5$	$C_6H_5CH(A)COC_6H_5$	13
Dibenzoylmethane	$NaOC_2H_5$	$(C_6H_5CO)_2CHA$ (1)	125

Note: References 491–1045 are on pp. 545–555.

|| Two isomeric acids and a non-acidic product, $C_{29}H_{26}O_4$, of unknown structure were obtained.

TABLE III—*Continued*

MICHAEL CONDENSATIONS WITH AROMATIC α,β-ETHYLENIC KETONES

Reactants	Catalyst	Product (Yield, %)	References
Chalcone, $C_6H_5CH{=}CHCOC_6H_5$, (*Cont.*) *and*		$A = C_6H_5CHCH_2COC_6H_5$	
Anthrone	$NaOCH_3$; NaOH, ethanol; *sec*-amines	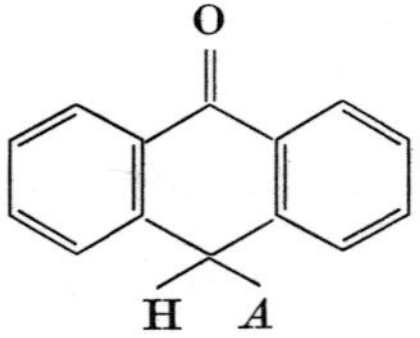 10-A-anthrone (10-H, 10-A) (77)	163, 613
2-Phenyl-2,3-dihydro-γ-pyrone	NaOH, ethanol	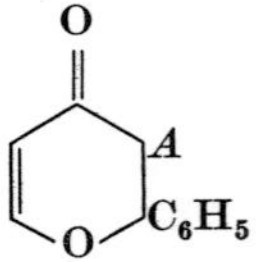 3-A-2-C_6H_5-2,3-dihydro-γ-pyrone	614
2-(3′,4′-Methylenedioxyphenyl)-2,3-dihydro-γ-pyrone	Na	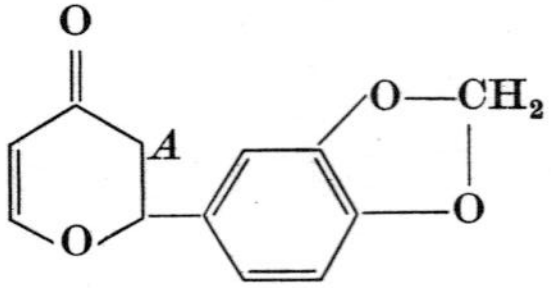 3-A-2-(3′,4′-methylenedioxyphenyl)-2,3-dihydro-γ-pyrone	614
2-Phenyl-2,3-dihydrobenzo-γ-pyrone	Aq. NaOH; $NaNH_2$; Na	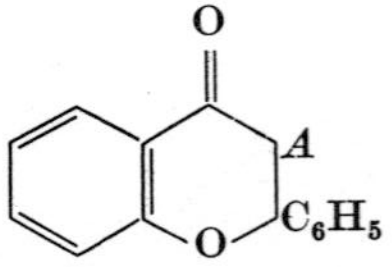 3-A-2-C_6H_5-2,3-dihydrobenzo-γ-pyrone	615

Cyclopentanone	NaOH, ethanol; $(C_2H_5)_2NH$	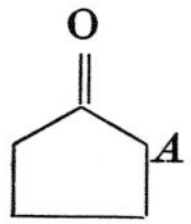 O, *A* (83)	616
Cyclohexanone	NaOH, ethanol	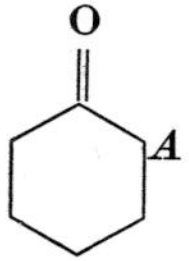 O, *A* (72–80)	613, 617
	$NaOC_2H_5$	Compound $C_{36}H_{34}O_3$	613
3-Methylcyclohexanone	NaOH, ethanol; piperidine	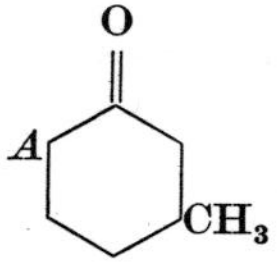 O, *A*, CH_3	613, 616
Menthone	$NaOC_2H_5$	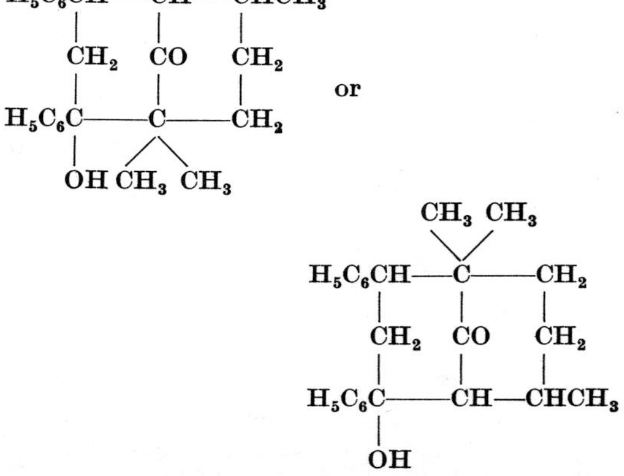 H_5C_6CH—CH—$CHCH_3$ / CH_2 CO CH_2 / H_5C_6C—C—CH_2 / OH CH_3 CH_3 or CH_3 CH_3 / H_5C_6CH—C—CH_2 / CH_2 CO CH_2 / H_5C_6C—CH—$CHCH_3$ / OH	616

Note: References 491–1045 are on pp. 545–555.

TABLE III—*Continued*

MICHAEL CONDENSATIONS WITH AROMATIC α,β-ETHYLENIC KETONES

Reactants	Catalyst	Product (Yield, %)	References
Chalcone, $C_6H_5CH{=}CHCOC_6H_5$, (*Cont.*) *and*		$A = C_6H_5\underset{\vert}{C}HCH_2COC_6H_5$	
Cyclohexane-1,3-dione	Piperidine	(58)	618
Nitromethane	$NaOCH_3$; NH_3, ethanol	ACH_2NO_2 (75, 88) and $(A)_2CHNO_2$ (small)	620, 209, 619
	$(C_2H_5)_2NH$	$(A)_2CHNO_2$ (two isomers, 77)	621
	CaH_2, CH_3OH	ACH_2NO_2 (65–92)	466*a*
Nitroethane	$(C_2H_5)_2NH$; $NaOCH_3$	$CH_3CH(A)NO_2$ (two isomers: 78 + 11; quant.)	209, 620
1-Nitropropane	$(C_2H_5)_2NH$	$CH_3CH_2CH(A)NO_2$ (97)	209
	CaH_2, CH_3OH	$CH_3CH_2CH(A)NO_2$ (65–92)	466*a*
2-Nitropropane	$(C_2H_5)_2NH$; $NaOCH_3$; CaH_2, CH_3OH	$(CH_3)_2C(A)NO_2$ (92–96)	209, 466*a*, 620
Ethyl nitroacetate	$(C_2H_5)_2NH$	$O_2NCH(A)CO_2C_2H_5$ (94)	622
Benzyl *p*-tolyl sulfone	$NaOCH_3$	$C_6H_5CH(A)SO_2C_6H_4CH_3$-*p* (two isomers: 15, 11)	74
Cyclopentadiene	Na derivative; piperidine	$CH(C_6H_5)CH(A)COC_6H_5$ (Small)	376
Fluorene	Pyridine, NaOH, H_2O	(Quant.)	362, 623

Reactant	Catalyst	Product (Yield, %)	Refs.
	$NaOC_2H_5$	9-A-fluorene (H, A at C-9) (10–27)	376
2,7-Dibromofluorene	$NaOC_2H_5$	2,7-dibromo-9-A-fluorene (H, A at C-9) (22)	376
4-Hydroxycoumarin	Pyridine	3-A-4-hydroxycoumarin (37)	169
2-Methylpyridine	$NaNH_2$	Tri- and tetra-molecular condensation products	374
2-Methylquinoline	$NaNH_2$	2-quinolyl-$CH_2CH(C_6H_5)CH(A)COC_6H_5$ or 2-quinolyl-$CH_2CH(C_6H_5)CH(COC_6H_5)CH(C_6H_5)$-$CH(A)COC_6H_5$ (60)	374
4-Methylquinoline	$NaNH_2$	4-(CH_2A)quinoline (27)	374

Note: References 491–1045 are on pp. 545–555.

TABLE III—*Continued*

MICHAEL CONDENSATIONS WITH AROMATIC α,β-ETHYLENIC KETONES

B. Substituted Chalcones

Substituent(s) in 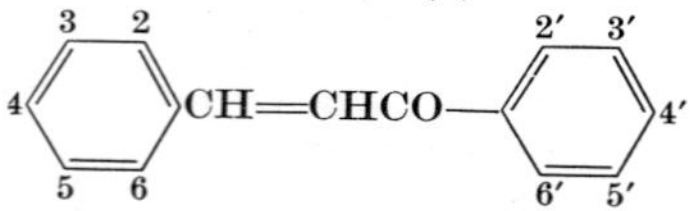 $C_6H_5CH{=}CHCOC_6H_5$ (ring positions 2–6, 2′–6′)	Addend	Catalyst	Product (Yield, %)	References
			A = Appropriately Substituted $C_6H_5CHCH_2COC_6H_5$ (point of attachment at CH)	
3-Br	CH_3NO_2	$NaOCH_3$	ACH_2NO_2	621
4-Br	CH_3NO_2	$NaOCH_3$	ACH_2NO_2	621
4′-Br	$CH_2(CO_2CH_3)_2$	$NaOCH_3$	$ACH(CO_2CH_3)_2$ (92)	624
	$CH_2(CO_2C_2H_5)_2$	$NaOC_2H_5$	$ACH(CO_2C_2H_5)_2$	624
	CH_3NO_2	$NaOC_2H_5$	ACH_2NO_2 (87)	625
	1,4-Pentadiene	$NaOC_2H_5$; $NaNH_2$, liq. NH_3	$(CH_2{=}CH)_2CHA$ (4) $(CH_2{=}CH)_2CHA$ (11)	376
	Fluorene	$NaOC_2H_5$	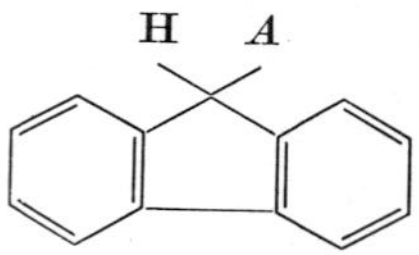 H A (15)	376
	2,7-Dibromofluorene	$NaOC_2H_5$	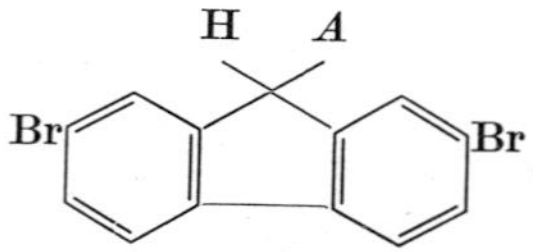 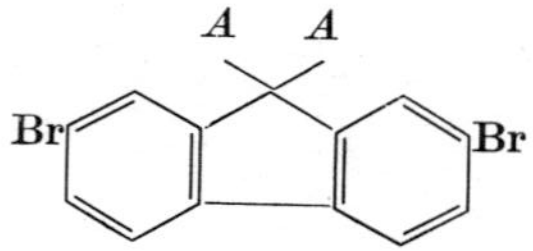 H A, Br Br (48) and A A, Br Br (12	376

4′-Cl	$CH_2(CO_2CH_3)_2$	$NaOCH_3$	$A CH(CO_2CH_3)_2$	609
	$NCCH_2CO_2CH_3$	$NaOCH_3$	$NCCH(A)CO_2CH_3$ (87)	609
	$CH_3CH(CN)CO_2CH_3$	$NaOCH_3$	$CH_3C(CN)(A)CO_2CH_3$	609
	Cyclohexanone	NaOH, ethanol	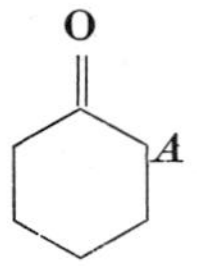 O, A	613
2-HO	$CH_3COCH_2CO_2C_2H_5$	$NaOC_2H_5$	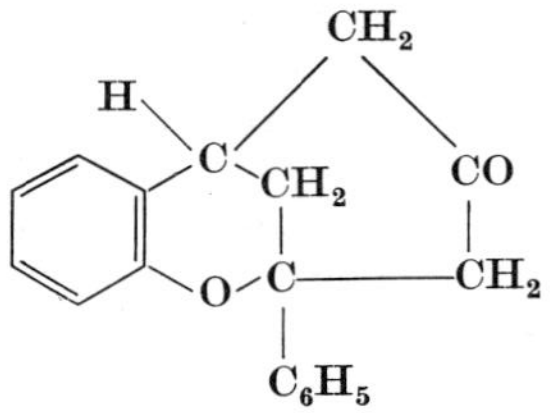 CH_2, H, C, CH_2, CO, O, C, CH_2, C_6H_5	586, cf. 202, 203
	$CH_3COCH(CH_3)$-$CO_2C_2H_5$	$NaOCH_3$	2,3-Dimethyl-4-phenacyl-1,4-benzopyran	38
	$CH_3COCH(C_6H_5)$-$CO_2C_2H_5$	$NaOC_2H_5$	2-Methyl-4-phenacyl-3-phenyl-1,4-benzopyran	38
	$C_6H_5COCH_2CO_2C_2H_5$	Aq. NaOH	4-Phenacyl-2-phenyl-1,4-benzopyran	434
	Deoxybenzoin	$NaOC_2H_5$	$C_6H_5CH(A)COC_6H_5$ (65)	626

Note: References 491–1045 are on pp. 545–555.

TABLE III—*Continued*

Michael Condensations with Aromatic α,β-Ethylenic Ketones

Substituent(s) in 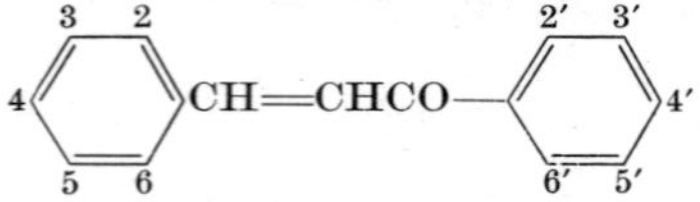 CH=CHCO (ring positions 2–6, 2′–6′)	Addend	Catalyst	Product (Yield, %)	References
			A = Appropriately Substituted $C_6H_5CHCH_2COC_6H_5$	
2-HO (*Cont.*)	Cyclopentanone	$(C_2H_5)_2NH$	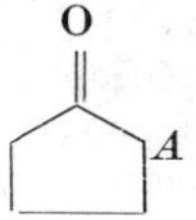 O, A (10)	626
	Cyclohexanone	NaOH, ethanol	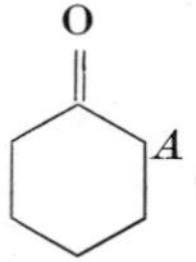 O, A (56)	626
2′-HO	4-Hydroxycoumarin	Pyridine	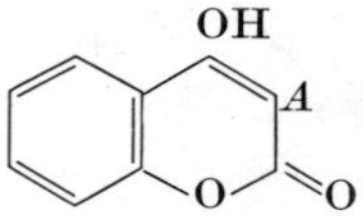 OH, A, O, O (34)	169
4-CH_3O	$CH_2(CO_2CH_3)_2$	$NaOCH_3$	ACH$(CO_2CH_3)_2$ (good)	627
	$CH_3COCH_2CO_2C_2H_5$	$NaOC_2H_5$	2-Carbethoxy-3-*p*-methoxyphenyl-5-phenyl-5-cyclohexen-1-one	628
	$NCCH_2CONH_2$	Na enolate	3-Cyano-2-hydroxy-4-*p*-methoxyphenyl-6-phenyl-4,5-dihydropyridine	594
	Cyclopentanone	*sec*-Amines	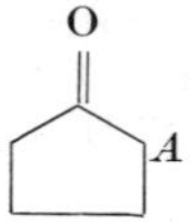 O, A	616

	3-Methylcyclohexanone	*sec*-Amines; KOH, C_2H_5OH	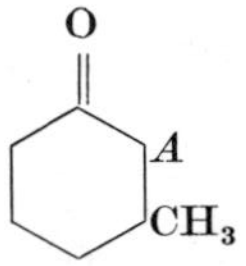 O, *A*, CH_3 (Two isomers)	616
	Deoxybenzoin	KOH, CH_3OH; $NaOCH_3$	$C_6H_5CH(A)COC_6H_5$ (42, little)	604, 629
	Nitromethane	$NaOCH_3$	$(A)_2CHNO_2$	621
4′-CH_3O	2-Phenyl-2,3-dihydro-γ-pyrone	$NaOC_2H_5$	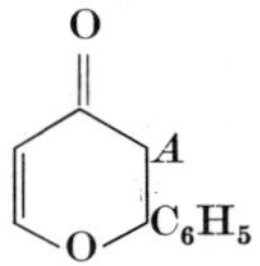 O, *A*, O, C_6H_5	614
3′-CH_3	Cyclohexanone	NaOH, ethanol	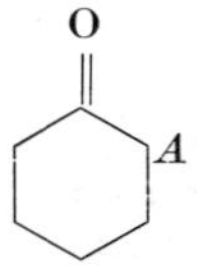 O, *A*	613
4-CH_3	CH_3NO_2	$NaOCH_3$	$(A)_2CHNO_2$	621
	2-Phenyl-2,3-dihydro-γ-pyrone	NaOH, ethanol	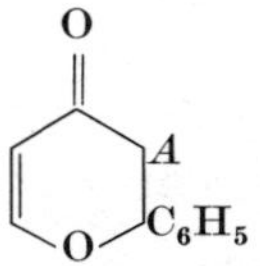 O, *A*, O, C_6H_5	614
4′-CH_3	$CH_3COCH_2CO_2C_2H_5$	$NaOC_2H_5$	2-Carbethoxy-3-methyl-5-*p*-tolyl-5-cyclohexen-1-one	630

Note: References 491–1045 are on pp. 545–555.

TABLE III—*Continued*

MICHAEL CONDENSATIONS WITH AROMATIC α,β-ETHYLENIC KETONES

Substituent(s) in $C_6H_5CH{=}CHCOC_6H_5$ (ring positions 2–6 and 2′–6′)	Addend	Catalyst	Product (Yield, %)	References
			A = Appropriately Substituted $C_6H_5\underset{\vert}{C}HCH_2COC_2H_5$	
4′-CH_3 (*Cont.*)	$NCCH_2CONH_2$	Piperidine	3-Cyano-6-hydroxy-4-phenyl-6-*p*-tolyl-2-piperidone (75)	439
		$NaOC_2H_5$	3-Cyano-2-keto-4-phenyl-6-*p*-tolyl 2,3,4,5-tetrahydropyridine (90)	439
3-NO_2	CH_3NO_2	$NaOCH_3$	$(A)_2CHNO_2$	621
3-Br, 4-CH_3O	$CH_2(CO_2CH_3)_2$	$NaOCH_3$	$ACH(CO_2CH_3)_2$	627
4,4′-Dimethoxy	2-Phenyl-2,3-dihydro-γ-pyrone	Na	O; A; O; C_6H_5	614
4-CH_3O, 4′-CH_3	$CH_3COCH_2CO_2C_2H_5$	$NaOC_2H_5$	O; $CO_2C_2H_5$; *p*-$CH_3H_4C_6$; $C_6H_4OCH_3$-*p*	628
	2-Phenyl-2,3-dihydro-γ-pyrone	Na	O; A; O; C_6H_5	614

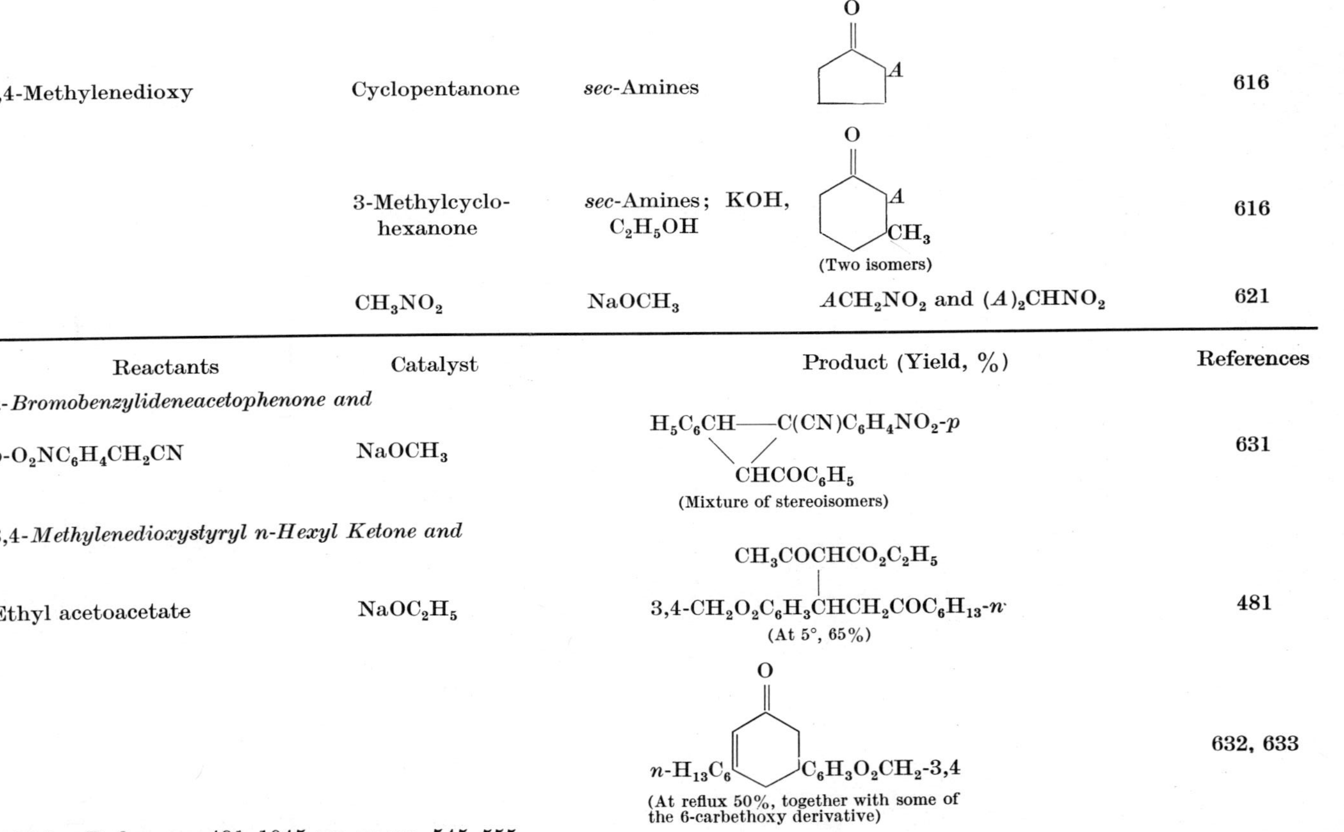

Reactants		Catalyst	Product (Yield, %)	References
3,4-Methylenedioxy	Cyclopentanone	*sec*-Amines	2-A-cyclopentanone (structure: O, A)	616
	3-Methylcyclohexanone	*sec*-Amines; KOH, C_2H_5OH	2-A-3-methylcyclohexanone (structure: O, A, CH_3) (Two isomers)	616
	CH_3NO_2	$NaOCH_3$	ACH_2NO_2 and $(A)_2CHNO_2$	621

Reactants	Catalyst	Product (Yield, %)	References
α-Bromobenzylideneacetophenone and			
p-$O_2NC_6H_4CH_2CN$	$NaOCH_3$	H_5C_6CH—$C(CN)C_6H_4NO_2$-p (cyclopropane ring with) $CHCOC_6H_5$ (Mixture of stereoisomers)	631
3,4-*Methylenedioxystyryl n-Hexyl Ketone and*			
Ethyl acetoacetate	$NaOC_2H_5$	$CH_3COCHCO_2C_2H_5$ (attached to) 3,4-$CH_2O_2C_6H_3CHCH_2COC_6H_{13}$-$n$ (At 5°, 65%)	481
		cyclohexenone (structure: O; n-$H_{13}C_6$; $C_6H_3O_2CH_2$-3,4) (At reflux 50%, together with some of the 6-carbethoxy derivative)	632, 633

Note: References 491–1045 are on pp. 545–555.

TABLE III—*Continued*

MICHAEL CONDENSATIONS WITH AROMATIC α,β-ETHYLENIC KETONES

Reactants	Catalyst	Product (Yield, %)	References
trans-Dibenzoylethylene and		$A = C_6H_5COCH_2\underset{\mid}{C}HCOC_6H_5$	
Diethyl benzylmalonate	$NaOC_2H_5$	$C_6H_5CH_2C(A)(CO_2C_2H_5)_2$ (20)	58
Acetophenone	$NaOCH_3$	1,2,3-Tribenzylpropane (1)	634
1,2-Dibenzoylethane	$NaOC_6H_5$	$C_6H_5COCH_2CH(A)COC_6H_5$ (62)	634
1,1-*Dibenzoylethane* (*Enol*) *and*			
Cyanoacetamide	$(C_2H_5)_2NH$	3-Cyano-5-methyl-4,6-diphenyl-2-pyridone	592
3,4-*Diphenyl*-3-*buten*-2-*one and*			
Phenylnitromethane	$(C_2H_5)_2NH$	1-Nitro-1,2,3-triphenylpentan-4-one (68)	29
2-*Benzoyl*-1-*phenylpropene and*			
Dimethyl malonate	$NaOCH_3$	$C_6H_5COCH(CH_3)CH(C_6H_5)CH(CO_2CH_3)_2$ (two isomers: 52 + 10)	76
2-*Methoxy*-1,3-*diphenyl*-2-*propen*-1-*one and*			
Cyanoacetamide	$NaOCH_3$	3-Cyano-5-methoxy-4,6-diphenyl-2-pyridone	631
Benzoyl-p-toluylmethane (*Enol*) *and*			
Cyanoacetamide	$(C_2H_5)_2NH$	3-Cyano-4-phenyl-6-*p*-tolyl-2-pyridone (34) and 3-cyano-6-phenyl-4-*p*-tolyl-2-pyridone (17)	370

Reactants	Catalyst	Product (Yield, %)	Refs.
2-*Benzylideneindan*-1,3-*dione and*			
Deoxybenzoin	$NaOC_2H_5$	2-[$CH(C_6H_5)CH(C_6H_5)COC_6H_5$]indan-1,3-dione (structure)	416
Styryl Phenethyl Ketone and		$A = C_6H_5CH_2CH_2COCH_2CHC_6H_5$ (A attached at the CH)	
Dimethyl malonate	$NaOCH_3$	ACH(CO_2CH_3)$_2$	423
Diethyl malonate	$NaOC_2H_5$	4-Carbethoxy-2-benzyl-5-phenylcyclohexane-1,3-dione (60)	198
3-*Benzoyl*-4-*phenyl*-3-*buten*-2-*one and*			
Phenylnitromethane	$(C_2H_5)_2NH$	3-Benzoyl-5-nitro-4,5-diphenylpentan-2-one (38)	29
p-$CH_3C_6H_4COCH_2C({=}NH)CH_3$	None	5-Acetyl-2-methyl-4,6-diphenyl-3-*p*-toluoyl-3,4-dihydropyridine	398
3-*Methoxy*-3-*phenyl*-1-*p*-*tolyl*-2-*propen*-1-*one and*			
Cyanoacetamide	$(C_2H_5)_2NH$	3-Cyano-4-phenyl-6-*p*-tolyl-2-pyridone	370
3-*Methoxy*-1-*phenyl*-3-*p*-*anisyl*-2-*propen*-1-*one and*			
Cyanoacetamide	$(C_2H_5)_2NH$	3-Cyano-4-*p*-anisyl-6-phenyl-2-pyridone	594
Fluorenylideneacetophenone¶ *and*			
Acetophenone	KOH, acetal	9,9-Diphenacylfluorene	635
5-*Mesitoylacenaphthylene and*			
Diethyl malonate	$NaOC_2H_5$	5-Mesitoylacenaphthene-1-acetic acid** (50)	636

Note: References 491–1045 are on pp. 545–555.

¶ The unsaturated ketone was formed *in situ* from fluorenone and acetophenone.

** The acid was obtained after hydrolysis of the adduct.

TABLE IV

MICHAEL CONDENSATIONS WITH ETHYLENIC KETONES OF THE DIBENZYLIDENE- AND DICINNAMYLIDENE-ACETONE TYPE

Reactants	Catalyst	Product (Yield, %)	References
Dibenzylideneacetone and		$A = C_6H_5CH{=}CHCOCH_2CHC_6H_5$ (with a bond drawn down from the second CH)	
Dimethyl malonate	Piperidine	ACH(CO_2CH_3)$_2$ (59)	198
	$NaOCH_3$	Dimethyl 2,6-diphenyl-4-oxocyclohexane-1,1-dicarboxylate	198
Diethyl malonate	Piperidine	ACH($CO_2C_2H_5$)$_2$	198
	$NaOCH_3$	Diethyl 2,6-diphenyl-4-oxocyclohexane-1,1-dicarboxylate	198
Ethyl acetoacetate	$(C_2H_5)_2NH$	$CH_3COCH(A)CO_2C_2H_5$ (38)	21
Methyl cyanoacetate	$NaOCH_3$	4-Carbomethoxy-4-cyano-3,5-diphenylcyclohexan-1-one (72)	198, 199
	NaOH	4-Carbomethoxy-4-cyano-3,5-diphenylcyclohexan-1-one	199
Ethyl cyanoacetate	$NaOC_2H_5$	4-Carbethoxy-4-cyano-3,5-diphenylcyclohexan-1-one (88)	200
3-Methylcyclohexanone	$(C_2H_5)_2NH$	O, A, CH_3 or O, A, CH_3	616
Benzyl cyanide	$NaOCH_3$	γ-Cinnamoyl-α,β-diphenylbutyronitrile (two isomers), and 4-cyano-3,4,5-triphenylcyclohexan-1-one (total 44) or 4-Cyano-3,4,5-triphenylcyclohexan-1-one (52)	952
Nitromethane	$NaOCH_3$	4-Nitro-3,5-diphenylcyclohexan-1-one	198

Substituted Dibenzylideneacetones

Substituent(s) in 2,3,4,5,6-C_6H_5CH=CHCOCH=CHC_6H_5-2′,3′,4′,5′,6′	Addend	Catalyst	Substituents in Product (Yield, %) [cyclohex-2-en-1-one, positions 2–6]	References
2-Cl	$CH_3COCH_2CO_2C_2H_5$	$NaOC_2H_5$; piperidine	3-*o*-ClC_6H_4CH=CH—, 5-C_6H_5, 6-$C_2H_5O_2C$— (35)	201
3-Cl	$CH_3COCH_2CO_2C_2H_5$	$NaOC_2H_5$; piperidine	3-*m*-ClC_6H_4CH=CH—, 5-C_6H_5—, 6-$C_2H_5O_2C$— (88)	201
4-Cl	$CH_3COCH_2CO_2C_2H_5$	$NaOC_2H_5$; piperidine	3-*p*-ClC_6H_4CH=CH—, 5-C_6H_5—, 6-$C_2H_5O_2C$—	201
2,3′-Di-Cl	$CH_3COCH_2CO_2C_2H_5$	$NaOCH_3$	3-*o*-ClC_6H_4—, 5-*m*-ClC_6H_4CH=CH—, 6-$C_2H_5O_2C$—	201
2,4′-Di-Cl	$CH_3COCH_2CO_2C_2H_5$	$NaOCH_3$	3-*o*-ClC_6H_4—, 5-*p*-ClC_6H_4CH=CH, 6-$C_2H_5O_2C$—	201
3,4′-Di-Cl	$CH_3COCH_2CO_2C_2H_5$	$NaOCH_3$	3-*m*-ClC_6H_4—, 5-*p*-ClC_6H_4CH=CH—, 6-$C_2H_5O_2C$—	198
4-CH_3O	$CH_2(CO_2CH_3)_2$	Piperidine	*p*-$CH_3OC_6H_4CH$=$CHCOCH_2CH(C_6H_5)$-$CH(CO_2CH_3)_2$	198
		$NaOCH_3$	3-*p*-Anisyl-4,4-dicarbomethoxy-5-phenylcyclohexan-1-one	198

Note: References 491–1045 are on pp. 545–555.

TABLE IV—*Continued*

MICHAEL CONDENSATIONS WITH ETHYLENIC KEYTONES OF THE DIBENZYLIDENE- AND DICINNAMYLIDENE-ACETONE TYPE

Substituted Dibenzylideneacetones—Continued

Substituent(s) in 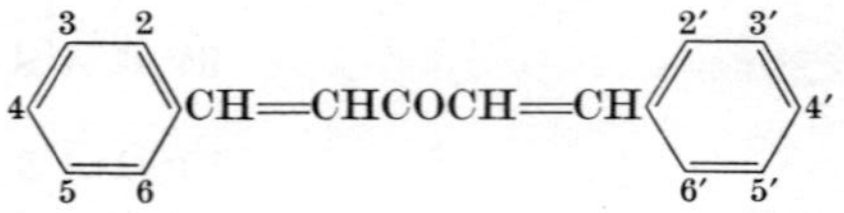 (3,2,4,5,6)-C$_6$H$_5$CH=CHCOCH=CH-C$_6$H$_5$(2′,3′,4′,5′,6′)	Addend	Catalyst	Substituents in Product (Yield, 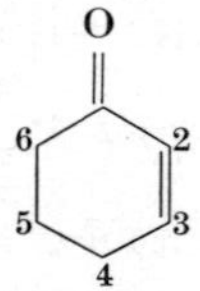 %) [cyclohexenone, positions 2–6]	References
2-HO, 2′-Cl	$CH_3COCH_2CO_2C_2H_5$	NaOH, aq. ethanol	3-o-ClC$_6$H$_4$CH=CH—, 5-o-HOC$_6$H$_4$—, 6-C$_2$H$_5$O$_2$C— (28)	203
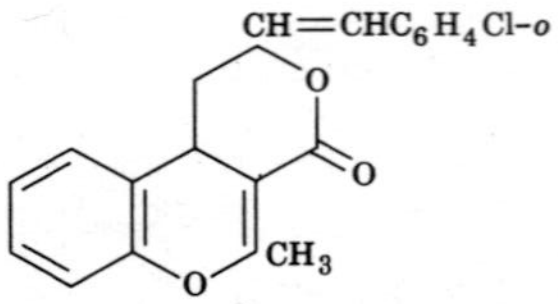 CH=CHC$_6$H$_4$Cl-o; O; O; CH$_3$ (15)				203
	$C_6H_5COCH_2CO_2C_2H_5$	$NaOC_2H_5$	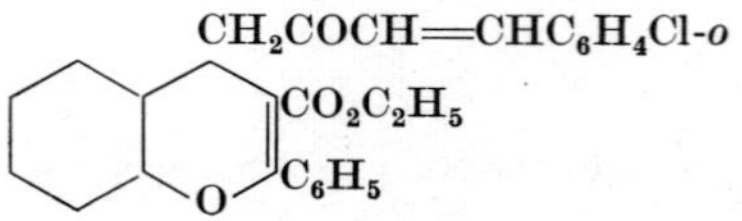 CH$_2$COCH=CHC$_6$H$_4$Cl-o; CO$_2$C$_2$H$_5$; C$_6$H$_5$; O	203

2-HO, 3′-Cl	$CH_3COCH_2CO_2C_2H_5$	NaOH, aq. ethanol	3-*m*-$ClC_6H_4CH{=}CH$—, 5-*o*-HOC_6H_4—, 6-$C_2H_5O_2C$— (3)	203
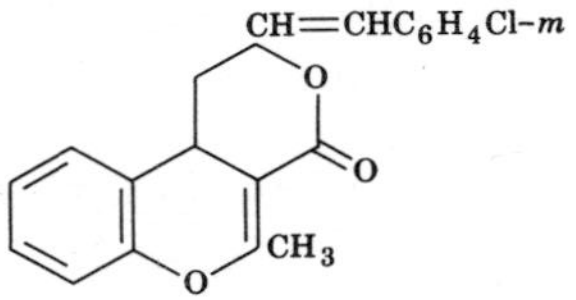 $CH{=}CHC_6H_4Cl$-*m*; O; O; CH_3; (8)				203
2-HO, 4′-Cl	$CH_3COCH_2CO_2C_2H_5$	NaOH, aq. ethanol	3-*p*-$ClC_6H_4CH{=}CH$—, 5-*o*-HOC_6H_4—, 6-$C_2H_5O_2C$— (33)	203
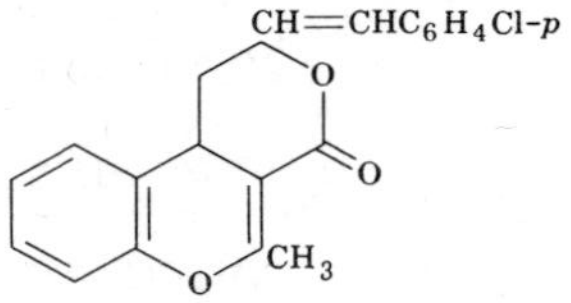 $CH{=}CHC_6H_4Cl$-*p*; O; O; CH_3; (11)				203
3-Cl, 4′-HO	$CH_3COCH_2CO_2C_2H_5$	NaOH, aq. ethanol	3-*m*-$ClC_6H_4CH{=}CH$—, 5-*p*-HOC_6H_4—, 6-$C_2H_5O_2C$— (65)	204
4-Cl, 4′-HO	$CH_3COCH_2CO_2C_2H_5$	NaOH, aq. ethanol	3-*p*-$ClC_6H_4CH{=}CH$—, 5-*p*-HOC_6H_4—, 6-$C_2H_5O_2C$— (70)	204
3-Cl, 4′-CH_3O	$CH_3COCH_2CO_2C_2H_5$	NaOH, aq. ethanol	3-*p*-$CH_3OC_6H_4CH{=}CH$—, 5-*m*-ClC_6H_4—, 6-$C_2H_5O_2C$— (55)	204
4-Cl, 4-CH_3O	$CH_3COCH_2CO_2C_2H_5$	NaOH, aq. ethanol	3-*p*-$CH_3OC_6H_4CH{=}CH$—, 5-*p*-ClC_6H_4—, 6-$C_2H_5O_2C$— (45)	204

TABLE IV—*Continued*

MICHAEL CONDENSATIONS WITH ETHYLENIC KEYTONES OF THE DIBENZYLIDENE- AND DICINNAMYLIDENE-ACETONE TYPE

Substituted Dibenzylideneacetones—Continued

Substituent(s) in $C_6H_5CH{=}CHCOCH{=}CHC_6H_5$ (ring positions 2–6, 2′–6′)	Addend	Catalyst	Substituents in Product (Yield, %) (cyclohex-2-en-1-one, positions 2–6)	References
2,2′-Di-HO	$CH_3COCH_2CO_2C_2H_5$	NaOH, aq. ethanol	3-*o*-$HOC_6H_4CH{=}CH$—, 5-*o*-HOC_6H_4— (24)	202, 586
2-HO, 2′-CH_3O	$CH_3COCH_2CO_2C_2H_5$	NaOH, aq. ethanol	3-*o*-$CH_3OC_6H_4CH{=}CH$—, 5-*o*-HOC_6H_4—	202
2,2′-Di-CH_3O	$CH_3COCH_2CO_2C_2H_5$	NaOH, aq. ethanol	3-*o*-$CH_3OC_6H_4CH{=}CH$—, 5-*o*-$CH_3OC_6H_4$— (88)	202
	$CH_3COCH_2COCH_3$	NaOH, aq. ethanol	3-*o*-$CH_3OC_6H_4CH{=}CH$—, 5-*o*-$CH_3OC_6H_4$—, 2-CH_3CO—	202
4,4′-Di-CH_3	$CH_2(CO_2CH_3)_2$	$NaOCH_3$	4,4-Dicarbomethoxy-3,5-di-*p*-methoxyphenylcyclohexan-1-one	198
	$NCCH_2CO_2CH_3$	$NaOCH_3$	3,5-Di-(*p*-methoxyphenyl)-4-carbomethoxy-4-cyanocyclohexan-1-one	199
4,4′-Di-$(CH_3)_2N$	$CH_3COCH_2CO_2C_2H_5$	NaOH, aq. ethanol	3-*p*-$(CH_3)_2NC_6H_4CH{=}CH$—, 5-*p*-$(CH_3)_2NC_6H_4$—, 6-$C_2H_5O_2C$—	205
2-HO, 4′-$(CH_3)_2N$	$CH_3COCH_2CO_2C_2H_5$	KOH, aq. ethanol	3-*o*-$HOC_6H_4CH{=}CH$—, 5-*p*-$(CH_3)_2NC_6H_4$—, 6-$C_2H_5O_2C$—	205
	$NCCH_2CO_2C_2H_5$	NaOH, aq. ethanol	*p*-$(CH_3)_2NC_6H_4CH{=}CHCOCH_2$-$CH(C_6H_4OH$-*o*$)CH(CO_2H)_2$*	205

2-CH_3O, 4′-$(CH_3)_2N$	$CH_3COCH_2CO_2C_2H_5$	NaOH, aq. ethanol	3-*o*-$CH_3OC_6H_4CH{=}CH$—, 5-*p*-$(CH_3)_2NC_6H_4$—, 6-$C_2H_5O_2C$—	205
2-HO, 3-CH_3O, 4′-$(CH_3)_2N$	$CH_3COCH_2CO_2C_2H_5$	NaOH, aq. ethanol	3-(2-HO-3-$CH_3OC_6H_3$)$CH{=}CH$—, 5-*p*-$(CH_3)_2NC_6H_4$—, 6-$C_2H_5O_2C$—	205
2-HO, 4-CH_3O, 4′-$(CH_3)_2N$	$CH_3COCH_2CO_2C_2H_5$	NaOH, aq. ethanol	3-*p*-$(CH_3)_2NC_6H_4CH{=}CH$—, 5-(2-HO-4-$CH_3OC_6H_3$)—, 6-$C_2H_5O_2C$—	205
2-HO, 5-CH_3O, 4′-$(CH_3)_2N$	$CH_3COCH_2CO_2C_2H_5$	NaOH, aq. ethanol	3-(2-HO-5-$CH_3OC_6H_3$)$CH{=}CH$—, 5-*p*-$(CH_3)_2NC_6H_4$—, 6-$C_2H_5O_2C$—	205
2-OCH_3, 4′-Cl	$CH_3COCH_2CO_2C_2H_5$	$NaOCH_3$	3-*p*-$ClC_6H_4CH{=}CH$—, 5-*o*-$CH_3OC_6H_4$—, 6-$C_2H_5O_2C$— (57)	203

Reactants	Catalyst	Product (Yield, %)	References
Benzylidenecinnamylideneacetone and			
Dimethyl malonate	$NaOCH_3$	4,4-Dicarbomethoxy-3-phenyl-5-styrylcyclohexan-1-one	198
p-Methoxybenzylidenecinnamylideneacetone and			
Dimethyl malonate	$NaOCH_3$	4,4-Dicarbomethoxy-3-*p*-methoxyphenyl-5-styrylcyclohexan-1-one	198
Dicinnamylideneacetone and			
Dimethyl malonate	$NaOCH_3$	4,4-Dicarbomethoxy-3,5-distyrylcyclohexan-1-one	198
2,6-*Dibenzylidenecyclohexanone and*			
Cyanoacetamide	$NaOC_2H_5$	Compound $C_{23}H_{22}N_2O_2$	224

* The acid was obtained after hydrolysis of the adduct.

TABLE V

MICHAEL CONDENSATIONS WITH UNSATURATED KETONES CONTAINING HETEROCYCLIC RINGS

Reactants	Catalyst	Product (Yield, %)	References
Furfurylideneacetone and		$A = \text{(2-furyl)}\underset{\vert}{\text{C}}\text{HCH}_2\text{COCH}_3$	
Benzyl cyanide	$NaOCH_3$	$C_6H_5CH(A)CN$ (81)	121
1-Nitropropane	$(C_2H_5)_2NH$	$CH_3CH_2CH(A)NO_2$ (75)	209
2-Nitropropane	$(C_2H_5)_2NH$	$(CH_3)_2C(A)NO_2$ (95)	209
Triethyl phosphonoacetate	$NaOC_2H_5$	$(C_2H_5O)_2P(O)CH(A)CO_2C_2H_5$ (9)	124
Furfurylideneacetophenone and		$A = \text{(2-furyl)}\underset{\vert}{\text{C}}\text{HCH}_2\text{COC}_6\text{H}_5$	
Diethyl malonate	$NaOC_2H_5$	$ACH(CO_2C_2H_5)_2$ (75)	210
Acetophenone	$NaOC_2H_5$	$C_6H_5COCH_2A$ (25)	207
Nitromethane	$NaOCH_3$	ACH_2NO_2	208
1-Nitropropane	$(C_2H_5)_2NH$	$CH_3CH_2CH(A)NO_2$ (79)	209
2-Nitropropane	$(C_2H_5)_2NH$	$(CH_3)_2C(A)NO_2$ (90)	209
Phenylnitromethane	$NaOCH_3$	$C_6H_5CH(A)NO_2$	208

Furfurylideneacetophenones Containing a Substituent in the Phenyl Group

Substituent in 2-furyl-CH=CHCO-C$_6$H$_5$ (positions 2, 3, 4, 5, 6)	Adduct	Catalyst	Product (Yield, %) A = 2-furyl-CH(—)CH$_2$COC$_6$H$_4$R with Substituent R as Indicated	References
4-Br	CH_3NO_2	$NaOCH_3$	ACH_2NO_2, R = 4-Br (75)	208
	$C_6H_5CH_2NO_2$	$NaOCH_3$	$C_6H_5CH(A)NO_2$, R = 4-Br (29)	208
4-CH_3O	$CH_2(CO_2C_2H_5)_2$	$NaOCH_3$	$ACH(CO_2H)_2$,* R = 4-CH_3O	210
4-Cyclohexyl	$CH_2(CO_2CH_3)_2$	$NaOCH_3$	$ACH(CO_2CH_3)_2$, R = 4-cyclohexyl (50)	210

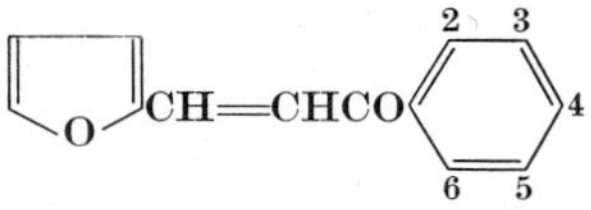

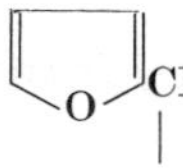

Reactants	Catalyst	Product (Yield, %)	References
2-*Furylidene*-1-*tetralone and* Ethyl acetoacetate	$NaOC_2H_5$	O, $CO_2C_2H_5$ and O, $CO_2C_2H_5$	393
2-*Furylidene*-6-*methoxy*-1-*tetralone and* Ethyl acetoacetate	$NaOC_2H_5$	O, $CO_2C_2H_5$, CH_3O	393

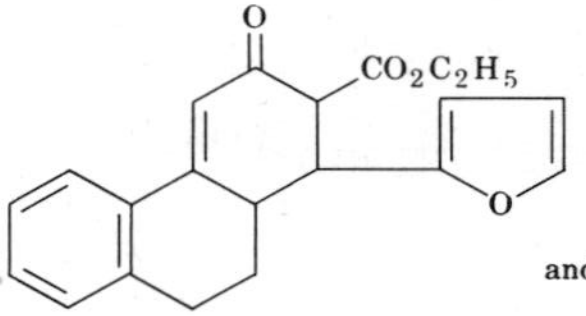

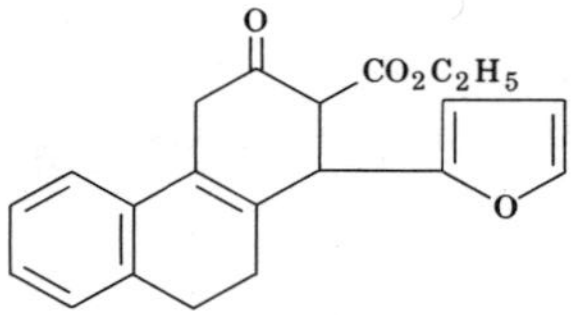

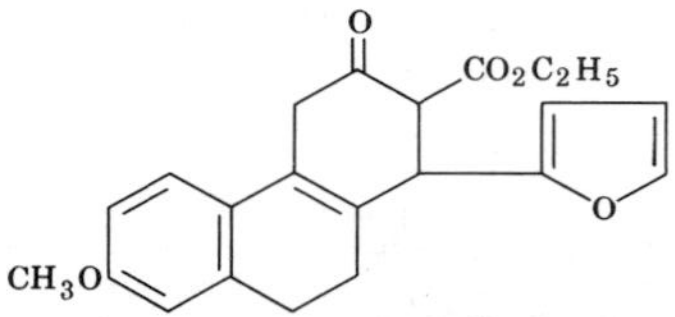

* The malonic ester adduct could not be obtained crystalline so it was hydrolyzed to the acid

TABLE V—*Continued*

MICHAEL CONDENSATIONS WITH UNSATURATED KETONES CONTAINING HETEROCYCLIC RINGS

Reactants	Catalyst	Product (Yield, %)	References
Benzylidene-2-acetylcoumarone and			
2-Acetylcoumarone†	Aq. NaOH	(2-Benzofuryl-$COCH_2$—$)_2CHC_6H_5$ and 2-Benzofuryl-$COCH_2CH(C_6H_5)CHCO$-2-benzofuryl, with 2-Benzofuryl-$COCH_2CHC_6H_5$ attached at the CH	637
Hydroxymethylene-2-acetylthiophene and			
Diethyl acetone-1,3-dicarboxylate	$NaOC_2H_5$	Diethyl 2-hydroxy-4-(α-thienyl)isophthalate (61)	427
Hydroxymethylene-2-acetylpyridine and			
Diethyl acetone-1,3-dicarboxylate	$NaOC_2H_5$	Diethyl 2-hydroxy-4-(α-pyridyl)isophthalate (76)	427
Phenyl β-(4-Quinolyl)vinyl Ketone and			
Acetophenone‡	NaOH	1,5-Diphenyl-3-(4-quinolyl)pentane-1,5-dione (87)	638

Note: References 491–1045 are on pp. 545–555.

† A mixture of benzaldehyde and 2-acetylcoumarone was used.

‡ A mixture of acetophenone and quinoline-4-carboxaldehyde was used.

TABLE VI

Michael Condensations with 3-Acylcoumarins and Related Compounds

Reactants	Catalyst	Product (Yield, %)	References
3-*Acetylcoumarin and*		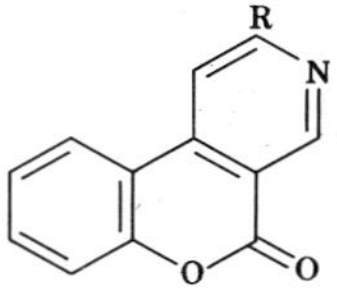 unless complete structure is shown	
Cyanoacetamide	None	R = 3-Coumarinyl (45–52)*	211
Acetone	Piperidine	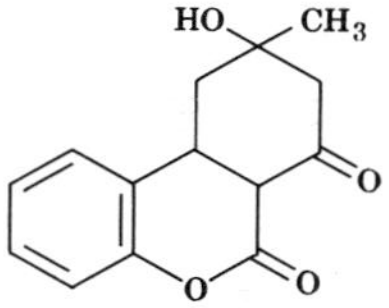	212
	$NH_3(NCCH_2CONH_2)$†	R = CH_3 (32)	211
Methyl ethyl ketone	$NH_3(NCCH_2CONH_2)$†	R = C_2H_5 (42)	211
Acetophenone	$NH_3(NCCH_2CONH_2)$†	R = C_6H_5 (21)	211
3-Acetylcoumarin	$NH_3(NCCH_2CONH_2)$†	R = 3-Coumarinyl	212

* The cyanoacetamide could be replaced by malonamide, formamide, or urea without changing the product. The same product was obtained when piperidine was used as a catalyst. The earlier report (ref. 213) that the product with cyanoacetamide and piperidine was 3-acetyldihydrocoumarin-4-(α-cyanoacetamide) could not be confirmed.

† In these experiments cyanoacetamide was present; its decomposition furnished the ammonia.

TABLE VI—*Continued*

MICHAEL CONDENSATIONS WITH 3-ACYLCOUMARINS AND RELATED COMPOUNDS

Reactants	Catalyst	Product (Yield, %)	References
3-*Acetylcoumarin* (*Cont.*) *and*		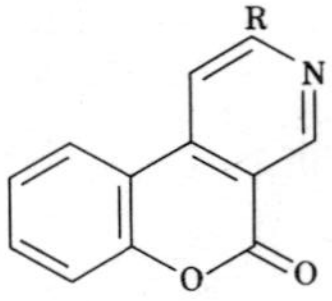 unless complete structure is shown	
3-Acetylcoumarin	Piperidine	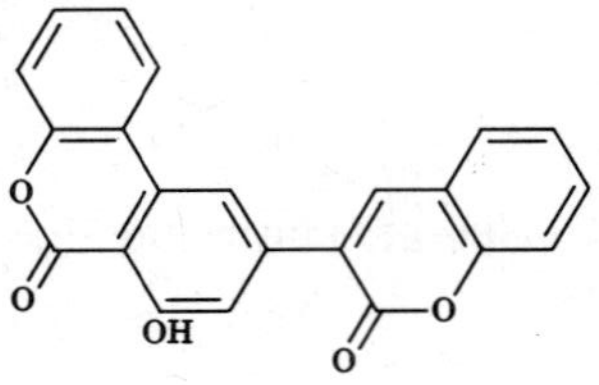 (18)	
Cyclohexanone	$NH_3(NCCH_2CONH_2)$†	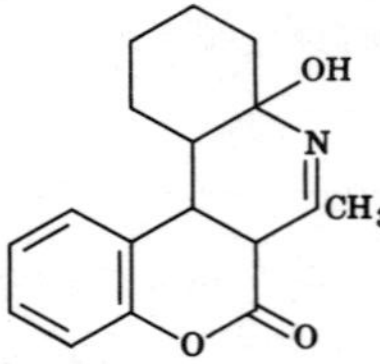 (47)	211

Reactants	Catalyst	Product (Yield, %)	Refs.
3-*Benzoylcoumarin and*			
Cyanoacetamide	Piperidine	3-Benzoyldihydrocoumarin-4-(α-cyanoacetamide)	213
7-*Hydroxycoumarin and*			
Cyanoacetamide	Piperidine	7-Hydroxydihydrocoumarin-4-(α-cyanoacetamide) (90)	639
7-*Methoxycoumarin and*			
Cyanoacetamide	Piperidine	7-Methoxydihydrocoumarin-4-(α-cyanoacetamide) (90)	639
2-(*p*-*Methoxybenzylidene*)*coumaran*-2-*one*‡ *and*		*A* = [3-oxo-coumaran-2-yl]–$CHCHC_6H_4OCH_3$-*p*	
Ethyl acetoacetate	$NaOC_2H_5$	$CH_3COCH(A)CO_2C_2H_5$	214
Deoxybenzoin	$NaOC_2H_5$	$C_6H_5COCH(A)C_6H_5$	214
Cyclohexanone	$NaOC_2H_5$	2-*A*-cyclohexanone	214

Note: References 491–1045 are on pp. 545–555.

† In these experiments cyanoacetamide was present; its decomposition furnished the ammonia.

‡ The corresponding 5-methoxy compound behaves analogously with ethyl acetoacetate, deoxybenzoin, and cyclohexanone; ref. 214*a*.

TABLE VI—*Continued*

MICHAEL CONDENSATIONS WITH 3-ACYLCOUMARINS AND RELATED COMPOUNDS

Reactants	Catalyst	Product (Yield, %)	References
γ-Pyrone and			
Diethyl malonate	$NaOC_2H_5$	Ethyl *p*-hydroxybenzoate	215
Alkylidenerhodanines and			
Rhodanine §	NH_4OH, NH_4Cl	α,α-Bis-(2-thio-4-ketotetrahydro-5-thiazolyl)ethane and homologs (22–55)	216
5-*Ethoxymethylene*-3-*methylrhodanine and*			
3-Methylrhodanine	*t*-Amines	5,5′-Methylidynebis-(3-methylrhodanine) (34–69)	640
3-Phenylrhodanine	$(C_2H_5)_3N$	O O ‖ ‖ C—C═CH—CH—C H_3CN | | NC_6H_5 (88) C—S S—C ‖ ‖ S S	640

Reactants	Catalyst	Product (Yield, %)	Refs.
5-Ethoxymethylene-3-phenylrhodanine and			
3-Methylrhodanine	$(C_2H_5)_3N$	(structure below) (94)	640

```
          O                    O
          ‖                    ‖
         C—C═CH—CH—C
        /  |      |     \
  H5C6N    |      |      NCH3 (94)
        \  |      |     /
         C—S      S—C
         ‖             ‖
         S             S
```

Reactants	Catalyst	Product (Yield, %)	Refs.
3,3′-Ethylenebis-(5-ethoxymethylenerhodanine) and			
3-Methylrhodanine	$(C_2H_5)_3N$	Salt of 3,3′-ethylenebis-5-(2″-thiono-4″-keto-3″-methyl-5″-thiazolidylmethylenerhodanine) (50)	640
3-Phenylrhodanine	$(C_2H_5)_3N$	Salt of 3,3′-ethylenebis-5-(2″-thiono-4″-keto-3″-phenyl-5″-thiazolidylmethylenerhodanine) (37)	640
Pyrazol blue and			
1-Phenyl-3-methyl-2-pyrazolin-5-one	None	1,1′,1″-Triphenyl-3,3′,3″-trimethyl-(4,4′,4″-ter-2-pyrazoline)-5,5′,5″-trione	641
1-(*p*-Bromophenyl)-3-methyl-2-pyrazolin-5-one	None	1,1′-Diphenyl-1″-(*p*-bromophenyl)-3,3′,3″-trimethyl-(4,4′,4″-ter-2-pyrazoline)-5,5′,5″-trione	641

Note: References 491–1045 are on pp. 545–555.

§ The actual ingredients used were rhodanine and various aliphatic aldehydes.

TABLE VII

Michael Condensations with Cycloalkenones and Acyl Cycloalkenes

Reactants	Catalyst	Product (Yield, %)	References
2-*Hydroxymethylenecyclopentanone and*			
Ethyl acetoacetate	$NaOC_2H_5$	5-Indanol-6-carboxylic acid (18)	427
Diethyl acetone-1,3-dicarboxylate	$NaOC_2H_5$	Diethyl 5-indanol-4,6-dicarboxylate (92)	427
Ethyl β-aminocrotonate	—	6-Methyl-2,3-dihydro-β-pyridindene*	445
2-*Cyclohexen*-1-*one and*		*A* 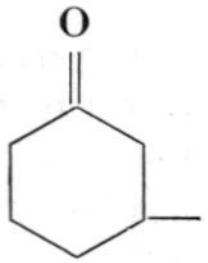 = [3-oxocyclohexyl structure]	
Diethyl malonate	$NaOC_2H_5$	$ACH(CO_2C_2H_5)_2$ (90)	642
Nitromethane	$NaOCH_3$	ACH_2NO_2 (50)	643
Nitroethane	$NaOCH_3$	$CH_3CH(A)NO_2$ (57)	643
3-*Chloro*-2-*cyclohexen*-1-*one and*			
Dimethyl methylmalonate	$NaOCH_3$	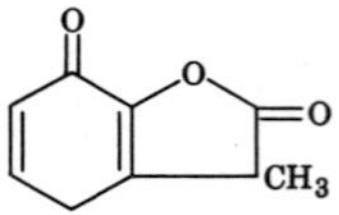 [structure: O, O, =O, CH_3]	436
1-*Acetyl*-1-*cyclopentene and*		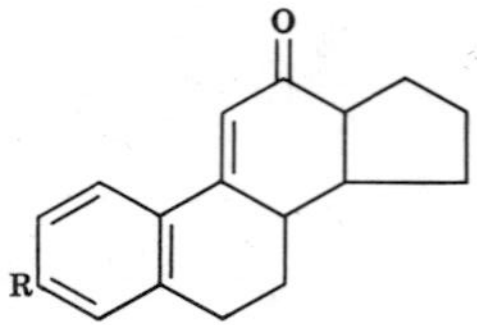 [structure: O, R]	

1-Tetralone	$NaNH_2$	R = H	98, 217
6-Methoxy-1-tetralone	$NaNH_2$	R = CH_3O (55)	206
6-Ethoxy-1-tetralone	$NaNH_2$	R = C_2H_5O	217
Cycloheptanone	KOC_4H_9-*t*	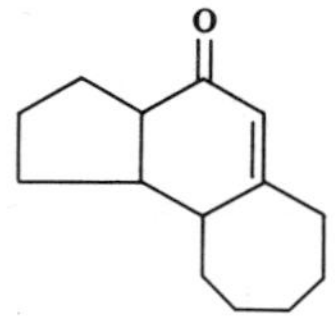 (41)	644
2-*Methylenecyclohexanone*† *and*			
Ethyl acetoacetate	NaOH	2-Oxo-2,3,4,5,6,7,8,10-octahydronaphthalene	528
Methyl ethyl ketone	KOH, CH_3OH	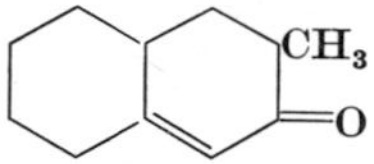	645
Cyclohexanone	KOH, CH_3OH	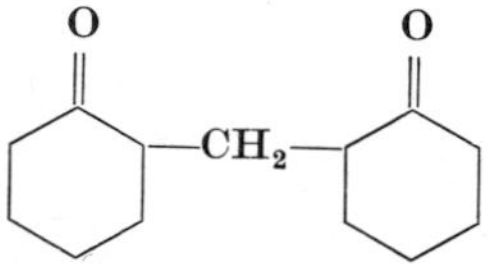 —CH_2— (68)	645, 646‡

Note: References 491–1045 are on pp. 545–555.

* This product was obtained after hydrolysis and decarboxylation.

† 2-Hydroxymethylcyclohexanone was used in these experiments.

‡ A mixture of cyclohexanone and formaldehyde was employed.

TABLE VII—*Continued*

MICHAEL CONDENSATIONS WITH CYCLOALKENONES AND ACYL CYCLOALKENES

Reactants	Catalyst	Product (Yield, %)	References
3-*Methyl-2-cyclohexen-1-one and*			
Diethyl malonate	$[C_6H_5CH_2N(CH_3)_3]OCH_3$	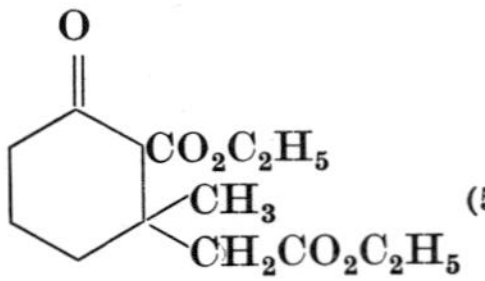 (50)	62, 647, cf. 69, 175
Ethyl acetoacetate	$NaOC_2H_5$	1-Methylbicyclo[3.3.1]nonan-5-ol-7-one	648, 69
Ethyl cyanoacetate	$NaOC_2H_5$	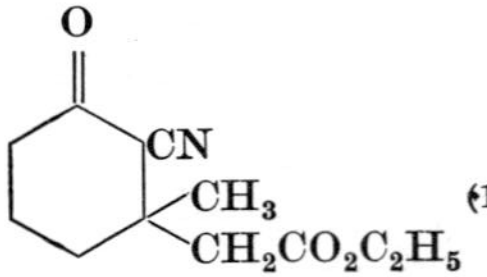 (13–21)	62, 647, cf. 18, 70
Ethyl cyanoacetate	NH_3	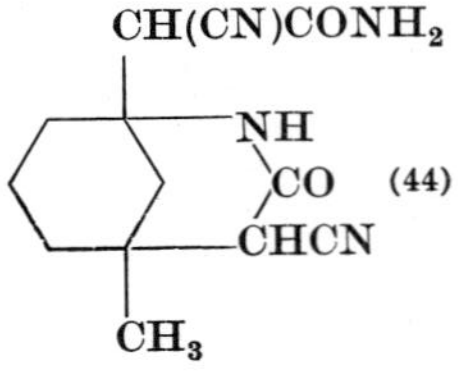 (44)	649

Cyanoacetamide	Piperidine	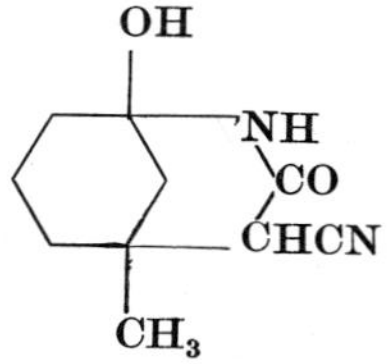 (77)	649
Nitromethane	$[C_6H_5CH_2N(CH_3)_3]OCH_3$	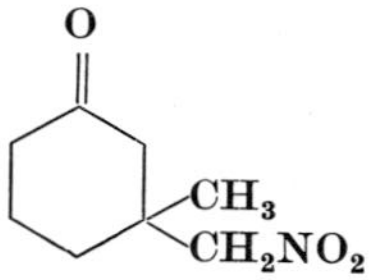 (65)	62
	Piperidine, 1/15 mole	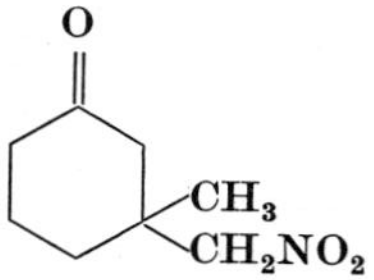 (37)	650
1,3-Dimethylindole	HCl	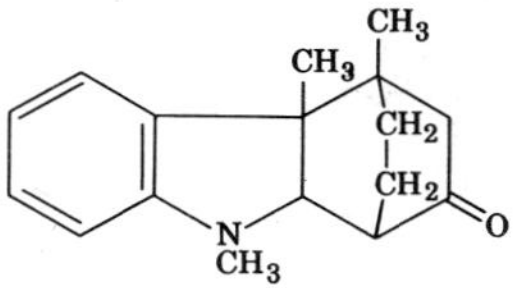	651

Note: References 491–1045 are on pp. 545–555.

TABLE VII—*Continued*

MICHAEL CONDENSATIONS WITH CYCLOALKENONES AND ACYL CYCLOALKENES

Reactants	Catalyst	Product (Yield, %)	References
2-*Hydroxymethylenecyclohexanone and*			
Ethyl acetoacetate	$NaOC_2H_5$	Ethyl 6-hydroxytetralin-7-carboxylate (50)	427
Diethyl acetone-1,3-dicarboxylate	$NaOC_2H_5$	Diethyl 6-hydroxytetralin-5,7-dicarboxylate (83)	427
Cyanoacetamide	Piperidine; $(C_2H_5)_2NH$	3-Cyano-5,6,7,8-tetrahydroquinolin-2-ol	224
$CH_3C({=}NH)CH_2CO_2C_2H_5$	None	Ethyl 2-methyl-5,6,7,8-tetrahydroquinoline-3-carboxylate§	443, 652
$CH_3C({=}NH)CH_2CN$	None	3-Cyano-2-methyl-5,6,7,8-tetrahydroquinoline	653
$CH_3C({=}NH)CH_2COCH_3$	None	3-Acetyl-2-methyl-5,6,7,8-tetrahydroquinoline	653
$CH_3C({=}NH)CH_2COC_6H_5$	None	3-Benzoyl-2-methyl-5,6,7,8-tetrahydroquinoline	653
2-*Aminomethylenecyclohexanone and*			
Ethyl cyanoacetate	Na	4-Cyano-3-oxo-2,3,5,6,7,8-hexahydroisoquinoline	446
1-*Acetyl*-2-*methyl*-1-*cyclopentene and*			
Diethyl malonate	$NaOC_2H_5$	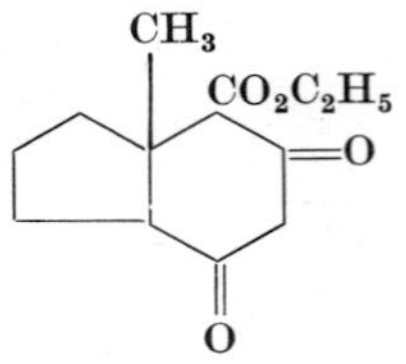 CH_3 $CO_2C_2H_5$ =O O	424
Diethyl phenethylmalonate	$NaOC_2H_5$	Acid, $C_{19}H_{26}O_3$ (poor)	218

Reactants	Catalyst	Product (Yield, %)	Refs.
Cyclopentylideneacetone and			
Diethyl malonate	$NaOC_2H_5$	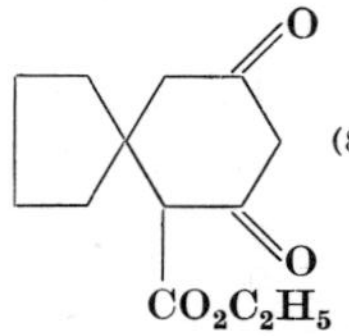 O, O, $CO_2C_2H_5$ (80)	221
1-*Acetyl*-1-*cyclohexene and*			
Diethyl malonate	$NaOC_2H_5$	*cis*- and *trans*-4-Carbethoxydecalin-1,3-dione (7, 87, 60)	94, 95, 96, 654
Ethyl acetoacetate	$NaOC_2H_5$	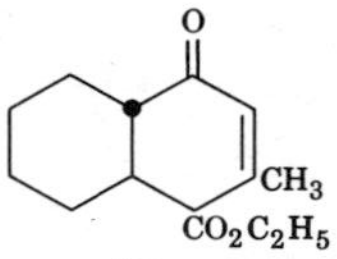 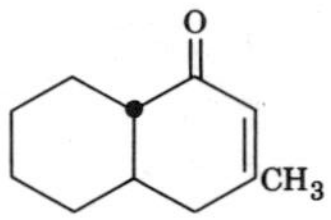 O, CH_3, $CO_2C_2H_5$ (30) and O, CH_3 (10)	93
Cyclohexanone	$NaNH_2$	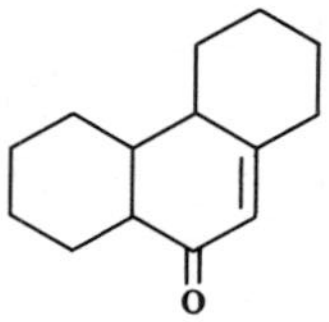 O (80)	99, cf. 98

Note: References 491–1045 are on pp. 545–555.

§ At 0° the product is ethyl 9-hydroxy-2-methyl-5,6,7,8,9,10-hexahydroquinoline-3-carboxylate.

TABLE VII—*Continued*

MICHAEL CONDENSATIONS WITH CYCLOALKENONES AND ACYL CYCLOALKENES

Reactants	Catalyst	Product (Yield, %)	References
1-*Acetyl*-1-*cyclohexene* (*Cont.*) *and*			
Cycloheptanone	KOC_4H_9-*t*	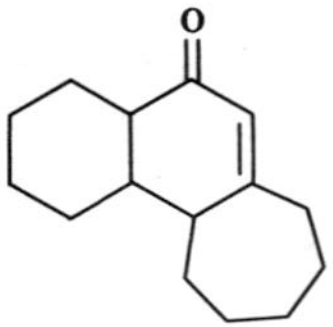 (56)	644
1-Acetyl-1-cyclohexene	$NaNH_2$	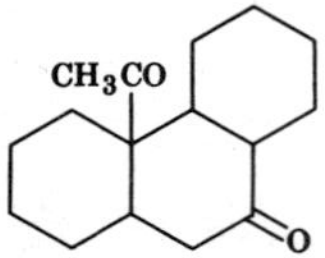 CH_3CO … O (Mixture of isomers)	97
1-Tetralone	$NaNH_2$	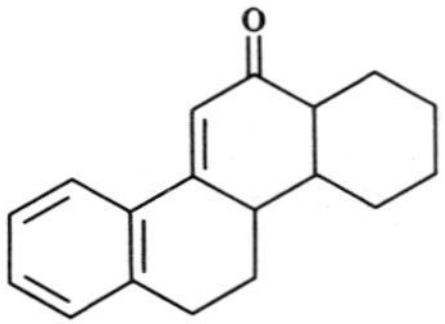 O	212

Reactant	Catalyst	Product (Yield, %)	Refs.
6-Methoxy-1-tetralone	$NaNH_2$	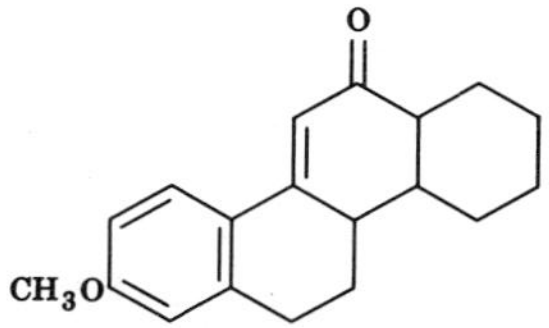 [structure, CH_3O] (Mixture of isomers)	98
cis-1-Decalone	$NaNH_2$	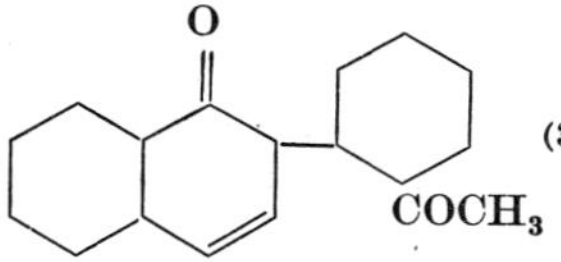 [structure, $COCH_3$] (35)	655
1-Oxo-9-methyl-1,2,5,6,7,8,9,10-octahydronaphthalene	$NaNH_2$	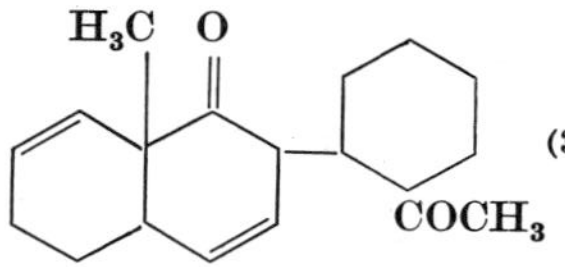 [structure, H_3C, $COCH_3$] (30)	655
3,8-Dimethyl-4,7,8,9-tetrahydroindan-1-one	$NaNH_2$	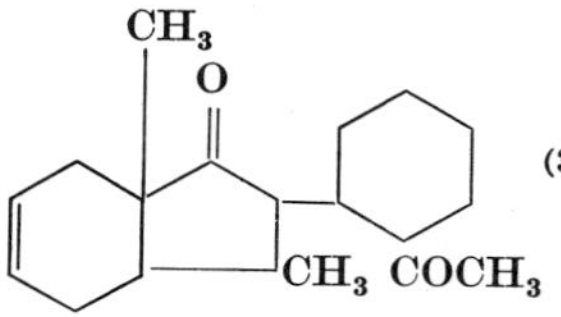 [structure, CH_3, CH_3, $COCH_3$] (35)	655
2-Methoxymethylenecyclohexan-1-one and			
Ethyl acetoacetate	$NaOC_2H_5$	2-Hydroxy-5,6,7,8-tetrahydro-3-naphthoic acid and ethyl α-acetyl-β-(2-ketocyclohexyl)acrylate	656

Note: References 491–1045 are on pp. 545–555.

TABLE VII—*Continued*

MICHAEL CONDENSATIONS WITH CYCLOALKENONES AND ACYL CYCLOALKENES

Reactants	Catalyst	Product (Yield, %)	References
2-(α-Hydroxyethylidene)cyclohexan-1-one and			
Diethyl acetone-1,3-dicarboxylate	$NaOC_2H_5$	5,7-Dicarbethoxy-8-methyl-6-hydroxy-1,2,3,4-tetrahydronaphthalene (36)	427
Cyanoacetamide	Piperidine; $NaOC_2H_5$	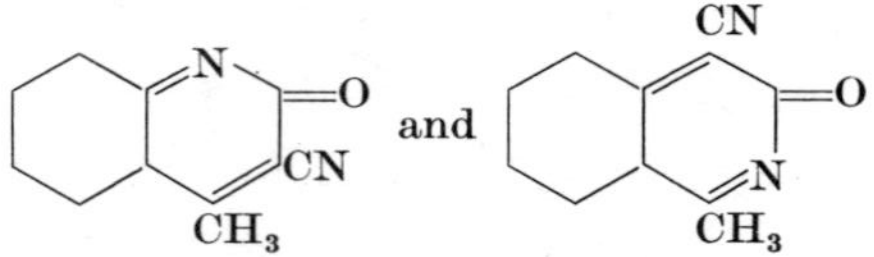	941
N-Methylcyanoacetamide	Piperidine; $NaOC_2H_5$	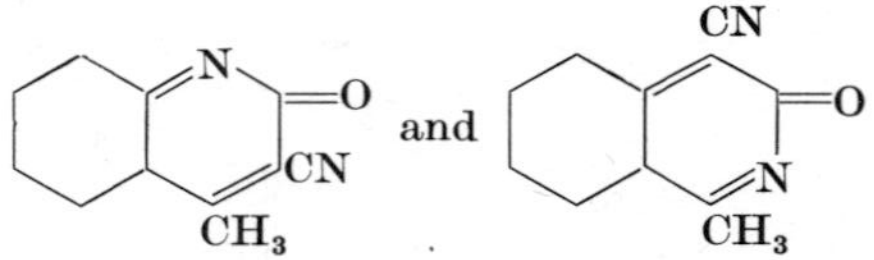	941
3,5-Dimethyl-2-cyclohexen-1-one and			
Ethyl acetoacetate	$NaOC_2H_5$	1,3-Dimethyl-5-hydroxybicyclo[3.3.1]nonan-7-one	657
2-Hydroxymethylene-5-methylcyclohexanone and			
Ethyl cyanoacetate	$(C_2H_5)_2NH$	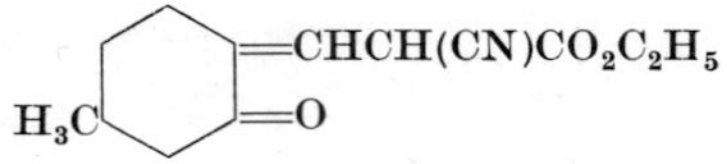	224
Cyanoacetamide	Piperidine; $(C_2H_5)_2NH$	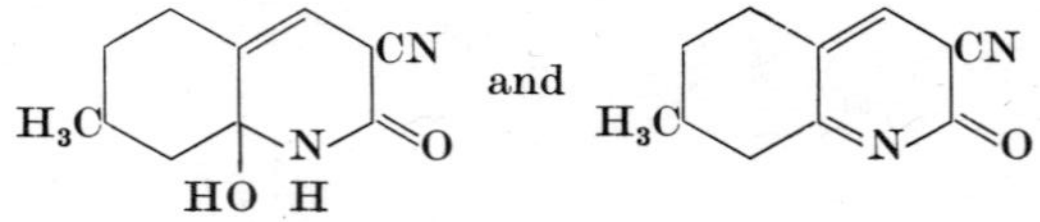	224

2-*Aminomethylene*-3-*methylcyclohexanone and*			
Ethyl cyanoacetate	Na	5-Methyl-3-oxo-2,3,5,6,7,8-hexahydroisoquinoline-4-carbonamide	446
2-*Hydroxymethylene*-4-*methylcyclohexanone and*			
Cyanoacetamide	*sec*-Amine	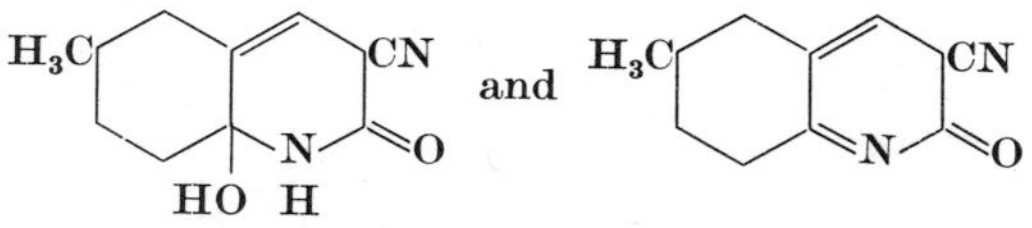 H_3C CN N O HO H and H_3C CN N O	224
$CH_3C(=NH)CH_2CO_2C_2H_5$	None	Ethyl 2,6-dimethyl-5,6,7,8-tetrahydroquinoline-3-carboxylate	443
$CH_3C(=NH)CH_2COCH_3$	None	3-Acetyl-2,6-dimethyl-5,6,7,8-tetrahydroquinoline	653
$CH_3C(=NH)CH_2COC_6H_5$	None	3-Benzoyl-2,6-dimethyl-5,6,7,8-tetrahydroquinoline	443
2-*Aminomethylene*-4-*methylcyclohexanone and*			
Ethyl cyanoacetate	Na	6-Methyl-3-oxo-2,3,5,6,7,8-hexahydroisoquinoline-4-carbonitrile	446
2-*Hydroxymethylene*-5-*methylcyclohexanone and*			
$CH_3C(=NH)CH_2CO_2C_2H_5$	None	Ethyl 2,7-dimethyl-5,6,7,8-tetrahydroquinoline-3-carboxylate	443
$CH_3C(=NH)CH_2COCH_3$	None	3-Acetyl-2,7-dimethyl-5,6,7,8-tetrahydroquinoline	653
$CH_3C(=NH)CH_2COC_6H_5$	None	3-Benzoyl-2,7-dimethyl-5,6,7,8-tetrahydroquinoline	653
2-*Aminomethylene*-5-*methylcyclohexanone and*			
Ethyl cyanoacetate	Na	7-Methyl-3-oxo-2,3,5,6,7,8-hexahydroisoquinoline-4-carbonitrile	446

Note: References 491–1045 are on pp. 545–555.

TABLE VII—*Continued*

MICHAEL CONDENSATIONS WITH CYCLOALKENONES AND ACYL CYCLOALKENES

Reactants	Catalyst	Product (Yield, %)	References
2-*Hydroxymethylene-6-methylcyclohexanone and*			
Cyanoacetamide	*sec*-Amine	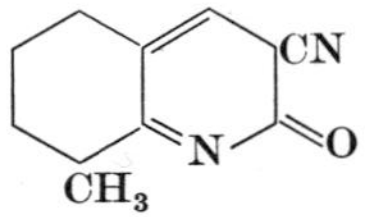	224
$CH_3C(=NH)CH_2CO_2C_2H_5$	None	Ethyl 2,8-dimethyl-5,6,7,8-tetrahydroquinoline-3-carboxylate (42)	653
2-*Methylene-3-methylcyclohexan-1-one and*			
3-Methylcyclohexanone	KOH, C_2H_5OH	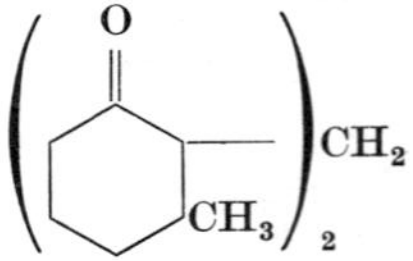	646
2-(α-*Hydroxyethylidene*)-4-*methylcyclohexan-1-one and*			
Cyanoacetamide	Piperidine; $NaOC_2H_5$	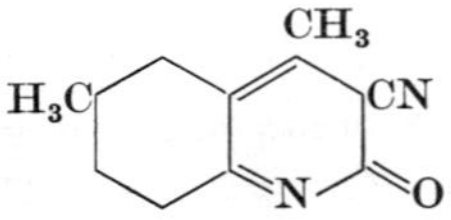 and 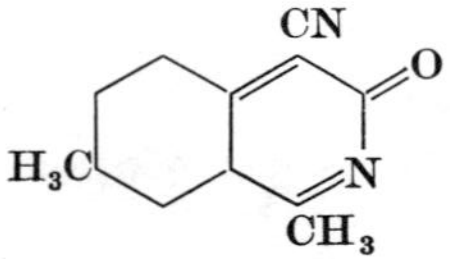	941

2-(α-*Hydroxyethylidene*)-5-*methylcyclohexan*-1-*one and*			
Cyanoacetamide	Piperidine; $NaOC_2H_5$	and	941
2-(α-*Hydroxyethylidene*)-6-*methylcyclohexan*-1-*one and*			
Cyanoacetamide	Piperidine; $NaOC_2H_5$	and	941
2-*Hydroxymethylenecycloheptanone and*			
Diethyl acetone-1,3-dicarboxylate	$NaOC_2H_5$	Diethyl 3-hydroxybicyclo[5.4.0]hendeca-1(6),2,4-triene-2,4-dicarboxylate (61)	428
$CH_3C({=}NH)CH_2CO_2C_2H_5$	None	Ethyl 6-methyl-2,3-dihydropyridindene 7-carboxylate	652
Methyl α-Cyclopentylideneëthyl Ketone and			
Diethyl malonate	$NaOC_2H_5$	1-Methylspiro[5.4]decane-2,4-dione (low)	220
3-*Methylcyclopentylideneacetone and*			
Diethyl malonate	$NaOC_2H_5$	8-Methylspiro[5.4]decane-2,4-dione	658
Cyclohexylideneacetone and			
Diethyl malonate	$NaOC_2H_5$	1-Carbethoxyspiro[5.5]hendecane-2,4-dione (84)	221, 390
	$NaOCH_3$	Spiro[5.5]hendecane-2,4-dione (70–80)	654

Note: References 491–1045 are on pp. 545–555.

TABLE VII—*Continued*

MICHAEL CONDENSATIONS WITH CYCLOALKENONES AND ACYL CYCLOALKENES

Reactants	Catalyst	Product (Yield, %)	References
2-*Methylene*-3,3-*dimethylcyclohexanone and*			
Ethyl acetoacetate	$NaOC_2H_5$	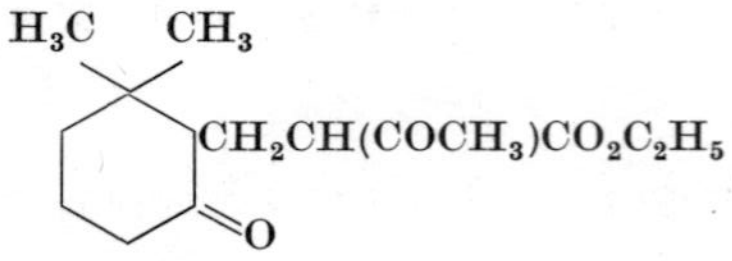 H_3C CH_3 ; $CH_2CH(COCH_3)CO_2C_2H_5$; O (8–20) or 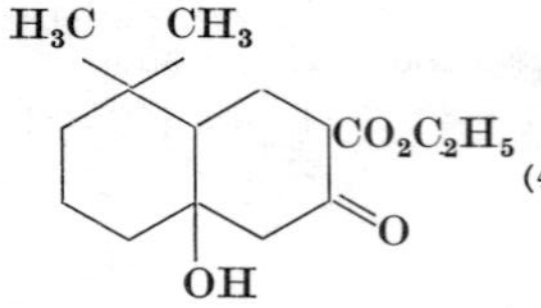 H_3C CH_3 ; $CO_2C_2H_5$; O ; OH (42)	659
2-*Hydroxymethylene*-4,5-*dimethylcyclohexanone and*			
$CH_3C({=}NH)CH_2CO_2C_2H_5$	None	Ethyl 2,6,7-trimethyl-5,6,7,8-tetrahydroquinoline-3-carboxylate	653
Isophorone and			
Nitromethane	Piperidine	5-Nitromethyl-3,3,5-trimethylcyclohexanone (9)	650
1-*Acetyl*-2-*methyl*-1-*cyclohexene and*			
Diethyl malonate	$NaOC_2H_5$	10-Methyldecalin-1,3-dione (low)	96
		4-Carbethoxy-10-methyldecalin-1,3-dione (good)	660

Cyclohexanone	KOC_4H_9-*t*	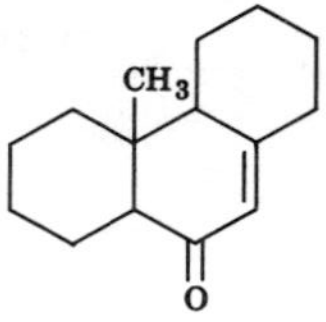 (Mixture of isomers, 22[‖])	401, 384
1-*Acetyl*-6-*methyl*-1-*cyclohexene and*			
Cyclohexanone	KOC_4H_9-*t*	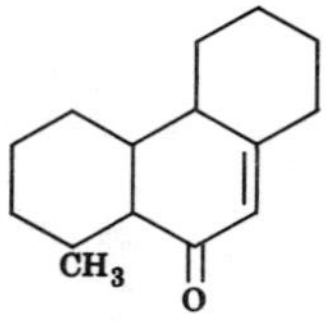 (Mixture of isomers, 19[¶])	401

Note: References 491–1045 are on pp. 545–555.

‖ A 50% yield of

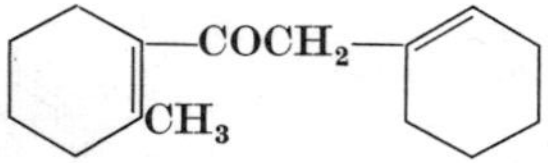

—$COCH_2$— CH_3

was also obtained. Other authors (ref. 387) describe this compound as the only product of the reaction.

¶ In addition, a 46% yield of

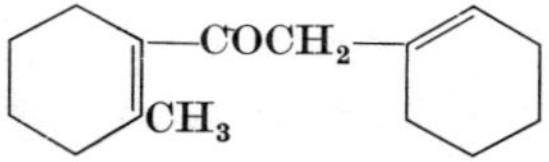

—$COCH_2$— CH_3

was obtained.

TABLE VII—*continued*

MICHAEL CONDENSATIONS WITH CYCLOALKENONES AND ACYL CYCLALKENES

Reactants	Catalyst	Product (Yield, %)	References
2-*Methyl-3-vinyl-2-cyclohexen-1-one and*			
2-Methylcyclohexanone-1,3-dione	$(C_2H_5)_2NH$	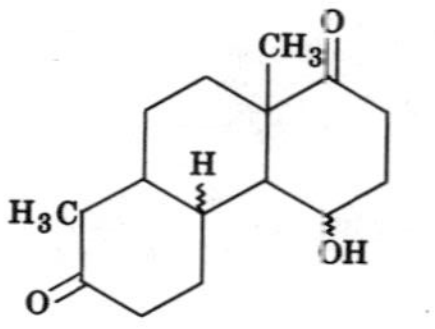 (42)	661
1-*Acetylcycloheptene and*			
Cyclopentanone	$NaOCH_3$	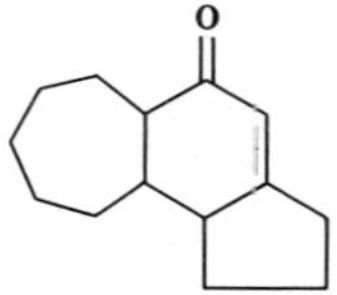 (26 crude)	644
Cyclohexanone	KOC_4H_9-*t*	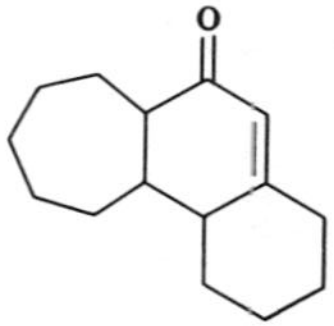 (55)	644

Reactants	Catalyst	Product (Yield, %)	Refs.
Cycloheptanone	KOC_4H_9-*t*	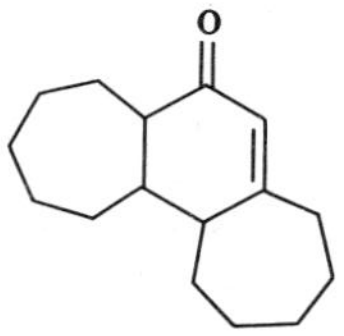 (41)	644
2-*Hydroxymethylenecycloöctanone and*			
Diethyl acetone-1,3-dicarboxylate	$NaOC_2H_5$	Diethyl 3-hydroxybicyclo[6.4.0]dodeca-1(6),2,4-triene-2,4-dicarboxylate (59)	428
3-*Methyl-5-n-propyl-2-cyclohexen-1-one and*			
Nitromethane	Piperidine	3-Methyl-3-nitromethyl-5-*n*-propylcyclohexanone (25)	650
2-*Methylcyclohexylideneacetone and*			
Diethyl malonate	$NaOC_2H_5$	1-Carbethoxy-7-methylspiro[5.5]hendecane-2,4-dione	220

Note: References 491–1045 are on pp. 545–555.

** This product is formed from an intermediate of the formula

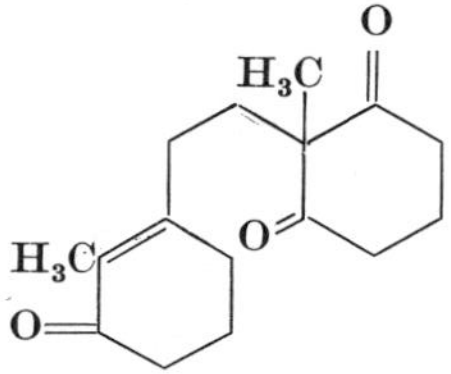

which has, however, not been isolated.

TABLE VII—*Continued*

MICHAEL CONDENSATIONS WITH CYCLOALKENONES AND ACYL CYCLOALKENES

Reactants	Catalyst	Product (Yield, %)	References
3-*Methylcyclohexylideneacetone and*			
Diethyl malonate	$NaOC_2H_5$	8-Methylspiro[5.5]hendecane-2,4-dione	220
Cyanoacetamide	$NaOC_2H_5$	[structure: spiro compound with CH_3, OH, NH, CN, O, CH_3] (58)	662
4-*Methylcyclohexylideneacetone and*			
Ethyl cyanoacetate	$NaOC_2H_5$	9-Methylspiro[5.5]hendecane-2,4-dione	220
Cyanoacetamide	$NaOC_2H_5$	[structure: spiro compound with H_3C, CH_3, OH, NH, CN, O]	662
Carvone and			
Ethyl acetoacetate	$NaOC_2H_5$	5-Hydroxy-3-isopropenyl-9-methylbicyclo[3.3.1]-nonan-7-one (54)	431
Ethyl cyanoacetate	$(C_2H_5)_2NH$	Ethyl 2-methyl-5-isopropenylcyclohexanone-3-cyanoacetate (25–33)	20

Reactants	Catalyst	Product (Yield, %)	Refs.
Umbellulone and			
Diethyl malonate	$NaOC_2H_5$	CH_3 $CH(CO_2C_2H_5)_2$ [bicyclic ketone with C_3H_7-*i*] (85)	143
1-*Acetyl*-2,6-*dimethylcyclohexene and*			
Diethyl malonate	$NaOC_2H_5$	*trans*(?)-8,10-Dimethyldecalin-1,3-dione	96
		4-Carbethoxy-8,10-dimethyldecalin-1,3-dione (42)	660, 96
1-*Acetyl*-6,6-*dimethylcyclohexene and*			
Diethyl α-acetyladipate	Na	$(CH_3)_2$-cyclohexyl(COCH$_3$)–$C(COCH_3)(CO_2C_2H_5)(CH_2)_3CO_2C_2H_5$ (85)	663
6-*Carbethoxy*-6-*methyl*-2-*cyclohexen*-1-*one and*			
Diethyl malonate	$NaOC_2H_5$	2-$C_2H_5O_2C$-2-CH_3-3-$CH(CO_2C_2H_5)_2$-cyclohexanone (74)	664
Diethyl methylmalonate	$NaOC_2H_5$	2-$C_2H_5O_2C$-2-CH_3-3-$C(CH_3)(CO_2C_2H_5)_2$-cyclohexanone (78)	188

Note: References 491–1045 are on pp. 545–555.

TABLE VII—*Continued*

MICHAEL CONDENSATIONS WITH CYCLOALKENONES AND ACYL CYCLOALKENES

Reactants	Catalyst	Product (Yield, %)	References
1-*Butyryl-2-methyl-1-cyclohexene and*			
Diethyl malonate	$NaOC_2H_5$	*trans*(?)-2-Ethyl-10-methyldecalin-1,3-dione	96
2-*Hydroxymethylenementhone and*			
Cyanoacetamide	*sec*-Amine	CH_3, CN, N, O, C_3H_7-*i* (20)	224
2-*Hydroxymethylenecamphor and*			
Malonic acid	None	β-Camphorylidenepropionic acid (50)	366
Cyanoacetic acid	None	β-Camphorylidenepropionitrile (80)	366
10-*Methyl-2-oxo-2,3,4,5,6,10-hexahydronaphthalene and*			
Diethyl malonate	$NaOC_2H_5$	CH_3, O, $CH(CO_2C_2H_5)_2$ (33)	190
2-*Hydroxymethylenecyclodecanone and*			
Diethyl acetone-1,3-dicarboxylate	$NaOC_2H_5$	Diethyl 3-hydroxybicyclo[8.4.0]tetradeca-1(6),2,4-triene-2,4-dicarboxylate (60)	428
2-*Phenyl-2-cyclopenten-1-one and*			
Diethyl malonate	$NaOC_2H_5$	Diethyl 2-phenylcyclopentan-1-one-3-malonate (67)	665
Dibenzyl malonate	KOC_4H_9-*t*	3-Oxo-2-phenylcyclopentane-1-acetic acid (53)‡‡	666

1-*Benzoylcyclopentene and*			
Dibenzyl malonate	KOC_4H_9-*t*	*trans*(?)-2-Benzoylcyclopentylmalonic acid	667
2-*Phenyl*-2-*cyclohexen*-1-*one and*			
Diethyl malonate	$NaOC_2H_5$	Diethyl *trans*-2-phenylcyclohexan-1-one-3-malonate (96)	105, 106, 668, 669
Dibenzyl malonate	KOC_4H_9-*t*	Dibenzyl *trans*-2-phenylcyclohexan-1-one-3-malonate (96)	108, 669
Methyl cyanoacetate	$NaOCH_3$	Methyl 2-phenylcyclohexan-1-one-3-cyanoacetate (80)	106, 668
Benzyl cyanoacetate	KOC_4H_9-*t*	*trans*-3-Cyanomethyl-2-phenylcyclohexan-1-one (86)	108
Nitromethane	$[C_6H_5CH_2N(CH_3)_3]OCH_3$	2-Phenyl-3-nitromethylcyclohexan-1-one (80)	106, 668
Methyl nitroacetate	$[C_6H_5CH_2N(CH_3)_3]OCH_3$	Methyl *trans*-2-phenylcyclohexan-1-one-3-nitroacetate (90)	106, 668
6-*Phenyl*-2-*cyclohexen*-1-*one and*			
Dibenzyl malonate††	KOC_4H_9-*t*	*trans*-6-Phenylcyclohexanone-3-acetic acid‡‡	107
4-*Phenyl*-2-*cyclohexen*-1-*one and*			
Dibenzyl malonate††	KOC_4H_9-*t*	*trans*-4-Phenylcyclohexanone-3-acetic acid‡‡	107
Cyclohexylidenecyclohexanone and			
Cyanoacetamide	$NaOC_2H_5$	Compound $C_{15}H_{20}N_2O$	670
1-*Butyryl*-2,6-*dimethylcyclohexene and*			
Diethyl malonate	$NaOC_2H_5$	*trans*(?)-2-Ethyl-8,10-dimethyldecalin-1,3-dione	96

Note: References 491–1045 are on pp. 545–555.

†† A mixture of 4- and 6-phenyl-2-cyclohexen-1-one was used in this experiment.

‡‡ The product was obtained after hydrolysis and partial decarboxylation.

TABLE VII—*Continued*

Michael Condensations with Cycloalkenones and Acyl Cycloalkenes

Reactants	Catalyst	Product (Yield, %)	References
2-*Hydrindanylideneacetone and*			
Diethyl malonate	$NaOC_2H_5$	(90)	222
Cyanoacetamide	$NaOC_2H_5$	(Quant.)	49
1,10-*Dimethyl*-2-*oxo*-2,3,4,5,6,10-*hexahydronaphthalene and*			
Diethyl malonate	$NaOC_2H_5$		671
Diethyl methylmalonate	—	‡‡	672

Reactants	Catalyst	Product (Yield, %)	Refs.
1-*Benzoylcyclohexene and*			
Dibenzyl malonate	KOC_4H_9-*t*	*trans*(?)-2-Benzoylcyclohexylmalonic acid (64)	667
2-*Phenyl*-2-*cyclohepten*-1-*one and*			
Dibenzyl malonate	KOC_4H_9-*t*	Dibenzyl 2-phenylcycloheptan-1-one-3-malonate (90)	108
1-*Acetyl*-9-*methyl*-6-*oxo*-3,4,6,7,8,9-*hexahydronaphthalene and*			
Diethyl α-acetyladipate	Na	and	663
1-*Acetyl*-6-*methoxy*-3,4-*dihydronaphthalene and*			
Ethyl acetoacetate	$NaOC_2H_5$		673
Cyclohexane-1,2-dione	—		674

Note: References 491–1045 are on pp. 545–555.

‡‡ The product was obtained after hydrolysis and partial decarboxylation.

TABLE VII—*Continued*

MICHAEL CONDENSATIONS WITH CYCLOALKENONES AND ACYL CYCLOALKENES

Reactants	Catalyst	Product (Yield, %)	References
Methyl α-Hydrindanylideneëthyl Ketone and			
Diethyl malonate	Na	[structure: spiro compound, CH3, CH2, CH2, O, O]	223
2-*Hydroxymethylenecyclododecanone and*			
Diethyl acetone-1,3-dicarboxylate	$NaOC_2H_5$	Diethyl 3-hydroxybicyclo[10.4.0]-1(6),2,4-triene-2,4-dicarboxylate	428
2-(2′,3′-*Dimethoxyphenyl*)-2-*cyclohexen*-1-*one and*		*A* = [structure: 2-(2′,3′-dimethoxyphenyl)cyclohexanone-3-yl; O, CH_3O, OCH_3]	
Dimethyl malonate	$NaOCH_3$	ACH$(CO_2CH_3)_2$ (97)	106, 668
Diethyl malonate	$NaOC_2H_5$	ACH$(CO_2C_2H_5)_2$ (94)	106, 668
Dibenzyl malonate	KOC_4H_9-*t*	ACH$(CO_2CH_2C_6H_5)_2$ (88)	108, 669
Methyl cyanoacetate	$NaOCH_3$	ACH(CN)CO_2CH_3 (95)	106, 668
Ethyl cyanoacetate	$NaOC_2H_5$	ACH(CN)$CO_2C_2H_5$ (90)	106, 668
Benzyl cyanoacetate	KOC_4H_9-*t*	$A$$CH_2CN$ (82)§§	108, 669
Methyl nitroacetate	$[C_6H_5CH_2N(CH_3)_3]OCH_3$	ACH$(NO_2)CO_2CH_3$ (90)	106, 668
1-*Benzoylcycloheptene and*			
Dibenzyl malonate	KOC_4H_9-*t*	*trans*(?)-2-Benzoylcycloheptylmalonic acid (46)‖‖	667

2-Isopropoxymethylene-1-tetralone and

Reactants	Catalyst	Product(s) (Yield, %)	Refs.
Biacetyl monodimethyl ketal	Na	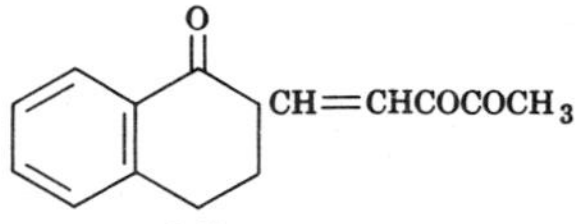 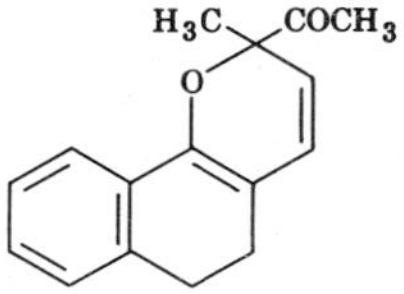 O, CH=CHCOCOCH$_3$ (69)¶¶ and H$_3$C, COCH$_3$, O (Low)	675

2-(2′,3′,4′-Trimethoxyphenyl)-2-cyclohepten-1-one and

Reactants	Catalyst	Product(s) (Yield, %)	Refs.
Diethyl malonate	KOC_4H_9-*t*	3-Oxo-2-(2′,3′,4′-trimethoxyphenyl)cycloheptane-1-acetic acid (72)‡‡	676

Zerumbone

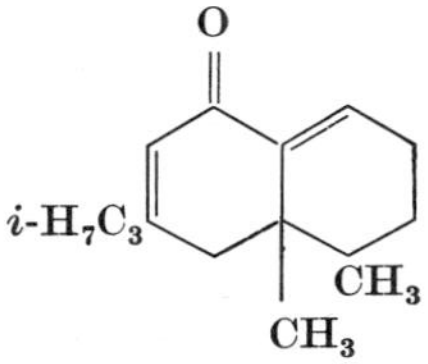

O, *i*-H_7C_3, CH_3, CH_3

and

Reactants	Catalyst	Product(s) (Yield, %)	Refs.
Ethyl cyanoacetate	—	Compound $C_{25}H_{36}N_2O_5$	677

Note: References 491–1045 are on pp. 545–555.

‡‡ The product was obtained after hydrolysis and partial decarboxylation.

§§ This product was obtained after partial hydrolysis and decarboxylation.

|||| The product was obtained after hydrolysis.

¶¶ This product results from spontaneous dehydrogenation or disproportionation of the expected compound.

TABLE VII—*Continued*

MICHAEL CONDENSATIONS WITH CYCLOALKENONES AND ACYL CYCLOALKENES

Reactants	Catalyst	Product (Yield, %)	References
2-*Isopropoxymethylenebenzosuberone and*			
Biacetyl monodimethyl ketal	Na	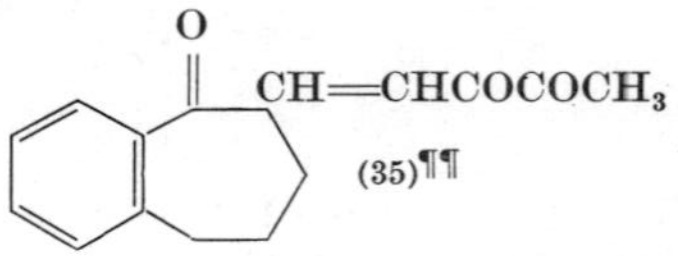 1-Benzosuberone bearing $CH{=}CHCOCOCH_3$ at C-2 (structure) (35)¶¶	675
2-*Cyclopentadecen*-1-*one and*			
Diethyl malonate	$NaOC_2H_5$	Diethyl cyclopentadecan-1-one-3-malonate (41)	532
2-*Hydroxymethylenecyclopentadecanone and*			
Diethyl acetone-1,3-dicarboxylate	$NaOC_2H_5$	Diethyl 3-hydroxybicyclo[13.4.0]nonadeca-1(6),2,4,-triene-2,4-dicarboxylate (79)	428
2-*Hydroxymethylenecyclohexadecanone and*			
Diethyl acetone-1,3-dicarboxylate	$NaOC_2H_5$	Diethyl 3-hydroxybicyclo[14.4.0]eicosa-1(6),2,4-triene-2,4-dicarboxylate (35)	428

Reactants	Catalyst	Product (Yield, %)	Refs.
3,5-*Cholestadien-7-one and*			
Diethyl malonate	$NaOC_2H_5$; piperidine	Diethyl 7-oxo-5-cholestene-3-malonate (50)	678
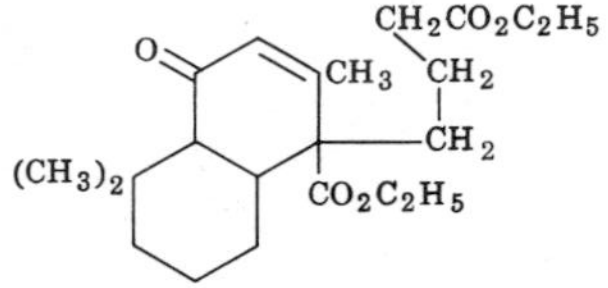 $(CH_3)_2$, CH_3, $CH_2CO_2C_2H_5$, CH_2, CH_2, $CO_2C_2H_5$	$C_6H_5N(CH_3)MgBr$	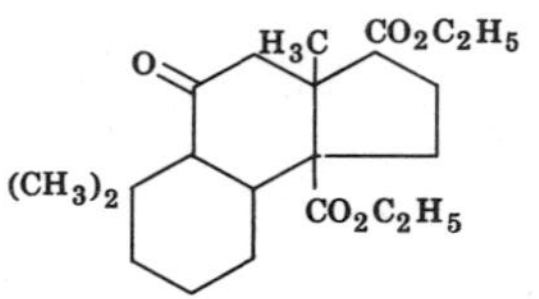 $(CH_3)_2$, H_3C, $CO_2C_2H_5$, $CO_2C_2H_5$ ***	663

Note: References 491–1045 are on pp. 545–555.

¶¶ This product results from spontaneous dehydrogenation or disproportionation of the expected compound.

*** This reaction takes place when

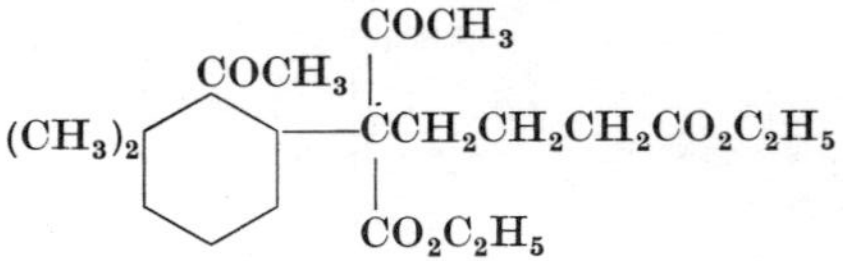

$(CH_3)_2$, $COCH_3$, $COCH_3$, $CCH_2CH_2CH_2CO_2C_2H_5$, $CO_2C_2H_5$

is treated with the reagent or when 1-acetyl-6,6-dimethyl-1-cyclohexene is condensed with ethyl α-acetyladipate in the presence of sodium amide.

TABLE VIII

ROBINSON'S MODIFICATION OF THE MICHAEL CONDENSATION OF α,β-ETHYLENIC KETONES

Substituent R in $CH_3COCH_2CH_2R$	Addend	Catalyst	Product (Yield, %) $A = CH_3COCH_2CH_2$—	References
$(CH_3)_2N$	$CH_2(CO_2C_2H_5)_2$	$NaOC_2H_5$	$ACH(CO_2C_2H_5)_2$	679
$(C_2H_5)_2N\cdot CH_3I$	$C_6H_5CH(CO_2C_2H_5)_2$	$NaNH_2$	$C_6H_5C(A)(CO_2C_2H_5)_2$	680
$(CH_3)_2N$	$CH_3COCH_2CO_2C_2H_5$	$NaOC_2H_5$	4-Carbethoxy-3-methyl-2-cyclohexen-1-one	629, 681
$(CH_3)_2N\cdot CH_3I$	$CH_3COCH(CH_3)CO_2C_2H_5$	—	3,6-Dimethyl-2-cyclohexen-1-one	682
$(C_2H_5)_2N\cdot CH_3I$	$CH_3COCH(CH_2C_6H_5)CO_2C_2H_5$	—	6-Benzyl-3-methyl-2-cyclohexen-1-one	683
	Ethyl isobutyrylacetate	$NaOC_2H_5$	Ethyl 2-isobutyryl-5-oxohexanoate (65)	684
O N·CH_3I	Ethyl α-acetylisovalerate	$NaOC_2H_5$	6-Isopropyl-3-methyl-2-cyclohexen-1-one* (50)	100
$(C_2H_5)_2N\cdot CH_3I$	Diethyl α-methyloxalacetate	$NaOC_2H_5$	Ethyl 1-methyl-2,4-dioxocyclohexane-1-pyruvate	685
	Dimethyl α-methyl-β-oxoadipate	$NaOCH_3$, pyridine	O; $CH_2CH_2CO_2CH_3$; CH_3 CO_2CH_3 (8)	686
$(C_2H_5)_2N$	2-Carbethoxycyclohexan-1-one	$NaOC_2H_5$, pyridine	2-(β-Acetylethyl)-2-carbethoxycyclohexan-1-one	230

$(C_2H_5)_2N \cdot CH_3I$	2-Carbethoxycyclohexan-1-one	$NaOC_2H_5$	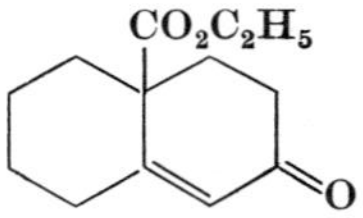 $CO_2C_2H_5$ O (70)	68, 229
	2-Carbomethoxycycloheptan-1-one	$NaOCH_3$	2-(β-Acetylethyl)-2-carbomethoxycyclo-heptan-1-one (86)	688
	2-Carbethoxycyclioöctan-1-one	$NaOCH_3$	2-(β-Acetylethyl)-2-carbethoxycycloöctan-1-one (78)	689, 690
	2-Carbethoxycyclononan-1-one	$NaOCH_3$	2-(β-Acetylethyl)-2-carbethoxycyclononan-1-one (80)	689, 690
	2-Carbomethoxycyclopentadecan-1-one	$NaOCH_3$	2-(β-Acetylethyl)-2-carbomethoxycyclo-pentadecan-1-one (78)	688
	Methyl 1-oxo-1,2,3,4-tetrahydro-phenanthrene-2-carboxylate	$NaOCH_3$	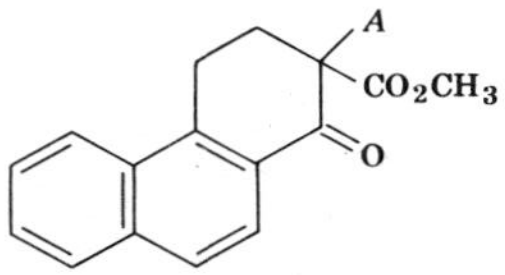 *A* CO_2CH_3 O (92)	485

Note: References 491–1045 are on pp. 545–555.

* This product, piperitone, results from hydrolysis and decarboxylation.

TABLE VIII—*Continued*

ROBINSON'S MODIFICATION OF THE MICHAEL CONDENSATION OF α,β-ETHYLENIC KETONES

Substituent R in $CH_3COCH_2CH_2R$	Addend	Catalyst	Product (Yield, %) $A = CH_3COCH_2CH_2—$	References
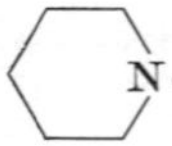 $N \cdot CH_3I$ (piperidine ring)	Methyl 1-oxo-1,2,3,4-tetrahydrophenanthrene-2-carboxylate	$NaOCH_3$	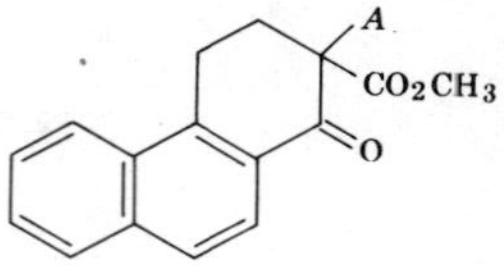 A, CO_2CH_3, O (95)	532
	Methyl 4-oxo-1,2,3,4-tetrahydrophenanthrene-3-carboxylate	$NaOCH_3$	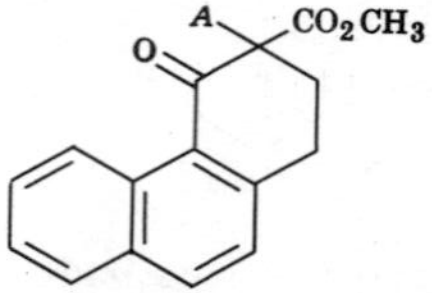 A, CO_2CH_3, O (92)	533
$(C_2H_5)_2N$	CH_3COCH_3	None	3-Methyl-2-cyclohexen-1-one (16)	691
	Cyclopentanone	None	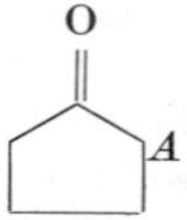 O, A (28)	691
$(C_2H_5)_2N \cdot CH_3I$	2-Methylcyclopentanone	$NaNH_2$; $NaOC_2H_5$	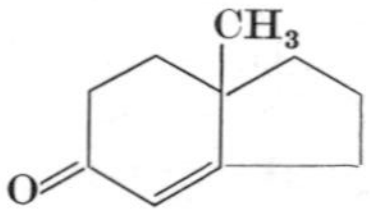 CH_3, O	229, 230

Reactant	Catalyst	Product (Yield, %)	Refs.
2-Methylcyclohexanone	$NaNH_2$	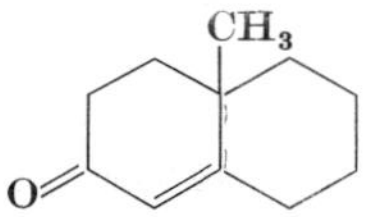 [structure: 10-methyl-Δ1(9)-octal-2-one, CH_3] (35–40, 10–15)	229, 687
	KOC_4H_9-*t*	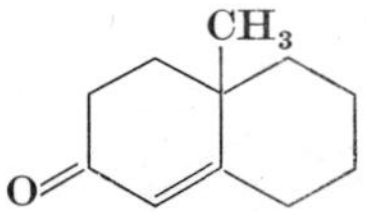 [structure, CH_3] (28)	687
	$(C_6H_5)_3CNa$	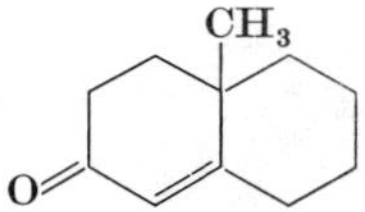 [structure, CH_3] (26–30)	692
	KOH, ethanol	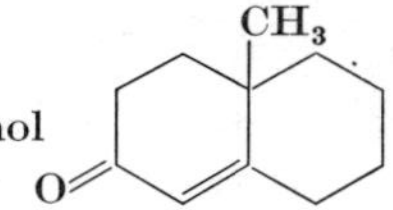 [structure, CH_3]	693
	$NaOCH_3$	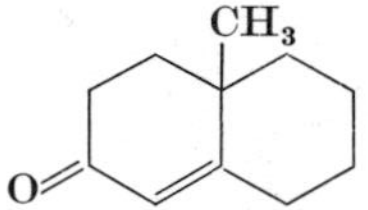 [structure, CH_3] (17)	664, 190
2-Formylcyclohexanone	$NaOCH_3$	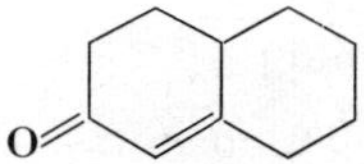 [structure: Δ1(9)-octal-2-one] (68)	694

Note: References 491–1045 are on pp. 545–555.

TABLE VIII—*Continued*

ROBINSON'S MODIFICATION OF THE MICHAEL CONDENSATION OF α,β-ETHYLENIC KETONES

Substituent R in $CH_3COCH_2CH_2R$	Addend	Catalyst	Product (Yield, %) $A = CH_3COCH_2CH_2—$	References
$(C_2H_5)_2N \cdot CH_3I$ (*Cont.*)	5-Carbomethoxymethyl-2-methyl-cyclohexan-1-one	$NaOCH_3$	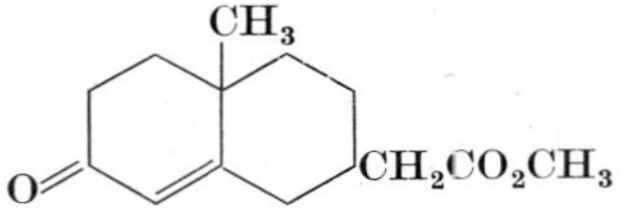 CH_3, O, $CH_2CO_2CH_3$ (12)	664
		$NaNH_2$	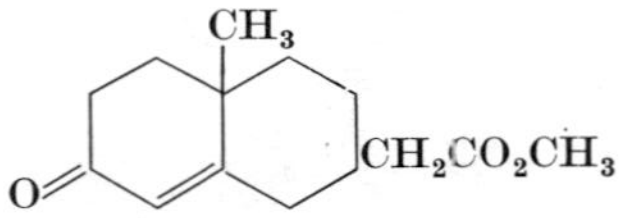 CH_3, O, $CH_2CO_2CH_3$ (12)	664
	2-Acetyl-3,3-dimethylcyclohexane-1-one	$NaOCH_3$	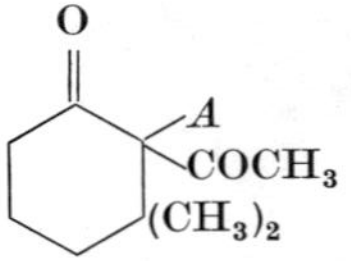 O, A, $COCH_3$ (40), $(CH_3)_2$	695
	trans-2-Decalone	$NaNH_2$	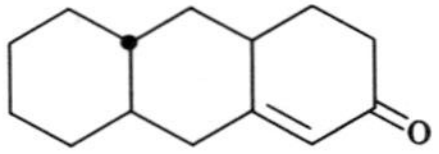 O	229
	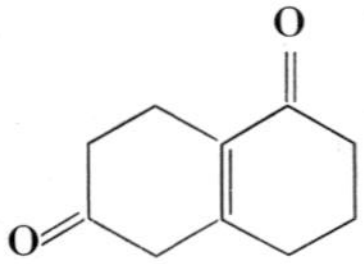 O, O †	$NaOCH_3$	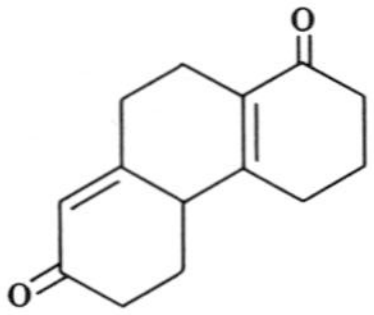 O, O	537

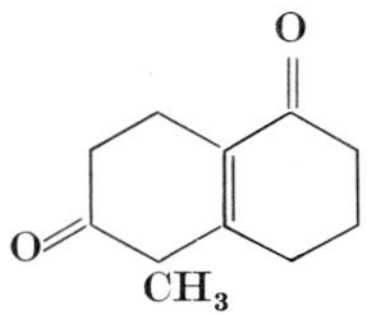 ‡	$NaOCH_3$	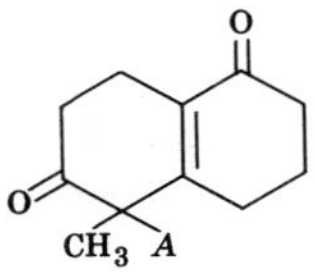	537
1-Methyl-2-decalone	$NaNH_2$	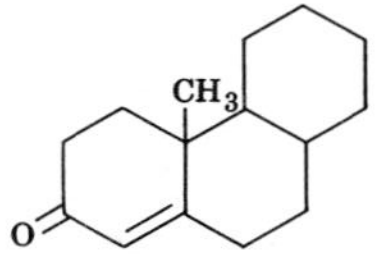	696

Note: References 491–1045 are on pp. 545–555.

† The compound actually employed was the isomer of the structure

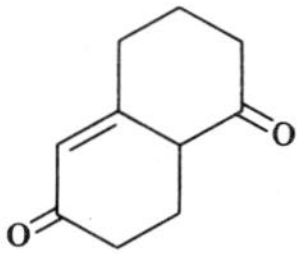

‡ A mixture of this compound with the isomer of the structure

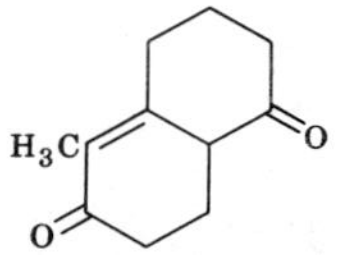

was used. Part of the material was dehydrogenated to 6-hydroxy-5-methyl-1-tetralone.

TABLE VIII—*Continued*

ROBINSON'S MODIFICATION OF THE MICHAEL CONDENSATION OF α,β-ETHYLENIC KETONES

Substituent R in $CH_3COCH_2CH_2R$	Addend	Catalyst	Product (Yield, %) $A = CH_3COCH_2CH_2$—	References
$(C_2H_5)_2N \cdot CH_3I$ (*Cont.*)	10-Methyl-2-decalone	$NaNH_2$	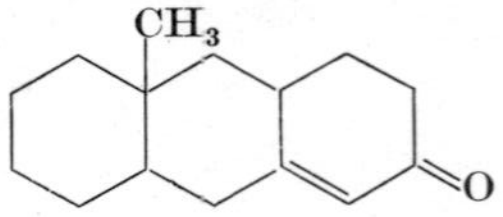	230
	1,4-Dihydroxy-8-methyl-7-decalone	$[(C_6H_5CH_2N(CH_3)_3]OH$	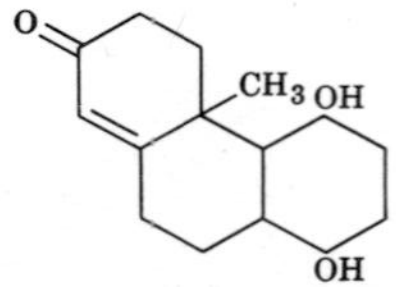	540
$(CH_3)_2N$	2-Phenylcyclohexanone	$NaNH_2$	2-Oxo-10-phenyl-2,3,4,5,6,7,8,10-octahydronaphthalene (42)	113
$(C_2H_5)_2N \cdot CH_3I$	1-Methyl-6-methoxy-2-decalone	$NaNH_2$	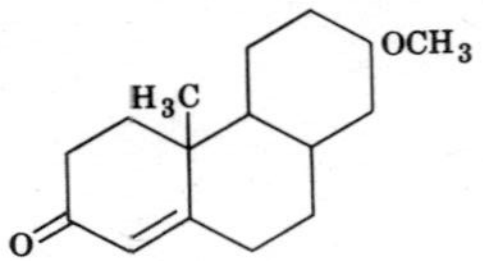	692
	1-Methyl-5-methoxy-2-tetralone	$NaNH_2$	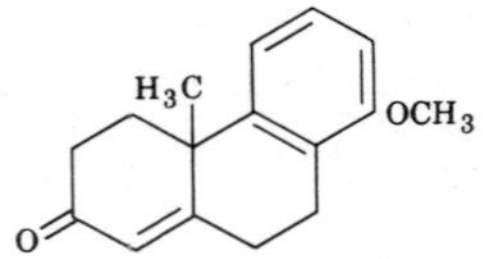 (55)	698

Reactant	Catalyst	Product (Yield, %)	Refs.
	KOC_2H_5	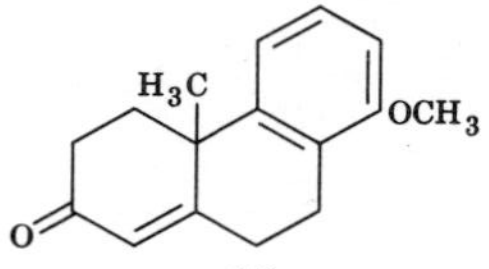 (70)	318
	KOH, ethanol	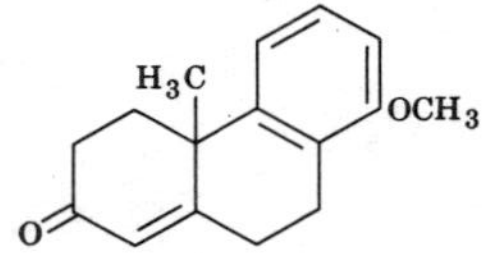	693
5-Hydroxy-1-methyl-8-methoxy-2-tetralone	Aq. KOH	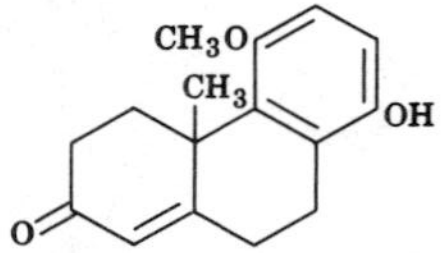 (30)	693
5,8-Dimethoxy-1-methyl-2-tetralone	$NaNH_2$	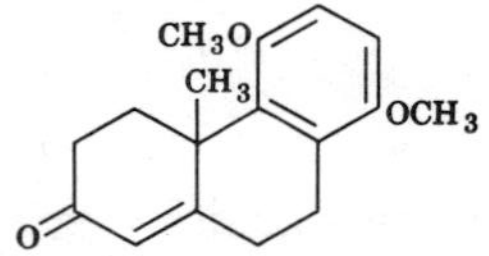	699

Note: References 491–1045 are on pp. 545–555.

TABLE VIII—*Continued*

ROBINSON'S MODIFICATION OF THE MICHAEL CONDENSATION OF α,β-ETHYLENIC KETONES

Substituent R in $CH_3COCH_2CH_2R$	Addend	Catalyst	Product (Yield, %) $A = CH_3COCH_2CH_2$—	References
$(C_2H_5)_2N \cdot CH_3I$ (*Cont.*)	4-Cyclohexyl-2-hydroxymethylene-cyclohexan-1-one	$NaOCH_3$	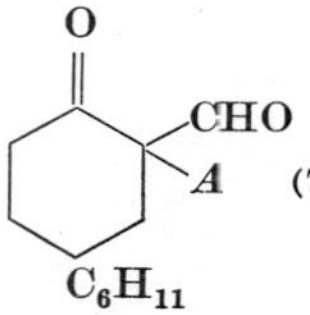 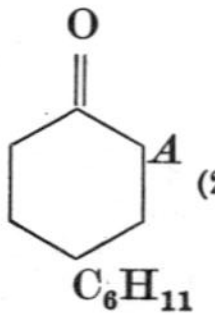 O, CHO, A, C_6H_{11} (76) and O, A, C_6H_{11} (21)	700
	2-Hydroxymethylene-4-(*trans*-4′-hydroxycyclohexyl)cyclohexan-1-one	$NaOCH_3$	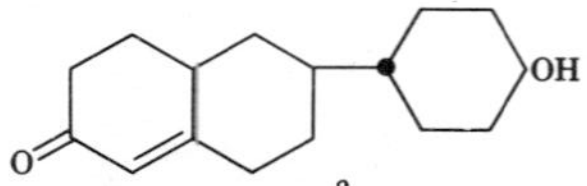 O, OH (35)§	532
$(C_2H_5)_2N$	2-Hydroxymethylene-4-(*trans*-4′-hydroxycyclohexyl)cyclohexan-1-one	$NaOCH_3$	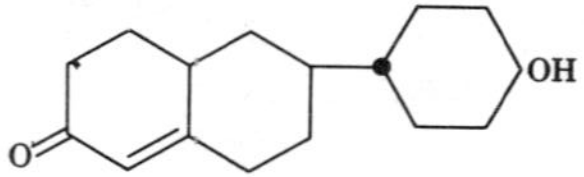 O, OH (29)§	692
$(C_2H_5)_2N \cdot CH_3I$	2-Hydroxymethylene-4-(*cis*-4′-oxo-cyclohexyl)cyclohexan-1-one	$NaOCH_3$	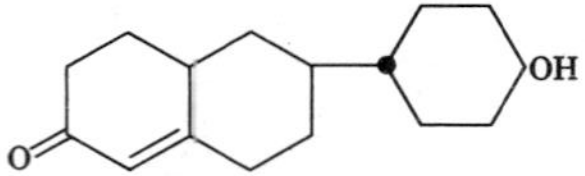 O, OH (40)§	532

$(C_2H_5)_2N$	2-Hydroxymethylene-4-(*cis*-4′-oxo-cyclohexyl)cyclohexan-1-one	$NaOCH_3$	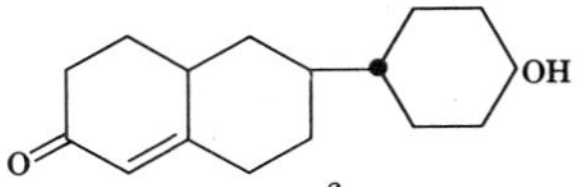 (34)§	692
$(C_2H_5)_2N \cdot CH_3I$	2-Hydroxymethylene-4-(4′-oxo-cyclohexyl)cyclohexan-1-one	$NaOCH_3$	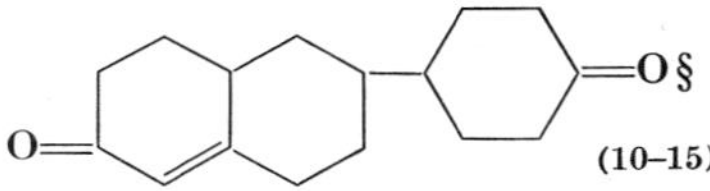 § (10–15)	532, 692
	6-Carbethoxy-1-methyl-2-decalone	$NaNH_2$	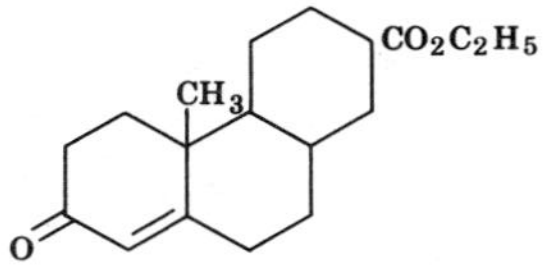	697
	7,8-Dimethoxy-1-ethyl-2-tetralone	$NaNH_2$	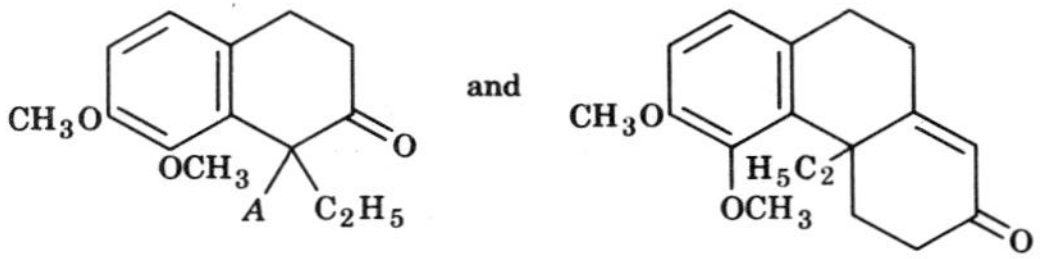 and	701
$(CH_3)_3N \cdot I$	2-Hydroxymethylene-4-(4′-carboxy-cyclohexyl)cyclohexan-1-one	$NaOCH_3$	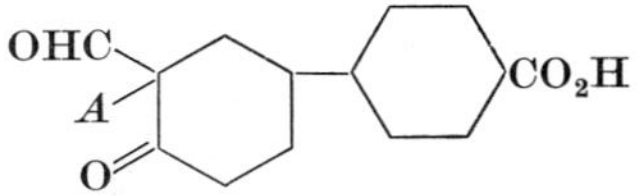 (81–88)	702

Note: References 491–1045 are on pp. 545–555.

§ This product resulted from the cyclization of the primary product, which has not been isolated.

TABLE VIII—*Continued*

ROBINSON'S MODIFICATION OF THE MICHAEL CONDENSATION OF α,β-ETHYLENIC KETONES

Substituent R in $CH_3COCH_2CH_2R$	Addend	Catalyst	Product (Yield, %) $A = CH_3COCH_2CH_2$—	References
$(CH_3)_3N \cdot I$ (*Cont.*)	2-Hydroxymethylene-4-(4′-carboxyphenyl)cyclohexan-1-one	$NaOCH_3$	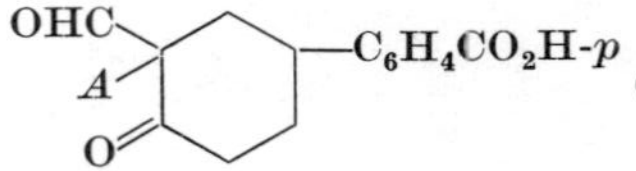 OHC, A, O; —$C_6H_4CO_2H$-*p* (51)	702
	2-Hydroxymethylene-4-(4′-carbomethoxycyclohexyl)cyclohexan-1-one	$NaOCH_3$	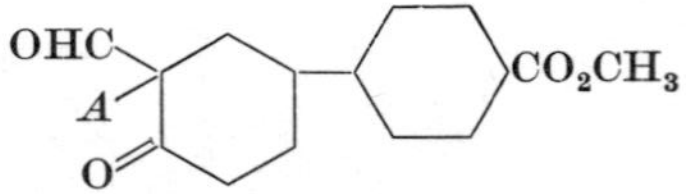 OHC, A, O; CO_2CH_3	702
	2-Hydroxymethylene-4-(4′-carbomethoxyphenyl)cyclohexan-1-one	$NaOCH_3$	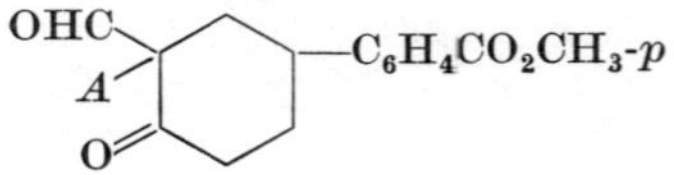 OHC, A, O; —$C_6H_4CO_2CH_3$-*p* (51)	702
$(C_2H_5)_2N \cdot CH_3I$	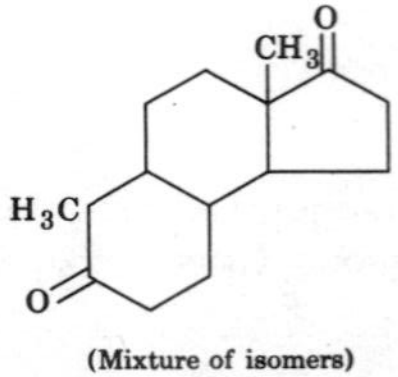 H_3C, CH_3, O, O (Mixture of isomers)	$NaNH_2$	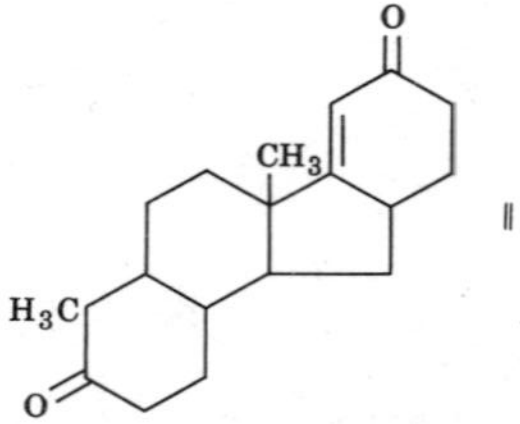 H_3C, CH_3, O, O	703

	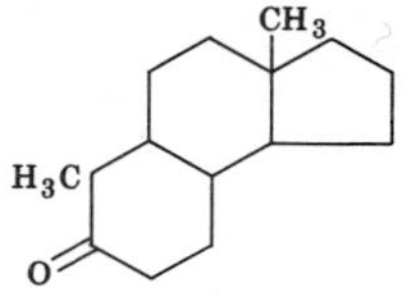 H_3C / CH_3 / O	$NaNH_2$	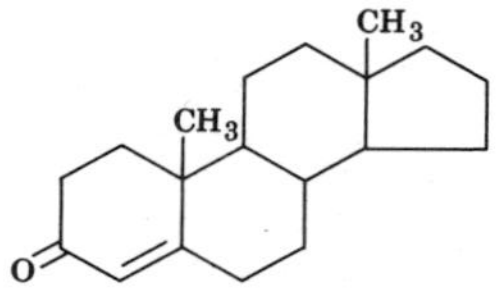 CH_3 / CH_3 / O	704
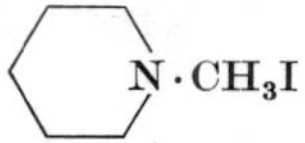 (piperidine) $N \cdot CH_3I$	2-Hydroxymethylene-1-oxo-1,2,3,4-tetrahydrophenanthrene	$NaOCH_3$	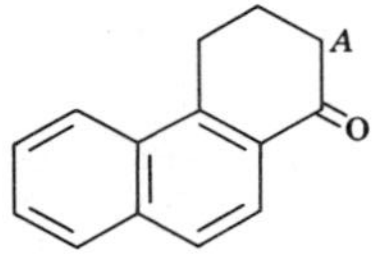 A / O (60)	532
	3-Hydroxymethylene-4-oxo-1,2,3,4-tetrahydrophenanthrene	$NaOCH_3$	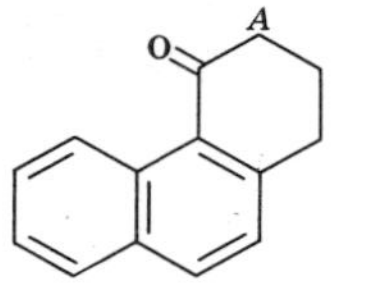 O / A (40)	533
$(CH_3)_2N \cdot CH_3I$	2,2′-Dimethoxydeoxybenzoin	$NaOC_2H_5$	3,4-Di-(2-methoxyphenyl)-2-cyclohexen-1-one (52–56)	705
$(C_2H_5)_2N \cdot CH_3I$	1-Hydroxymethylene-3-methyl-anilinomethylene-*trans*-2-decalone	$NaOCH_3$	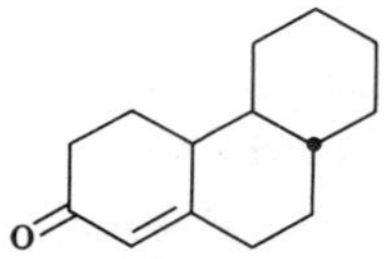 O (24)	694

Note: References 491–1045 are on pp. 545–555.
‖ This is the structure assumed by the authors.

TABLE VIII—*Continued*

ROBINSON'S MODIFICATION OF THE MICHAEL CONDENSATION OF α,β-ETHYLENIC KETONES

Substituent R in $CH_3COCH_2CH_2R$	Addend	Catalyst	Product (Yield, %) $A = CH_3COCH_2CH_2$—	References
$(C_2H_5)_2N \cdot CH_3I$ (*Cont.*)	2-Methylcyclopentane-1,3-dione	$NaOCH_3$	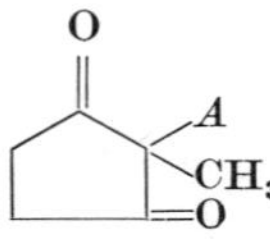 (37) and 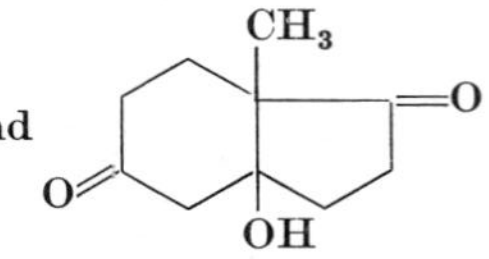	528, 706
	Cyclohexane-1,3-dione	Piperidine	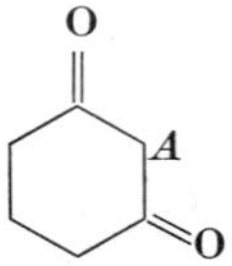	532
	2-Methylcyclohexane-1,3-dione	None	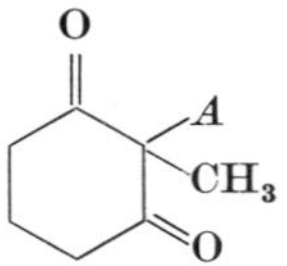	663
		$NaOCH_3$; $NaNH_2$; $(C_2H_5)_2NH$; pyridine; $NaOC_2H_5$	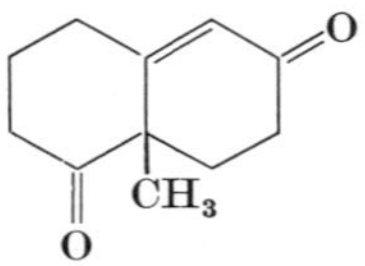	663, 706, 707

		$NaOC_2H_5$	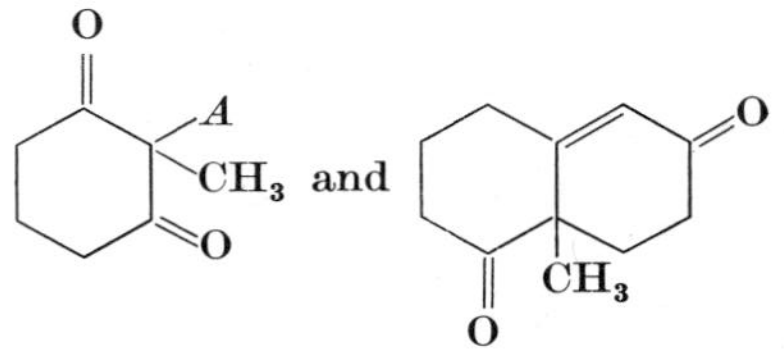 O, A, CH_3 and O, O, CH_3, O	528
$(C_2H_5)_2N$	2-Methylcyclohexane-1,3-dione	None	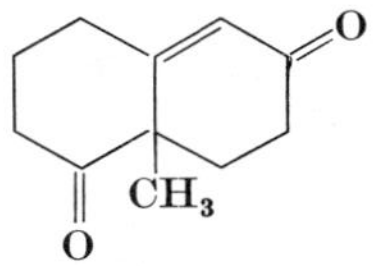 O, CH_3, O (8)	538
$(C_2H_5)_2N \cdot CH_3I$	2-Methylcyclohexane-1,3-dione	$NaOCH_3$	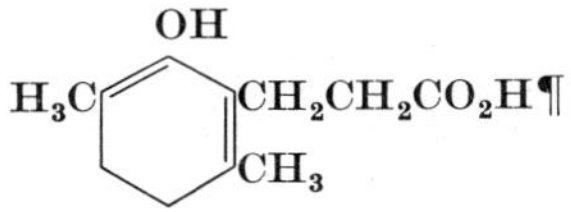 OH, H_3C, $CH_2CH_2CO_2H$¶, CH_3	708, 709
$(C_2H_5)_2N$	5,5-Dimethylcyclohexane-1,3-dione	None	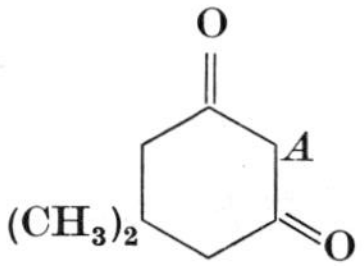 O, A, $(CH_3)_2$, O	538
$(CH_3)_2N$	Nitromethane	$NaOC_2H_5$	ACH_2NO_2	710
$(C_2H_5)_2N$	2-Nitropropane	NaOH	$(CH_3)_2C(A)NO_2$ (85)	691

Note: References 491–1045 are on pp. 545–555.

¶ This compound is formed by ring fission of the primary product.

TABLE VIII—*Continued*

ROBINSON'S MODIFICATION OF THE MICHAEL CONDENSATION OF α,β-ETHYLENIC KETONES

Substituent R in $CH_3COCH_2CH_2R$	Addend	Catalyst	Product (Yield, %)	References
			$A = CH_3COCH_2CH_2$—	
$(C_2H_5)_2N \cdot CH_3I$	CH_3O, O, =O	$NaNH_2$	OCH_3, O, =O, CH_3O, O	711
O N $\cdot CH_3I$	Methyl fluorene-9-carboxylate	KOH	Methyl 9-(β-acetylethyl)fluorene-9-carboxylate (45)	544

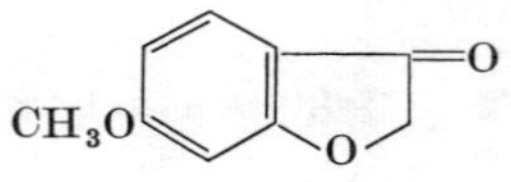

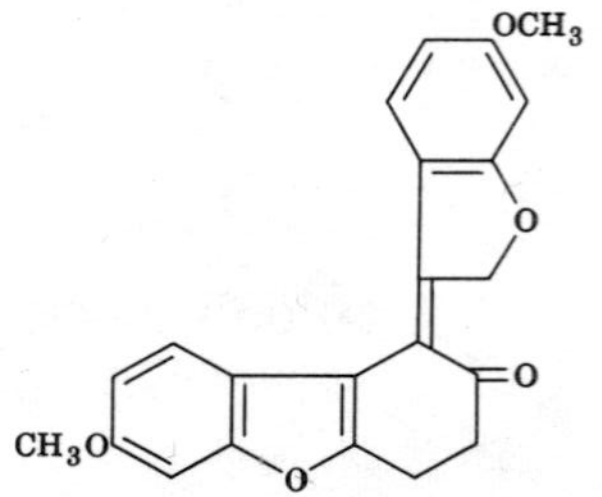

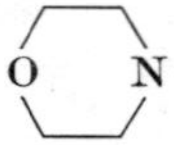

Reactants	Catalyst	Product (Yield, %)	References
O= *$NCH_3 \cdot CH_3I$ and*		$A = (CH_3)_2NCH_2CH_2COCH_2CH_2$—	
Diethyl malonate	KOC_2H_5	$A$$CH(CO_2C_2H_5)_2$ (25)	681
Ethyl acetoacetate	KOC_2H_5	$CH_3COCH(A)CO_2C_2H_5$	681

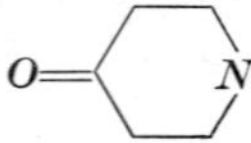

2-Carbethoxycyclopentanone	KOC_2H_5	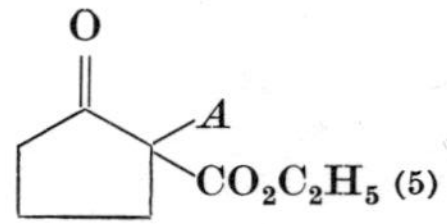 O, A, $CO_2C_2H_5$ (5)	681
2-Carbethoxycyclohexanone	KOC_2H_5	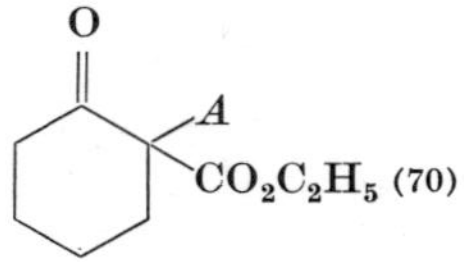 O, A, $CO_2C_2H_5$ (70)	681
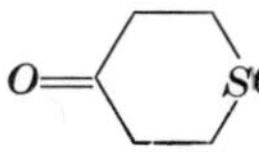 O=⟨ ⟩SCH_3I *and*		$A = CH_3SCH_2CH_2COCH_2CH_2—$	
Diethyl malonate	KOC_2H_5	$ACH(CO_2C_2H_5)_2$ (42)	712
Dimethyl β-keto-α-methyladipate	$KOCH_3$	$CH_3O_2C(CH_2)_2COC(A)(CH_3)CO_2CH_3$ (70)	712
2-Carbethoxycyclopentanone	KOC_2H_5	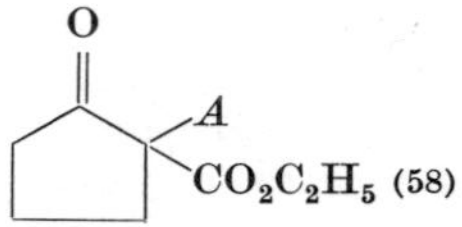 O, A, $CO_2C_2H_5$ (58)	712
2-Nitropropane	KOC_2H_5	$(CH_3)_2C(A)NO_2$ (41)	712

Note: References 491–1045 are on pp. 545–555.

‖ This is the structure assumed by the authors.

TABLE VIII—*Continued*

ROBINSON'S MODIFICATION OF THE MICHAEL CONDENSATION OF α,β-ETHYLENIC KETONES

Reactants	Catalyst	Product (Yield, %)	References
$CH_3CH_2COCH_2CH_2N(C_2H_5)_2 \cdot CH_3I$ and			
2-Carbethoxycyclohexanone**	$NaOC_2H_5$	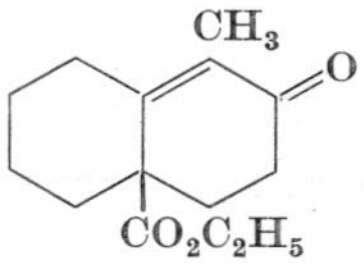 [structure: CH_3, O, $CO_2C_2H_5$]	231
Methyl 1-oxo-1,2,3,4-tetrahydrophenanthrene-2-carboxylate	$NaOCH_3$	Methyl 1-oxo-2-(β-propionylethyl)-1,2,3,4-tetrahydrophenanthrene-2-carboxylate (96)	532
Methyl 4-oxo-1,2,3,4-tetrahydrophenanthrene-3-carboxylate	$NaOCH_3$	Methyl 4-oxo-3-(β-propionylethyl)-1,2,3,4-tetrahydrophenanthrene-3-carboxylate (87)	533
Cyclohexane-1,3-dione	$(C_2H_5)_3N$	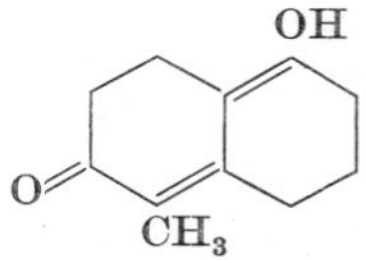 [structure: OH, O, CH_3] (Enol)	115, 532
2-Hydroxycyclohexanone	None	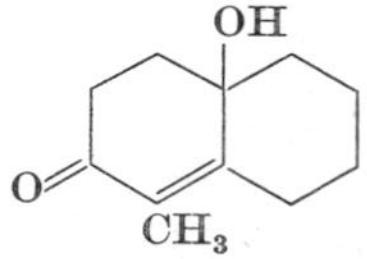 [structure: OH, O, CH_3] (Quant.)	713
2-Methylcyclohexanone	$NaNH_2$	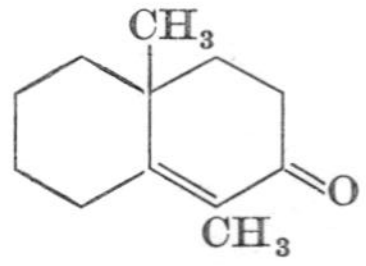 [structure: CH_3, O, CH_3] (28–38) and 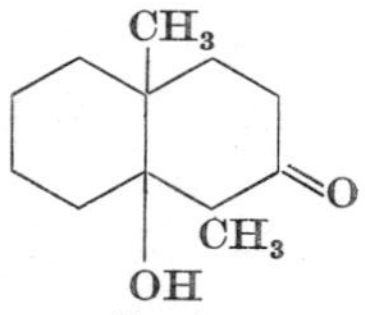 [structure: CH_3, O, CH_3, OH] (Low)	714

2-Acetoxycyclohexanone	$NaOCH_3$	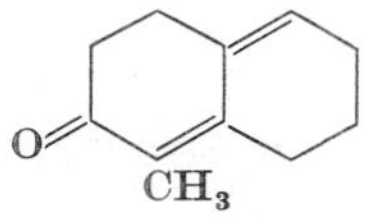 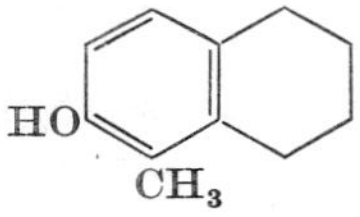 CH_3 (23) and HO CH_3 (32)	713
Carvenone	—	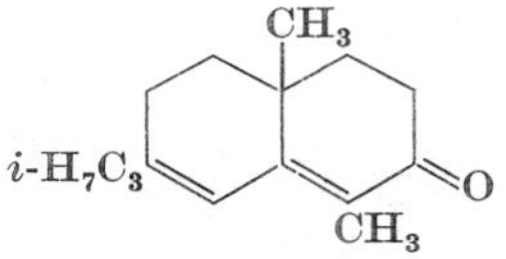 CH_3, $i\text{-}H_7C_3$, CH_3, O (Cyperone, 35–40††)	715
(+)-Dihydrocarvone	$NaNH_2$	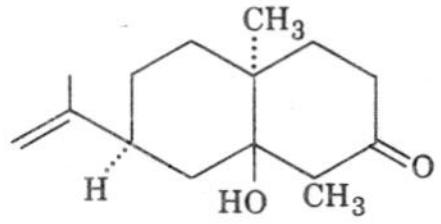 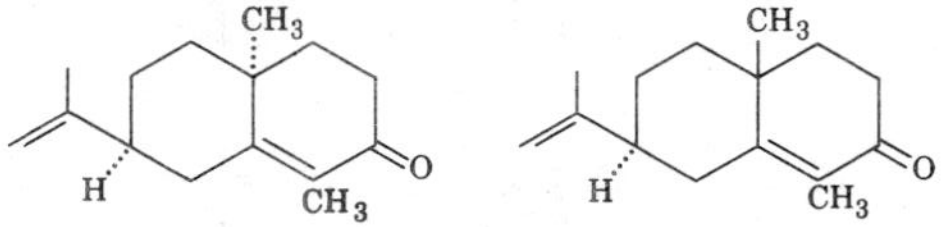 CH_3, H, HO, CH_3, O (36) and CH_3, H, CH_3, O; CH_3, H, CH_3, O (Mixture, 11)	716

Note: References 491–1045 are on pp. 545–555.

** In this instance, the tertiary base was used instead of the quaternary methiodide.

†† This compound resulted from the treatment of the crude primary product with boiling potassium hydroxide solution.

TABLE VIII—*Continued*

ROBINSON'S MODIFICATION OF THE MICHAEL CONDENSATION OF α,β-ETHYLENIC KETONES

Reactants	Catalyst	Product (Yield, %)	References
$CH_3CH_2COCH_2CH_2N(C_2H_5)_2 \cdot CH_3I$ *(Cont.) and*			
(−)-Dihydrocarvone	$NaNH_2$	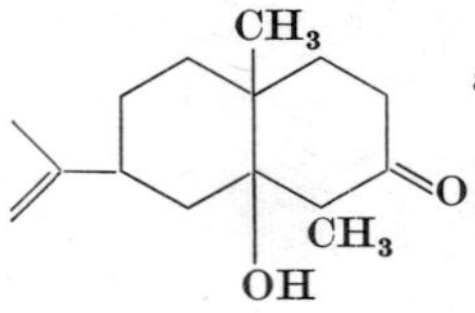 CH_3, CH_3, OH, O and CH_3, CH_3, O 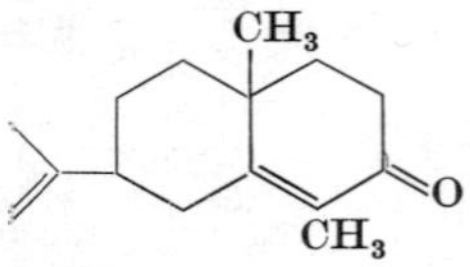	714
		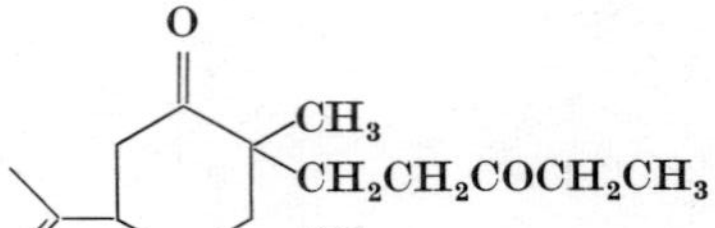 O, CH_3, $CH_2CH_2COCH_2CH_3$ (30)	717
5-(α-Carbomethoxyethyl)-2-methylcyclohexanone	$NaOCH_3$	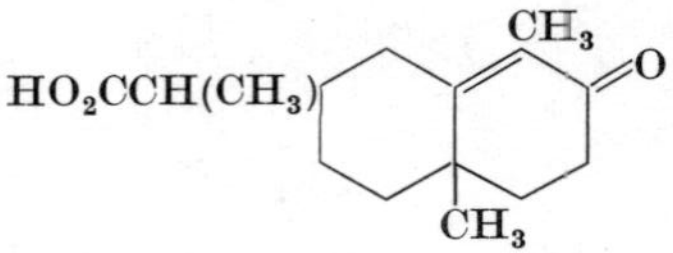 $HO_2CCH(CH_3)$, CH_3, O, CH_3 (15‡‡, 70§§)	664, 718
	$NaNH_2$	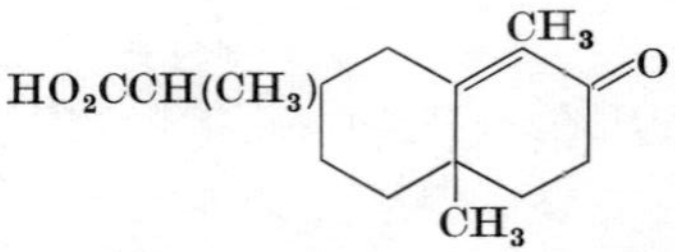 $HO_2CCH(CH_3)$, CH_3, O, CH_3 (45, 10)	188, 718

Reactants	Catalyst	Product (Yield, %)	Refs.
	$(C_6H_5)_3CNa$	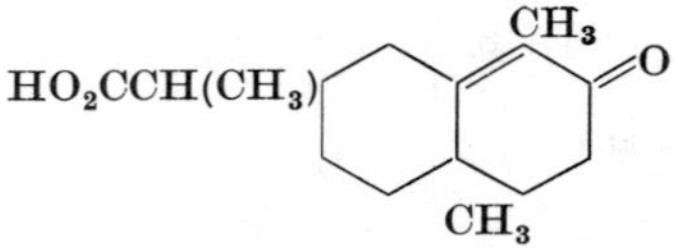 $HO_2CCH(CH_3)$–, CH_3, CH_3, O (23‖‖)	187
9-Methylhydrindan-6-one	$NaNH_2$	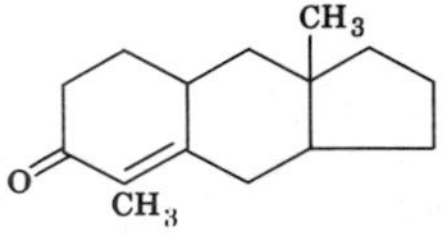 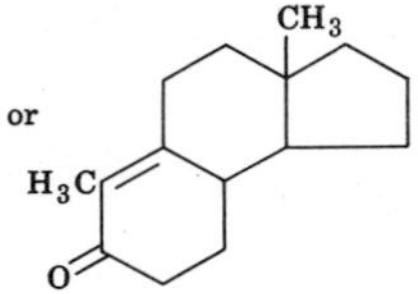 CH_3, O, CH_3 or CH_3, H_3C, O	230
$CH_3COCH(CH_3)CH_2N$(piperidino)$\cdot CH_3I$ *and*			
Ethyl isobutyrylacetate	—	CH_3, O, C_3H_7-*i* (Carvenone)	684
Ethyl α-acetylpropionate	$NaOC_2H_5$	3,4,6-Trimethyl-2-cyclohexen-1-one (65)	100
Hydroxymethylenecarvotanacetone	$NaOC_2H_5$	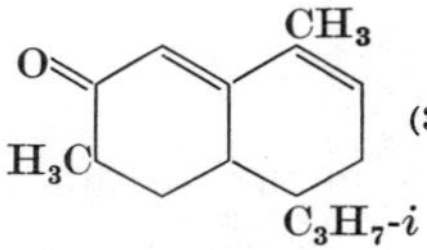 O, H_3C, CH_3, C_3H_7-*i* (35††)	720

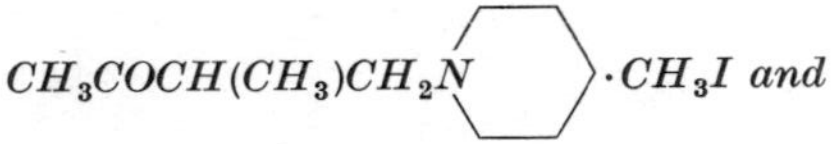

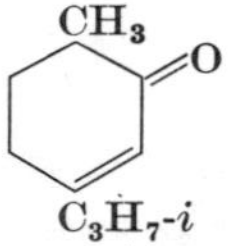

Note: References 491–1045 are on pp. 545–555.
†† This compound resulted from the treatment of the crude primary product with boiling potassium hydroxide solution.
‡‡ About two-thirds of the keto ester failed to enter into the reaction.
§§ One-quarter of the keto ester could be recovered unchanged.
‖‖ The ester obtained in the reaction was hydrolyzed.

TABLE VIII—*Continued*

ROBINSON'S MODIFICATION OF THE MICHAEL CONDENSATION OF α,β-ETHYLENIC KETONES

Reactants	Catalyst	Product (Yield, %)	References
$CH_3COCH[CH_2N(CH_3)_2 \cdot C_2H_5I]_2$ *and*		$A = CH_3COC(=CH_2)CH_2$—	
2-Carbethoxycyclohexanone	$NaOCH_3$	2-A-2-$CO_2C_2H_5$-cyclohexanone (74, conversion 65¶¶)	689
2-Carbethoxycycloheptanone	$NaOCH_3$	2-A-2-$CO_2C_2H_5$-cycloheptanone (67)	689
2-Carbomethoxycycloöctanone	$NaOCH_3$	2-A-2-CO_2CH_3-cyclooctanone (66, conversion 89¶¶)	689

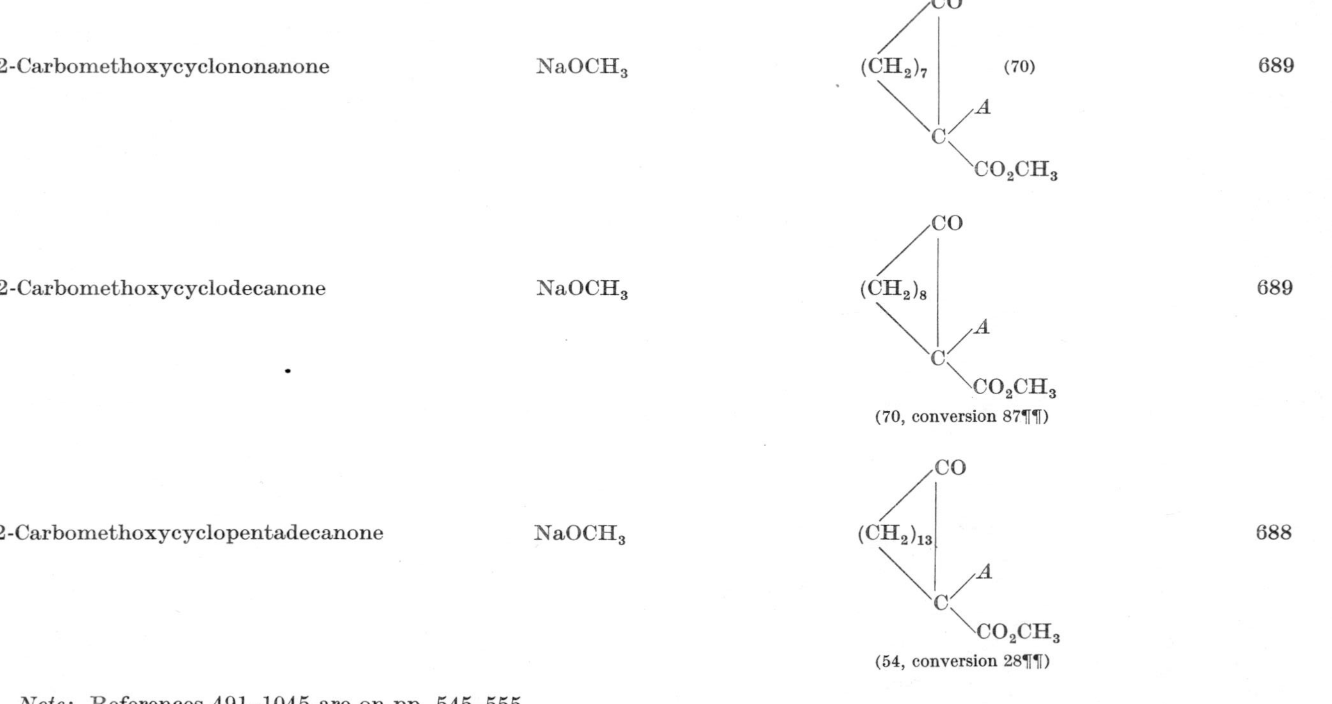

2-Carbomethoxycyclononanone	$NaOCH_3$	$(CH_2)_7$ ring: CO, C(A)(CO_2CH_3) (70)	689
2-Carbomethoxycyclodecanone	$NaOCH_3$	$(CH_2)_8$ ring: CO, C(A)(CO_2CH_3) (70, conversion 87¶¶)	689
2-Carbomethoxycyclopentadecanone	$NaOCH_3$	$(CH_2)_{13}$ ring: CO, C(A)(CO_2CH_3) (54, conversion 28¶¶)	688

Note: References 491–1045 are on pp. 545–555.

¶¶ Only the indicated amount of the keto ester entered into the reaction; the balance could be recovered unchanged.

TABLE VIII—*Continued*

ROBINSON'S MODIFICATION OF THE MICHAEL CONDENSATION OF α,β-ETHYLENIC KETONES

Reactants	Catalyst	Product (Yield, %)	References
$CH_3OCH_2COCH_2CH_2N(C_2H_5)_2$ and $CH_3COCH(OCH_3)CH_2N(C_2H_5)_2$ (mixture) and			
2-Methylcyclohexane-1,3-dione	Pyridine	O H_3C CH_3O O and O H_3C O OCH_3	721

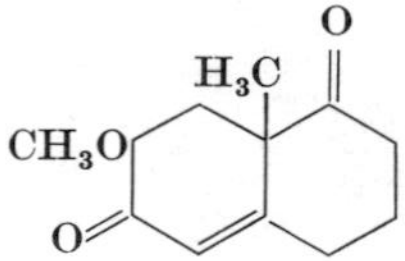

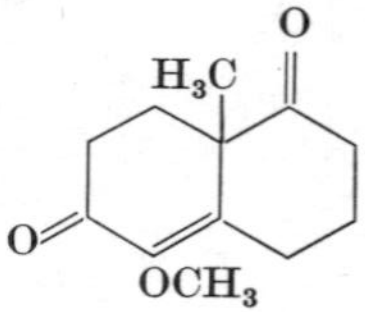

Substituent R in $(CH_3)_2CHCOCH_2CH_2R$	Addend	Catalyst	Product (Yield, %)	References
$(CH_3)_2N$	Ethyl acetoacetate	—	3-Isopropyl-2-cyclohexen-1-one	722
 O N·CH_3I	Ethyl methylacetoacetate	$NaOC_2H_5$	Carvenone (43)	100

Reactants	Catalyst	Product (Yield, %)	References
$(CH_3)_2CHCH_2COCH_2CH_2N$ O·CH_3I and			
Ethyl acetoacetate	$NaOC_2H_5$	3-Isobutyl-2-cyclohexen-1-one (45)	100
$(CH_3)_3CCOCH_2CH_2N$ O·CH_3I and			
Ethyl acetoacetate	$NaOC_2H_5$	3-*t*-Butyl-2-cyclohexen-1-one (45)	100

2-Diethylaminomethyl-5-methylcyclopentanone methiodide and

Ethyl acetoacetate	$NaOC_2H_5$	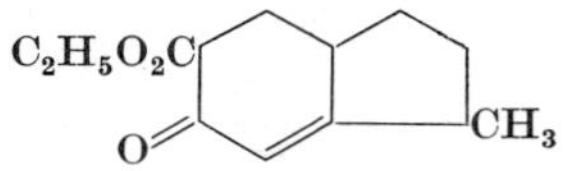 $C_2H_5O_2C$, O, CH_3	229

Substituent R in 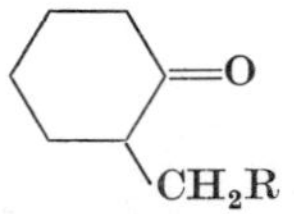 (2-CH_2R-cyclohexanone)	Addend	Catalyst	Product (Yield, %) A 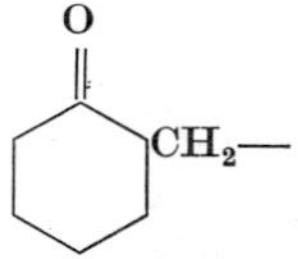 = 2-oxocyclohexyl-CH_2—	References
$(CH_3)_2N$	Diethyl malonate	$NaOC_2H_5$	$ACH(CO_2C_2H_5)_2$ (60–66)	114, 723
$(CH_3)_2N\cdot CH_3I$	Diethyl malonate	$NaOC_2H_5$	$ACH(CO_2C_2H_5)_2$ (60–66)	114, 723
$(CH_3)_2N$	Ethyl acetoacetate	$NaOC_2H_5$	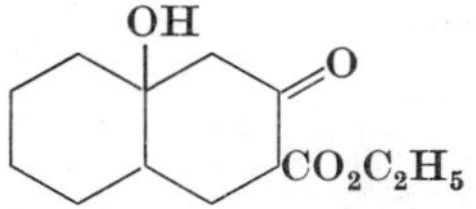 OH, O, $CO_2C_2H_5$ (70)	724
$(CH_3)_2N\cdot CH_3I$	Ethyl methylacetoacetate	$NaOC_2H_5$; $NaOC_3H_7$-*i*	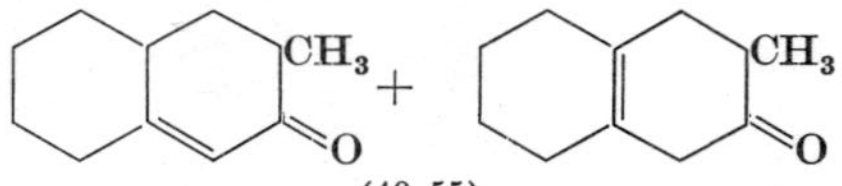 CH_3, O + CH_3, O (40–55)	725
	Ethyl ethylacetoacetate	$NaOC_2H_5$; $NaOC_3H_7$-*i*	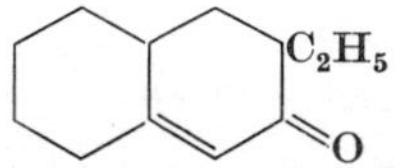 C_2H_5, O (35–40)	725

Note: References 491–1045 are on pp. 545–555.

TABLE VIII—*Continued*

ROBINSON'S MODIFICATION OF THE MICHAEL CONDENSATION OF α,β-ETHYLENIC KETONES

Substituent R in 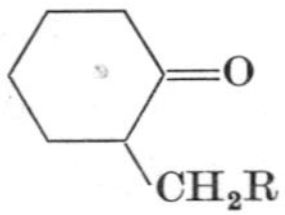 2-(CH_2R)cyclohexanone	Addend	Catalyst	Product (Yield, %)	References
			A 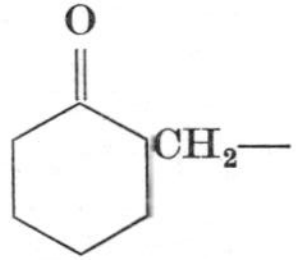 = 2-oxocyclohexyl-CH_2—	
$(CH_3)_2N \cdot CH_3I$ (*Cont.*)	Ethyl *n*-propylacetoacetate	$NaOC_2H_5$	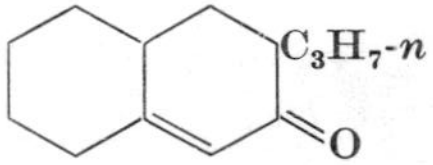 [bicyclic enone, C_3H_7-*n*, =O] (30–35)	725
	Ethyl allylacetoacetate	$NaOC_2H_5$	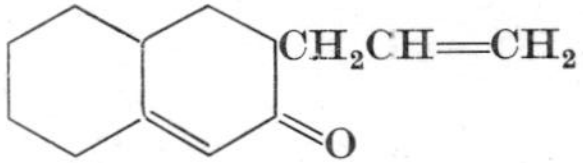 [bicyclic enone, $CH_2CH{=}CH_2$, =O] (20)	726
	Ethyl phenylacetoacetate	$NaOC_2H_5$	$CH_3COC(A)(C_6H_5)CO_2C_2H_5$	725
	Ethyl benzylacetoacetate	$NaOC_2H_5$	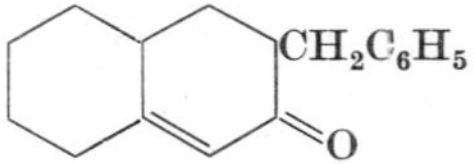 [bicyclic enone, $CH_2C_6H_5$, =O] (35–40)	725
	Acetylacetone	None	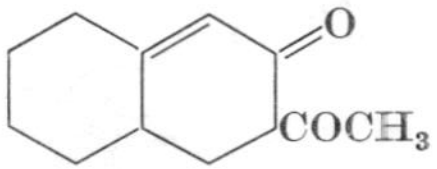 [bicyclic enone, =O, $COCH_3$] (60)	691
$(CH_3)_2N$	Cyclopentanone	None	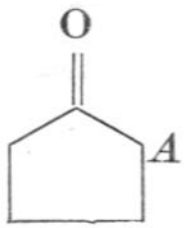 [2-A-cyclopentanone] (73)	691

Reactants	Catalyst	Product (Yield, %)	References
Hexane-2,5-dione	None	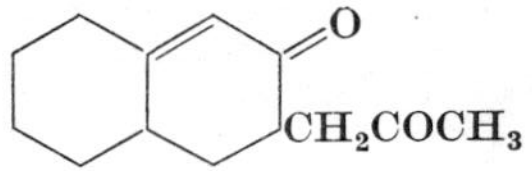 O, CH_2COCH_3 (29)	691
Cyclohexanone	None	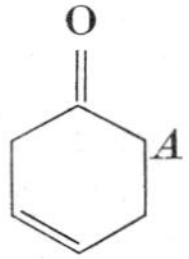 O, *A* (63)	691
Nitromethane	$NaOC_2H_5$	ACH_2NO_2	710
Nitroethane	$NaOC_2H_5$	$ACH(CH_3)NO_2$	726
1-Nitropropane	NaOH	$ACH(C_2H_5)NO_2$ (78)	691
2-Nitropropane	NaOH	$(CH_3)_2C(A)NO_2$ (81)	691

Reactants	Catalyst	Product (Yield, %)	References
2-*Diethylaminomethyl*-6-*methylcyclohexanone Methiodide and*			
Diethyl malonate	$NaOC_2H_5$	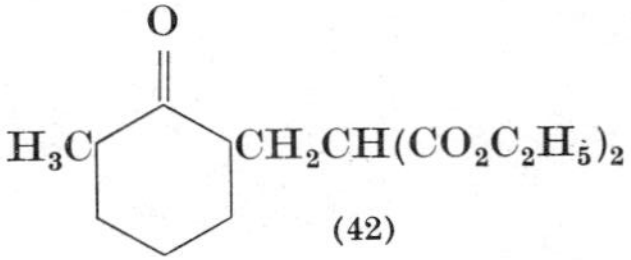 O, H_3C, $CH_2CH(CO_2C_2H_5)_2$ (42)	114
Ethyl acetoacetate	$NaOC_2H_5$	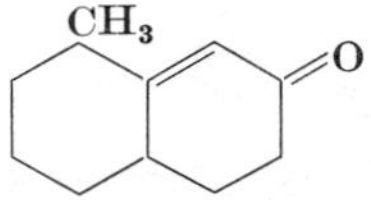 CH_3, O (60)	229

Note: References 491–1045 are on pp. 545–555.

TABLE VIII—*Continued*

ROBINSON'S MODIFICATION OF THE MICHAEL CONDENSATION OF α,β-ETHYLENIC KETONES

Reactants	Catalyst	Product (Yield, %)	References
2-*Diethylaminomethyl-4-methylcyclohexanone Methiodide and*			
Diethyl malonate	$NaOC_2H_5$	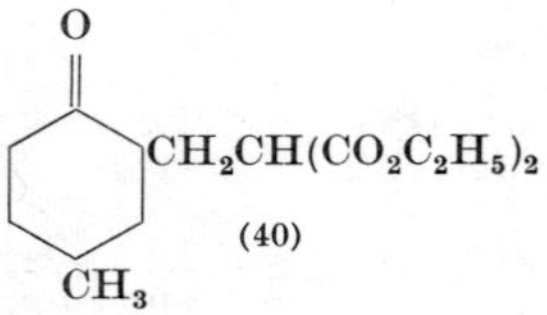 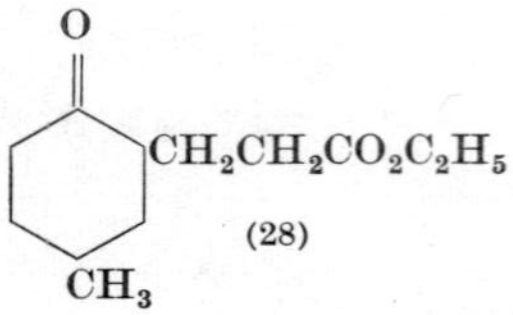 O, $CH_2CH(CO_2C_2H_5)_2$, CH_3 (40); O, $CH_2CH_2CO_2C_2H_5$, CH_3 (28)	114
2-*Diethylaminomethyl-4-methoxycyclohexanone Methiodide and*			
Ethyl acetoacetate	$NaOC_2H_5$	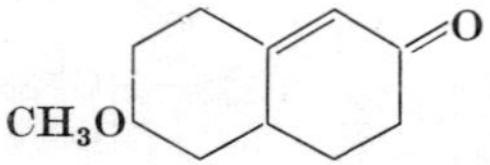 CH_3O, O	697
Ethyl β-oxovalerate	$NaOC_2H_5$	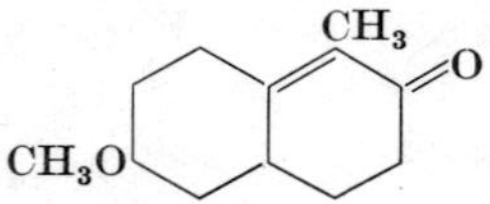 CH_3O, CH_3, O	697
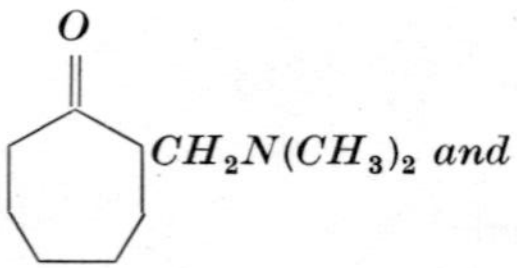 *O*, $CH_2N(CH_3)_2$ *and*			
Diethyl malonate	$NaOC_2H_5$	Diethyl 2-(2′-oxocycloheptyl)ethane-1,1-dicarboxylate	727

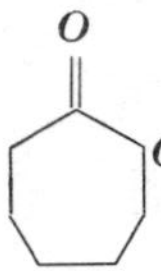

2-(Dimethylaminomethyl)cycloheptanone $CH_2N(CH_3)_2 \cdot CH_3I$ *and*

Reactant	Catalyst	Product (Yield, %)	Refs.
Ethyl acetoacetate	$NaOC_2H_5$	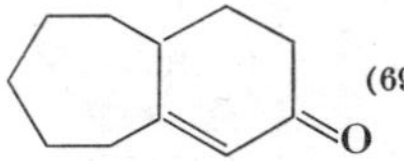 O (69)	727, 728
6-Dimethylaminomethyl-3-methyl-2-cyclohexen-1-one Methiodide and			
Ethyl acetoacetate	—	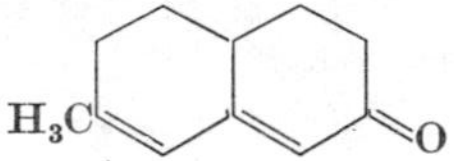 H_3C, O	682
Ethyl propionylacetate	—	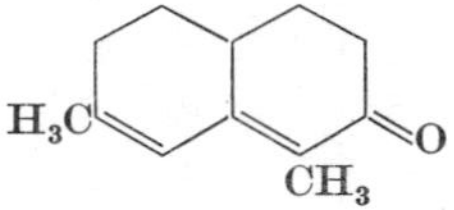 H_3C, O, CH_3	682
Ethyl 7-piperidino-5-oxoheptanoate and			
2-Methylcyclohexane-1,3-dione	Pyridine	O, CH_3, $(CH_2)_2CO(CH_2)_3CO_2C_2H_5$, O (50–55)	708
		CH_3, O, $CH_2CH_2CO_2H$, $CH_2CH_2CH_2CO_2H$ (3–4***)	
		O, CH_3, O, $CH_2CH_2CO_2C_2H_5$ (Low)	

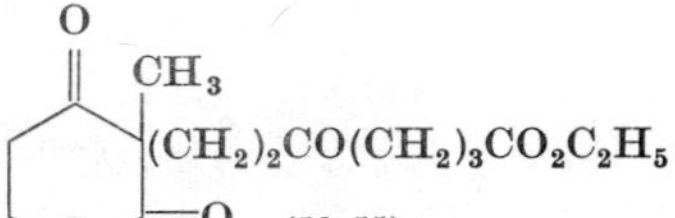

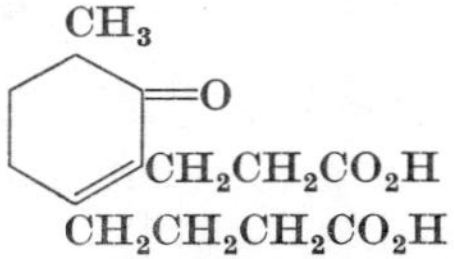

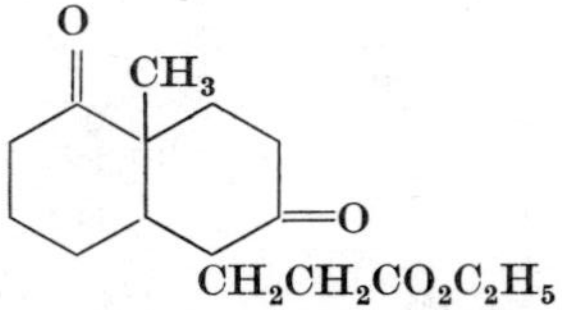

Note: References 491–1045 are on pp. 545–555.

*** This compound is formed by ring fission of the primary product and recyclization. When the methiodide of ethyl 7-piperidino-5-oxoheptanoate was employed in conjunction with sodium methoxide, the dibasic acid was the main product of the reaction.

TABLE VIII—*Continued*

ROBINSON'S MODIFICATION OF THE MICHAEL CONDENSATION OF α,β-ETHYLENIC KETONES

Reactants	Catalyst	Product (Yield, %)	References
β-Dimethylaminoethyl Cyclohexyl Ketone Hydrochloride and			
Methyl acetoacetate	KOC_4H_9-*t*	3-Cyclohexyl-2-cyclohexen-1-one (30)	729
1-(*β-Dimethylaminopropionyl*)-1-*cyclohexene Hydrochloride and*			
Methyl acetoacetate	KOC_4H_9-*t*	4-Acetyl-4-carbomethoxy-1-decalone (47)	729
1-(*β-Morpholinopropionyl*)-1-*cyclohexene Methiodide and*			
Diethyl malonate	$NaOC_2H_5$	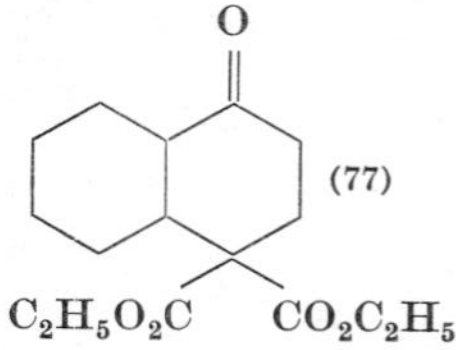 O; $C_2H_5O_2C$ $CO_2C_2H_5$ (77)	100

Substituent R in $RCH_2CH_2COC_6H_5$	Addend	Catalyst	Product (Yield, %) $A = —CH_2CH_2COC_6H_5$	References
$(CH_3)_2N \cdot HCl$	Methyl acetoacetate	KOC_4H_9-*t*	3-Phenyl-2-cyclohexen-1-one (60)	729
	Ethyl acetoacetate	KOC_4H_9-*t*	3-Phenyl-2-cyclohexen-1-one (60)	730
$(CH_3)_2N$	Ethyl acetoacetate	$NaOC_2H_5$	6-Carbethoxy-3-phenyl-2-cyclohexen-1-one	574
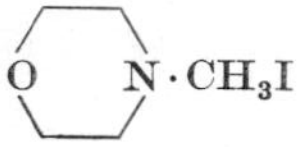 O N·CH_3I	Ethyl acetoacetate	$NaOC_2H_5$	3-Phenyl-2-cyclohexen-1-one (60)	100

$(CH_3)_2N$	Cyclopentanone	None	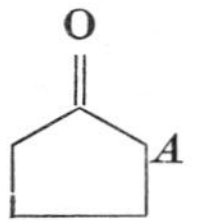 O, A (95)	691
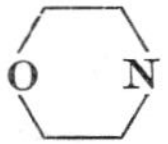 O N	Cyclopentanone	None	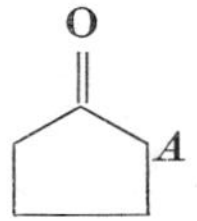 O, A (83)	691
$(CH_3)_2N$	Acetylacetone	None	6-Acetyl-3-phenyl-2-cyclohexen-1-one (50)	691
	Cyclohexanone	NaOH, C_2H_5OH	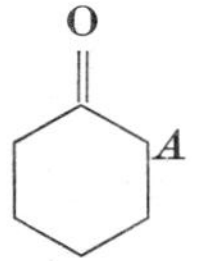 O, A (50)	731
		None	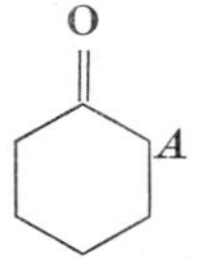 O, A (95)	691
 O N	Cyclohexanone	None	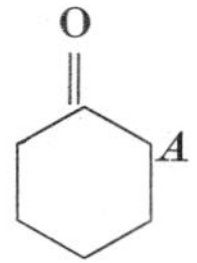 O, A (73)	691

Note: References 491–1045 are on pp. 545–555.

TABLE VIII—*Continued*

ROBINSON'S MODIFICATION OF THE MICHAEL CONDENSATION OF α,β-ETHYLENIC KETONES

Substituent R in $RCH_2CH_2COC_6H_5$	Addend	Catalyst	Product (Yield, %) $A = —CH_2CH_2COC_6H_5$	References
$(CH_3)_2N$	Hexane-2,5-dione	None	6-Acetonyl-3-phenyl-2-cyclohexen-1-one (22)	691
	Acetophenone	None	$ACH_2COC_6H_5$ (40)	691
	Deoxybenzoin	None	$C_6H_5CH(A)COC_6H_5$ (9)	691
	Nitromethane	$NaOC_2H_5$	ACH_2NO_2, $(A)_2CHNO_2$, $(A)_3CNO_2$	710
		NaOH	ACH_2NO_2 (13)	691
		None	ACH_2NO_2 (15)	691
$(C_2H_5)_2N$	Nitroethane	NaOH	$ACH(CH_3)NO_2$ (7) and $A_2C(CH_3)NO_2$ (50)	691
O N	Nitroethane	NaOH	$A_2C(CH_3)NO_2$ (30)	691
		$NaOC_2H_5$	$ACH(CH_3)NO_2$ (48) and $A_2C(CH_3)NO_2$ (30)	691
$(CH_3)_2N$	1-Nitropropane	NaOH	$ACH(C_2H_5)NO_2$ (80)	691
$(C_2H_5)_2N$	1-Nitropropane	$NaOC_2H_5$	$ACH(C_2H_5)NO_2$ (60)	691
$(CH_3)_2N$	2-Nitropropane	NaOH	$(CH_3)_2C(A)NO_2$ (12)	691
O N	2-Nitropropane	NaOH	$(CH_3)_2C(A)NO_2$ (84)	691
$(CH_3)_2N$	1-Nitro-2-phenylethane	NaOH	$C_6H_5CH_2CH(A)NO_2$ (68) and $C_6H_5CH_2C(A)_2NO_2$ (7)	691

Reactants		Catalyst	Product (Yield, %)	References
$(C_2H_5)_2N \cdot (CH_3)_2SO_4$	Methyl fluorene-9-carboxylate	KOH	*A*, CO_2CH_3 (83)	544
β-Dimethylamino-p-hydroxypropiophenone Hydrochloride and			O, R′, R″, C_6H_4OH-*p*	
Ethyl acetoacetate		KOC_4H_9-*t*	R′ = R″ = H (30)	729
Ethyl ethylacetoacetate		KOC_4H_9-*t*	R′ = C_2H_5, R″ = H (71)	729
Ethyl isopropylacetoacetate		KOC_4H_9-*t*	R′ = $(CH_3)_2CH$ and $CO_2C_2H_5$, R″ = H (30)	729
Ethyl α-propionylpropionate		KOC_4H_9-*t*	R′ = R″ = CH_3 (56)	729
Ethyl α,γ-diphenylacetoacetate		KOC_4H_9-*t*	R′ = R″ = C_6H_5 (15)	729
Acetylacetone		KOC_4H_9-*t*	R′ = CH_3CO, R″ = H (12)	729
4-*Carbethoxy-2-diethylaminomethylcyclohexanone Methiodide and*				
Ethyl β-oxovalerate		$NaOC_2H_5$	$C_2H_5O_2C$, CH_3, O	697
2-*Morpholinomethyl*-1-*hydrindone Methiodide and*				
Ethyl acetoacetate		$NaOC_2H_5$	O, $CO_2C_2H_5$	732

Note: References 491–1045 are on pp. 545–555.

TABLE VIII—*Continued*

ROBINSON'S MODIFICATION OF THE MICHAEL CONDENSATION OF α,β-ETHYLENIC KETONES

Reactants	Catalyst	Product (Yield, %) 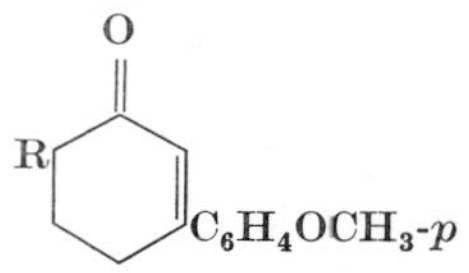	References
β-Dimethylaminoethyl p-Methoxyphenyl Ketone Hydrochloride and		[structure: 2-R-3-($C_6H_4OCH_3$-*p*)-2-cyclohexen-1-one]	
Ethyl acetoacetate	KOC_4H_9-*t*	R = H (40)	729
Ethyl ethylacetoacetate	KOC_4H_9-*t*	R = C_2H_5 (64)	729
Ethyl isopropylacetoacetate	KOC_4H_9-*t*	R = $(CH_3)_2CH$ (30)	729
Acetylacetone	KOC_4H_9-*t*	R = CH_3CO (36)	729
Nitromethane†††	KOC_4H_9-*t*	*p*-Methoxy-ω-nitrobutyrophenone	710
β-Dimethylaminoisopropyl Phenyl Ketone Hydrochloride and			
Ethyl acetoacetate	KOC_4H_9-*t*	4-Methyl-3-phenyl-2-cyclohexen-1-one (40, 38)	729, 730
β-Morpholino-α-phenylethyl Methyl Ketone and			
2-Nitropropane	NaOH	2-Methyl-2-nitro-4-phenylhexan-5-one (89)	691
6-*Isopropyl*-3-*methyl*-2-*morpholinomethylcyclohexan*-1-*one Methiodide and*			
Ethyl acetoacetate	$NaOC_2H_5$	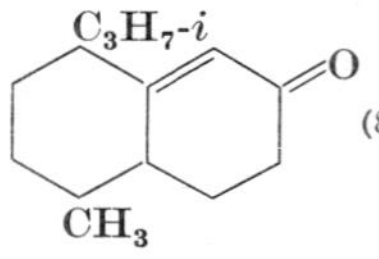 [structure: bicyclic enone with C_3H_7-*i*, =O, CH_3] (82)	733

2-*Dimethylaminomethyl*-1-*tetralone and*		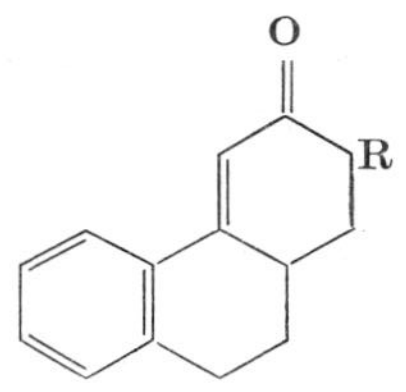	
Ethyl acetoacetate	$NaOC_2H_5$	R = H	724
Ethyl methylacetoacetate	$NaOC_2H_5$	R = CH_3	724
β-Dimethylamino-α-(p-methoxyphenyl)ethyl Methyl Ketone Methiodide and			
2-Hydroxymethylene-6-methoxy-1-tetralone	$NaOCH_3$	2-(*p*-Methoxyphenyl)-3-oxo-7-methoxy-1,2,3,9,10,10*a*-hexahydrophenanthrene (46)	734
3,4-*Dimethoxyphenyl β-Dimethylaminoethyl Ketone and*			
Nitromethane	$NaOC_2H_5$	1-(3′,4′-Dimethoxyphenyl)-4-nitrobutan-1-one	710
β-Dimethylamino-β-(p-methoxyphenyl)ethyl Methyl Ketone and			
Nitromethane	$NaOC_2H_5$	4-(*p*-Methoxyphenyl)-5-nitropentan-2-one	710
β-Dimethylamino-β-(3,4-*dimethoxyphenyl)ethyl Methyl Ketone and*			
Nitromethane	$NaOC_2H_5$	4-(3′,4′-Dimethoxyphenyl)-5-nitropentan-2-one	710

Note: References 491–1045 are on pp. 545–555.

††† The free base was employed, instead of the hydrochloride.

TABLE VIII—*Continued*

ROBINSON'S MODIFICATION OF THE MICHAEL CONDENSATION OF α,β-ETHYLENIC KETONES

Reactants	Catalyst	Product (Yield, %)	References
β-Dimethylamino-β-(3,4-methylenedioxyphenyl)ethyl Methyl Ketone and			
Nitromethane	$NaOC_2H_5$	4-(3′,4′-Methylenedioxyphenyl)-5-nitropentan-2-one	710
2-*Dimethylaminomethylbenzosuberone and*			
Biacetyl mono dimethyl ketal	Na enolate	O $CHCH_2COCOCH_3$ (Small)	394
β-Dimethylaminoethyl 6-*Methoxy-2-naphthyl Ketone Hydrochloride and*			
Methyl acetoacetate	KOH, $(CH_3)_2CHOH$	3-(6′-Methoxy-2′-naphthyl)cyclohexen-1-one (70)	735
β-Dimethylamino-β-phenylethyl 2-*Nitro-4,5-dimethoxyphenyl Ketone and*			
Nitromethane	$NaOC_2H_5$	4-Nitro-1-(2′-nitro-4′,5′-dimethoxyphenyl)-3-phenylbutan-1-one	710

Substituent R in 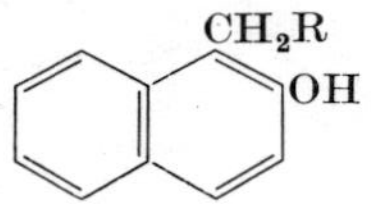 2-hydroxy-1-naphthylmethyl (CH_2R, OH)	Addend	Catalyst	Product (Yield, %)	References
C_2H_5S	Diethyl malonate	KOH	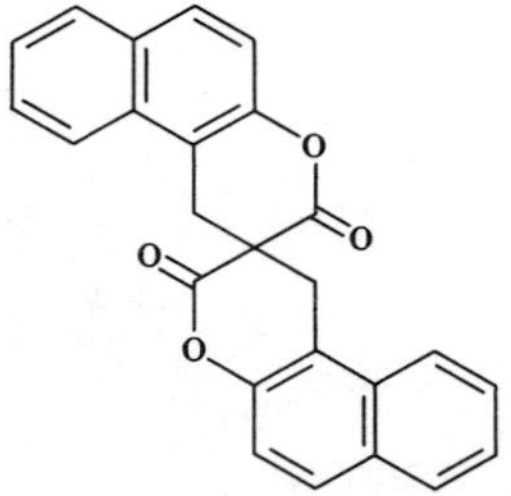 Spiro bis(naphthopyranone) (68)	155
	Diethyl acetamidomalonate	KOH	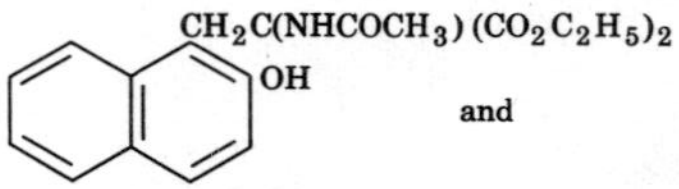 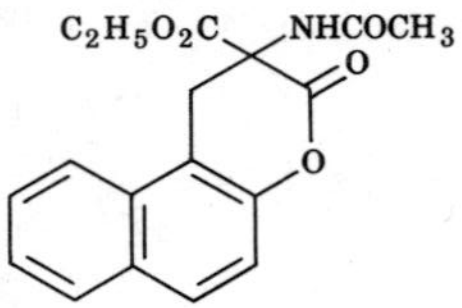 1-[$CH_2C(NHCOCH_3)(CO_2C_2H_5)_2$]-2-naphthol (8) and naphthopyranone with $C_2H_5O_2C$, $NHCOCH_3$ (42)	155

Note: References 491–1045 are on pp. 545–555.

TABLE VIII—*Continued*

ROBINSON'S MODIFICATION OF THE MICHAEL CONDENSATION OF α,β-ETHYLENIC KETONES

Substituent R in 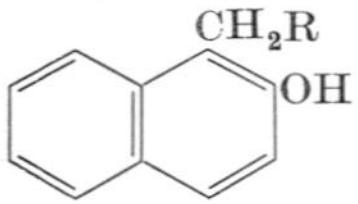 CH_2R, OH (naphthalene)	Addend	Catalyst	Product (Yield, %)	References
 O N	Dibenzoylmethane	HCl, C_2H_5OH	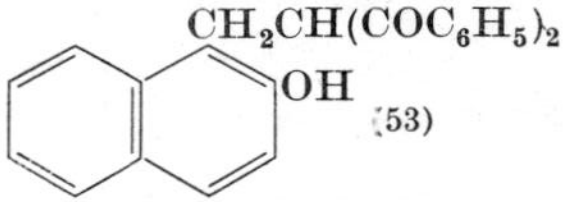 $CH_2CH(COC_6H_5)_2$, OH (53)	736, cf. 737, 738
C_2H_5S	2-Nitropropane	NaOH	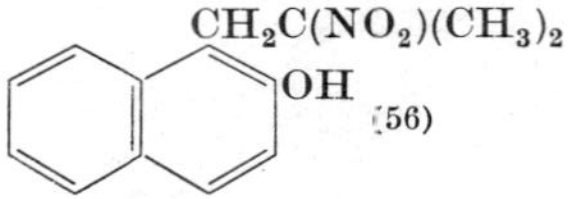 $CH_2C(NO_2)(CH_3)_2$, OH (56)	155
	Indole	KOH	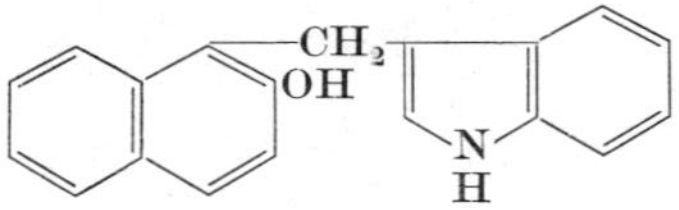 CH_2, OH, N H (52)	155
Substituent R in $RCH_2CH(NO_2)CH_3$			$A = CH_3CH(NO_2)CH_2$—	
$(i\text{-}C_3H_7)_2N$	Diethyl malonate	$NaOC_4H_9\text{-}n$	$A CH(CO_2C_2H_5)_2$ (37)	251
		$NaOC_2H_5$	$A CH(CO_2C_2H_5)_2$ (25)	251
		$[C_6H_5CH_2N(CH_3)_3]OH$	$A CH(CO_2C_2H_5)_2$ (47)	251

N	Diethyl malonate	$NaOC_4H_9$-*n*	$ACH(CO_2C_2H_5)_2$ (13)	251
$(i\text{-}C_3H_7)_2N$	Ethyl acetoacetate	$NaOC_2H_5$; $NaOC_4H_9$-*n*	$CH_3COCH(A)CO_2C_2H_5$ (46)	251
N	Ethyl acetoacetate	$NaOC_4H_9$-*n*	$CH_3COCH(A)CO_2C_2H_5$ (17)	251
$(i\text{-}C_3H_7)_2N$	Ethyl α-acetylsuccinate	$NaOC_4H_9$-*n*	$C_2H_5O_2CC(A)(COCH_3)CH_2CO_2C_2H_5$ (72)	251
N	Ethyl α-acetylsuccinate	$NaOC_4H_9$-*n*	$C_2H_5O_2CC(A)(COCH_3)CH_2CO_2C_2H_5$ (8)	251
$(i\text{-}C_3H_7)_2N$	1-Nitropropane	$[C_6H_5CH_2N(CH_3)_3]OH$	$CH_3CH_2CH(A)NO_2$ (33)	251
		NaOH	$CH_3CH_2CH(A)NO_2$ (50)	251
	2-Nitropropane	$[C_6H_5CH_2N(CH_3)_3]OH$	$(CH_3)_2C(A)NO_2$ (52)	251
		NaOH	$(CH_3)_2C(A)NO_2$ (43)	251
Substituent R in $RCH_2CH(NO_2)CH_2CH_3$			$A = CH_3CH_2CH(NO_2)CH_2$—	
$(CH_3)_2N$	1-Nitropropane	NaOH	$CH_3CH_2CH(A)NO_2$ (34)	251, 739
$(C_2H_5)_2N$	1-Nitropropane	NaOH	$CH_3CH_2CH(A)NO_2$ (18)	251, 739
$(i\text{-}C_3H_7)_2N$	1-Nitropropane	$[C_6H_5CH_2N(CH_3)_3]OH$	$CH_3CH_2CH(A)NO_2$ (15)	251
		NaOH	$CH_3CH_2CH(A)NO_2$ (18)	251, 739
$(CH_3)_2N$	2-Nitropropane	NaOH	$(CH_3)_2C(A)NO_2$ (55)	251
$(i\text{-}C_3H_7)_2N$	2-Nitropropane	$[C_6H_5CH_2N(CH_3)_3]OH$	$(CH_3)_2C(A)NO_2$ (50)	251
		NaOH	$(CH_3)_2C(A)NO_2$ (44)	251

Note: References 491–1045 are on pp. 545–555.

TABLE IX

Michael Condensations with Quinones and Their Derivatives

Reactants	Catalyst	Product (Yield, %)	References
p-Benzoquinone and			
Ethyl acetoacetate	$ZnCl_2$(!)	HO, O, $CO_2C_2H_5$, CH_3	256
		H_3C, O, $CO_2C_2H_5$, $C_2H_5O_2C$, O, CH_3	
$CH_3C({=}NH)CH(CH_3)CO_2C_2H_5$	None	HO, $C(CH_3)(CO_2C_2H_5)C({=}NH)CH_3$, OH (31)	377
$C_2H_5OC({=}NH)CH_2CO_2C_2H_5$	None	Ethyl 2-ethoxy-5-hydroxyindole-3-carboxylate (38)	377
Ethyl cyanoacetate	NH_3, ethanol	$CH(CN)CO_2C_2H_5$, HO, OH, $CH(CN)CO_2C_2H_5$ (15)	252
Cyanoacetamide	NH_3, ethanol	$CH(CN)CONH_2$, HO, OH, $CH(CN)CONH_2$ (16)	252

Malononitrile	NH_3, ethanol	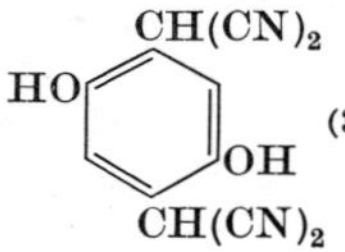 (31)	252
Acetylacetone	Pyridine	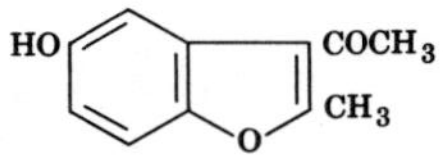 (5)	740
		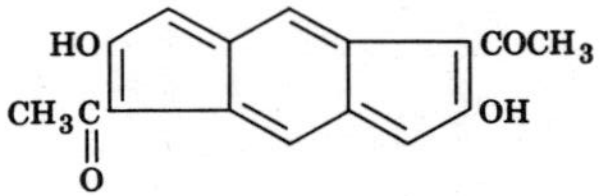	741
2,6-*Dichlorobenzoquinone and*			
Ethyl acetoacetate	Pyridine	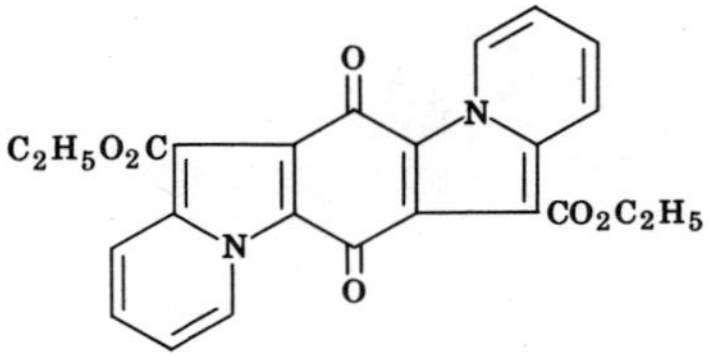	272
		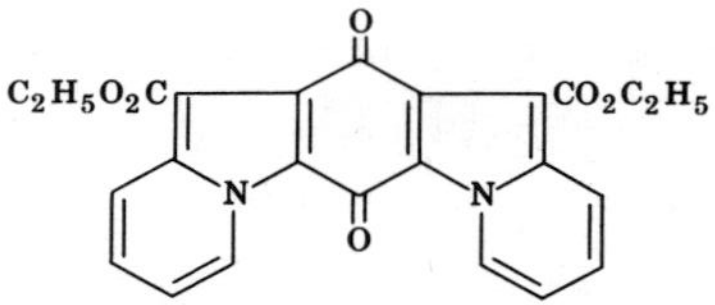	

Note: References 491–1045 are on pp. 545–555.
* This is the formula assumed by the author.

TABLE IX—*Continued*

MICHAEL CONDENSATIONS WITH QUINONES AND THEIR DERIVATIVES

Reactants	Catalyst	Product (Yield, %)	References
Chloranil and			
Ethyl acetoacetate	Pyridine	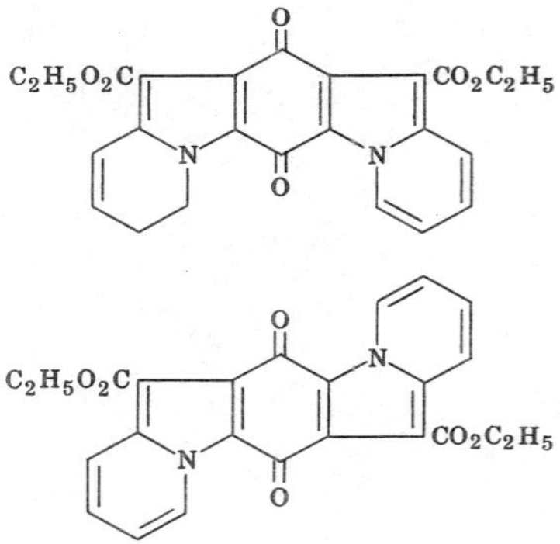	272
β-Naphthol	Pyridine	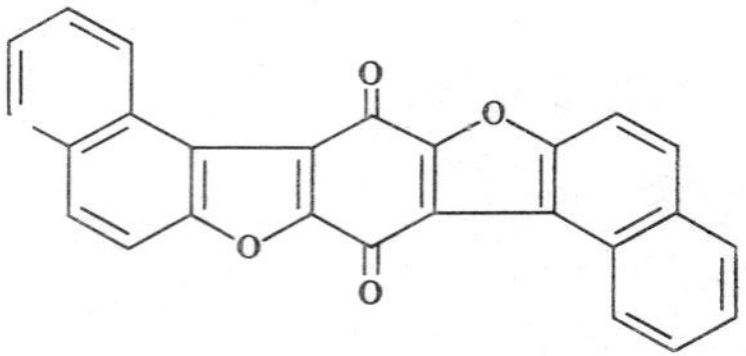	272

Reactants	Catalyst	Product (Yield, %)	Refs.
2-Hydroxy-3-naphthanilide	Pyridine	C_6H_5NHCO … O … O … O … O … $CONHC_6H_5$	272
Methoxybenzoquinone and			
$CH_3C(=NH)CH(CH_3)CO_2C_2H_5$	None	HO … OCH_3† OH $C(CH_3)(CO_2C_2H_5)C(=NH)CH_3$ (72)	377
$C_2H_5OC(=NH)CH_2CO_2C_2H_5$	None	Ethyl 2-ethoxy-5-hydroxy-6-methoxyindole-3-carboxylate† (46)	377
p-Xyloquinone and			
Diethyl malonate	$NaOC_2H_5$	O—CO $CHCO_2C_2H_5$ H_3C CH_3 OH (41)	742
		O—CO H_3C $CHCO_2C_2H_5$ $C_2H_5O_2CHC$ CH_3 OC—O (Small)	

Note: References 491–1045 are on pp. 545–555.

† The position of the methoxyl group has not been determined.

TABLE IX—*Continued*

MICHAEL CONDENSATIONS WITH QUINONES AND THEIR DERIVATIVES

Reactants	Catalyst	Product (Yield, %)	References
2-*Bromo*-3,5-*dimethylbenzoquinone and*			
Diethyl malonate	$NaOC_2H_5$	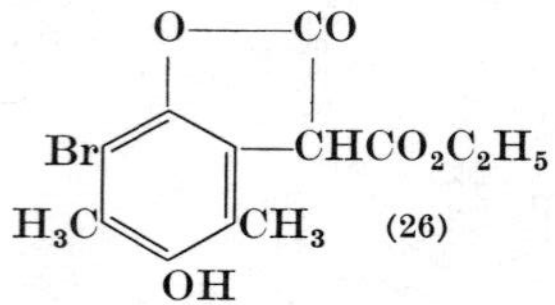 (26)	743
3,5-*Dibromo*-2,6-*dimethylbenzoquinone and*			
Diethyl malonate	Na	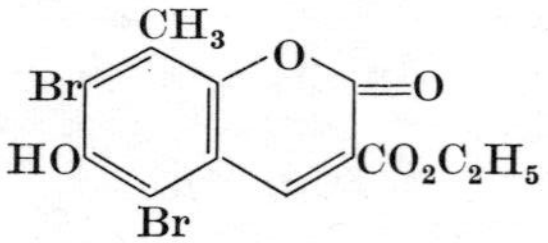 (44)	744
Trimethylbenzoquinone and		*A* 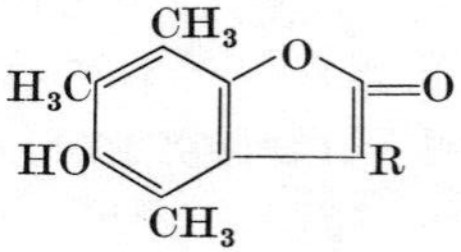 = ; *B* 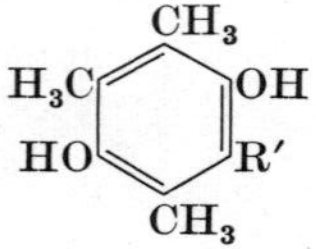 =	
Diethyl malonate	$NaOC_2H_5$	*A*, R = H	253, 745
Ethyl acetoacetate	$NaOC_2H_5$; Na	*A*, R = H (4), and 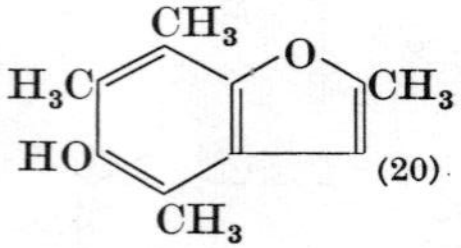 (20)	745
	$NaOC_2H_5$	*A*, R = $COCH_3$ (55)	745
Ethyl palmitoylacetate	$NaOC_2H_5$	*A*, R = $COC_{15}H_{31}$-*n*	746
Ethyl stearoylacetate	$NaOC_2H_5$	*A*, *R* = $COC_{17}H_{35}$-*n* (27)	746

Diethyl isobutyrylmalonate	$NaOC_2H_5$; $Mg(OC_2H_5)_2$	*A*, *R* = $CO_2C_2H_5$ (56)	253
Ethyl cyanoacetate	Na	Ethyl trimethylhydroquinonecyanoacetate (32)	388
Trimethylbenzoquinone and		*A* 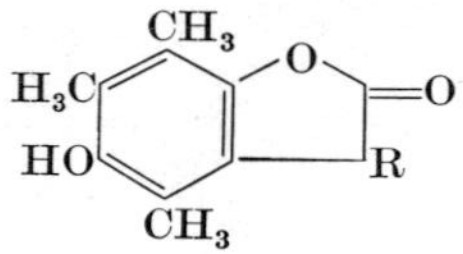 = [structure: benzofuranone with H_3C, HO, two CH_3, O, =O, R] *B* = [structure: benzene ring with H_3C, CH_3, OH, HO, R′, CH_3] 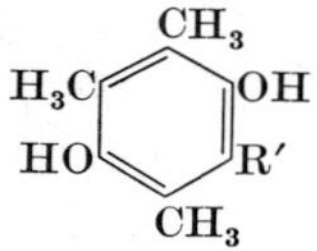	
Cyanoacetamide	$NaOCH_3$	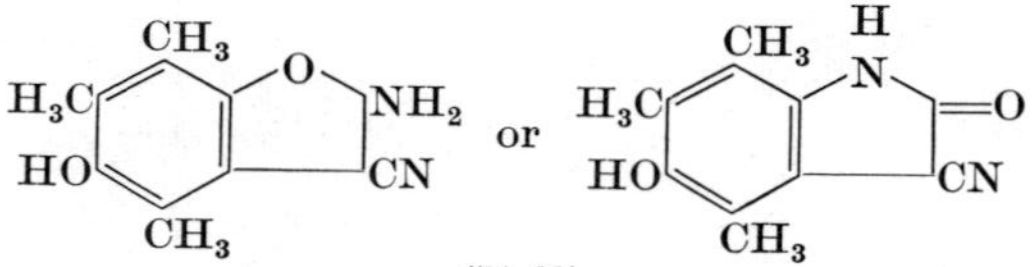 [structure: H_3C, HO, CH_3, CH_3 benzofuran with NH_2, CN] or [structure: H_3C, HO, CH_3, CH_3 indolinone with N–H, =O, CN] (74–83)	388
Benzyl cyanide	$NaOCH_3$	*A*, R = C_6H_5 (32)	388
Acetylacetone	$NaOC_2H_5$	*B*, R′ = $CH_3CO\overset{\vert}{C}HCOCH_3$ (72)	259
Isobutyrylacetone	$NaOC_2H_5$	*B*, R′ = $CH_3CO\overset{\vert}{C}HCOCH(CH_3)_2$ (81)	259
2,6-Dimethylheptane-3,5-dione	$NaOC_2H_5$	*B*, R′ = $(CH_3)_2CHCO\overset{\vert}{C}HCOCH(CH_3)_2$ (76)	260
Heptadecane-2,4-dione	$NaOC_2H_5$	*B*, R′ = $CH_3CO\overset{\vert}{C}HCOC_{13}H_{27}$-*n* (14)	254
5,9,13,17-Tetramethylocta-decane-2,4-dione	$NaOC_2H_5$	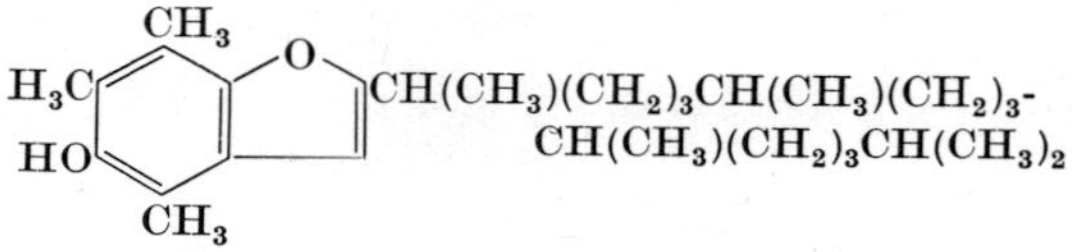 [structure: H_3C, HO, CH_3, CH_3 benzofuran with O] $CH(CH_3)(CH_2)_3CH(CH_3)(CH_2)_3$-$CH(CH_3)(CH_2)_3CH(CH_3)_2$ (21)	254
Acetomesitylene	Bromomagnesium enolate	*B*, R′ = $CH_2COC_6H_2(CH_3)_3$ (90)	253

Note: References 491–1045 are on pp. 545–555.

TABLE IX—*Continued*

MICHAEL CONDENSATIONS WITH QUINONES AND THEIR DERIVATIVES

Reactants	Catalyst	Product (Yield, %)	References
Bromotrimethylbenzoquinone and			
Diethyl malonate	$NaOC_2H_5$	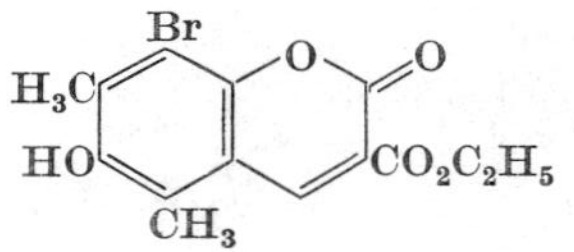 Br, H_3C, HO, CH_3, O, O, $CO_2C_2H_5$ (25)	747
Duroquinone and		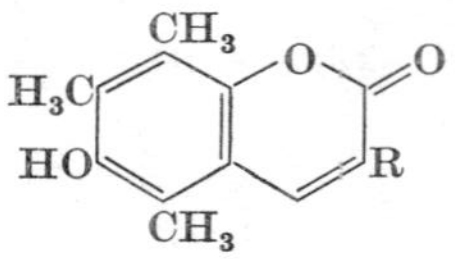 CH_3, H_3C, HO, CH_3, O, O, R	
Diethyl malonate	Na	R = $CO_2C_2H_5$	201, cf. 747*a*, 747*b*
Ethyl acetoacetate	Na	R = $COCH_3$ (25)	263
Methyl cyanoacetate	Na	R = CN (26)	262
Trimethylethylbenzoquinone and			
Diethyl malonate	Na	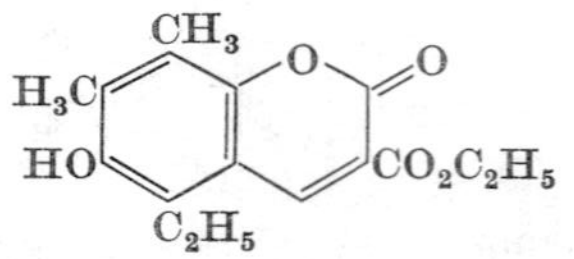 CH_3, H_3C, HO, C_2H_5, O, O, $CO_2C_2H_5$	748

		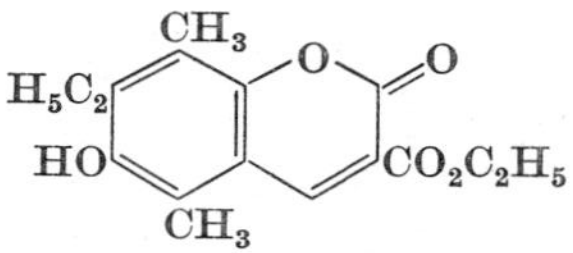CH3 H5C2 HO O O CO2C2H5 CH3 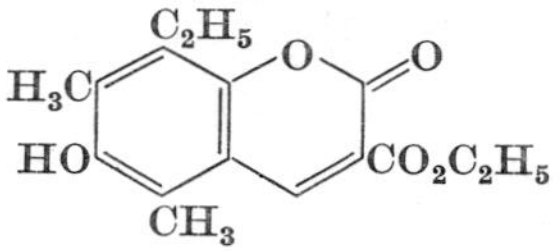C2H5 H3C HO O O CO2C2H5 CH3 (Mixture, 90)	
1,4-*Naphthoquinone and*			
Diethyl malonate	Pyridine	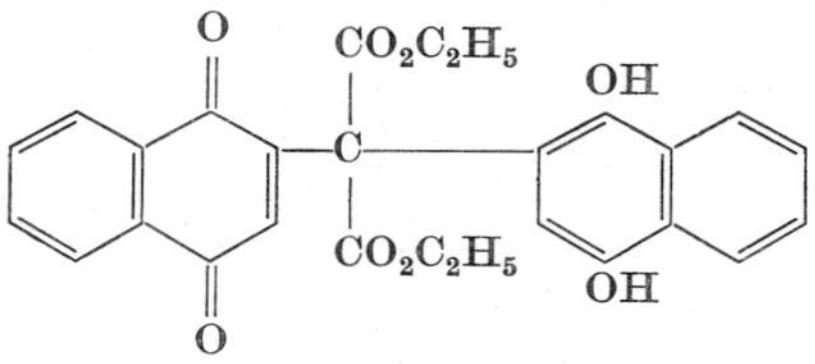O CO2C2H5 C CO2C2H5 O OH OH (15)	267
Ethyl acetoacetate	NaOH, ethanol	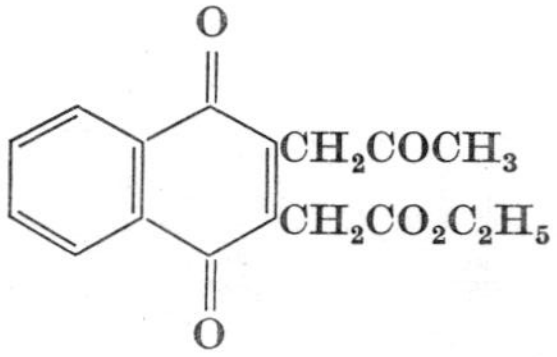O CH2COCH3 CH2CO2C2H5 O (25)	266

Note: References 491–1045 are on pp. 545–555.

TABLE IX—*Continued*

Michael Condensations with Quinones and Their Derivatives

Reactants	Catalyst	Product (Yield, %)	References
1,4-*Naphthoquinone* (*Cont.*) *and*			
Ethyl acetoacetate (*Cont.*)	Pyridine, pyridine hydrochloride	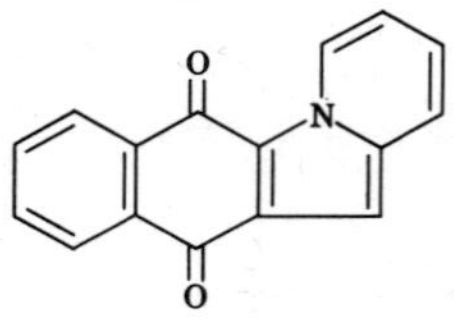 (14)	266
Ethyl benzoylacetate	Pyridine, pyridine hydrochloride	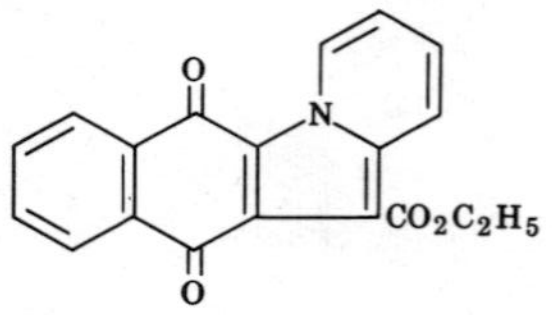 $CO_2C_2H_5$ (16)	269
Potassium 1,4-*naphthoquinone*-2-*sulfonate and*			
Diethyl malonate	Pyridine	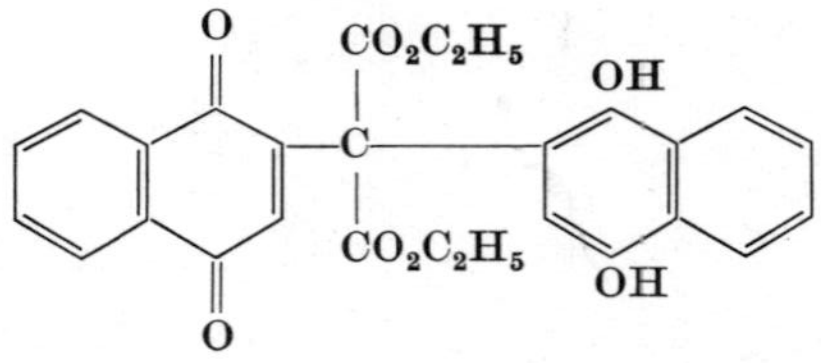 O, O, $CO_2C_2H_5$, C, $CO_2C_2H_5$, OH, OH (40)	267

Reactants	Catalyst	Product (Yield, %)	Refs.
Ethyl acetoacetate	$(CH_3)_4NOH$	2-(CH_2COCH_3)-3-($CH_2CO_2C_2H_5$)-1,4-naphthoquinone (40)	266
2-Bromo-1,4-naphthoquinone and			
Ethyl acetoacetate	KOH, aq. ethanol	2-(CH_2COCH_3)-3-($CH_2CO_2C_2H_5$)-1,4-naphthoquinone (32)	266

TABLE IX—*Continued*

Michael Condensations with Quinones and Their Derivatives

Reactants	Catalyst	Product (Yield, %)	References
2,3-*Dichloro*-1,4-*naphthoquinone and*	A = 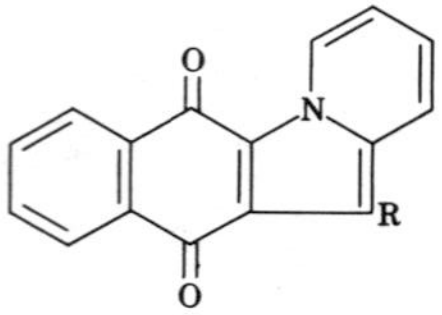	B = 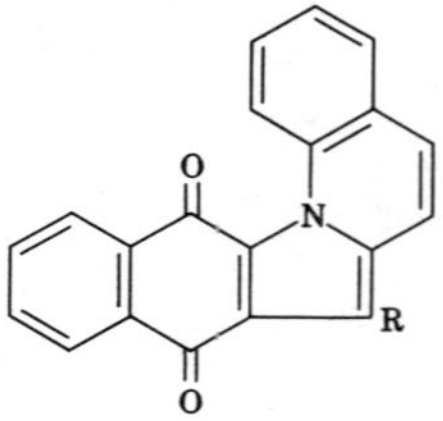	
Dimethyl malonate	Quinoline, quinoline hydrochloride	B, R = CO_2CH_3 (20)	266
Diethyl malonate	Pyridine	A, R = $CO_2C_2H_5$ (6)	269
	Quinoline, quinoline hydrochloride	B, R = $CO_2C_2H_5$ (11)	266
Methyl acetoacetate	Pyridine, pyridine hydrochloride	A, R = CO_2CH_3 (51)	266
	Quinoline, quinoline hydrochloride	B, R = CO_2CH_3 (39)	266
Ethyl acetoacetate	Pyridine, pyridine hydrochloride	A, R = $CO_2C_2H_5$ (49, 62)	266, 269
		or	
		O, O; CH_2COCH_3; $CH_2CO_2C_2H_5$ (50)	266

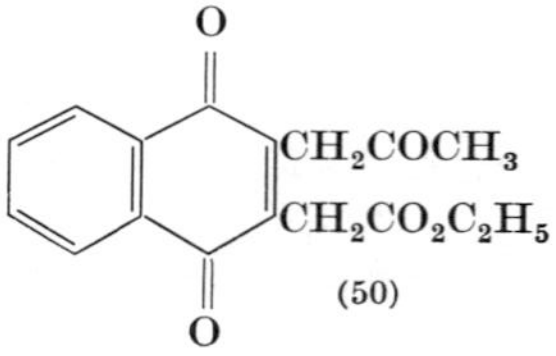

	Quinoline, quinoline hydrochloride	B, R = $CO_2C_2H_5$ (45)	266
Acetoacetanilide	Pyridine	A, R = $COCH_3$ (31) and A, R = $CONHC_6H_5$ (8)	271, 272
Acetoacet-*o*-chloroanilide	Pyridine	A, R = $COCH_3$	271, 272
Acetoacet-*o*-toluide	Pyridine	A, R = $COCH_3$	271, 272
2-(Acetoacetamido)-6-ethoxy-benzothiazole	Pyridine	A, R = $COCH_3$	271, 272
Acetylacetone	Pyridine	A, R = $COCH_3$ (36)	269
Acetophenone	Pyridine	A, R = COC_6H_5 (13)	273
Dibenzoylmethane	Pyridine	A, R = COC_6H_5 (3)	273
CH_2 ‡ O *and*			
Diethyl malonate	Na	$CO_2C_2H_5$, O, O (Small)	265
2,3-*Dimethyl*-1,4-*naphthoquinone and*			
Diethyl malonate	Na	O, O, $CO_2C_2H_5$, CH_3, OH (45)	749

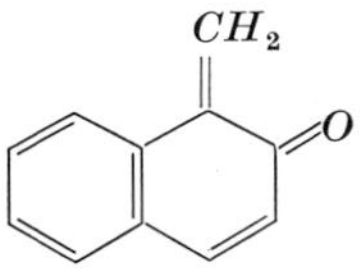

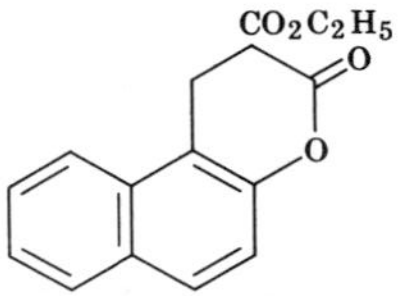

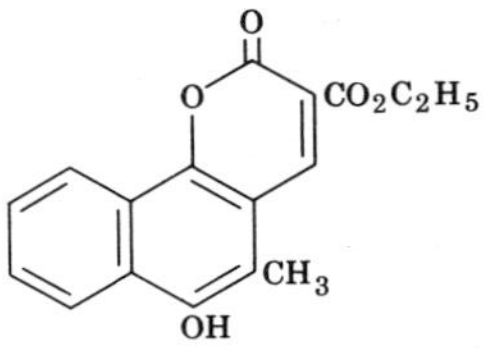

Note: References 491–1045 are on pp. 545–555.
‡ This quinone was introduced as its dimer.

TABLE IX—*Continued*

MICHAEL CONDENSATIONS WITH QUINONES AND THEIR DERIVATIVES

Reactants	Catalyst	Product (Yield, %)	References
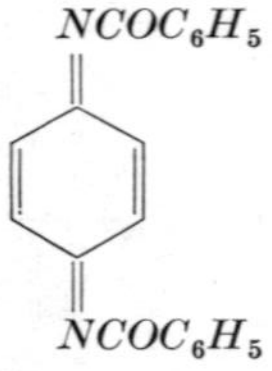 $NCOC_6H_5$ / (ring) / $NCOC_6H_5$ *and*		$A =$ (ring with $NHCOC_6H_5$ above and $NHCOC_6H_5$ below) 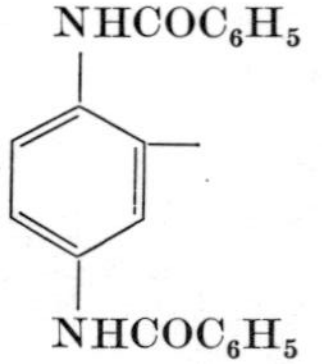	
Diethyl malonate	$NaOCH_3$	$ACH(CO_2C_2H_5)_2$ (76)	749*a*
Acetylacetone	$NaOCH_3$	$CH_3COCH(A)COCH_3$ (75)	749*a*
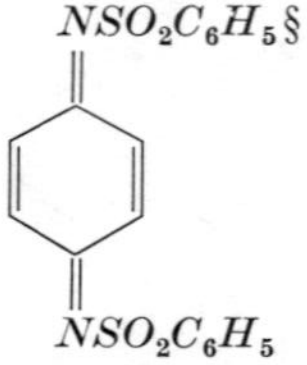 $NSO_2C_6H_5$§ / (ring) / $NSO_2C_6H_5$ *and*		$A =$ (ring with $NHSO_2C_6H_5$ above and $NHSO_2C_6H_5$ below) 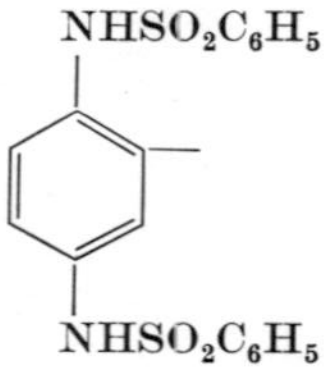	
Diethyl malonate	$NaOCH_3$	$ACH(CO_2C_2H_5)_2$ (57)	750
Ethyl acetoacetate	$NaOCH_3$	$CH_3COCH(A)CO_2C_2H_5$ (90 crude)	750
2-Carbethoxycyclopentanone	$NaOCH_3$	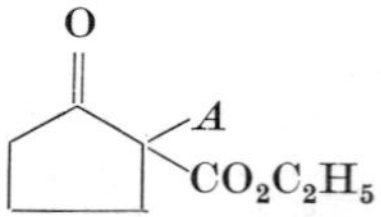 O (cyclopentanone ring bearing A and $CO_2C_2H_5$) (97 crude)	750
Ethyl benzoylacetate	$NaOCH_3$	$C_6H_5COCH(A)CO_2C_2H_5$ (94 crude)	750
Acetylacetone	$NaOCH_3$	$CH_3COCH(A)COCH_3$ (25 crude)	750

Cyclohexane-1,3-dione	$NaOCH_3$	2-A-cyclohexane-1,3-dione (76)	750
2-Chloro-*p*-quinone di(benzenesulfonimide) ($NSO_2C_6H_5$) and		A = 2-chloro-1,4-bis($NHSO_2C_6H_5$)phen-5-yl ($NHSO_2C_6H_5$, $NHSO_3C_6H_5$)	
Diethyl malonate	$NaOCH_3$	$ACH(CO_2C_2H_5)_2$ (62)	750
Ethyl acetoacetate	$NaOCH_3$	$CH_3COCH(A)CO_2C_2H_5$ (97 crude)	750
Acetylacetone	$NaOCH_3$	$CH_3COCH(A)COCH_3$ (94 crude)	750
2-Methyl-*p*-quinone di(benzenesulfonimide) (H_3C, $NSO_2C_6H_5$) and		A = 2-methyl-1,4-bis($NHSO_2C_6H_5$)phen-5-yl (H_3C, $NHSO_2C_6H_5$)	
Diethyl malonate	$NaOCH_3$	$ACH(CO_2C_2H_5)_2$ (82)	750
Ethyl acetoacetate	$NaOCH_3$	$CH_3COCH(A)CO_2C_2H_5$ (95 crude)	750
Acetylacetone	$NaOCH_3$	$CH_3COCH(A)COCH_3$ (79)	750

Note: References 491–1045 are on pp. 545–555.

§ With this compound, ethyl cyanoacetate, malononitrile, nitromethane, nitroethane and 2-nitropropane gave only tarry products.

TABLE IX—*Continued*

MICHAEL CONDENSATIONS WITH QUINONES AND THEIR DERIVATIVES

Reactants	Catalyst	Product (Yield, %)	References
1,4-Naphthoquinone di($NSO_2C_6H_5$) (structure) *and*		A = 2-(1,4-bis($NHSO_2C_6H_5$)naphthyl) (structure)	
Diethyl malonate	$(C_2H_5)_3N$	$ACH(CO_2C_2H_5)_2$ (83)	751
Ethyl benzoylacetate	$(C_2H_5)_3N$	$C_6H_5COCH(A)CO_2C_2H_5$ (90)	751
Acetylacetone	$(C_2H_5)_3N$	$CH_3COCH(A)COCH_3$ (84)	751
Nitromethane	$(C_2H_5)_3N$	$(A)_2CHNO_2$ (84)	751
Nitroethane	$(C_2H_5)_3N$	$ACH(CH_3)NO_2$ (64)	751
o-Benzoquinone di($NCOC_6H_5$) (structure) *and*		A = 2,3-bis($NHCOC_6H_5$)phenyl (structure)	
Diethyl malonate	$NaOCH_3$	$ACH(CO_2C_2H_5)_2$‖ (96)	752
Acetylacetone	$NaOCH_3$	$CH_3COCH(A)COCH_3$‖ (99)	752
Cl-o-benzoquinone di($NCOC_6H_5$)¶ (structure) *and*			
Acetylacetone	$NaOCH_3$	Cl-C_6H_2($NHCOC_6H_5$)$_2$$CH(COCH_3)_2$‖ (97)	752

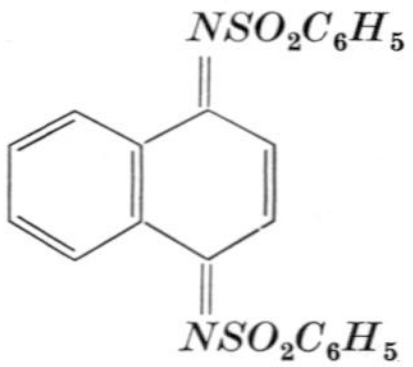

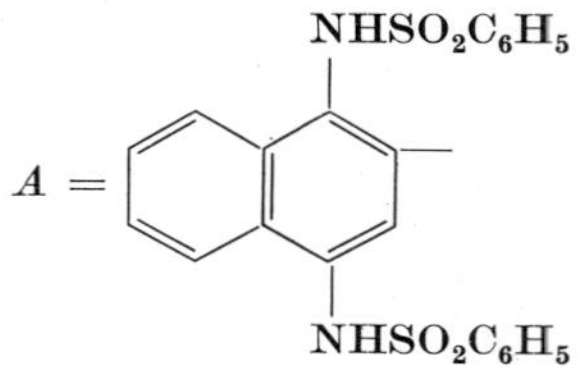

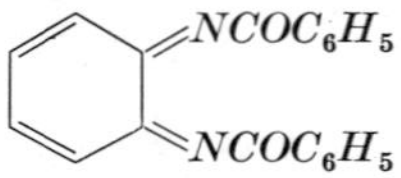

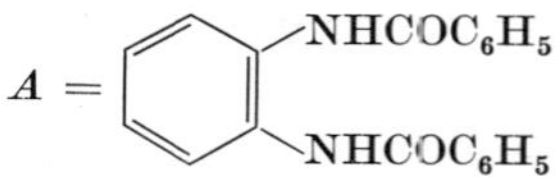

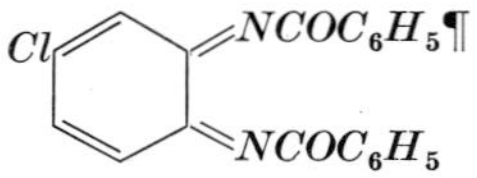

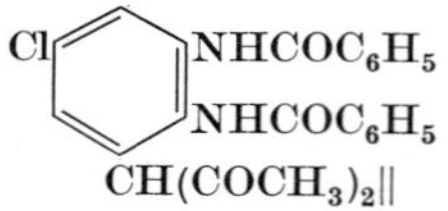

Note: References 491–1045 are on pp. 545–555.

‖ The position in which the substitution has taken place has not been determined.

¶ With diethyl malonate, this compound gave only an oily product.

TABLE X

Michael Condensations with Acrylonitrile*

Reactants	Catalyst	Product (Yield, %)	References
A. Hydrocarbons		A = —CH_2CH_2CN	
Cyclopentadiene	$[C_6H_5CH_2N(CH_3)_3]OH$	Hexa-(β-cyanoethyl)cyclopentadiene (9)	288
Indene	$[C_6H_5CH_2N(CH_3)_3]OH$	x,x-Bis-(β-cyanoethyl)indene (14) 1,1,3-Tris-(β-cyanoethyl)indene 35)	288
1-Isopropylideneindene	$[C_6H_5CH_2N(CH_3)_3]OH$	A; $C(CH_3)_2$ or A; CH_3, C, CH_2 (22)	288
Fluorene	$[C_6H_5CH_2N(CH_3)_3]OH$	9,9-Di-(β-cyanoethyl)fluorene (74)	288, 753
1-Methylfluorene	$[C_6H_5CH_2N(CH_3)_3]OH$	9,9-Di-(β-cyanoethyl)-1-methylfluorene (70)	482
2-Nitrofluorene	$[C_6H_5CH_2N(CH_3)_3]OH$	9,9-Di-(β-cyanoethyl)-2-nitrofluorene (70)	288
2,7-Dibromofluorene	Not indicated	2,7-Dibromo-9,9-di-(β-cyanoethyl)fluorene	754
4,5-Methylenephenanthrene	$[C_6H_5CH_2N(CH_3)_3]OH$	4,5-[Di-(β-cyanoethyl)methylene]phenanthrene	754, 755
9-Phenylfluorene	$[C_6H_5CH_2N(CH_3)_3]OH$	9-(β-Cyanoethyl)-9-phenylfluorene (73)	289
9-Fluorenol	$[C_6H_5CH_2N(CH_3)_3]OH$	9-(β-Cyanoethyl)-9-fluorenol	289
1,2,3,4-Tetrahydrofluoranthene	$[C_6H_5CH_2N(CH_3)_3]OH$	1-(β-Cyanoethyl)-1,2,3,4-tetrahydrofluoranthene	754, 755
2,2,4-Trimethyl-1,2-dihydrofluoranthene	$[C_6H_5CH_2N(CH_3)_3]OH$	1-(β-Cyanoethyl)-2,2,4-trimethyl-1,2-dihydrofluoranthene	754, 755
B. Aldehydes		A = —CH_2CH_2CN	
Acetaldehyde	—	$(A)_2CHCHO$, $(A)_3CCHO$	756
Propionaldehyde	—	$CH_3CH(A)CHO$, $CH_3C(A)_2CHO$	756

Note: References 491–1045 are on pp. 545–555.

* Compare the review by Bruson.[274]

TABLE X—*Continued*

MICHAEL CONDENSATIONS WITH ACRYLONITRILE*

Reactants	Catalyst	Product (Yield, %)	References
B. Aldehydes (Cont.)		$A = —CH_2CH_2CN$	
Isobutyraldehyde	Quaternized polyvinylpyridine resin; aq. KCN	$(CH_3)_2C(A)CHO$ (40, 79)	478, 756, 757
Diethylacetaldehyde	KOH, CH_3OH	$(C_2H_5)_2C(A)CHO$ (75–80)	278, 284
2-Ethyl-2-hexenal	KOH	$CH_3CH_2CH{=}CHC(A)(C_2H_5)CHO$ (50)	284
2-Ethylhexanal	KOH, CH_3OH	$C_4H_9C(A)(C_2H_5)CHO$ (75, 80)	278, 284
α-Phenylpropionaldehyde	KOH	$(C_6H_5)(CH_3)C(A)CHO$ (74)	758
C. Ketones		$A = —CH_2CH_2CN$	
Acetone	Quaternized polyvinylpyridine resin	CH_3COCH_2A (19) and $CH_3COC(A)_3$ (32)	478
	NaOH	CH_3COCH_2A (8), $CH_3COCH(A)_2$ (14), $CH_3COC(A)_3$ (24)	759
	$[C_6H_5CH_2N(CH_3)_3]OH$	$CH_3COC(A)_3$(75–80) and $(A)_2CHCOC(A)_3$	760, 761
	$[C_6H_5CH_2N(CH_3)_3]OH$	CH_3COCH_2A (18)†	762
Methyl ethyl ketone	Na; $[C_6H_5CH_2N(CH_3)_3]OH$	$CH_3COC(A)_2CH_3$ (51, 90) and $(A)_2CHCOC(A)_2CH_3$	763, 761
	KOH, C_2H_5OH; $[C_6H_5CH_2N(CH_3)_3]OH$	$CH_3COCH(A)CH_3$ (6, 20) and $CH_3COC(A)_2CH_3$ (47)‡	275, 278
	$[C_6H_5CH_2N(CH_3)_3]OH$	$CH_3COCH(A)CH_3$ and $CH_3COC(A)_2CH_3$ (24–30)†	762
	Polyvinylpyridine resin	$CH_3COCH(A)CH_3$ and $CH_3COC(A)_2CH_3$ (total, 47)	478
Methyl β-cyanoethyl ketone	Aq. KCN	$CH_3COC(A)_2CH_2CN$ (82)	123
Methyl *n*-propyl ketone	KOH, C_2H_5OH; $[C_6H_5CH_2N(CH_3)_3]OH$; quaternized polyvinylpyridine resin	$CH_3COCH(A)C_2H_5$ (15, 20), $CH_3COC(A)_2C_2H_5$ (14, 43), and $ACH_2COC(A)_2C_2H_5$	275, 278, 478, 761

Methyl isopropyl ketone	KOH, C_2H_5OH; $[C_6H_5CH_2N(CH_3)_3]OH$	$CH_3COC(A)(CH_3)_2$ (54)‡	275
Diethyl ketone	$[C_6H_5CH_2N(CH_3)_3]OH$	$CH_3CH(A)COC(A)_2CH_3$ (31)	761
Methyl isobutyl ketone	KOH, C_2H_5OH; $[C_6H_5CH_2N(CH_3)_3]OH$	$CH_3COCH(A)CH(CH_3)_2$ (17) and $CH_3COC(A)_2CH(CH_3)_2$ (15)‡	275, 761
Mesityl oxide	$[C_6H_5CH_2N(CH_3)_3]OH$	$CH_3COC(A)_2C(CH_3){=}CH_2$ (35, 74) and $CH_3COC(A){=}C(CH_3)_2$ (10–15)	764, 283
Methyl *n*-amyl ketone	KOH, C_2H_5OH; $[C_6H_5CH_2N(CH_3)_3]OH$	$CH_3COCH(A)C_4H_9$-*n* (19) and $CH_3COC(A)_2C_4H_9$-*n* (40)‡	275, 761
Diisopropyl ketone	$[C_6H_5CH_2N(CH_3)_3]OH$	$(CH_3)_2C(A)COCH(CH_3)_2$ (40, 10) and $(CH_3)_2C(A)COC(A)(CH_3)_2$ (1)‡	274, 275, 765
	Aq. NaOH	$(CH_3)_2C(A)COCH(CH_3)_2$ (28) and $(CH_3)_2C(A)COC(A)(CH_3)_2$ (small)	766
Methyl hexyl ketone	$[C_6H_5CH_2N(CH_3)_3]OH$; KOH, C_2H_5OH	$CH_3COCH(A)C_5H_{11}$-*n* (19) and $CH_3COC(A)_2C_5H_{11}$-*n* (31)‡	275, 761
Diisobutyl ketone	KOH, C_2H_5OH; $[C_6H_5CH_2N(CH_3)_3]OH$	$(CH_3)_2CHCH(A)COCH_2CH(CH_3)_2$ (35) and $(CH_3)_2CHCH(A)COCH(A)CH(CH_3)_2$ (19)‡	275
Isopropyl *n*-amyl ketone	KOH, CH_3OH	*n*-$C_5H_{11}COC(A)(CH_3)_2$	276
Isopropyl *n*-nonyl ketone	KOH, CH_3OH	*n*-$C_9H_{19}COC(A)(CH_3)_2$	276
Acetylacetone	$[C_6H_5CH_2N(CH_3)_3]OH$ or OC_4H_9-*n*	$CH_3COC(A)_2COCH_3$ (49–55)	277
Acetonylacetone	$[C_6H_5CH_2N(CH_3)_3]OH$ or OC_4H_9-*n*	$CH_3COC(A)_2CH_2COCH_3$ (46–50)	277
Cyclopentanone	$[C_6H_5CH_2N(CH_3)_3]OH$; KOH	2,2,5,5-Tetra-(β-cyanoethyl)cyclopentanone (97)	761
	$[C_6H_5CH_2N(CH_3)_3]OH$; $[C_6H_5N(CH_3)_3]OC_2H_5$	2,2,5,5-Tetra-(β-cyanoethyl)cyclopentanone (95–97)	767

Note: References 491–1045 are on pp. 545–555.

* Compare the review by Bruson.[274]

† A large excess of the ketone was used in this experiment.

‡ The acrylonitrile was formed *in situ* from β-chloropropionitrile in the experiments described in ref. 275.

TABLE X—*Continued*

MICHAEL CONDENSATIONS WITH ACRYLONITRILE*

Reactants	Catalyst	Product (Yield, %)	References
C. Ketones (Cont.)		$A = —CH_2CH_2CN$	
Cyclohexanone	KOH, C_2H_5OH; $[C_6H_5CH_2N(CH_3)_3]OH$	2-(β-Cyanoethyl)cyclohexanone (16–19) and 2,2-di-(β-cyanoethyl)cyclohexanone (44)‡	114, 234, 275
	$[C_6H_5CH_2N(CH_3)_3]OH$	2-(β-Cyanoethyl)cyclohexanone (47) or 2,2-di-(β-cyanoethyl)cyclohexanone (18–20)	762, 168
	$NaNH_2$	2,2,6,6-Tetra-(β-cyanoethyl)cyclohexanone (12)§	275, 284
	Na; $[C_6H_5CH_2N(CH_3)_3]OH$; KOH	2,2,6,6-Tetra-(β-cyanoethyl)cyclohexanone (81, 80–95)	761, 763
	NaOH	2-(β-Cyanoethyl)cyclohexanone (20) and 2,2-Di-(β-cyanoethyl)cyclohexanone (40)	768
	Enamine of the ketone with pyrrolidine	2-(β-Cyanoethyl)cyclohexanone (80)	535
	$NaOC_2H_5$	2-(β-Cyanoethyl)cyclohexanone (5), 2,2-di-(β-cyanoethyl)cyclohexanone (5), and 2,2,6,6-tetra-(β-cyanoethyl)cyclohexanone	766
	KOH	2-(β-Cyanoethyl)cyclohexanone (29) and 2,2-di-(β-cyanoethyl)cyclohexanone (26)	769
Cyclohexane-1,3-dione	$NaOCH_3$	2-(β-Cyanoethyl)cyclohexane-1,3-dione (23)	770
2,4-Dimethylcyclopentan-1-one	KOH	O, *A*, CH_3, H_3C (73)	769

2,4-Dimethyl-2-cyclopenten-1-one	Not indicated	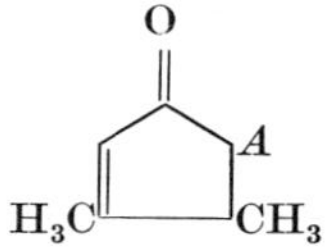 O, A, H_3C, CH_3 (12)	769
3,5-Dimethyl-2-cyclopenten-1-one	Not indicated	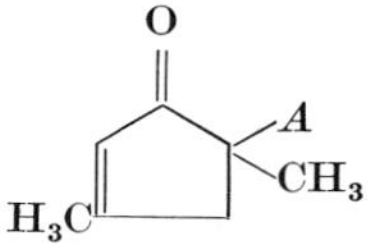 O, A, CH_3, H_3C (24 crude)	769
2-Methylcyclohexanone	$[C_6H_5CH_2N(CH_3)_3]OH$	2-Methyl-2-(β-cyanoethyl)cyclohexanone (80)	114
	$[C_6H_5CH_2N(CH_3)_3]OH$; KOH	2-Methyl-2,6,6-tri-(β-cyanoethyl)cyclohexanone (38)	761
4-Methylcyclohexanone	$[C_6H_5CH_2N(CH_3)_3]OH$	2-(β-Cyanoethyl)-4-methylcyclohexanone (21)	114
2-Methylcyclohexane-1,3-dione	$NaOCH_3$	2-(β-Cyanoethyl)-2-methylcyclohexane-1,3-dione (82)‖	769
	$NaOC_2H_5$	1-Carbethoxy-7-cyano-5-methylheptan-4-one (63)	771
Cycloheptanone	Enamine of the ketone	2-(β-Cyanoethyl)cycloheptan-1-one	535
2-Cyanocycloheptanone	KOH, CH_3OH	2-(β-Cyanoethyl)-2-cyanocycloheptan-1-one (65)	772
5,5-Dimethylcyclohexane-1,3-dione	$NaOCH_3$	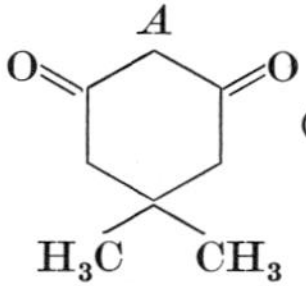 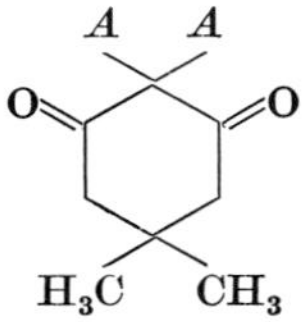 A, O, O, H_3C, CH_3 (56) or A, A, O, O ¶, H_3C, CH_3 (81)	769

Note: References 491–1045 are on pp. 545–555.

* Compare the review by Bruson.[274]

‡ The acrylonitrile was formed from β-chloropropionitrile in the experiments described in reference 275.

§ The acrylonitrile was formed *in situ* from the methiodide of 2-diethylaminoethyl cyanide.

‖ Under more drastic conditions, this product is hydrolyzed to 7-cyano-5-methyl-4-oxoheptane-1-carboxylic acid (74).

¶ Under more drastic conditions, part of the product was hydrolyzed to 5-(β-cyanoethyl)-7-cyano-2,2-dimethyl-4-oxoheptane-1-carboxylic acid.

TABLE X—*Continued*

MICHAEL CONDENSATIONS WITH ACRYLONITRILE*

Reactants	Catalyst	Product (Yield, %)	References
C. Ketones (Cont.)		A = —CH_2CH_2CN	
5,5-Dimethylcyclohexane-1,3-dione (*Cont.*)	$NaOC_2H_5$	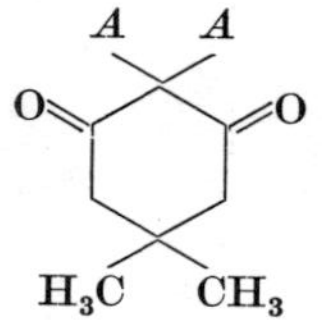 A, A, O, O, H_3C, CH_3 (83) **	234
	$NaNH_2$	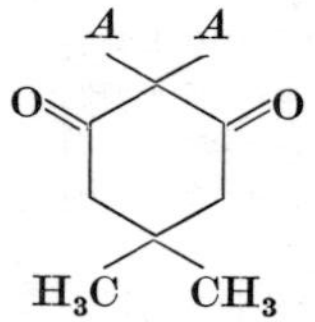 A, A, O, O, H_3C, CH_3 §	234
Isophorone	$[C_6H_5CH_2N(CH_3)_3]OH$	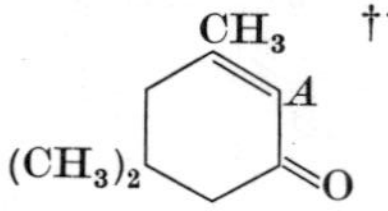 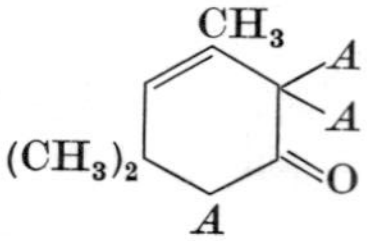 CH_3, A, $(CH_3)_2$, O (9) 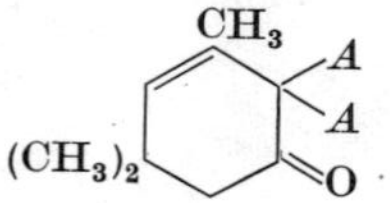 ††; CH_3, A, A, $(CH_3)_2$, O (22); CH_3, A, A, $(CH_3)_2$, O, A (1)	285

Reactant	Catalyst	Product (Yield, %)	Ref.
	$NaOC_5H_{11}$-*t*	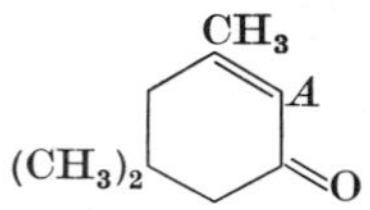 CH_3, A, $(CH_3)_2$, O (cyclohexenone structure)	286
4-*t*-Amylcyclohexanone	$[C_6H_5CH_2N(CH_3)_3]OH$; KOH	2,2,6,6-Tetra-(β-cyanoethyl)-4-*t*-amylcyclohexanone (80–95)	761
2-(Cyclohex-1′-enyl)cyclohexanone	$[C_6H_5CH_2N(CH_3)_3]OH$	2-Cyclohex-1′-enyl-2-(β-cyanoethyl)cyclohexanone (50) and 2-cyclohex-1′-enyl-2,6,6-tri-(β-cyanoethyl)cyclohexanone (29)	279
4-Cyclohexylcyclohexanone	$[C_6H_5CH_2N(CH_3)_3]OH$; KOH	2,2,6,6-Tetra-(β-cyanoethyl)-4-cyclohexylcyclohexanone (80–95)	761
3-Oxo-2-phenylcyclohexylacetonitrile	$[C_6H_5CH_2N(CH_3)_3]OH$	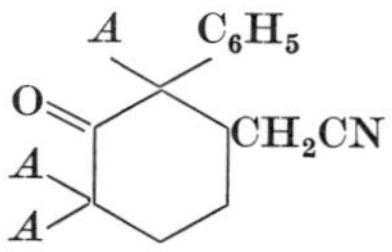 A, C_6H_5, O, CH_2CN, A, A (cyclohexanone structure) (16)	108

Note: References 491–1045 are on pp. 545–555.

* Compare the review by Bruson.[281]

§ The acrylonitrile was formed *in situ* from the methiodide of 2-diethylaminoethyl cyanide.

** The diketone was recovered to an extent of 34%. When β-chloropropionitrile was employed instead of acrylonitrile, the yield was 21%, and 52% of the diketone was recovered.

†† This structure has been proven (ref. 286) by ozonization to 3,3-dimethyl-5-oxohexane-1-carboxylic acid. In ref. 285, the isomeric formula

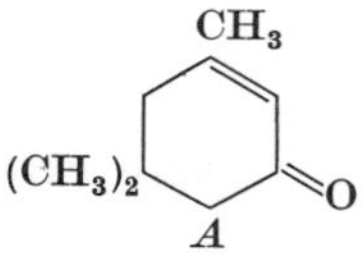

CH_3, $(CH_3)_2$, O, A (cyclohexenone structure)

was incorrectly assigned to the monosubstitution product.

TABLE X—*Continued*

MICHAEL CONDENSATIONS WITH ACRYLONITRILE*

Reactants	Catalyst	Product (Yield, %)	References
		A = —CH_2CH_2CN	
C. Ketones (Cont.)			
2-Phenylcyclohexanone	$NaNH_2$	2-(β-Cyanoethyl)-2-phenylcyclohexanone (63–70)	112
	$[C_6H_5CH_2N(CH_3)_3]OH$	2-(β-Cyanoethyl)-2-phenylcyclohexanone	113
	Na	2-(β-Cyanoethyl)-2-phenylcyclohexanone (60)	773
4-($\alpha,\alpha,\gamma,\gamma$-Tetramethylbutyl)-cyclohexanone	$[C_6H_5CH_2N(CH_3)_3]OH$	2,2,6,6-Tetra-(β-cyanoethyl)-4-($\alpha,\alpha,\gamma,\gamma$-tetramethylbutyl)cyclohexanone (80–95)	761
2-Benzylidene-6-phenylcyclohexanone	$[C_6H_5CH_2N(CH_3)_3]OH$	2-Benzylidene-6-(β-cyanoethyl)-6-phenylcyclohexanone (83)	112
α-Tetralone	$[C_6H_5CH_2N(CH_3)_3]OH$; KOH	O; A; A	761
1-Methyl-*cis*-2-decalone	$[C_6H_5CH_2N(CH_3)_3]OH$	H_3C; $CH_2CH_2CO_2H$; O (50) ‡‡	368
1-Methyl-*trans*-2-decalone	$[C_6H_5CH_2N(CH_3)_3]OH$	H_3C; H; O; $CH_2CH_2CO_2H$ (40) ‡‡	368

Reactant	Catalyst	Product (Yield, %)	Refs.
3-(Methylanilinomethylene)-1-methyl-*trans*-2-decalone	$[C_6H_5CH_2N(CH_3)_3]OH$	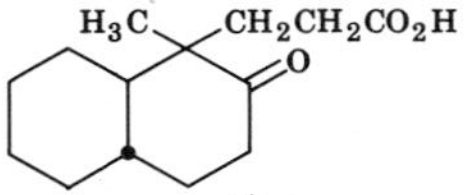 H_3C, $CH_2CH_2CO_2H$, O (10)‡‡	368
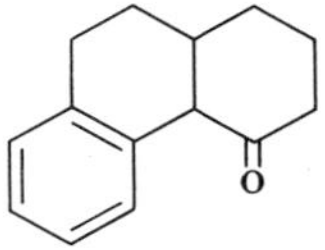 O	$[C_6H_5CH_2N(CH_3)_3]OH$	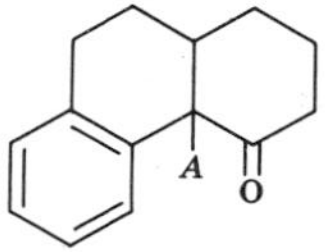 *A*, O (75)	108
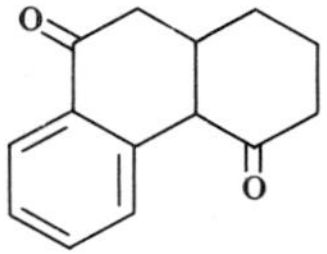 O, O	$[C_6H_5CH_2N(CH_3)_3]OH$	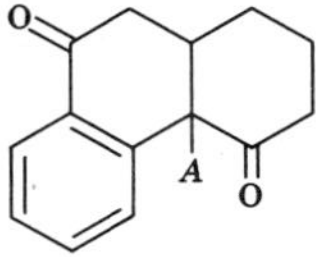 O, *A*, O (71)	108
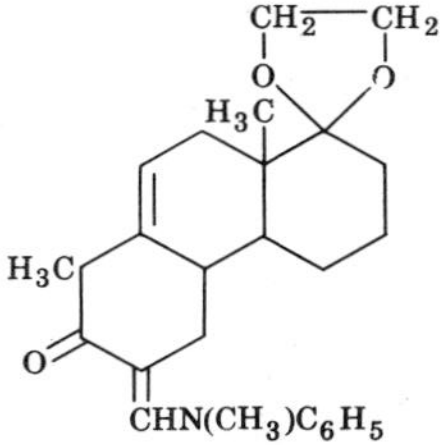 CH_2—CH_2, O, O, H_3C, H_3C, O, $CHN(CH_3)C_6H_5$	$[C_6H_5N(CH_3)_3]OH$	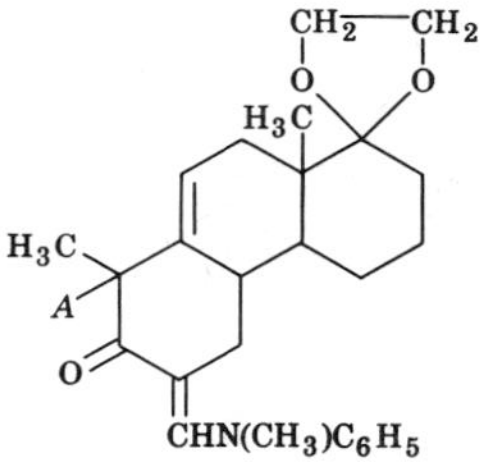 CH_2—CH_2, O, O, H_3C, H_3C, *A*, O, $CHN(CH_3)C_6H_5$ (56)	542

Note: References 491–1045 are on pp. 545–555.

* Compare the review by Bruson.[274]

‡‡ This product was isolated after saponification of the adduct.

TABLE X—*Continued*

MICHAEL CONDENSATIONS WITH ACRYLONITRILE*

Reactants	Catalyst	Product (Yield, %)	References
C. Ketones (Cont.)		$A = —CH_2CH_2CN$	
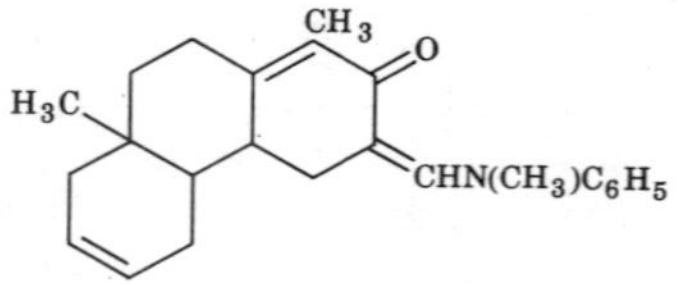 H_3C, CH_3, O, $CHN(CH_3)C_6H_5$	$[C_6H_5N(CH_3)_3]OH$	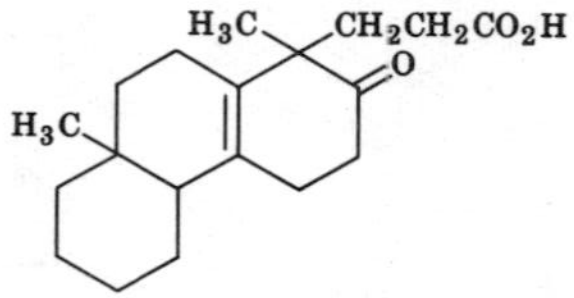 H_3C, H_3C, $CH_2CH_2CO_2H$, O (22)	774
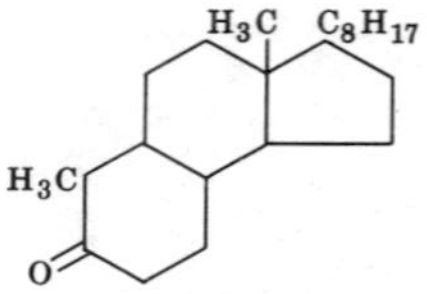 H_3C, C_8H_{17}, H_3C, O (Inhoffen ketone)	$[C_6H_5N(CH_3)_3]OH$	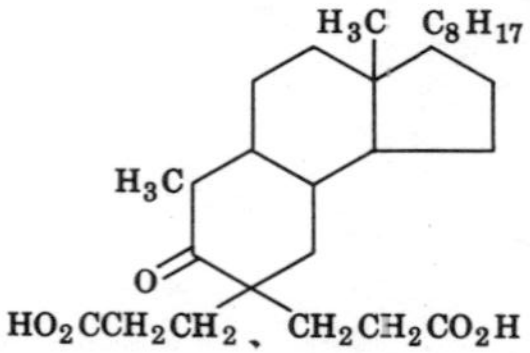 H_3C, C_8H_{17}, H_3C, O, $HO_2CCH_2CH_2$, $CH_2CH_2CO_2H$ (11)	368
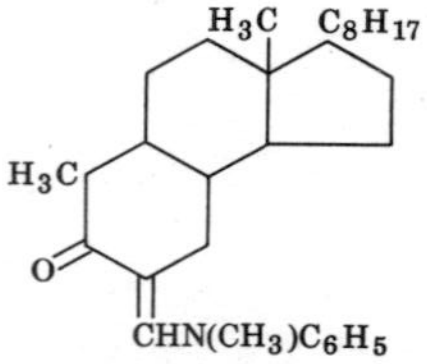 H_3C, C_8H_{17}, H_3C, O, $CHN(CH_3)C_6H_5$	$[C_6H_5N(CH_3)_3]OH$	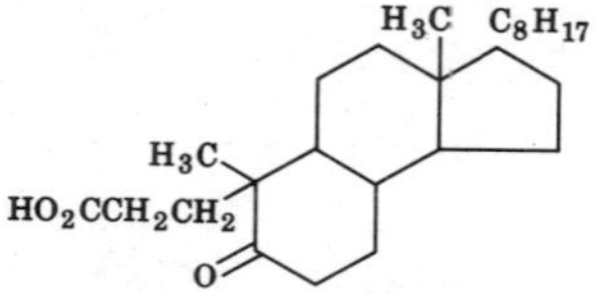 H_3C, C_8H_{17}, H_3C, $HO_2CCH_2CH_2$, O (Windaus acid)	368, 775

Reactant	Catalyst	Product (Yield, %)	Refs.
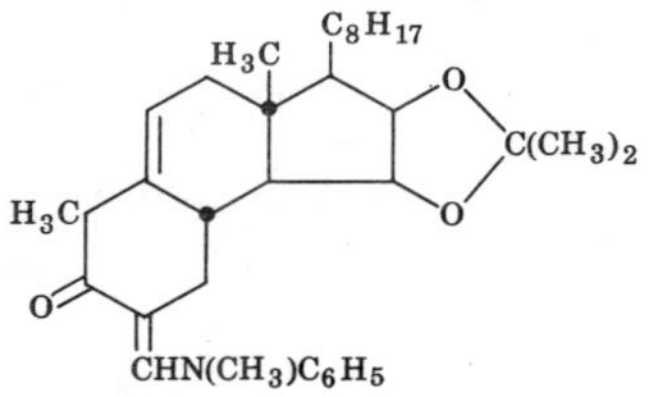	$[C_6H_5N(CH_3)_3]OH$	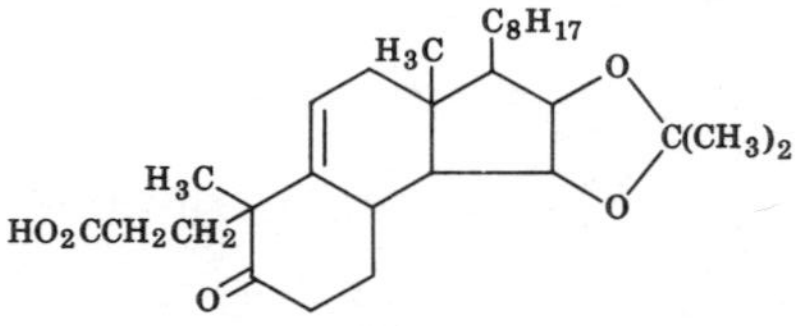 (33% α and 46% β isomer)	551
Acetophenone	$[C_6H_5CH_2N(CH_3)_3]OH$ or OC_4H_9-n	$C_6H_5COC(A)_3$ (57–64)	277, 279, 761
	Aq. KCN	$C_6H_5COCH(A)_2$ (30) and $C_6H_5COC(A)_3$ (small)	776
	$[C_6H_5N(CH_3)_3]OC_2H_5$	$C_6H_5COC(A)_3$ (65)	767
	$[C_6H_5CH_2N(CH_3)_3]$-OC_4H_9-n	$C_6H_5COC(A)_3$ (64)	767
	$[C_6H_5CH_2N(CH_3)_3]OH$	$C_6H_5COC(A)_3$ (57)	767
4-Chloroacetophenone	$[C_6H_5CH_2N(CH_3)_3]OH$; KOH	p-$ClC_6H_4COC(A)_3$	761
4-Bromoacetophenone	$[C_6H_5CH_2N(CH_3)_3]OH$; KOH	p-$BrC_6H_4COC(A)_3$	761
4-Methylacetophenone	$[C_6H_5CH_2N(CH_3)_3]OH$; KOH	p-$CH_3C_6H_4COC(A)_3$	761
4-Methoxyacetophenone	$[C_6H_5CH_2N(CH_3)_3]OH$; KOH	p-$CH_3OC_6H_4COC(A)_3$	761
Propiophenone	$[C_6H_5CH_2N(CH_3)_3]OH$; KOH	$C_6H_5COC(A)_2CH_3$ (quant.)	761
Phenylacetone	$[C_6H_5CH_2N(CH_3)_3]OH$; KOH	$C_6H_5C(A)_2COCH_3$ (86)	761
	Na enolate	$C_6H_5CH(A)COCH_3$ (80)	107

Note: References 491–1095 are on pp. 545–555.

* Compare the review by Bruson.[274]

TABLE X—*Continued*

MICHAEL CONDENSATIONS WITH ACRYLONITRILE*

Reactants	Catalyst	Product (Yield, %)	References
C. Ketones (Cont.)		$A = -CH_2CH_2CN$	
Isobutyrophenone	KOH, CH_3OH	$C_6H_5COC(A)(CH_3)_2$	276
Benzoylacetone	$[C_6H_5CH_2N(CH_3)_3]OH$ or OC_4H_9-*n*	$C_6H_5COC(A)_2COCH_3$	277
2,4,6-Trimethylacetophenone	$[C_6H_5CH_2N(CH_3)_3]OH$; KOH	2,4,6-$(CH_3)_3C_6H_2COC(A)_3$ (30)	761
Isopropyl benzyl ketone	KOH, CH_3OH	$C_6H_5CH_2COC(A)(CH_3)_2$	276
Methyl β-naphthyl ketone	$[C_6H_5CH_2N(CH_3)_3]OH$	β-$C_{10}H_7COC(A)_3$	761
α-*n*-Butylpropiophenone	KOH, CH_3OH	$C_6H_5COC(A)(CH_3)C_4H_9$-*n*	276
α-*n*-Propylbutyrophenone	KOH, CH_3OH	$C_6H_5COC(A)(C_2H_5)C_3H_7$-*n*	276
Deoxybenzoin	$[C_6H_5CH_2N(CH_3)_3]OH$; KOH	$C_6H_5C(A)_2COC_6H_5$ (80)	761
Anthrone	$[C_6H_5CH_2N(CH_3)_3]OH$	9,9-Di-(β-cyanoethyl)-10-anthrone (89)	288
	KOC_4H_9-*t*	O; H, $CH_2CH_2CO_2H$ (90–95) §§	777
4-Phenylacetophenone	$[C_6H_5CH_2N(CH_3)_3]OH$; KOH	4-$C_6H_5C_6H_4COC(A)_3$	761
Dibenzyl ketone	$[C_6H_5CH_2N(CH_3)_3]OH$; KOH	$C_6H_5C(A)_2COCH(A)C_6H_5$	761

α-*n*-Octylpropiophenone	KOH, CH_3OH	$C_6H_5COC(A)(CH_3)C_8H_{17}$-*n*	276
Methyl α-phenylnonyl ketone	KOH, CH_3OH	$CH_3COC(A)(C_8H_{17}$-*n*$)C_6H_5$	276
2-Acetylfuran	$[C_6H_5CH_2N(CH_3)_3]OH$ or OC_4H_9-*n*	[furan ring, O] $COC(A)_3$ (90–93)	277, 279
2-Acetyl-5-methylfuran	$[C_6H_5CH_2N(CH_3)_3]OH$	H_3C [furan ring, O] $COC(A)_3$ (71)	778
2-Propionylfuran	$[C_6H_5CH_2N(CH_3)_3]OH$	[furan ring, O] $COC(A)_2CH_3$ (Quant.)	279
3-Acetyl-2,5-dimethylfuran	$[C_6H_5CH_2N(CH_3)_3]OH$	H_3C [furan ring, O] CH_3, $COC(A)_3$ (16)	778
2-Propionyl-5-methylfuran	$[C_6H_5CH_2N(CH_3)_3]OH$	H_3C [furan ring, O] $COC(A)_2CH_3$ (62)	778
2-*n*-Butyrylfuran	$[C_6H_5CH_2N(CH_3)_3]OH$	[furan ring, O] $COC(A)_2CH_2CH_3$ (70)	279
2,5-Dimethyl-3-propionylfuran	$[C_6H_5CH_2N(CH_3)_3]OH$	H_3C [furan ring, O] CH_3, $COCH(A)CH_3$ (27); H_3C [furan ring, O] CH_3, $COC(A)_2CH_3$ (45)	778

Note: References 491–1045 are on pp. 545–555.

* Compare the review by Bruson.[274]

§§ Acrylonitrile was formed *in situ* from β-chloropropionitrile.

TABLE X—*Continued*

MICHAEL CONDENSATIONS WITH ACRYLONITRILE*

Reactants	Catalyst	Product (Yield, %)	References
		A = $—CH_2CH_2CN$	
C. Ketones (Cont.)			
2-*n*-Butyryl-5-methylfuran	$[C_6H_5CH_2N(CH_3)_3]OH$	H_3C–(O)–$COCH(A)C_2H_5$ (23); H_3C–(O)–$COC(A)_2C_2H_5$ (47)	778
3-*n*-Butyryl-2,5-dimethylfuran	$[C_6H_5CH_2N(CH_3)_3]OH$	H_3C–(O)–CH_3, $COC(A)_2C_2H_5$ (54)	778
2-Acetylthiophene	$[C_6H_5CH_2N(CH_3)_3]OH$ or OC_4H_9-*n*	(S)–$COC(A)_3$ (87–89)	277, 279
2-Acetyl-5-methylthiophene	$[C_6H_5CH_2N(CH_3)_3]OH$	H_3C–(S)–$COC(A)_3$ (80)	778
2-Propionylthiophene	$[C_6H_5CH_2N(CH_3)_3]OH$	(S)–$COC(A)_2CH_3$ (98)	279
5-Methyl-2-propionylthiophene	$[C_6H_5CH_2N(CH_3)_3]OH$	H_3C–(S)–$COC(A)_2CH_3$ (70)	778
2-*n*-Butyrylthiophene	$[C_6H_5CH_2N(CH_3)_3]OH$	(S)–$COCH(A)C_2H_5$ (36); (S)–$COC(A)_2C_2H_5$ (48)	778

2-Acetoxyacetylthiophene	$[C_6H_5CH_2N(CH_3)_3]OH$	2-thienyl-$COC(A)_2OCOCH_3$ (40)	277
5-Methyl-2-*n*-butyrylthiophene	$[C_6H_5CH_2N(CH_3)_3]OH$	5-H_3C-2-thienyl-$COCH(A)C_2H_5$ (43) 5-H_3C-2-thienyl-$COC(A)_2C_2H_5$ (27)	778
1,2,5-Trimethyl-4-piperidone	KOH	4-piperidone (O), 2-H_3C, 3-A, 3-CH_3, N-CH_3 (90)	769
2,5-Dimethyl-1-ethyl-4-piperidone	KOH	4-piperidone (O), 2-H_3C, 3-A, 3-CH_3, N-C_2H_5 (90)	769
1,2,3,6-Tetramethyl-4-piperidone	KOH	4-piperidone (O), 6-H_3C, 3-A, 3-CH_3, 2-CH_3, N-CH_3 (70)	769

Note: References 491–1045 are on pp. 545–555.

* Compare the review by Bruson.[274]

TABLE X—*Continued*

MICHAEL CONDENSATIONS WITH ACRYLONITRILE*

Reactants	Catalyst	Product (Yield, %)	References
C. Ketones (Cont.)		$A = —CH_2CH_2CN$	
1,2-Dimethyloctahydro-4-(1H)-quinolone	KOH	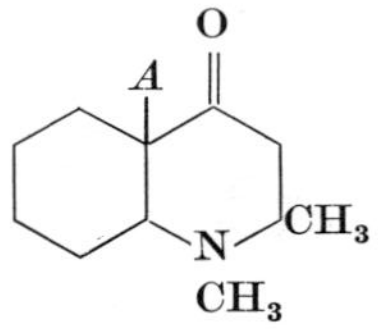 O; A; N; CH_3; CH_3 (91)	769
2,2-Dimethyl-4-pyranone	KOH	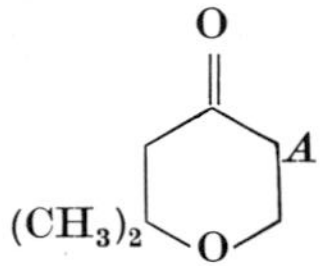 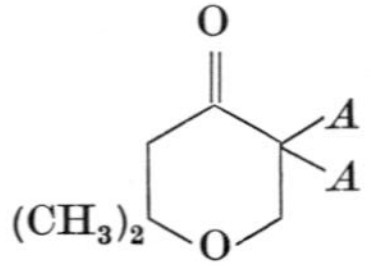 O; A; $(CH_3)_2$; O (25); O; A; A; $(CH_3)_2$; O (50)	769
Kojic acid	$[C_6H_5CH_2N(CH_3)_3]OH$	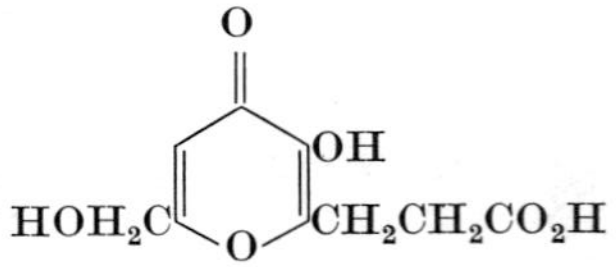 O; OH; HOH_2C; O; $CH_2CH_2CO_2H$ ‡‡ (47)	170
3-Oxo-2,2,5,5-tetramethyltetrahydrofuran	$[C_6H_5CH_2N(CH_3)_3]OH$; KOH	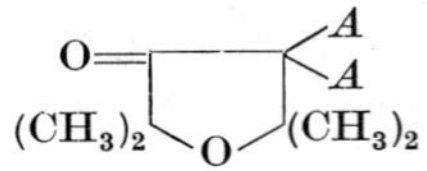 O=; A; A; $(CH_3)_2$; O; $(CH_3)_2$ (63)	761
3-Ethyl-1-methyloxindole	$[C_6H_5CH_2N(CH_3)_3]OH$	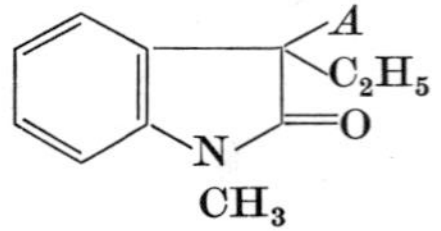 A; C_2H_5; =O; N; CH_3 (71)	779

D. Esters and Amides			
Diethyl malonate	$NaOC_2H_5$; Na	$A CH(CO_2C_2H_5)_2$ (57–63); $(A)_2C(CO_2C_2H_5)_2$ (12)	780, 781, 288, 781*a*
	$[C_6H_5CH_2N(CH_3)_3]OH$	$(A)_2C(CO_2C_2H_5)_2$ (82)	288
	$[C_6H_5N(CH_3)_3]OC_2H_5$	$A CH(CO_2C_2H_5)_2$ (27); $(A)_2C(CO_2C_2H_5)_2$ (10)‖‖	767
Malonamide	$[C_6H_5CH_2N(CH_3)_3]OH$	$(A)_2C(CONH_2)_2$ (14)	282
Diethyl methylmalonate	$[C_6H_5CH_2N(CH_3)_3]OH$	$A C(CH_3)(CO_2C_2H_5)_2$ (93)	782
	KOH, CH_3OH	α-Methylglutaric acid‡‡	783
Diethyl *n*-propylmalonate	KOH, CH_3OH	α-Propylglutaric acid‡‡	783
Diethyl *n*-butylmalonate	KOH, CH_3OH	α-*n*-Butylglutaric acid‡‡	783
	Na; $NaOCH_3$; $NaOC_2H_5$; $[C_6H_5CH_2N(CH_3)_3]OH$	n-$C_4H_9C(A)(CO_2C_2H_5)_2$ (87–94)	282, 781, 784
Diethyl *n*-hexylmalonate	$NaOCH_3$; $NaOC_2H_5$	n-$C_6H_{13}C(A)(CO_2C_2H_5)_2$ (82)	784
Diethyl *n*-octylmalonate	$NaOCH_3$; $NaOC_2H_5$	n-$C_8H_{17}C(A)(CO_2C_2H_5)_2$ (90)	784
Diethyl *n*-decylmalonate	$NaOCH_3$; $NaOC_2H_5$	n-$C_{10}H_{21}C(A)(CO_2C_2H_5)_2$ (89)	784
Diethyl *n*-dodecylmalonate	$NaOCH_3$; $NaOC_2H_5$	n-$C_{12}H_{25}C(A)(CO_2C_2H_5)_2$ (92)	784
Diethyl *n*-tetradecylmalonate	$NaOCH_3$; $NaOC_2H_5$	n-$C_{14}H_{29}C(A)(CO_2C_2H_5)_2$ (86)	784
Diethyl cetylmalonate	$NaOCH_3$; $NaOC_2H_5$	n-$C_{16}H_{33}(A)(CO_2C_2H_5)_2$ (89)	784
Tetraethyl ethane-1,1,2,2-tetracarboxylate	$[C_6H_5CH_2N(CH_3)_8]OH$	$(C_2H_5O_2C)_2C(A)CH(CO_2C_2H_5)_2$ (77)	367
Diethyl phenylmalonate	KOH, CH_3OH	α-Phenylglutaric acid‡‡	783
	$NaOC_2H_5$	$C_6H_5C(A)(CO_2C_2H_5)_2$ (72)	785
Diethyl benzylmalonate	KOH, CH_3OH	α-Benzylglutaric acid‡‡	783
	$[C_6H_5CH_2N(CH_3)_3]OH$	$C_6H_5CH_2C(A)(CO_2C_2H_5)_2$ (81)	283
Diethyl phenethylmalonate	KOH, CH_3OH	α-Phenethylglutaric acid‡‡	783
Diethyl 1-naphthylmalonate	KOH, CH_3OH	α-(1-Naphthyl)glutaric acid‡‡	783

Note: References 491–1045 are on pp. 545–555.

* Compare the review by Bruson.[274]

‡‡ This product was isolated after saponification of the adduct.

‖‖ β-Ethoxypropionitrile was employed instead of acrylonitrile.

TABLE X—*Continued*

MICHAEL CONDENSATIONS WITH ACRYLONITRILE*

Reactants	Catalyst	Product (Yield, %)	References
D. Esters and Amides (*Cont.*)		A = —CH_2CH_2CN	
Diethyl 2-naphthylmalonate	KOH, CH_3OH	α-(2-Naphthyl)glutaric acid‡‡	783
Diethyl (1-naphthylmethyl)-malonate	KOH, CH_3OH	α-(1-Naphthylmethyl)glutaric acid‡‡	783
Diethyl (2-naphthylmethyl)-malonate	KOH, CH_3OH	α-(2-Naphthylmethyl)glutaric acid‡‡	783
Diethyl (β-1-naphthylethyl)-malonate	KOH, CH_3OH	α-(β-1-Naphthylethyl)glutaric acid‡‡	783
Diethyl (β-2-naphthylethyl)-malonate	KOH, CH_3OH	α-(β-2-Naphthylethyl)glutaric acid‡‡	783
Vinylacetamide (or crotonamide)	$[C_6H_5CH_2N(CH_3)_3]OH$	CH_2=$CHC(A)_2CONH_2$ (18)	283
Diethyl β-(4-methoxy-1-naphthyl)ethylmalonate	KOH, CH_3OH, $(CH_3)_3COH$	4-Methoxy-1-naphthyl–$CH_2CH_2CHCO_2H$‡‡ with $CH_2CH_2CO_2H$ on the CH (40) [structure: 4-OCH_3 naphthalene]	786
Diethyl β-(5-methoxy-1-naphthyl)ethylmalonate	KOH, CH_3OH, $(CH_3)_3COH$	5-Methoxy-1-naphthyl–$CH_2CH_2CHCO_2H$‡‡ with $CH_2CH_2CO_2H$ on the CH (32) [structure: 5-OCH_3 naphthalene]	786

Diethyl β-(6-methoxy-1-naphthyl)ethylmalonate	KOH, CH_3OH, $(CH_3)_3COH$	CH_3O–[naphthalene ring]–$CH_2CH_2CHCO_2H$‡‡ with $CH_2CH_2CO_2H$ (61)	786
Diethyl β-(7-methoxy-1-naphthyl)ethylmalonate	KOH, CH_3OH, $(CH_3)_3COH$	CH_3O–[naphthalene ring]–$CH_2CH_2CHCO_2H$‡‡ with $CH_2CH_2CO_2H$	786
Diethyl formamidomalonate	$NaOC_2H_5$	Glutamic acid‡‡ (55)	459
Diethyl acetamidomalonate	$NaOC_2H_5$	$CH_3CONHC(A)(CO_2C_2H_5)_2$ (95)	458
Ethyl cyanoacetate	Aq. NaOH	$NCCH(A)CO_2C_2H_5$, $NCC(A)_2CO_2C_2H_5$	469
	$[C_6H_5CH_2N(CH_3)_3]OH$	$NCC(A)_2CO_2C_2H_5$ (quant.)	367, 282
	NaCN	$NCCH(A)CO_2C_2H_5$ and a little $NCC(A)_2CO_2C_2H_5$	469
Cyanoacetamide	$[C_6H_5CH_2N(CH_3)_3]OH$	$NCC(A)_2CONH_2$ (56)	282
Ethyl α-isopropylcyanoacetate	KOH, CH_3OH	α-Isopropylglutaric acid‡‡	783
Diethyl α-methyl-α′-cyanosuccinate	$NaOCH_3$	$C_2H_5O_2CCH(CH_3)C(CN)(A)CO_2C_2H_5$ (94)	787
Ethyl α,β-dicyano-β-methylbutyrate	$[C_6H_5CH_2N(CH_3)_3]OH$	$(CH_3)_2C(CN)C(A)(CN)CO_2C_2H_5$ (89)	788, 789
Diethyl α-cyano-β,β-dimethylglutarate	Not indicated	$C_2H_5O_2CCH_2C(CH_3)_2C(A)(CN)CO_2C_2H_5$ (72)	790
Diethyl 3,4-dicyano-3-methylbutane-1,4-dicarboxylate	$[C_6H_5CH_2N(CH_3)_3]OH$	$AC(CN)(CO_2C_2H_5)C(CN)(CH_3)CH_2CH_2CO_2C_2H_5$ (83)	791

Note: References 491–1045 are on pp. 545–555.

* Compare the review by Bruson.[274]

‡‡ This product was isolated after saponification of the adduct.

TABLE X—*Continued*

MICHAEL CONDENSATIONS WITH ACRYLONITRILE*

Reactants	Catalyst	Product (Yield, %)	References
D. Esters and Amides (*Cont.*)		$A = —CH_2CH_2CN$	
Ethyl phenylcyanoacetate	KOH, CH_3OH	$C_6H_5C(A)(CN)(CO_2C_2H_5)$ (69–83)	792
Diethyl 1,2-dicyano-2-methyl-pentane-1,5-dicarboxylate	$[C_6H_5CH_2N(CH_3)_3]OH$	$C_2H_5O_2C(CH_2)_3C(CN)(CH_3)C(A)(CN)CO_2C_2H_5$ (99)	793
Methyl ethylphenylacetate	$NaOCH_3$	$(C_6H_5)(C_2H_5)C(A)CO_2CH_3$	794
Methyl *n*-propylphenylacetate	$NaOCH_3$	$(C_6H_5)(n\text{-}C_3H_7)C(A)CO_2CH_3$	794
Methyl *n*-butylphenylacetate	$NaOCH_3$	$(C_6H_5)(n\text{-}C_4H_9)C(A)CO_2CH_3$	794
Methyl isobutylphenylacetate	$NaOCH_3$	$C_6H_5(i\text{-}C_4H_9)C(A)CO_2CH_3$	794
Methyl diphenylacetate	$NaOCH_3$	$(C_6H_5)_2C(A)CO_2CH_3$	794
Methyl fluorene-9-carboxylate	KOH	9-Carbomethoxy-9-(β-cyanoethyl)fluorene (94)	795
Ethyl 1-methylfluorene-9-carboxylate	NaOH, pyridine	9-Carbethoxy-9-(β-cyanoethyl)-1-methylfluorene (78)	482
Ethyl 2,7-dibromofluorene-9-carboxylate	$[C_6H_5CH_2N(CH_3)_3]OH$	9-Carbethoxy-9-(β-cyanoethyl)-2,7-dibromofluorene (93)	796
Methyl 4-cyclopenta[*def*]-phenanthrene-4-carboxylate	$[C_6H_5CH_2N(CH_3)_3]OH$	H, $CH_2CH_2CO_2H$ (90)	797
Ethyl α-furylacetate	$[C_6H_5CH_2N(CH_3)_3]OH$ or $OC_4H_9\text{-}n$	O, $C(A)_2CO_2C_2H_5$ (25)	277

Ethyl α-thienylacetate	$[C_6H_5CH_2N(CH_3)_3]OH$ or OC_4H_9-n	2-thienyl-$C(A)_2CO_2C_2H_5$ (32)	277
Ethyl 2-pyridylacetate	Na	2-pyridyl-$CH(A)CO_2C_2H_5$ (72)	798
E. Keto Esters and Amides			
Methyl acetoacetate	$[C_6H_5CH_2N(CH_3)_3]OH$	$CH_3COC(A)_2CO_2CH_3$ (49)	760, 761
Ethyl acetoacetate	$[C_6H_5CH_2N(CH_3)_3]OH$ or OC_4H_9-n	$CH_3COC(A)_2CO_2C_2H_5$ (79–80) or $CH_3COCH(A)CO_2C_2H_5$ (79–80)	277, 760, 761, 767
	$[C_6H_5CH_2N(CH_3)_3]OC_2H_5$	$CH_3COC(A)_2CO_2C_2H_5$ (83)	767
	$NaOC_2H_5$	$CH_3COCH(A)CO_2C_2H_5$ (40)	799
Ethyl methylacetoacetate	KOH, CH_3OH, $(CH_3)_3COH$	$CH_3COC(CH_3)(A)CO_2C_2H_5$ (58, 57)	766, 800
		α-Methylglutaric acid (51)‡‡	800
	$NaOC_2H_5$	$CH_3COC(CH_3)(A)CO_2C_2H_5$ (61)	782
	—	$CH_3COCH(A)CH_3$ (34)‡‡	801
Ethyl ethylacetoacetate	KOH, CH_3OH, $(CH_3)_3COH$	$CH_3COC(C_2H_5)(A)CO_2C_2H_5$ (62)	800
		α-Ethylglutaric acid (62)‡‡	800
	—	$CH_3COCH(A)CH_2CH_3$ (43)‡‡	801
Ethyl *n*-propylacetoacetate	KOH, CH_3OH, $(CH_3)_3COH$	$CH_3COC(C_3H_7$-$n)(A)CO_2C_2H_5$ (88)	800
	—	α-*n*-Propylglutaric acid (88)‡‡	800
		$CH_3COCH(A)CH_2CH_2CH_3$ (36)‡‡	801

Note: References 491–1045 are on pp. 545–555.

* Compare the review by Bruson.[274]

‡‡ This product was isolated after saponification of the adduct.

TABLE X—*Continued*

MICHAEL CONDENSATIONS WITH ACRYLONITRILE*

Reactants	Catalyst	Product (Yield, %)	References
E. Keto Esters and Amides (*Cont.*)		A = —CH_2CH_2CN	
Ethyl isopropylacetoacetate	KOH, CH_3OH, $(CH_3)_3COH$	$CH_3COC(C_3H_7\text{-}i)(A)CO_2C_2H_5$ (37, 43)	591, 800
		α-Isopropylglutaric acid (43)‡‡	800
Ethyl allylacetoacetate	KOH, CH_3OH, $(CH_3)_3COH$	$CH_3COC(C_3H_5)(A)CO_2C_2H_5$ (76)	800
		α-Allylglutaric acid (76)‡‡	800
Ethyl *n*-butylacetoacetate	KOH, CH_3OH, $(CH_3)_3COH$	$CH_3COC(C_4H_9\text{-}n)(A)CO_2C_2H_5$ (74–75)	119, 800
		α-*n*-Butylglutaric acid (75)‡‡	800
	—	$CH_3COCH(A)CH_2CH_2CH_2CH_3$ (35)‡‡	801
Ethyl *n*-amylacetoacetate	KOH, CH_3OH, $(CH_3)_3COH$; Na	$CH_3COC(C_5H_{11}\text{-}n)(A)CO_2C_2H_5$ (71)	781, 800
		α-*n*-Amylglutaric acid (71)‡‡	800
	—	$CH_3COCH(A)(CH_2)_4CH_3$ (32)‡‡	801
Ethyl isoamylacetoacetate	KOH, CH_3OH, $(CH_3)_3COH$	$CH_3COC(C_5H_{11}\text{-}i)(A)CO_2C_2H_5$ (72)	800
		α-Isoamylglutaric acid (72)‡‡	800
Ethyl *n*-hexylacetoacetate	KOH, CH_3OH, $(CH_3)_3COH$	$CH_3COC(C_6H_{13}\text{-}n)(A)CO_2C_2H_5$ (84)	800
		α-*n*-Hexylglutaric acid (84)‡‡	800
Ethyl phenylacetoacetate	$NaOC_2H_5$; KOH, CH_3OH, $(CH_3)_3COH$	$CH_3COC(C_6H_5)(A)CO_2C_2H_5$ (27)	802
Ethyl benzylacetoacetate	$NaOC_2H_5$	$CH_3COC(CH_2C_6H_5)(A)CO_2C_2H_5$ (85)	581
	KOH, CH_3OH, $(CH_3)_3COH$	$CH_3COC(CH_2C_6H_5)(A)CO_2C_2H_5$ (66)	800
		α-Benzylglutaric acid (66)‡‡	800
	—	$CH_3COCH(A)CH_2C_6H_5$ (31)‡‡	801
Ethyl *n*-butyrylacetate	$[C_6H_5CH_2N(CH_3)_3]OH$ or $OC_4H_9\text{-}n$	$n\text{-}C_3H_7COC(A)_2CO_2C_2H_5$ (34–36, 74)	217, 119
	$NaOC_2H_5$	$n\text{-}C_3H_7COCH(A)CO_2C_2H_5$ (52)	799

Ethyl isobutyrylacetate	$[C_6H_5CH_2N(CH_3)_3]OH$ or OC_4H_9-*n*	$(CH_3)_2CHCOC(A)_2CO_2C_2H_5$ (65–68)	277
	$NaOC_2H_5$	$(CH_3)_2CHCOCH(A)CO_2C_2H_5$ (53)	799
Ethyl isovalerylacetate	$NaOC_2H_5$	*i*-$C_4H_9COCH(A)CO_2C_2H_5$ (46)	799
Ethyl hexanoylacetate	$NaOC_2H_5$	*n*-$C_5H_{11}COCH(A)CO_2C_2H_5$ (38, 67)	799, 803
Ethyl heptanoylacetate	$NaOC_2H_5$	*n*-$C_6H_{13}COCH(A)CO_2C_2H_5$ (35)	799
Ethyl benzoylacetate	$[C_6H_5CH_2N(CH_3)_3]OH$ or OC_4H_9-*n*	$C_6H_5COC(A)_2CO_2C_2H_5$ (53)	277
	$NaOC_2H_5$	$C_6H_5COCH(A)CO_2C_2H_5$ (86, 43)	581, 799
Ethyl 2-furoylacetate	$NaOC_2H_5$	2-Furyl-$COCH(A)CO_2C_2H_5$ (37)	799
Ethyl 2-thenoylacetate	$NaOC_2H_5$	2-Thienyl-$COCH(A)CO_2C_2H_5$ (64)	799
2-Carbethoxycyclohexanone	KOH, C_2H_5OH; $NaOC_2H_5$; $NaNH_2$; $[C_6H_5CH_2N(CH_3)_3]OH$	2-$CO_2C_2H_5$-2-*A*-cyclohexanone (85)	119, 121, 694
Methyl camphor-3-carboxylate	KOH, C_2H_5OH	3-Carbomethoxy-3-(*β*-cyanoethyl)camphor (78)	119
2-Carbomethoxy-1-tetralone	$[C_6H_5CH_2N(CH_3)_3]OH$	2-CO_2CH_3-2-*A*-1-tetralone (92)	804

Note: References 491–1045 are on pp. 545–555.

* Compare the review by Bruson.[274]

‡‡ This product was isolated after saponification of the adduct.

TABLE X—*Continued*

MICHAEL CONDENSATIONS WITH ACRYLONITRILE*

Reactants	Catalyst	Product (Yield, %)	References
		A = —CH_2CH_2CN	
E. Keto Esters and Amides (Cont.)			
Acetoacetanilide	$[C_6H_5CH_2N(CH_3)_3]OH$	$CH_3COC(A)_2CONHC_6H_5$	760
Acetoacet-2-chloroanilide	$[C_6H_5CH_2N(CH_3)_3]OH$	$CH_3COC(A)_2CONHC_6H_4Cl$-*o*	760
Acetoacet-2,5-dichloroanilide	$[C_6H_5CH_2N(CH_3)_3]OH$	$CH_3COC(A)_2CONHC_6H_3Cl_2$-2,5	760
Acetobutyrolactone	$NaOC_2H_5$	2-Aceto-2-(β-cyanoethyl)butyrolactone (86–92)	581
F. Nitriles			
Allyl cyanide (or crotononitrile)	$[C_6H_5CH_2N(CH_3)_3]OH$	$CH_3CH{=}C(A)CN$ (9)	283
		$CH_2{=}CHC(A)_2CN$ (23)	
Isopropenyl cyanide (or β,β-dimethylacrylonitrile)	$[C_6H_5CH_2N(CH_3)_3]OH$	$(CH_3)_2C{=}C(A)CN$ (5)	
		$CH_2{=}C(CH_3)C(A)_2CN$ (11)	283
Benzyl cyanide	Aq. NaCN	$C_6H_5CH(A)CN$ (80)	469
	$[C_6H_5CH_2N(CH_3)_3]OH$	$C_6H_5C(A)_2CN$ (94)	282
	$NaOC_2H_5$	$C_6H_5C(A)_2CN$ (46)	805
	KOH, CH_3OH, $(CH_3)_3COH$	$C_6H_5C(A)_2CN$ (70)	767
	$[C_6H_5N(CH_3)_3]OC_2H_5$	$C_6H_5C(A)_2CN$ (90)	767
p-Nitrobenzyl cyanide	$[C_6H_5CH_2N(CH_3)_3]OH$	*p*-$O_2NC_6H_4C(A)_2CN$ (90)	282
o-Chlorobenzyl cyanide	KOH, CH_3OH, $(CH_3)_3COH$	*o*-$ClC_6H_4C(A)_2CN$ (47)	806
m-Chlorobenzyl cyanide	KOH, CH_3OH, $(CH_3)_3COH$	*m*-$ClC_6H_4C(A)_2CN$ (64)	806
p-Chlorobenzyl cyanide	KOH	*p*-$ClC_6H_4C(A)_2CN$ (80)	807
m-Bromobenzyl cyanide	KOH, CH_3OH, $(CH_3)_3COH$	*m*-$BrC_6H_4C(A)_2CN$ (89)	806
p-Bromobenzyl cyanide	KOH, CH_3OH, $(CH_3)_3COH$	*p*-$BrC_6H_4C(A)_2CN$ (84)	806
m-Methylbenzyl cyanide	KOH, CH_3OH, $(CH_3)_3COH$	*m*-$CH_3C_6H_4C(A)_2CN$ (88)	806
p-Methylbenzyl cyanide	KOH, CH_3OH, $(CH_3)_3COH$	*p*-$CH_3C_6H_4C(A)_2CN$ (95)	806
α-Phenylpropionitrile	KOH, CH_3OH, $(CH_3)_3COH$	$(C_6H_5)(CH_3)C(A)CN$ (55)	758

p-Isopropylbenzyl cyanide	KOH	p-$(CH_3)_2CHC_6H_4C(A)_2CN$	807
Cyclohexenylacetonitrile	$[C_6H_5CH_2N(CH_3)_3]OH$	$C(A)_2CN$ (37)	283
α-(2-Thienyl)benzyl cyanide	$[C_6H_5CH_2N(CH_3)_3]OH$	S; $C(A)(C_6H_5)CN$	808
α-Naphthylacetonitrile	$[C_6H_5CH_2N(CH_3)_3]OH$	α-$C_{10}H_7C(A)_2CN$ (55)	807
α-(1-Cyclohexenyl)benzyl cyanide	$[C_6H_5CH_2N(CH_3)_3]OH$	$C(A)(C_6H_5)CN$	808
1-Cyano-2-benzoyl-1,2-dihydro-isoquinoline	Li salt	N; C_6H_5; $CONH_2$	805*a*
G. Nitro Compounds			
Nitromethane	$NaOCH_3$; aq. K_2CO_3	$(A)_2CHNO_2$ (low); $(A)_3CNO_2$ (52)	117, 281
	$[C_6H_5CH_2N(CH_3)_3]OH$	$(A)_3CNO_2$ (45)	282
Nitroethane	$(C_2H_5)_2NH$; $NaOCH_3$	$CH_3CH(A)NO_2$ (30)	117, 280
	Aq. K_2CO_3	$CH_3C(A)_2NO_2$ (67)	281
2-Nitropropane	Aq. KOH	$(CH_3)_2C(A)NO_2$ (78)	117
Nitrocyclohexane	Aq. KOH	1-Nitro-1-(β-cyanoethyl)cyclohexane (40)	117
$O_2NCH{=}NO_2K$	Aq. solution	$(A)_2C(NO_2)_2$ (34); $(A)_3CNO_2$ (12)	809

Note: References 491–1045 are on pp. 545–555.

* Compare the review by Bruson.[274]

TABLE X—*Continued*

MICHAEL CONDENSATIONS WITH ACRYLONITRILE*

Reactants	Catalyst	Product (Yield, %)	References
G. Nitro Compounds (Cont.)		A = —CH_2CH_2CN	
$CH_3O_2CCH_2CH_2C(NO_2){=}NO_2Na$	Aq. solution	$AC(NO_2)_2CH_2CH_2CO_2CH_3$	810
p-Bromophenylnitromethane	$[C_6H_5CH_2N(CH_3)_3]OH$	*p*-$BrC_6H_4C(A)_2NO_2$ (15)	117
Methyl 2-nitro-1-phenylpropyl ether	Aq. NaOH	3-Nitro-3-methyl-4-methoxy-4-phenylvaleronitrile (30)	117
n-Butyl 3-nitro-*n*-butyl sulfone	$[CH_3N(C_2H_5)_3]OH$	3-Nitro-3-methyl-5-(butylsulfonyl)-1-pentanecarbonitrile	117
Ethyl nitroacetate	KOH, ethanol	Ethyl α-nitro-γ-cyanobutyrate (19)	811
	$[C_6H_5CH_2N(CH_3)_3]OH$	$O_2NCH(A)CO_2C_2H_5$ (52)	812
		$O_2NC(A)_2CO_2C_2H_5$ (80)	812
	$(C_2H_5)_2NH$	$O_2NCH(A)CO_2C_2H_5$ (diethylamine salt) (81)	622
Methyl γ,γ-dinitrobutyrate	Na derivative in water	Methyl 6-cyano-4,4-dinitrohexanoate (51)	810
Endo(nitroethylene)anthracene	$NaOCH_3$	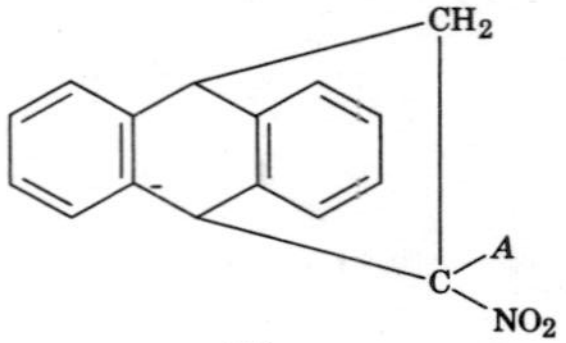 CH_2, A, NO_2 (48)	813

Reactant	Catalyst	Product (Yield, %)	Refs.
H. Sulfones			
Phenyl benzyl sulfone	$[C_6H_5CH_2N(CH_3)_3]OH$	$C_6H_5SO_2C(A)_2C_6H_5$ (60)	279, 814
Allyl *p*-tolyl sulfone	$[C_6H_5CH_2N(CH_3)_3]OH$	*p*-$CH_3C_6H_4SO_2CH(A)CH{=}CH_2$ and *p*-$CH_3C_6H_4SO_2C(A)_2CH{=}CH_2$	814
p-$CH_3C_6H_4SO_2CH_2CO_2C_2H_5$	KOH, CH_3OH	*p*-$CH_3C_6H_4SO_2C(A)_2CO_2C_2H_5$	814
Phenyl *p*-chlorobenzyl sulfone¶¶	$[C_6H_5CH_2N(CH_3)_3]OH$	*p*-$ClC_6H_4C(A)_2SO_2C_6H_5$ (60)	815
I. Phosphonoacetates			
Triethyl phosphonoacetate	$[C_6H_5CH_2N(CH_3)_3]OH$	$(C_2H_5O)_2P(O)C(A)_2CO_2C_2H_5$ (87)	816
	$NaOC_2H_5$	$(C_2H_5O)_2P(O)CH(A)CO_2C_2H_5$ (28)	
		$(C_2H_5O)_2P(O)C(A)_2CO_2C_2H_5$ (27)	124
	Na	$(C_2H_5O)_2P(O)CH(A)CO_2C_2H_5$ (40)	817
		$(C_2H_5O)_2P(O)C(A)_2CO_2C_2H_5$ (19)	
	K	$(C_2H_5O)_2P(O)C(A)_2CO_2C_2H_5$ (68)	817
Diethyl cyanomethanephosphonate	$[C_6H_5CH_2N(CH_3)_3]OH$	$(C_2H_5O)_2P(O)C(CN)(A_2)$ (90)	816
	K	$(C_2H_5O)_2P(O)C(CN)(A)_2$ (80)	817
Triethyl α-phosphonopropionate	$NaOC_2H_5$	$(C_2H_5O)_2P(O)C(CH_3)(A)CO_2C_2H_5$ (58)	124
Triethyl α-phosphonohexanoate	$NaOC_2H_5$	$(C_2H_5O)_2P(O)C(C_4H_9\text{-}n)(A)CO_2C_2H_5$ (71)	124
	K	$(C_2H_5O)_2P(O)C(C_4H_9\text{-}n)(A)CO_2C_2H_5$ (73)	817

Note: References 491–1045 are on pp. 545–555.

* Compare the review by Bruson.[274]

¶¶ The ortho and meta isomers give analogous reactions. From *o*- and *m*-methyl benzylphenyl sulfone only undefined oils were formed; the para isomer failed to react.

TABLE XI

MICHAEL CONDENSATIONS WITH UNSATURATED NITRILES OTHER THAN ACRYLONITRILE

Reactants	Catalyst	Product (Yield, %)	References
Crotononitrile (or Allyl Cyanide) and		$A = CH_3\overset{\vert}{C}HCH_2CN$	
Ethyl cyanoacetate	$NaOC_2H_5$	$ACH(CN)CO_2C_2H_5$ (90)	77
Ethyl α-cyanopropionate	$NaOC_2H_5$	$CH_3C(A)(CN)CO_2C_2H_5$	77
Benzyl cyanide	$NaOC_2H_5$; $NaOCH_3$	$C_6H_5CH(A)CN$ (76)	27
1-Nitropropane	Aq. NaOH	$C_2H_5CH(A)NO_2$ (80)	117
2-Nitropropane	$[CH_3N(C_2H_5)_3]OH$	$(CH_3)_2C(A)NO_2$ (80)	117
Fluorene	$[C_6H_5CH_2N(CH_3)_3]OH$	9-H, 9-A-fluorene (structure: H A) (51)	282
Methyl fluorene-9-carboxylate	KOH	9-A-9-CO_2CH_3-fluorene (structure: A CO_2CH_3) (73)	291
Ethyl fluorene-9-carboxylate	KOH	9-A-9-$CO_2C_2H_5$-fluorene (structure: A $CO_2C_2H_5$) (70)	291
Methacrylonitrile and			
1,2,3,4-Tetrahydrofluoranthene	$[C_6H_5CH_2N(CH_3)_3]OH$	1-(β-Cyanopropyl)-1,2,3,4-tetrahydrofluoranthene	754, 755

Reactants	Catalyst	Product (Yield, %)	Refs.
γ-Methoxycrotononitrile and		$A = CH_3OCH_2\overset{\vert}{C}HCH_2CN$	
Diethyl malonate	$NaOC_2H_5$	ACH$(CO_2C_2H_5)_2$ (74)	818, cf. 819
Diethyl ethylmalonate	$NaOC_2H_5$	AC$(C_2H_5)(CO_2C_2H_5)_2$ (36)	820
Diethyl β-methoxyethylmalonate	$NaOC_2H_5$	AC$(CH_2CH_2OCH_3)(CO_2C_2H_5)_2$ (40–50)	820
Diethyl β-ethoxyethylmalonate	$NaOC_2H_5$	AC$(CH_2CH_2OC_2H_5)(CO_2C_2H_5)_2$ (42)	820
3-*Cyano*-1,2,5,6-*tetrahydropyridine and*			
Diethyl malonate	$NaOC_2H_5$	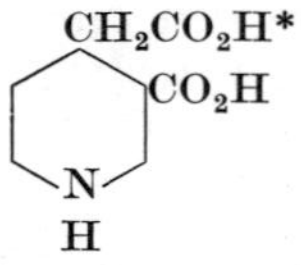 CH_2CO_2H* / CO_2H / N / H (Cincholoiponic acid, 2 isomers)	87
Cyclopentylideneacetonitrile and			
Cyanoacetamide	$NaOC_2H_5$	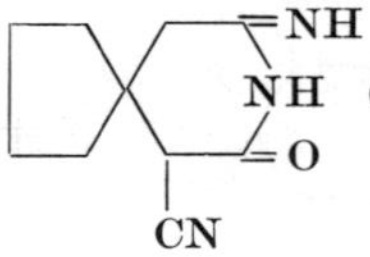 =NH / NH / =O / CN (< 30)	821
1-*Cyano*-2-*methyl*-1-*cyclohexene and*			
Diethyl malonate	$NaOC_2H_5$	Diethyl (2-cyano-1-methylcyclohexyl)malonate (low)	822
Cyclohexylideneacetonitrile and			
Cyanoacetamide	$NaOC_2H_5$	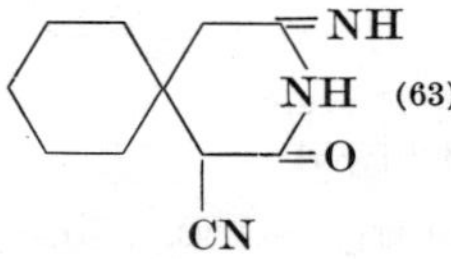 =NH / NH / =O / CN (63)	821

Note: References 491–1045 are on pp. 545–555.

* This product was obtained after hydrolysis and partial decarboxylation.

TABLE XI—*Continued*

MICHAEL CONDENSATIONS WITH UNSATURATED NITRILES OTHER THAN ACRYLONITRILE

Reactants	Catalyst	Product (Yield, %)	References
(3-*Methylcyclohexylidene*)*acetonitrile and*			
Cyanoacetamide	$NaOC_2H_5$	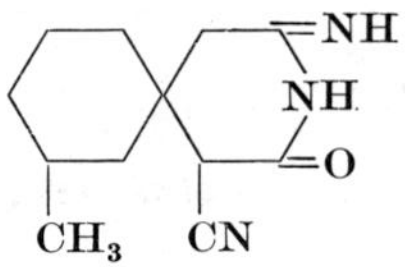 [structure: spiro compound with =NH, NH, =O, CH_3, CN] (25)	402*a*
(4-*Methylcyclohexylidene*)*acetonitrile and*			
Cyanoacetamide	$NaOC_2H_5$	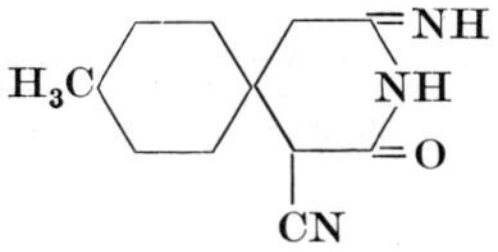 [structure: H_3C-substituted spiro compound with =NH, NH, =O, CN] (25)	402*a*
Cinnamonitrile and		$A = C_6H_5CHCH_2CN$ (with free bond on CH)	
Diethyl malonate	$NaOC_2H_5$	$ACH(CO_2C_2H_5)_2$ (83)	290
Ethyl phenylacetate	$NaOC_2H_5$; $NaOCH_3$	$C_6H_5CH(A)CO_2C_2H_5$ (50)	27
Benzyl cyanide	$NaOC_2H_5$; $NaOCH_3$	$C_6H_5CH(A)CN$ (80–87)	27, 805
p-Methoxybenzyl cyanide	$NaOC_2H_5$; $NaOCH_3$	*p*-$CH_3OC_6H_4CH(A)CN$ (23)	27
m-Aminobenzyl cyanide	$NaOC_2H_5$; $NaOCH_3$	*m*-$H_2NC_6H_4CH(A)CN$ (Two isomers: 17, 30)	27
Fluorene	$[C_6H_5CH_2N(CH_3)_3]OH$	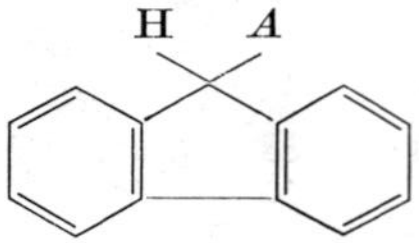 [structure: 9-fluorenyl with H and *A* at C-9] (50)	289

p-Methoxycinnamonitrile and			
Benzyl cyanide	$NaOC_2H_5$; $NaOCH_3$	$C_6H_5CH(CN)CH(C_6H_4OCH_3\text{-}p)CH_2CN$ (72)	27
2-*Hydrindanylideneacetonitrile and*			
Cyanoacetamide	$NaOC_2H_5$	=O, NH, =O, CN and	90
		CH_2CN, $CH(CN)CONH_2$	
α-*Phenylcinnamonitrile and*		$A = C_6H_5CHCH(C_6H_5)CN$	
Nitromethane	$(C_2H_5)_2NH$	ACH_2NO_2 (11)	117
Nitroethane	$(C_2H_5)_2NH$	$CH_3CH(A)NO_2$ (57)	117
α-(*p-Bromophenyl*)*cinnamonitrile and*			
Nitroethane	Piperidine	$C_6H_5CH[CH(CH_3)NO_2]CH(CN)C_6H_4Br\text{-}p$	117
1-*Cyano*-1,3-*butadiene and*		$A = —CH_2CH{=}CHCH_2CN$	
Diethyl malonate	$[C_6H_5CH_2N(CH_3)_3]OH$	$(A)_2C(CO_2C_2H_5)_2$ (13)	91
Ethyl acetoacetate	$[C_6H_5CH_2N(CH_3)_3]OH$	$CH_3COC(A)_2CO_2C_2H_5$ (28)	91

Note: References 491–1045 are on pp. 545–555.

TABLE XI—*Continued*

MICHAEL CONDENSATIONS WITH UNSATURATED NITRILES OTHER THAN ACRYLONITRILE

Reactants	Catalyst	Product (Yield, %)	References
1-*Cyano*-1,3-*butadiene* (*Cont.*) *and*		$A = —CH_2CH{=}CHCH_2CN$	
Ethyl cyanoacetate	$[C_6H_5CH_2N(CH_3)_3]OH$	$(A)_2C(CN)CO_2C_2H_5$	91
Acetylacetone	$[C_6H_5CH_2N(CH_3)_3]OH$	$(A)_2C(COCH_3)_2$ (22)	91
Nitromethane	$[C_6H_5CH_2N(CH_3)_3]OH$	$(A)_3CNO_2$	293
Nitroethane	$[C_6H_5CH_2N(CH_3)_3]OH$	$CH_3CH(A)NO_2$ and $CH_3C(A)_2NO_2$ (total, 65)	293
1-Nitropropane	$[C_6H_5CH_2N(CH_3)_3]OH$	$C_2H_5CH(A)NO_2$	293
2-Nitropropane	$[C_6H_5CH_2N(CH_3)_3]OH$	$(CH_3)_2C(A)NO_2$ (77)	293
Nitrocyclohexane	$[C_6H_5CH_2N(CH_3)_3]OH$	[cyclohexane ring bearing NO_2 and A on the same carbon]	293

TABLE XIA

MICHAEL CONDENSATIONS WITH ACRYLAMIDE[295] AND METHACRYLAMIDE[823]

Reactants	Catalyst	Product (Yield, %)
Acrylamide and		
Cyclohexanone	NaH	2-Oxo-1,2,3,4,5,6,7,8-octahydroquinoline (10)
Acetophenone	KOC_4H_9-*t*	γ-Benzoylbutyric acid* (20)
Dibenzyl ketone	KOC_4H_9-*t*	$[C_6H_5CH(CH_2CH_2CONH_2)]_2CO$ (48)
2-Phenylcyclohexanone	KOC_4H_9-*t*	C_6H_5 HN O (39)
	$NaNH_2$	C_6H_5 HN O (29)
2-Phenylcycloheptanone	KOC_4H_9-*t*	Lactam of β-(2-keto-1-phenylcycloheptyl)propionic acid (31)
	$NaNH_2$	Lactam of β-(2-keto-1-phenylcycloheptyl)propionic acid (22)

* This product was obtained after hydrolysis.

TABLE XIA—*Continued*

MICHAEL CONDENSATIONS WITH ACRYLAMIDE[295] AND METHACRYLAMIDE[823]

Reactants	Catalyst	Product (Yield, %)
Acrylamide (Cont.) and		
4-Oxo-1,2,3,4,9,10,11,12-octahydrophenanthrene	KOC_4H_9-*t*	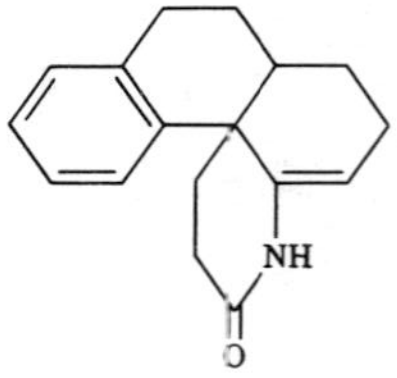 (50)†
4,9-Dioxo-1,2,3,4,9,10,11,12-octahydrophenanthrene	KOC_4H_9-*t*	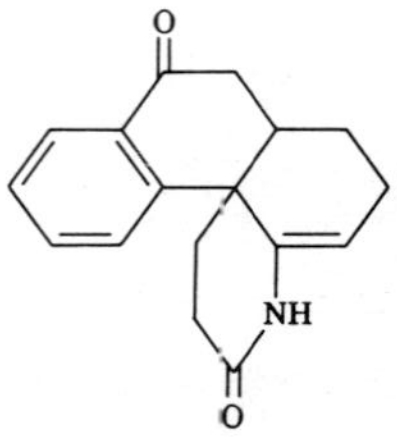 (23)

	NaH	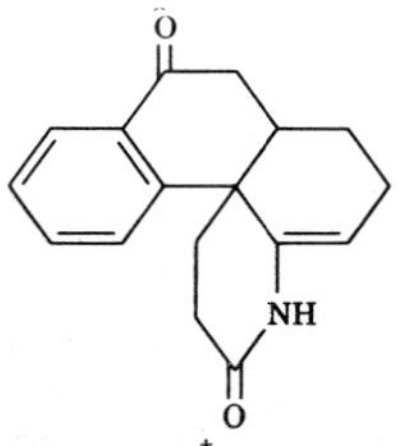 O; NH; O (41)‡
Methacrylamide and		
Diphenylacetonitrile	$NaOC_2H_5$	$(C_6H_5)_2$, CH_3, HN, N, H, O (35)

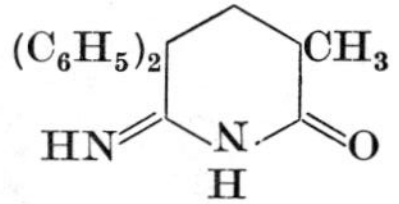

† The yield of lactam was 23%; when the residual reaction mixture was hydrolyzed, the yield of the corresponding acid was 27%.

‡ The yield of lactam was 57%; further work up of the mother liquor yielded an additional 16% of the lactam.

TABLE XII

MICHAEL CONDENSATIONS WITH ALIPHATIC α,β-ETHYLENIC ACID DERIVATIVES

Reactants	Catalyst	Product (Yield, %)	References
Methyl Acrylate and		$A = —CH_2CH_2CO_2CH_3$	
Diethyl malonate	Na	ACH($CO_2C_2H_5$)$_2$ (76)	525
Diethyl acetamidomalonate	$NaOC_2H_5$	Glutamic acid* (64)	463
Ethyl acetoacetate	$NaOC_2H_5$; Na	$CH_3COCH(A)CO_2C_2H_5$ (73, 38)	824, 525
Ethyl 5-ethoxy-3-oxopentanoate	Na	Methyl 5-oxo-6-heptenoate (19)†	538
Ethyl benzoylacetate	$[C_6H_5CH_2N(CH_3)_3]OH$	$C_6H_5COCH(A)CO_2C_2H_5$ (52)	536
Ethyl cyanoacetate	$NaOC_2H_5$	$NCCH(A)CO_2C_2H_5$ (73)	825
Malononitrile	$[C_6H_5CH_2N(CH_3)_3]OH$	$(A)_2C(CN)_2$	826
Diethyl 1,2-dicyano-2-methylpentane-1,5-dicarboxylate	KOC_2H_5	$(A)C(CN)(CO_2C_2H_5)C(CN)(CH_3)CH_2CH_2CH_2CO_2C_2H_5$ (65)	793
Benzyl cyanide	$NaOCH_3$; $NaNH_2$	$C_6H_5CH(A)CN$ (20–24)	27
α-Phenylpropionitrile	$NaOCH_3$	$C_6H_5C(A)(CH_3)CN$ (43)	758
α-Phenylbutyronitrile	$[C_6H_5CH_2N(CH_3)_3]OH$	$C_6H_5C(A)(C_2H_5)CN$	808
α-Isopropylbenzyl cyanide	$[C_6H_5CH_2N(CH_3)_3]OH$	$C_6H_5C(A)(C_3H_7\text{-}i)CN$	808
α-Isobutylbenzyl cyanide	$[C_6H_5CH_2N(CH_3)_3]OH$	$C_6H_5C(A)(C_4H_9\text{-}i)CN$	808
α-(2-Thienyl)benzyl cyanide	$[C_6H_5CH_2N(CH_3)_3]OH$	$C_6H_5C(A)(C_4H_3S)CN$	808
α-*n*-Pentylbenzyl cyanide	$[C_6H_5CH_2N(CH_3)_3]OH$	$C_6H_5C(A)(C_5H_{11}\text{-}n)CN$	808
α-(3-Methylbutyl)benzyl cyanide	$[C_6H_5CH_2N(CH_3)_3]OH$	$C_6H_5C(A)(CN)CH_2CH_2CH(CH_3)_2$	808
α-(2-Pyridyl)benzyl cyanide	$[C_6H_5CH_2N(CH_3)_3]OH$	$C_6H_5C(A)(C_5H_4N)CN$	808
α-(2-Pyridyl)-*p*-chlorobenzyl cyanide	$[C_6H_5CH_2N(CH_3)_3]OH$	$p\text{-}ClC_6H_4C(A)(C_5H_4N)CN$	808
α-(1-Cyclohexenyl)benzyl cyanide	$[C_6H_5CH_2N(CH_3)_3]OH$	$C_6H_5C(A)(C_6H_9)CN$	808
α-Cyclohexylbenzyl cyanide	$[C_6H_5CH_2N(CH_3)_3]OH$	$C_6H_5C(A)(C_6H_{11})CN$	808
Diphenylacetonitrile	$NaOCH_3$	$(C_6H_5)_2C(A)CN$	823
α-(*p*-Chlorophenyl)benzyl cyanide	$[C_6H_5CH_2N(CH_3)_3]OH$	$C_6H_5C(A)(C_6H_4Cl\text{-}p)CN$	808

Ethyl (α-tetralylidene)cyanoacetate‡	$NaOC_2H_5$	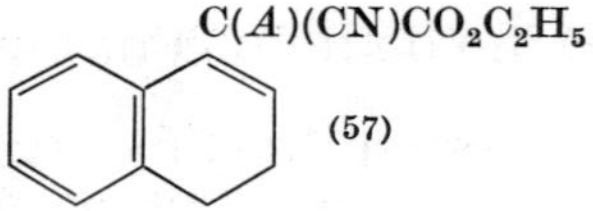 $C(A)(CN)CO_2C_2H_5$ (57)	827
2-(1′-Cyclohexenyl)cyclohexanone	$[C_6H_5CH_2N(CH_3)_3]OCH_3$	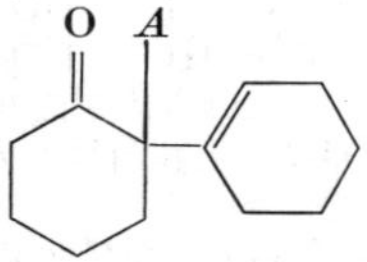 O A (40)	828
Oxindole	$NaOC_2H_5$	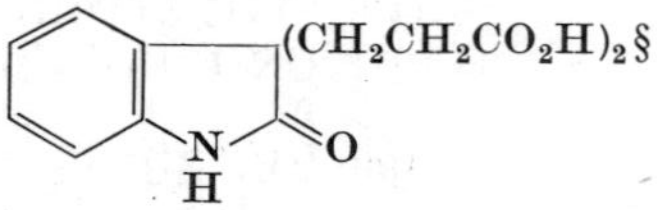 $(CH_2CH_2CO_2H)_2$§ N H O	829
1-Methyloxindole	$NaOC_2H_5$	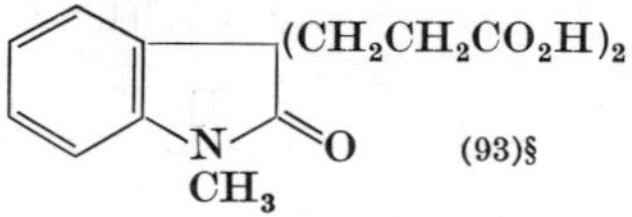 $(CH_2CH_2CO_2H)_2$ N CH_3 O (93)§	372
1-Ethyloxindole	$NaOC_2H_5$	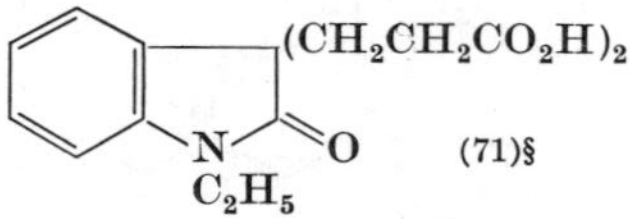 $(CH_2CH_2CO_2H)_2$ N C_2H_5 O (71)§	829

Note: References 491–1045 are on pp. 545–555.

* This acid was isolated after hydrolysis and partial decarboxylation.

† This compound was isolated by partial hydrolysis and decarboxylation, which were accompanied by elimination of one molecule of ethanol.

‡ This compound reacts in the tautomeric β,γ-unsaturated form.

§ This compound was isolated after saponification.

TABLE XII—*Continued*

MICHAEL CONDENSATIONS WITH ALIPHATIC α,β-ETHYLENIC ACID DERIVATIVES

Reactants	Catalyst	Product (Yield, %)	References
Methyl Acrylate (Cont.) and		$A = —CH_2CH_2CO_2CH_3$	
Methyl oxindole-3-propionate	$NaOC_2H_5$	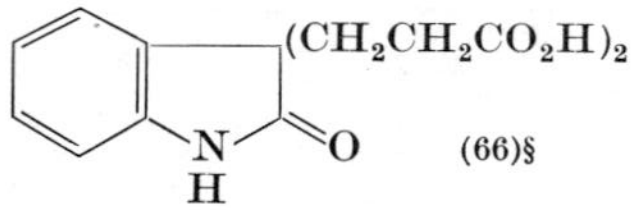 $(CH_2CH_2CO_2H)_2$ (66)§	829
Ethyl oxindole-3-propionate	$NaOC_2H_5$	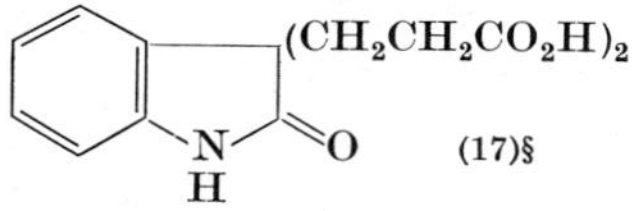 $(CH_2CH_2CO_2H)_2$ (17)§	372
Nitromethane	$[C_6H_5CH_2N(CH_3)_3]OH$	$(A)CH_2NO_2$ (35)	457, 830
		$(A)_2CHNO_2$	831
Nitroethane	$[C_6H_5CH_2N(CH_3)_3]OH$; $(C_2H_5)_3N$	$CH_3CH(A)NO_2$ (66)	832, 830, 833
1-Nitropropane	$(C_2H_5)_3N$	$C_2H_5CH(A)NO_2$ (80)	832
2-Nitropropane	$(C_2H_5)_3N$	$(CH_3)_2C(A)NO_2$ (81)	832
	$[C_6H_5CH_2N(CH_3)_3]OH$	$(CH_3)_2C(A)NO_2$ (80–86)	830, 834, 835
1-Nitrobutane	$[C_6H_5CH_2N(CH_3)_3]OH$	n-$C_3H_7CH(A)NO_2$ (51)	
		n-$C_3H_7C(A)_2NO_2$ (36)	453
2-Methyl-1-nitropropane	$[C_6H_5CH_2N(CH_3)_3]OH$	$(CH_3)_2CHCH(A)NO_2$ (59)	453
		$(CH_3)_2CHC(A)_2NO_2$ (9)	
Dinitromethane	—‖	$(A)_2C(NO_2)_2$ (60)	809
β,β-Dinitroethanol	—‖	$(A)C(NO_2)_2CH_2OH$ (20)	809, 810, 836, 837
Methyl γ,γ-dinitrobutyrate	—¶	$AC(NO_2)_2CH_2CH_2CO_2CH_3$ (45)	810

Methyl γ-isopropyl-γ-nitrobutyrate	$(C_2H_5)_2NH$	$(CH_3)_2CHC(A)_2NO_2$ (41)	453
	$[C_6H_5CH_2N(CH_3)_3]OH$	$(CH_3)_2CHC(A)_2NO_2$ (20)	
Endo(nitroethylene)anthracene	$NaOCH_3$	CH_2; C; A; NO_2 (51)	813
Triethyl phosphonoacetate	$NaOC_2H_5$	$(C_2H_5O)_2P(O)CH(A)CO_2C_2H_5$ (40)	124
	Na (small amount)	$(C_2H_5O)_2P(O)CH(A)CO_2C_2H_5$ (53)	817
	K (molar amount)	$(C_2H_5O)_2P(O)C(A)_2CO_2C_2H_5$ (67)	817
Triethyl α-phosphonohexanoate	$NaOC_2H_5$	$(C_2H_5O)_2P(O)C(A)(C_4H_9\text{-}n)CO_2C_2H_5$ (64)	124
	K (molar amount)	$(C_2H_5O)_2P(O)C(A)(C_4H_9\text{-}n)CO_2C_2H_5$ (73)	817
Diethyl malonate	$NaOC_2H_5$	$ACH(CO_2C_2H_5)_2$	66
	Anion exchange resin	$ACH(CO_2C_2H_5)_2$; $(A)_2C(CO_2C_2H_5)_2$	480
Diethyl methylmalonate	$NaOC_2H_5$	$AC(CH_3)(CO_2C_2H_5)_2$ (74)	66
Diethyl ethylmalonate**	$NaOC_2H_5$	$AC(C_2H_5)(CO_2C_2H_5)_2$ (79)	838
Diethyl *n*-butylmalonate††	$NaOC_2H_5$	$AC(C_4H_9\text{-}n)(CO_2C_2H_5)_2$ (88)	838
Diethyl *n*-hexylmalonate**	$NaOC_2H_5$	$AC(C_6H_{13}\text{-}n)(CO_2C_2H_5)_2$ (83)	838
Diethyl *n*-octylmalonate**	$NaOC_2H_5$	$AC(C_8H_{17}\text{-}n)(CO_2C_2H_5)_2$ (81)	838
Diethyl *n*-decylmalonate**	$NaOC_2H_5$	$AC(C_{10}H_{21}\text{-}n)(CO_2C_2H_5)_2$ (79)	838

Note: References 491–1045 are on pp. 545–555.

§ This compound was isolated after saponification.

|| The dinitro compound was used as its potassium salt in aqueous solution; no other catalyst was employed.

¶ The dinitro compound was employed as its *aci*-sodium salt in aqueous solution.

** In this experiment methyl acrylate was used as starting material; it was *trans*-esterified by the catalyst solution.

†† When methyl acrylate and sodium ethoxide were employed, an 85% yield of $n\text{-}C_4H_9C(A)(CO_2C_2H_5)_2$ was obtained.

TABLE XII—*Continued*

MICHAEL CONDENSATIONS WITH ALIPHATIC α,β-ETHYLENIC ACID DERIVATIVES

Reactants	Catalyst	Product (Yield, %)	References
Ethyl Acrylate and		$A = -CH_2CH_2CO_2C_2H_5$	
Diethyl *n*-dodecylmalonate**	$NaOC_2H_5$	$AC(C_{12}H_{25}\text{-}n)(CO_2C_2H_5)_2$ (80)	838
Diethyl *n*-tetradecylmalonate**	$NaOC_2H_5$	$AC(C_{14}H_{29}\text{-}n)(CO_2C_2H_5)_2$ (80)	838
Diethyl *n*-hexadecylmalonate**	$NaOC_2H_5$	$AC(C_{16}H_{33}\text{-}n)(CO_2C_2H_5)_2$ (83)	838
Ethyl 1-methyl-1,2,5,6-tetrahydropyridine-4-acetate	NaH	1-methyl-1,2,5,6-tetrahydropyridin-4-yl-$CH(A)CO_2C_2H_5$ (N–CH_3) (69)	467
Ethyl acetoacetate	$NaOC_2H_5$; NaOH	$CH_3COCH(A)CO_2C_2H_5$ (80, 67)	839, 119, 30
2-Carbethoxy-3,3-dimethylcyclohexanone	$NaOC_2H_5$	cyclohexanone with A, $CO_2C_2H_5$ at C-2 and $(CH_3)_2$ at C-3 (49)	840
Ethyl cyanoacetate	$NaOC_2H_5$	$ACH(CN)CO_2C_2H_5$	841, 842‡‡
Cyanoacetamide	Na deriv.	3-Cyano-2,6-dioxopiperidine	843
Cyclohexane-1,3-dione	$NaOC_2H_5$	Diethyl 3-(β-carbethoxyethyl)-4-oxoheptane-1,7-dicarboxylate (64)§§	844
2-Ethylcyclohexane-1,3-dione	$NaOC_2H_5$	Diethyl 3-ethyl-4-oxoheptane-1,7-dicarboxylate (61)§§	844
2-Allylcyclohexane-1,3-dione	$NaOC_2H_5$	Diethyl 3-allyl-4-oxoheptane-1,7-dicarboxylate (66)§§	771
2-Benzylcyclohexane-1,3-dione	$NaOC_2H_5$	Diethyl 3-benzyl-4-oxoheptane-1,7-dicarboxylate (61)§§	844

Oxindole	$NaOC_2H_5$	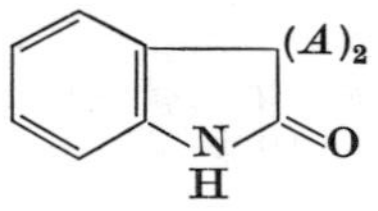 $(A)_2$; N; H; O	845
1-Methyloxindole	$NaOC_2H_5$	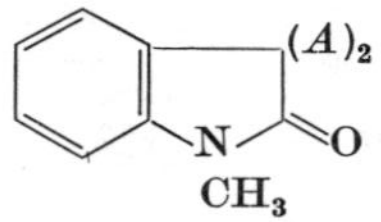 $(A)_2$; N; CH_3; O (69)	846
1,3-Dimethyloxindole	$NaOC_2H_5$	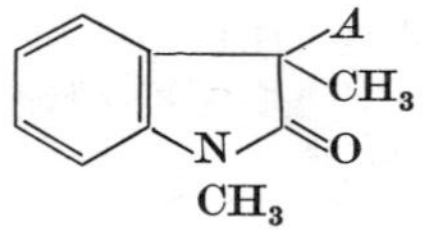 A; CH_3; N; CH_3; O (73)	846
Nitromethane	$[C_6H_5CH_2N(CH_3)_3]OH$	$(A)_2CHNO_2$	452
Nitroethane	$[C_6H_5CH_2N(CH_3)_3]OH$	$ACH(CH_3)NO_2$ (60) or $(A)_2C(CH_3)NO_2$	830, 452
1-Nitropropane	$[C_6H_5CH_2N(CH_3)_3]OH$	$C_2H_5CH(A)NO_2$	830
		$C_2H_5C(A)_2NO_2$	830
2-Nitropropane	$[C_6H_5CH_2N(CH_3)_3]OH$	$(CH_3)_2C(A)NO_2$	830
β,β-Dinitroethanol	—‖	$(NO_2)_2C(A)CH_2OH$ (35)	837
Ethyl nitroacetate	$[C_6H_5CH_2N(CH_3)_3]OH$	$ACH(NO_2)CO_2C_2H_5$ (55)	455
		$A_2C(NO_2)CO_2C_2H_5$ (22)	455
		$ACH(NO_2)CO_2C_2H_5$ (11)	811
	$[C_6H_5N(CH_3)_3]OH$	$ACH(NO_2)CO_2C_2H_5$	847

Note: References 491–1045 are on pp. 545–555.

‖ The dinitro compound was used as its potassium salt in aqueous solution; no other catalyst was employed.

** In this experiment methyl acrylate was used as starting material; it was *trans*-esterified by the catalyst solution.

‡‡ In this experiment, the condensation product was not isolated, but was treated directly with ethyl α-bromoisobutyrate.

§§ This product is formed by hydrolytic fission of the cyclohexane ring.

TABLE XII—*Continued*

MICHAEL CONDENSATIONS WITH ALIPHATIC α,β-ETHYLENIC ACID DERIVATIVES

Reactants	Catalyst	Product (Yield, %)	References
Ethyl Acrylate (Cont.) and		$A = —CH_2CH_2CO_2C_2H_5$	
Ethyl β-methyl-γ-nitrobutyrate	$[C_6H_5CH_2N(CH_3)_3]OH$	$ACH(NO_2)CH(CH_3)CH_2CO_2C_2H_5$ (63)	456
	$(i\text{-}C_3H_7)_2NH$	$ACH(NO_2)CH(CH_3)CH_2CO_2C_2H_5$ (46)	456
Ethyl γ-nitro β-*n*-propylbutyrate	$[C_6H_5CH_2N(CH_3)_3]OH$	$ACH(NO_2)CH(C_3H_7\text{-}n)CH_2CO_2C_2H_5$ (53)	116
Ethyl γ-acetoxy-β-nitromethylbutyrate	$[C_6H_5CH_2N(CH_3)_3]OH$	$ACH(NO_2)CH(CH_2OCOCH_3)CH_2CO_2C_2H_5$ (67)	457
Ethyl β-nitroisopropylmalonate	$[C_6H_5CH_2N(CH_3)_3]OH$	$ACH(NO_2)CH(CH_3)CH(CO_2C_2H_5)_2$ (65)	457
2-Benzoyl-1-cyano-1,2-dihydroisoquinoline	Li salt	1-isoquinolyl-$CH_2CH(COC_6H_5)CO_2C_2H_5$ (58)	805*a*
n-Butyl Acrylate and		$A = —CH_2CH_2CO_2C_4H_9\text{-}n$	
Methyl β-cyanoethyl ketone	Aq. KCN	$CH_3COCH(A)CH_2CN$ and $CH_3COC(A)_2CH_2CN$	123
β,β-Dinitroethanol	—‖	$AC(NO_2)_2CH_2OH$ (23)	837
γ-Hydroxycrotonolactone and			
Ethyl γ-ethoxyacetoacetate	Na	γ-butyrolactone with $CH(CO_2C_2H_5)COCH_2OC_2H_5$ substituent (O=C–O ring)	848
Ethyl β-Hydroxyacrylate and			
Nitromethane	Enolate	Ethyl β-hydroxy-γ-nitrobutyrate (quant.)	546
Nitroethane	Enolate	Ethyl β-hydroxy-γ-nitropentanoate (66)	546
1-Nitropropane	Enolate	Ethyl β-hydroxy-γ-nitrohexanoate (54)	546

Reactants	Catalyst	Product (Yield, %)	Refs.
Ethyl β-Ethoxyacrylate and			
Diethyl malonate	$NaOC_2H_5$	OH; $C_2H_5O_2C$, $CO_2C_2H_5$, $CO_2C_2H_5$ (14)	307
	$[C_6H_5CH_2N(CH_3)_3]OC_2H_5$	$C_2H_5O_2C$, $CO_2C_2H_5$, $CO_2C_2H_5$ (25)	307
Diethyl methylmalonate	$[C_6H_5CH_2N(CH_3)_3]OC_2H_5$	Diethyl 3-ethoxybutane-2,4-dicarboxylate (19) and diethyl carbonate; diethyl 1-butene-1,3-dicarboxylate (18)	307
	$NaOC_2H_5$	H_3C, HO, $CO_2C_2H_5$, $CO_2C_2H_5$ (47); $C_2H_5O_2C$, $CO_2C_2H_5$, $CO_2C_2H_5$ (Little)	307
Crotonic Acid and			
Kojic acid	$NaHCO_3$	O; OH; HOH_2C, O, $CH(CH_3)CH_2CO_2H$ (63)	849

Note: References 491–1045 are on pp. 545–555.

‖ The dinitro compound was used as its potassium salt in aqueous solution; no other catalyst was employed.

TABLE XII—*Continued*

MICHAEL CONDENSATIONS WITH ALIPHATIC α,β-ETHYLENIC ACID DERIVATIVES

Reactants	Catalyst	Product (Yield, %)	References
Ethyl Crotonate and		$A = —CH(CH_3)CH_2CO_2C_2H_5$	
Diethyl malonate	$NaOC_2H_5$	$ACH(CO_2C_2H_5)_2$ (38, 53, 95, 98)	5, 851, 50, 850, 7, 8
Diethyl methylmalonate	$NaOC_2H_5$ (1/6 mole)	2-Methylbutane-1,3,3-tricarboxylic acid§ and 2-methylbutane-1,1,3-tricarboxylic acid§ (9 : 1, 90)	50, cf. 607
	$NaOC_2H_5$ (1 mole)	2-Methylbutane-1,1,3-tricarboxylic acid§ (60)	50, cf. 607
Ethyl phenylacetate	K	$C_6H_5CH(A)CO_2C_2H_5$ (22)	852
Ethyl 3,4-dimethoxyphenyl-acetate	$NaOC_2H_5$	$3,4\text{-}(CH_3O)_2C_6H_3CH(A)CO_2C_2H_5$ (76)	853
Ethyl acetoacetate	$NaOC_2H_5$	$CH_3COCH(A)CO_2C_2H_5$ (60)	782
		O, O, $CO_2C_2H_5$, CH_3 (80, 65)	180, 854
		O, O, CH_3 (55)	855
2-Carbethoxycyclopentanone	KOC_2H_5	O, A, $CO_2C_2H_5$ and triethyl 2-methylhexane-1,3,6-tricarboxylate§§	856, 857, 858

2-Carbethoxy-5-methylcyclo- pentanone	KOC_2H_5	O, H_3C, A, $CO_2C_2H_5$ (66)	304, 305
Ethyl cyanoacetate	$NaOC_2H_5$	ACH(CN)$CO_2C_2H_5$¶¶	859, 860
Ethyl α-cyanopropionate	$NaOC_2H_5$	$CH_3C(A)(CN)CO_2C_2H_5$ (50)	77, 80
Ethyl α-cyanobutyrate	$NaOC_2H_5$	$C_2H_5C(A)(CN)CO_2C_2H_5$ (33)	77
Ethyl α-cyanohydrocinnamate	$NaOC_2H_5$	$C_6H_5CH_2C(A)(CN)CO_2C_2H_5$	80
Cyanoacetamide	Na enolate	3-Cyano-2,6-dioxo-4-methylpiperidine	349
Benzyl cyanide	$NaOC_2H_5$	$C_6H_5CH(A)CN$ (63–68)	27
1-(β-Diethylaminoethyl)-2- tetralone	$NaOC_2H_5$	A, $CH_2CH_2N(C_2H_5)_2$, O (23); O, O, CH_3, $CH_2CH_2N(C_2H_5)_2$	861
Nitromethane	$[C_6H_5CH_2N(CH_3)_3]OC_4H_9$	ACH_2NO_2 (55)	456
	$(C_2H_5)_2NH$	ACH_2NO_2 (15)	456
	$(i\text{-}C_3H_7)_2NH$	ACH_2NO_2 (25)	456
Triethyl phosphonoacetate	K	$(C_2H_5O)_2P(O)CH(A)CO_2C_2H_5$ (66)	817
Ethyl α-Chlorocrotonate and			
Ethyl acetoacetate	Na enolate	H_3C, $CO_2C_2H_5$, $C_2H_5O_2C$, O, CH_3	862

Note: References 491–1045 are on pp. 545–555.

§ This compound was isolated after saponification.

§§ This product is formed by hydrolytic fission of the alicyclic ring.

¶¶ This product has not been isolated, but was condensed with ethyl β-chloropropionate (ref. 859) or ethyl bromoacetate (ref. 860).

TABLE XII—*Continued*

MICHAEL CONDENSATIONS WITH ALIPHATIC α,β-ETHYLENIC ACID DERIVATIVES

Reactants	Catalyst	Product (Yield, %)	References
Ethyl β-Hydroxycrotonate and			
Cyanoacetamide	Piperidine	3-Cyano-6-hydroxy-4-methyl-2-pyridone	378
Ethyl β-Aminocrotonate and			
Malonoamide	Piperidine	6-Hydroxy-4-methyl-2-pyridone-3-carboxamide	378
Cyanoacetamide	Piperidine	3-Cyano-6-hydroxy-4-methyl-2-pyridone	391
Ethyl β-Ethoxycrotonate and			
Cyanoacetamide	Piperidine	3-Cyano-6-hydroxy-4-methyl-2-pyridone	378
Ethyl γ-Acetoxycrotonate and			
Nitromethane	$[C_6H_5CH_2N(CH_3)_3]OC_4H_9$	$CH_3CO_2CH_2CH(CH_2NO_2)CH_2CO_2C_2H_5$ (65)	457
Ethyl γ,γ,γ-Trifluorocrotonate and			
Nitromethane	$(C_2H_5)_3N$	$CF_3CH(CH_2NO_2)CH_2CO_2C_2H_5$ (68)	863
Methyl Methacrylate and		A = $—CH_2CH(CH_3)CO_2CH_3$	
Diethyl methylmalonate	$NaOC_2H_5$	Triethyl pentane-2,2,4-tricarboxylate (66)	864
Ethyl acetoacetate	$NaOC_2H_5$	$CH_3COCH(CO_2C_2H_5)CH_2CH(CH_3)CO_2CH_3$	782
2-Carbethoxycyclopentanone	$NaOCH_3$	2-Oxocyclopentane bearing $CH_2CH(CH_3)CO_2C_2H_5$ and $CO_2C_2H_5$ on C-1 (70)	865
Diphenylacetonitrile	$NaOC_2H_5$	$(C_6H_5)_2C(A)CN$ (80)	823

Reactant	Catalyst	Product (Yield, %)	Refs.
2-(1′-Cyclohexenyl)cyclohexanone	$[C_6H_5CH_2N(CH_3)_3]OCH_3$	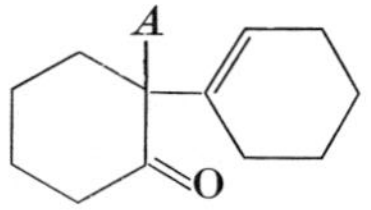 2-A-2-(1′-cyclohexenyl)cyclohexanone (structure) (31)	828
2-Nitropropane	$(C_2H_5)_2NH$	$(CH_3)_2C(A)NO_2$ (35)	832
Triethyl phosphonoacetate	$NaOC_2H_5$	$(C_2H_5O)_2P(O)CH(CO_2C_2H_5)CH_2CH(CH_3)CO_2CH_3$ (42)	124
Triethyl α-phosphonohexanoate	$NaOC_2H_5$	$(C_2H_5O)_2P(O)C(C_4H_9)(CO_2C_2H_5)CH_2CH(CH_3)CO_2CH_3$ (75)	124
Ethyl Methacrylate and		$A = —CH_2CH(CH_3)CO_2C_2H_5$	
Diethyl methylmalonate	$NaOC_2H_5$	$AC(CH_3)(CO_2C_2H_5)_2$	866
Ethyl acetoacetate	$NaOC_2H_5$	$CH_3COCH(A)CO_2C_2H_5$ (24)	867
Ethyl isobutyrylacetate	$NaOC_2H_5$	$CH_3CH(CO_2C_2H_5)CH_2CH(CO_2C_2H_5)CH(CH_3)_2$	320
2-Carbethoxycyclopentanone***	K	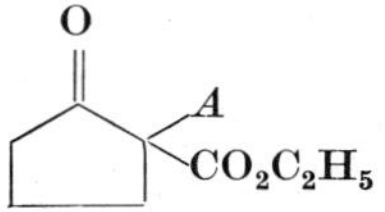 2-A-2-$CO_2C_2H_5$-cyclopentanone (structure) (17)	865
Ethyl cyanoacetate	Na; $NaOC_2H_5$	$ACH(CN)CO_2C_2H_5$	78, cf. 860
Ethyl β-Hydroxymethacrylate and			
Malonic acid	Pyridine, piperidine	*trans*-α-Methylglutaconic acid (47)*	366, 868
Cyanoacetic acid	Pyridine, piperidine	Ethyl 4-cyano-2-methyl-2-butenoate	366
Nitromethane	Ester enolate	Ethyl α-methyl-β-hydroxy-γ-nitrobutyrate	546
Dimethyl Methylenemalonate and			
o-Nitrophenylacetic acid	Na	3,3-Dicarbomethoxy-1-(*o*-nitrophenyl)butyric acid (58)	869

Note: References 491–1045 are on pp. 545–555.

* This acid was isolated after hydrolysis and partial decarboxylation.

*** The ethyl methacrylate was formed *in situ* from ethyl α-bromoisobutyrate.

TABLE XII—*Continued*

MICHAEL CONDENSATIONS WITH ALIPHATIC α,β-ETHYLENIC ACID DERIVATIVES

Reactants	Catalyst	Product (Yield, %)	References
Diethyl Methylenemalonate††† *and*			
Diethyl malonate	KOH, C_2H_5OH	$(C_2H_5O_2C)_2CHCH_2CH(CO_2C_2H_5)_2$ (quant.)	870
Tetraethyl propane-1,1,3,3-tetracarboxylate	KOH, C_2H_5OH	Hexaethyl pentane-1,1,3,3,5,5-hexacarboxylate	870
Ethyl *o*-nitrophenylacetate	$NaOC_2H_5$	*o*-$O_2NC_6H_4CH(CO_2C_2H_5)CH_2CH(CO_2C_2H_5)_2$ (60)	871, 829, 872
Ethyl acetoacetate	$NaOC_2H_5$	Triethyl 2-oxopentane-3,5,5-tricarboxylate (38)	867
Dimethyl Maleate and			
Diethyl *n*-butylmalonate	Not indicated	*n*-$C_4H_9CH(CO_2H)CH(CO_2H)CH_2CO_2H$*	873
Diethyl isoamylmalonate	Not indicated	*i*-$C_5H_{11}CH(CO_2H)CH(CO_2H)CH_2CO_2H$*	873
Diethyl *n*-hexylmalonate	Not indicated	*n*-$C_6H_{13}CH(CO_2H)CH(CO_2H)CH_2CO_2H$*	873
Diethyl cyclohexylmalonate	Not indicated	$C_6H_{11}CH(CO_2H)CH(CO_2H)CH_2CO_2H$*	873
Diethyl isoöctylmalonate	Not indicated	*i*-$C_8H_{17}CH(CO_2H)CH(CO_2H)CH_2CO_2H$*	873
Benzyl cyanide	$NaOCH_3$	$C_6H_5CH(CN)CH(CO_2CH_3)CH_2CO_2CH_3$ (50)	27
Dimethyl Maleate and			
2-Nitropropane‡‡‡	$(C_2H_5)_2NH \cdot CH_3CO_2H$	$(CH_3)_2C(NO_2)CH(CO_2CH_3)CH_2CO_2CH_3$ (69)	832
	C_2H_5NH	$(CH_3)_2C(NO_2)CH(CO_2CH_3)CH_2CO_2CH_3$ (80); $(CH_3)_2C{=}C(CO_2CH_3)CH_2CO_2CH_3$ (16)	832
	$(C_2H_5)_2NH$	$(CH_3)_2C(NO_2)CH(CO_2CH_3)CH_2CO_2CH_3$ (85)	832
Triethyl phosphonacetate	$NaOC_2H_5$	$(C_2H_5O)_2P(O)CH(CO_2C_2H_5)CH(CO_2CH_3)CH_2CO_2CH_3$ (13)	124
Diethyl Maleate and		A = —$CH(CO_2C_2H_5)CH_2CO_2C_2H_5$	
Diethyl malonate	Na; KOH, acetal	$ACH(CO_2C_2H_5)_2$ (72)	483, 6, 517, 518

Ethyl phenylacetate	$NaOC_2H_5$	$C_6H_5CH(A)CO_2C_2H_5$	874
Ethyl acetoacetate	KOH, acetal	$CH_3COCH(A)CO_2C_2H_5$ (72)	48
	Na; $NaOC_2H_5$	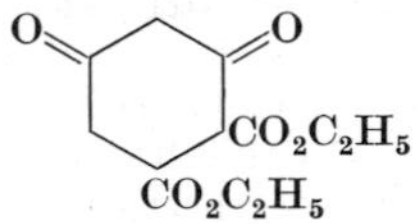 O, O, $CO_2C_2H_5$, $CO_2C_2H_5$	316, 875
2-Carbethoxycyclopentanone	Piperidine	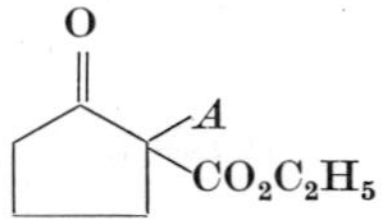 O, A, $CO_2C_2H_5$ (60)	876
	KOC_2H_5	Tetraethyl hexane-1,2,3,4-tetracarboxylate (96)§§	876
Benzyl cyanide	$NaOCH_3$; $NaOC_2H_5$	$C_6H_5CH(A)CN$ (52–58)	27
	KOH, acetal	$C_6H_5CH(A)CN$ (74)	483, 517, 518
2-Methylcyclohexane-1,3-dione	$NaOC_2H_5$	Triethyl 3-methyl-4-oxoheptane-1,2,7-tricarboxylate (62)§§	844
Dimethyl Fumarate and		$A = —CH(CO_2CH_3)CH_2CO_2CH_3$	
Diethyl malonate	$(C_2H_5)_2NH$	$ACH(CO_2C_2H_5)_2$ (5)	18
Ethyl cyanoacetate	$(C_2H_5)_2NH$	$ACH(CN)CO_2C_2H_5$ (10)	18
2-Nitropropane	$(C_2H_5)_2NH$; $(C_2H_5)_3N$	$(CH_3)_2C(A)NO_2$ (80–85)	832

Note: References 491–1045 are on pp. 545–555.

* This acid was isolated after hydrolysis and partial decarboxylation.

§§ This product is formed by hydrolytic fission of the alicyclic ring.

††† Instead of the unsaturated ester, dimethyl methoxymethylmalonate was employed.

‡‡‡ The reaction involves the preliminary isomerization of diethyl maleate to diethyl fumarate.

TABLE XII—*Continued*

Michael Condensations with Aliphatic α,β-Ethylenic Acid Derivatives

Reactants	Catalyst	Product (Yield, %)	References
Diethyl Fumarate (Cont.) and		$A = —CH(CO_2C_2H_5)CH_2CO_2C_2H_5$	
Diethyl malonate	Na; $NaOC_2H_5$	$ACH(CO_2C_2H_5)_2$ (90, 55)	77, 5, 7, 8, 6, 877, 878
Diethyl methylmalonate	$NaOC_2H_5$	$AC(CH_3)(CO_2C_2H_5)_2$	77, 878, 7, 8
Diethyl ethylmalonate	$NaOC_2H_5$	$AC(C_2H_5)(CO_2C_2H_5)_2$ (61, 80)	5, 879, 7, 8, 77, 878
Diethyl isopropylmalonate	$NaOC_2H_5$	$AC(C_3H_7\text{-}i)(CO_2C_2H_5)_2$	7, 878
Diethyl benzylmalonate	$NaOC_2H_5$	$AC(CH_2C_6H_5)(CO_2C_2H_5)_2$ (23–31)§§§	56, 880
Ethyl acetoacetate	Na; $NaOC_2H_5$	$CH_3COCH(A)CO_2C_2H_5$ and 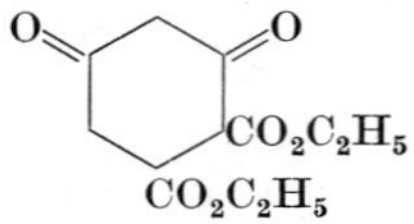 [cyclohexane-1,3-dione ring bearing $CO_2C_2H_5$ and $CO_2C_2H_5$]	875
Ethyl methylacetoacetate	$NaOC_2H_5$	$CH_3COC(CH_3)(A)CO_2C_2H_5$ and 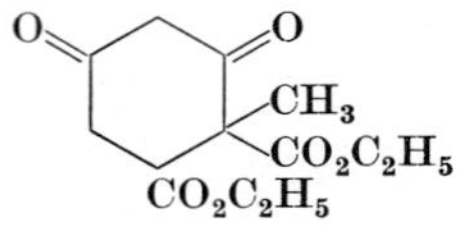 [cyclohexane-1,3-dione ring bearing CH_3, $CO_2C_2H_5$ and $CO_2C_2H_5$]	316, 878
Ethyl ethylacetoacetate	$NaOC_2H_5$	$CH_3COC(C_2H_5)(A)CO_2C_2H_5$	875
Ethyl propionylacetate	$NaOC_2H_5$	$C_2H_5COCH(A)CO_2C_2H_5$	879
Ethyl benzylacetoacetate	$NaOC_2H_5$	$CH_3COC(CH_2C_6H_5)(A)CO_2C_2H_5$	875
Ethyl cyanoacetate	Na	$NCCH(A)CO_2H$; $NCCH(A)CO_2C_2H_5$	316
Benzyl cyanide	$NaOC_2H_5$	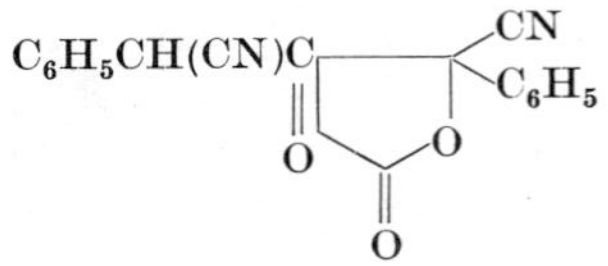 $C_6H_5CH(CN)C$ [ring structure: C=O, O, C=O, with CN and C_6H_5]	881

2-Nitropropane	$(C_2H_5)_2NH$ (0.2 mole)	$(CH_3)_2C(A)NO_2$ (90)	832
	$(C_2H_5)_2NH$ (1.25 mole)	$(CH_3)_2C{=}C(CO_2C_2H_5)CH_2CO_2C_2H_5$ (83)	832
Diethyl Chlorofumarate and			
Ethyl acetoacetate	$NaOC_2H_5$	$CH_3COC(CO_2C_2H_5){=}C(CO_2C_2H_5)CH_2CO_2C_2H_5$	882–885
Ethyl methylacetoacetate	$NaOC_2H_5$	O, O, CH_3, $CO_2C_2H_5$, $CO_2C_2H_5$ (21) ‖‖‖	882, 883 885, 862
Ethyl benzylacetoacetate	$NaOC_2H_5$	O, O, $CH_2C_6H_5$, $CO_2C_2H_5$, $CO_2C_2H_5$ ¶¶¶	862

Note: References 491–1045 are on pp. 545–555.

§§§ Gardner and Rydon (refs. 58–61) have ascribed to the product the isomeric structure $C_6H_5CH_2CH(CO_2C_2H_5)CH(CO_2C_2H_5)CH(CO_2C_2H_5)_2$.

‖‖‖ The formula

$C_2H_5O_2C$, $CO_2C_2H_5$, H_3C, O, $CO_2C_2H_3$

originally (refs. 882–883) assumed has been proven incorrect.

¶¶¶ By analogy with the behavior of ethyl methylacetoacetate, this formula is more probable than the one originally suggested:

$C_2H_5O_2C$, $CO_2C_2H_5$, $C_2H_5O_2C$, O, $CH_2C_6H_5$

TABLE XII—*Continued*

MICHAEL CONDENSATIONS WITH ALIPHATIC α,β-ETHYLENIC ACID DERIVATIVES

Reactants	Catalyst	Product (Yield, %)	References
Ethyl β,β-Dimethylacrylate and		$A = (CH_3)_2\overset{\mid}{C}CH_2CO_2C_2H_5$	
Diethyl malonate	KOC_2H_5; $NaOC_2H_5$	$ACH(CO_2C_2H_5)_2$ (35)	886, 11, 24
Ethyl acetoacetate	Na	O; $(CH_3)_2$; O; $CO_2C_2H_5$	415
Ethyl α-cyanopropionate	Na	$CH_3C(A)(CN)CO_2C_2H_5$****	23
Benzyl cyanide	$NaOC_2H_5$	$C_6H_5CH(A)CN$ (43)	27
Ethyl Tiglate and		$A = —CH(CH_3)CH(CH_3)CO_2C_2H_5$	
Diethyl malonate	$NaOC_2H_5$	$ACH(CO_2C_2H_5)_2$ (15, 63)	50, 59, cf. 887
Diethyl ethylmalonate	$NaOC_2H_5$	$AC(C_2H_5)(CO_2C_2H_5)_2$ (14)	59
Ethyl phenylacetate	K	$C_6H_5CH(A)CO_2C_2H_5$	852
Ethyl cyanoacetate	Na enolate	$ACH(CN)CO_2C_2H_5$ (42, 65)	50, 887, 888
Ethyl α-Ethylacrylate and			
Ethyl acetoacetate	$NaOC_2H_5$	$CH_3COCH(CO_2C_2H_5)CH_2CH(C_2H_5)CO_2C_2H_5$ (20), diethyl α-ethylglutarate	889

Dimethyl Glutaconate and		$A = —CH(CH_2CO_2CH_3)_2$	
Methyl cyanoacetate	$NaOCH_3$	ACH(CN)CO_2CH_3 (46)	890
Ethyl cyanoacetate	Na; $NaOCH_3$; $NaOC_2H_5$	ACH(CN)$CO_2C_2H_5$ (64)	890, 392
Nitromethane	$[C_6H_5CH_2N(CH_3)_3]OH$	ACH_2NO_2 (51)	891
Dimethyl Ethylidenemalonate and			
Deoxybenzoin	$NaOCH_3$	$C_6H_5COCH(C_6H_5)CH(CH_3)CH_2CO_2H$ (55)*	163
Diethyl Ethylidenemalonate and		$A = CH_3CHCH(CO_2C_2H_5)_2$ (with a bond drawn down from the middle CH)	
Diethyl malonate††††	None; Na	$ACH(CO_2C_2H_5)_2$ (95)	892, 893
Ethyl acetoacetate	$NaOC_2H_5$	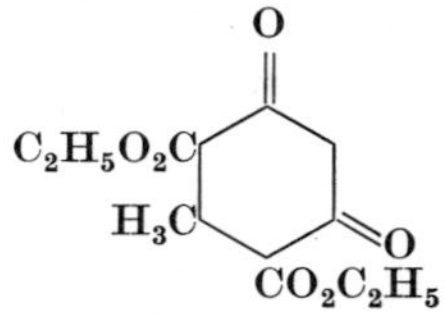	14
Nitromethane	$[C_6H_5CH_2N(CH_3)_3]OH$	ACH_2NO_2 (69)	457
Ethyl Ethylidenemalonamate‡‡‡‡ and			
Ethyl malonamate	KOH; $(C_2H_5)_2NH$	$CH_3CH[CH(CO_2C_2H_5)CONH_2]_2$ (73)	895

Note: References 491–1045 are on pp. 545–555.

* This acid was isolated after hydrolysis and partial decarboxylation.

**** The product has not been isolated, but has been methylated directly.

†††† The same reaction takes place when acetaldehyde and diethyl malonate react in the presence of secondary amines; the yield is from 11 (ref. 887) to 55% (ref. 894).

‡‡‡‡ This material is formed *in situ* from the aldehyde or ketone and the derivative of malonic or cyanoacetic acid.

TABLE XII—*Continued*

MICHAEL CONDENSATIONS WITH ALIPHATIC α,β-ETHYLENIC ACID DERIVATIVES

Reactants	Catalyst	Product (Yield, %)	References
Ethylidenecyanoacetamide‡‡‡‡ and			
Cyanoacetamide	KOH	$CH_3CH[CH(CONH_2)CN]_2$, 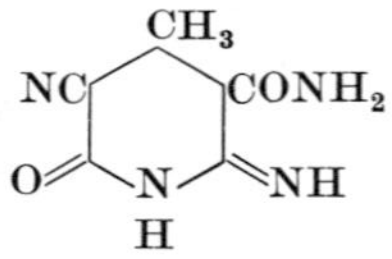 CH_3; NC; $CONH_2$; O; N; NH; H	896
Ethylidenemalononitrile‡‡‡‡ and			
Malononitrile	Piperidine	$CH_3CH[CH(CN)_2]_2$	897
Ethyl α-Ethylcrotonate and		$A = CH_3CHCH(C_2H_5)CO_2C_2H_5$	
Diethyl malonate	$NaOC_2H_5$	$ACH(CO_2C_2H_5)_2$ (48)	59
Diethyl ethylmalonate	$NaOC_2H_5$	$AC(C_2H_5)(CO_2C_2H_5)_2$ (39)	59
Ethyl cyanoacetate	$NaOC_2H_5$	$ACH(CN)CO_2C_2H_5$ (60)	77
Ethyl β-n-Propylacrylate and			
Ethyl acetoacetate	$NaOC_2H_5$	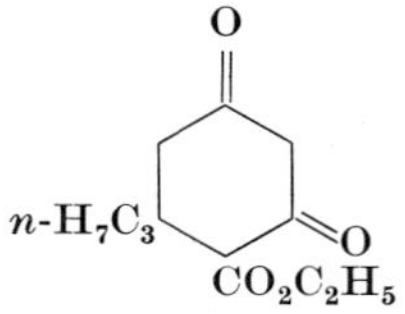 O; n-H_7C_3; O; $CO_2C_2H_5$	898
Nitromethane	$[C_6H_5CH_2N(CH_3)_3]OC_4H_9$	n-$C_3H_7CH(CH_2NO_2)CH_2CO_2C_2H_5$ (71)	116
Ethyl β-Isopropylacrylate and			
Diethyl malonate	$NaOC_2H_5$	i-$C_3H_7CH(CH_2CO_2C_2H_5)CH(CO_2C_2H_5)_2$	886

Reactants	Catalyst	Product (Yield, %)	Refs.
Ethyl α-n-Butylacrylate and			
Ethyl cyanoacetate	$NaOC_2H_5$	$CNCH(CO_2C_2H_5)CH_2CH(C_4H_9\text{-}n)CO_2C_2H_5$ (54)	889
Methyl β-n-Pentylacrylate and			
Ethyl acetoacetate	$NaOC_2H_5$	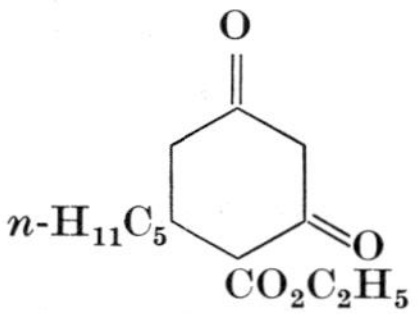 O, O, $n\text{-}H_{11}C_5$, $CO_2C_2H_5$ (71)	180
Dimethyl 1,2-Dihydromuconate and			
Ethyl cyanoacetate	$NaOC_2H_5$	(β-Carboxymethyl)adipic acid (79)*	899
Ethyl phenethylcyanoacetate	KOC_2H_5	$C_6H_5CH_2CH_2C(CN)(CO_2C_2H_5)CH(CH_2CO_2C_2H_5)\text{-}CH_2CH_2CO_2C_2H_5$ (46)	899
Diethyl 1,2-Dihydromuconate and			
Diethyl malonate	$NaOC_2H_5$	$C_2H_5O_2CCH_2CH_2CH(CH_2CO_2C_2H_5)CH(CO_2C_2H_5)_2$ (50), 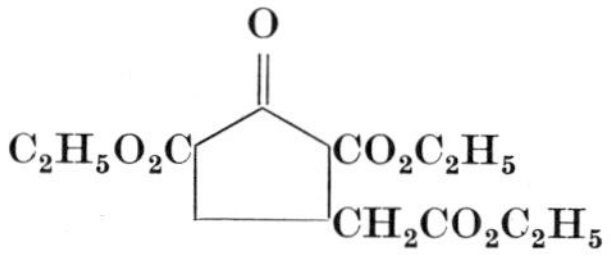 O, $C_2H_5O_2C$, $CO_2C_2H_5$, $CH_2CO_2C_2H_5$ (25)	900
Ethyl 4,4,5,5,6,6,6-Heptafluoro-2-hexenoate and			
Nitromethane	$(C_2H_5)_3N$	Ethyl 4,4,5,5,6,6,6-heptafluoro-3-nitromethylhexanoate (64)	863
Diethyl Propylidenemalonate and			
Diethyl malonate	Enolate	$C_2H_5CH[CH(CO_2C_2H_5)_2]_2$ (quant.)	901

Note: References 491–1045 are on pp. 545–555.

* This acid was isolated after hydrolysis and partial decarboxylation.

‡‡‡‡ This material is formed *in situ* from the aldehyde or ketone and the derivative of malonic or cyanoacetic acid.

TABLE XII—*Continued*

MICHAEL CONDENSATIONS WITH ALIPHATIC α,β-ETHYLENIC ACID DERIVATIVES

Reactants	Catalyst	Product (Yield, %)	References
Propylidenecyanoacetamide‡‡‡‡ and			
Cyanoacetamide	KOH	$C_2H_5CH[CH(CONH_2)CN]_2$ and 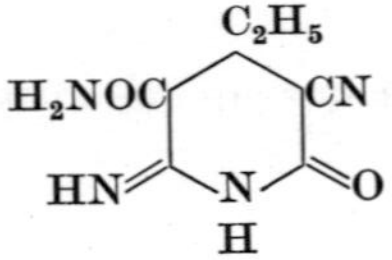 C_2H_5; H_2NOC; CN; HN; N; O; H	896
Diethyl Isopropylidenemalonate and			
Diethyl malonate	$NaOC_2H_5$; enolate	$(CH_3)_2C[CH(CO_2C_2H_5)_2]_2$ (95, 30, 8)	901, 902, 903, 904
Ethyl acetoacetate	$NaOC_2H_5$	$CH_3COCH(CO_2C_2H_5)C(CH_3)_2CH(CO_2C_2H_5)_2$, 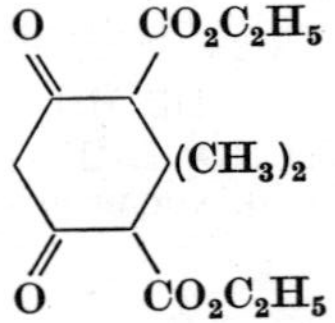 O; $CO_2C_2H_5$; $(CH_3)_2$; O; $CO_2C_2H_5$	905, 415
Cyanoacetone§§§§	$NaOC_2H_5$	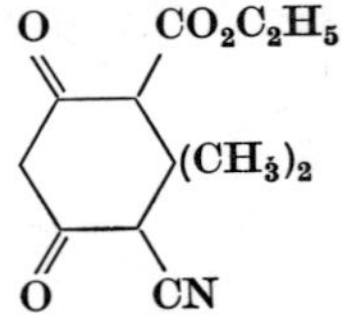 O; $CO_2C_2H_5$; $(CH_3)_2$; O; CN	415
Acetylacetone	$NaOC_2H_5$	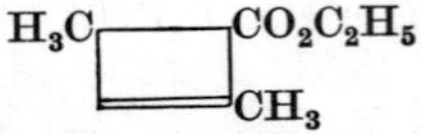 H_3C; $CO_2C_2H_5$; CH_3	415

Ethyl Isopropylidenecyanoacetate‡‡‡‡ *and*			
Ethyl cyanoacetate	$(C_2H_5)_2NH$	$(CH_3)_2C[CH(CN)CO_2C_2H_5]_2$ (10)	906
	NH_3	β,β-Dimethylglutarimide (quant.)	821
Nitromethane	$NaOCH_3$	Ethyl α-cyano-β,β-dimethyl-γ-nitrobutyrate (74)	907
Ethyl 4-Ethoxymethyl-2-hexenoate and			
Diethyl malonate	Na	$C_2H_5CH(CH_2OC_2H_5)CH(CH_2CO_2C_2H_5)CH(CO_2C_2H_5)_2$ (79)	908
Ethyl 4,4-Diethoxymethyl-2-hexenoate and			
Diethyl malonate	$NaOC_2H_5$	$C_2H_5CH[CH(OC_2H_5)_2]CH(CH_2CO_2C_2H_5)CH(CO_2C_2H_5)_2$ (48)	909
n-Butylidenecyanoacetamide‡‡‡‡ *and*			
Cyanoacetamide	KOH	n-$C_3H_7CH[CH(CN)CONH_2]_2$ and 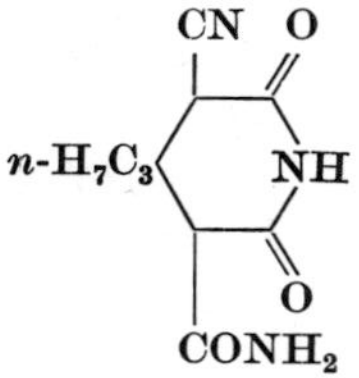	896
Diethyl Isobutylidenemalonate‡‡‡‡ *and*			
Diethyl malonate	Piperidine; $(C_2H_5)_2NH$	$(CH_3)_2CHCH[CH(CO_2C_2H_5)_2]_2$ (41)	894
Ethyl Isobutylidenecyanoacetate and			
Ethyl acetoacetate	$NaOC_2H_5$	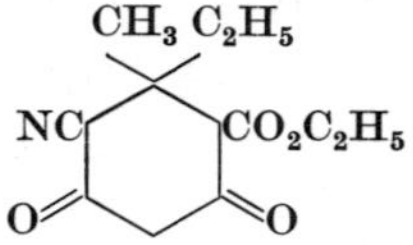	415

Note: References 491–1045 are on pp. 545–555.

‡‡‡‡ This material is formed *in situ* from the aldehyde or ketone and the derivative of malonic or cyanoacetic acid.

§§§§ Instead of cyanoacetone, α-methylisoxazole was employed.

TABLE XII—*Continued*

MICHAEL CONDENSATIONS WITH ALIPHATIC α,β-ETHYLENIC ACID DERIVATIVES

Reactants	Catalyst	Product (Yield, %)	References
Isobutylidenecyanoacetamide‡‡‡‡ and			
Cyanoacetamide	$(C_2H_5)_2NH$	$(CH_3)_2CHCH[CH(CN)CONH_2]_2$ (79)	910
		cyclic imide: ring bearing CN, O, i-H_7C_3, NH, =NH, $CONH_2$ (Small)	
Diethyl Itaconate and		A = $—CH_2CH(CO_2C_2H_5)CH_2CO_2C_2H_5$	
Diethyl malonate	$NaOC_2H_5$	$ACH(CO_2C_2H_5)_2$, triethyl cyclopentanone-2,3,5-tricarboxylate, ethyl cyclopentanone-3-carboxylate, diethyl cyclopentanone-2,4- (or 2,3-) dicarboxylate, cyclopentene bearing $CH(CO_2C_2H_5)_2$, $CO_2C_2H_5$, $CO_2C_2H_5$, $C_2H_5O_2CCH_2CH(CO_2C_2H_5)CH_2CH_2CO_2C_2H_5$	8, 317, 911, 912
Diethyl methylmalonate	$NaOC_2H_5$	cyclopentanone bearing $C_2H_5O_2C$, $C_2H_5O_2C$, CH_3, $CO_2C_2H_5$ and $AC(CH_3)(CO_2C_2H_5)_2$ (small)	317, 406

Tetraethyl 1,1,2,3-butanetetra-carboxylate‖‖‖	$NaOC_2H_5$	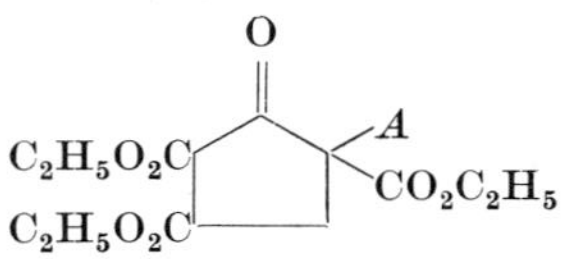 O; $C_2H_5O_2C$; $C_2H_5O_2C$; A; $CO_2C_2H_5$ (cyclopentanone ring)	911
Ethyl acetoacetate	$NaOC_2H_5$	$CH_3COCH(A)CO_2C_2H_5$	316
2-Carbethoxycyclopentanone	$[C_6H_5CH_2N(CH_3)_3]OH$	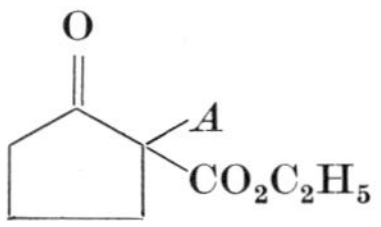 O; A; $CO_2C_2H_5$ (cyclopentanone ring) (90 crude)	913
Ethyl cyanoacetate‖‖‖	$NaOC_2H_5$	$ACH(CN)CO_2C_2H_5$	316
Nitromethane	$(C_2H_5)_2NH$; $(i\text{-}C_3H_7)_2NH$	ACH_2NO_2 (25)	891
Nitroethane	$(i\text{-}C_3H_7)_2NH$	$CH_3CH(A)NO_2$ (40)	891
Diethyl Mesaconate and			
Diethyl malonate	$NaOC_2H_5$	$C_2H_5O_2CCH(CH_3)CH(CO_2C_2H_5)CH(CO_2C_2H_5)_2$ (60–75)	6, 317
Diethyl Citraconate and			
Diethyl malonate	Na enolate	$C_2H_5O_2CCH_2C(CH_3)(CO_2C_2H_5)CH(CO_2C_2H_5)_2$ (72)	316, 317
	$NaOC_2H_5$	$C_2H_5O_2CCH_2CH(CO_2C_2H_5)CH_2CH(CO_2C_2H_5)_2$ (50)¶¶¶¶	316
	$NaOC_2H_5$	2,3,5-Tricarbethoxycyclopentanone	316

Note: References 491–1045 are on pp. 545–555.

‡‡‡‡ This material is formed *in situ* from the aldehyde or ketone and the derivative of malonic or cyanoacetic acid.

‖‖‖ Instead of diethyl itaconate, diethyl citraconate, which isomerizes under the conditions of the experiment, was employed.

¶¶¶¶ The citraconate is isomerized to itaconate.

TABLE XII—*Continued*

Michael Condensations with Aliphatic α,β-Ethylenic Acid Derivations

Reactants	Catalyst	Product (Yield, %)	References
Diethyl Citraconate (Cont.) and			
Diethyl malonate (*Cont.*)	$NaOC_2H_5$	Diethyl itaconate, diethyl mesaconate, 3-carbethoxycyclopentanone, 2,3-(or 3,4-)dicarbethoxycyclopentanone, 2,3,5-tricarbethoxycyclopentanone, 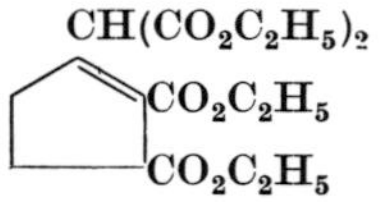 $CH(CO_2C_2H_5)_2$, $CO_2C_2H_5$, $CO_2C_2H_5$ (cyclopentene structure)	317, 912; cf. 5, 6, 8, 911
Diethyl ethylmalonate	Na enolate	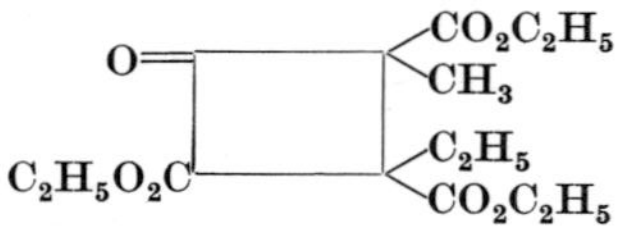 (cyclobutanone structure: O=, $C_2H_5O_2C$, $CO_2C_2H_5$, CH_3, C_2H_5, $CO_2C_2H_5$)	5
Ethyl acetoacetate	Na; dry $NaOC_2H_5$	$CH_3COCH(CO_2C_2H_5)C(CH_3)(CO_2C_2H_5)CH_2CO_2C_2H_5$; (cyclohexanedione structure: O, O, $CO_2C_2H_5$, CH_3, $CO_2C_2H_5$) 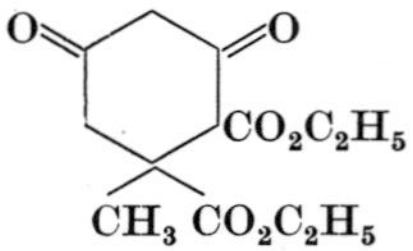	316
Ethyl methylacetoacetate	Na	$CH_3COC(CH_3)(CO_2C_2H_5)C(CH_3)(CO_2C_2H_5)CH_2CO_2C_2H_5$; 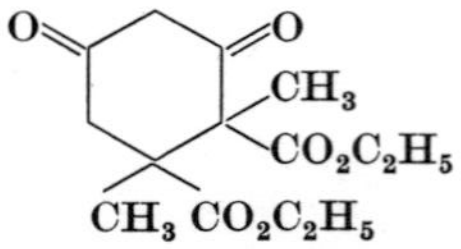 (cyclohexanedione structure: O, O, CH_3, $CO_2C_2H_5$, CH_3, $CO_2C_2H_5$)	316

Reactant	Catalyst	Product	Refs.
	$NaOC_2H_5$	$CH_3COC(CH_3)(CO_2C_2H_5)CH_2CH(CO_2C_2H_5)$-$CH_2CO_2C_2H_5$,¶¶¶¶	316
		2-methyl-2-carbethoxy-4-(carbethoxymethyl)cyclohexane-1,3-dione (H_3C, $C_2H_5O_2C$, $CH_2CO_2C_2H_5$)¶¶¶¶	
Ethyl cyanoacetate	Na	$NCCH(CO_2C_2H_5)C(CH_3)(CO_2C_2H_5)CH_2CO_2C_2H_5$	316
	$NaOC_2H_5$	$NCCH_2CH_2CH(CO_2C_2H_5)CH_2CO_2C_2H_5$¶¶¶¶	316
*Trimethyl Aconitate***** and*		$A = CH_3O_2CCH_2CH(CO_2CH_3)CHCO_2CH_3$	
Dimethyl malonate	Na enolate	$A$$CH(CO_2CH_3)_2$	914
Diethyl malonate	Na enolate	$A$$CH(CO_2C_2H_5)_2$	914
Ethyl acetoacetate	Na enolate	$A$$CH_3COCH(A)CO_2C_2H_5$	914
Triethyl Aconitate and			
Diethyl malonate	Dry $NaOC_2H_5$	Pentaethyl butane-1,1,2,3,4-pentacarboxylate	915, 878
	Na	Tetraethyl butane-1,2,3,4-tetracarboxylate, 2,4-dicarbethoxycyclopentanone	7, 9, 10
Ethyl acetoacetate	Na enolate	Tetraethyl 2-oxohexane-3,4,5,6-tetracarboxylate	875
Triethyl Isoaconitate and			
Ethyl cyanoacetate	Na	Diethyl α-cyanoglutaconate and diethyl malonate	916
Diethyl Ethylideneglutaconate and			
Diethyl glutaconate	$(C_2H_5)_2NH$	Tetraethyl ethylidenebisglutaconate	916*a*

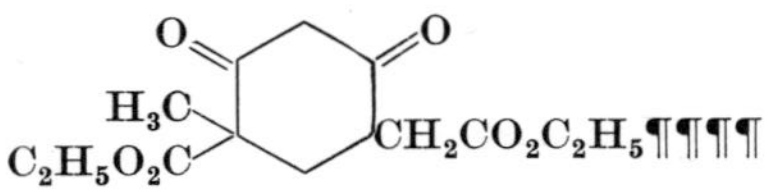

Note: References 491–1045 are on pp. 545–555.

***** Trimethyl chlorotricarballylate was employed instead of trimethyl aconitate.

¶¶¶¶ The citraconate is isomerized to itaconate.

TABLE XII—*Continued*

MICHAEL CONDENSATIONS WITH ALIPHATIC α,β-ETHYLENIC ACID DERIVATIVES

Reactants	Catalyst	Product (Yield, %)	References
Diethyl Isoamylidenemalonate‡‡‡‡ and			
Diethyl malonate	Na enolate; piperidine; $(C_2H_5)_2NH$	i-$C_4H_9CH[CH(CO_2C_2H_5)_2]_2$ (63)	894, 878, 917, 918
Isoamylidenecyanoacetic Acid‡‡‡‡ and			
Cyanoacetic acid	Piperidine	α,α'-Dicyano-β-isobutylglutaric acid	917
Isoamylidenecyanoacetamide‡‡‡‡ and			
Cyanoacetamide	$(C_2H_5)_2NH$	Ring: $CH_2CH(CH_3)_2$; H_2NOC, CN; HN=, N–H, =O (Small)	910
Ethyl (3-Pentylidene)cyanoacetate‡‡‡‡ and			
Ethyl cyanoacetate	NH_3	β,β-Diethylglutarimide (quant.)	821
Diethyl Heptylidenemalonate‡‡‡‡ and			
Diethyl malonate	Piperidine; $(C_2H_5)_2NH$	n-$C_6H_{13}CH[CH(CO_2C_2H_5)_2]_2$	894
Heptylidenecyanoacetic Acid‡‡‡‡ and			
Cyanoacetic acid	Piperidine	n-$C_6H_{13}CH[CH(CN)CO_2H]_2$	917
Heptylidenecyanoacetamide‡‡‡‡ and			
Cyanoacetamide	Piperidine	n-$C_6H_{13}CH[CH(CN)CONH_2]_2$ (87), Ring: C_6H_{13}-n; H_2NOC, CN; HN=, N–H, =O (Small)	910

Triethyl Ethylenetricarboxylate and			
Diethyl malonate	$NaOC_2H_5$	$(C_2H_5O_2C)_2CHCH(CO_2C_2H_5)CH(CO_2C_2H_5)_2$	878, 919
Triethyl 1-*Propylene*-1,1,2-*tricarboxylate and*			
Diethyl malonate	Na enolate	$(C_2H_5O_2C)_2CHC(CH_3)(CO_2C_2H_5)CH(CO_2C_2H_5)_2$ (43–49)	920
Triethyl 1-*Propylene*-2,3,3-*tricarboxylate and*			
Diethyl malonate	Na enolate	$(C_2H_5O_2C)_2CHCH(CO_2C_2H_5)CH_2CH(CO_2C_2H_5)_2$ (61)	920
Tetraethyl Ethylenetetracarboxylate and			
Diethyl malonate	Na	Tricarballylic acid*	893, 878
Tetraethyl 1-*Propylene*-1,1,3,3-*tetracarboxylate and*			
Ethyl cyanoacetate	Piperidine	Diethyl γ-carbethoxy-α-cyanoglutaconate and diethyl malonate	921
	$NaOC_2H_5$	Diethyl γ-carbethoxy-α-cyanoglutaconate, diethyl malonate, and diethyl α,γ-dicyanoglutarate	916
Triethyl 3-*Cyano*-1-*propylene*-1,1,3-*tricarboxylate and*			
Ethyl cyanoacetate	$NaOC_2H_5$	Diethyl α,γ-dicyanoglutaconate and diethyl malonate	916
Tetraethyl 1-*Butene*-1,1,3,3-*tetracarboxylate and*			
Ethyl cyanoacetate	$NaOC_2H_5$	Diethyl γ-carbethoxy-α-cyanoglutaconate and diethyl methylmalonate	916

Note: References 491–1095 are on pp. 545–555.

* This acid was isolated after hydrolysis and partial decarboxylation.

‡‡‡‡ This material is formed *in situ* from the aldehyde or ketone and the derivative of malonic or cyanoacetic acid.

TABLE XIII

MICHAEL CONDENSATIONS WITH ETHYL ETHOXYMETHYLENECYANOACETATE, DIETHYL ETHOXYMETHYLENEMALONATE, AND DIETHYL AMINOMETHYLENEMALONATE

Reactants	Catalyst	Product (Yield, %)	References
Ethyl Ethoxymethylenecyanoacetate and			
Ethyl acetoacetate	$NaOC_2H_5$	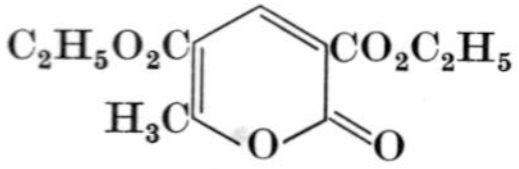 $C_2H_5O_2C$, $CO_2C_2H_5$, H_3C, O, O	310
Diethyl Ethoxymethylenemalonate and			
Diethyl malonate	$NaOC_2H_5$	$(C_2H_5O_2C)_2C{=}CHCH(CO_2C_2H_5)_2$	922
Ethyl phenylacetate	$NaOC_2H_5$	Diethyl 1-hydroxynaphthalene-2,4-dicarboxylate*	308
Ethyl *p*-chlorophenylacetate	$NaOC_2H_5$	Diethyl 7-chloro-1-hydroxynaphthalene-2,4-dicarboxylate* (7) and α-(*p*-chlorophenyl)glutaconic acid (11)†	309
Ethyl *p*-bromophenylacetate	$NaOC_2H_5$	Diethyl 7-bromo-1-hydroxynaphthalene-2,4-dicarboxylate* (11) and 7-bromo-1-hydroxynaphthalene-2,4-dicarboxylic acid (13)†	309
Ethyl α-naphthylacetate	$NaOC_2H_5$	1-Hydroxyphenanthrene-2,4-dicarboxylic acid (5)† and α-(1-naphthyl)glutaconic acid†	309
Methyl 2-pyridylacetate	None	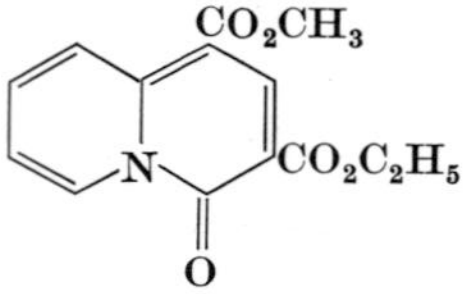 CO_2CH_3, N, $CO_2C_2H_5$, O (26)	923
Ethyl 2-pyridylacetate	None	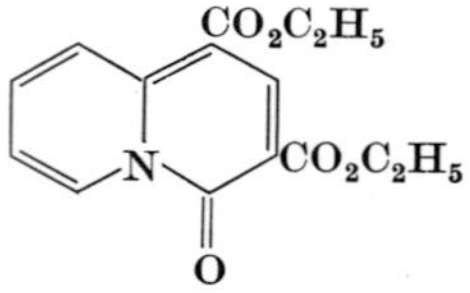 $CO_2C_2H_5$, N, $CO_2C_2H_5$, O (52)	923

Reactant	Catalyst	Product (Yield, %)	Refs.
Ethyl 6-methyl-2-pyridylacetate	None	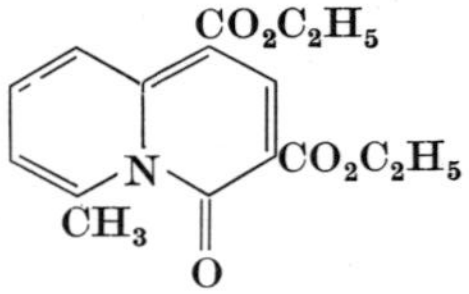 [structure: $CO_2C_2H_5$, $CO_2C_2H_5$, N, CH_3, O] (80)	924
Ethyl acetoacetate	$NaOC_2H_5$	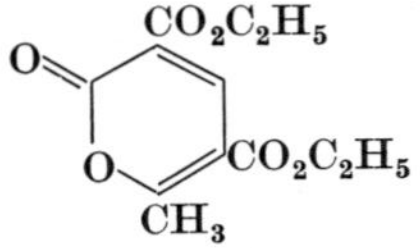 [structure: O, $CO_2C_2H_5$, $CO_2C_2H_5$, O, CH_3]	310
Ethyl β-aminocrotonate	None	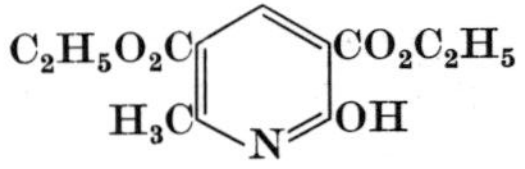 [structure: $C_2H_5O_2C$, $CO_2C_2H_5$, H_3C, N, OH]	441
Diethyl 2-*Aminoethylene*-1,1-*dicarboxylate and*			
Ethyl acetoacetate	HCl	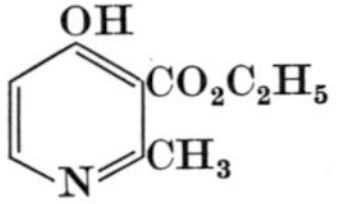 [structure: OH, $CO_2C_2H_5$, N, CH_3]	441
	Na enolate	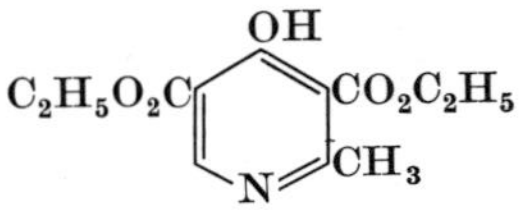 [structure: OH, $C_2H_5O_2C$, $CO_2C_2H_5$, N, CH_3]	441

Note: References 491–1045 are on pp. 545–555.

* This compound could be isolated only after distillation of the crude condensation product. Direct hydrolysis of this product proved that it consisted of diethyl α-carbethoxy-γ-phenylglutaconate, $C_2H_5O_2CCH(C_6H_5)CH{=\!=}C(CO_2C_2H_5)_2$.

† This acid was present in the crude product in the form of its ester, but was not isolated as such.

TABLE XIV

MICHAEL CONDENSATIONS WITH ALIPHATIC DIENIC AND TRIENIC ESTERS

Reactants	Catalyst	Product (Yield, %)	References
Methyl 1,3-Butadiene-1-carboxylate and		$A = —CH_2CH{=}CHCH_2CO_2CH_3$	
Dimethyl malonate	$NaOCH_3$; Na	$ACH(CO_2CH_3)_2$ (75)	397, 925, 926
Ethyl α-cyanopropionate	$NaOCH_3$ (1/8 mole)	$CH_3C(A)(CN)CO_2C_2H_5$	926
Methyl Sorbate and		$A = CH_3CHCH{=}CHCH_2CO_2CH_3$ |	
Dimethyl malonate	$NaOCH_3$	$ACH(CO_2CH_3)_2$ and $CH_3CH{=}CHCHCH_2CO_2CH_3$ | $CH(CO_2CH_3)_2$ (Mixture 9 : 1; 60–70, 80)	925–926, 927, 173
Ethyl α-cyanopropionate	$NaOCH_3$ (1/8 mole)	$AC(CH_3)(CN)CO_2C_2H_5$ (60–70)	926
Nitromethane	$(i\text{-}C_3H_7)_2NH$	ACH_2NO_2 (21)	116
Methyl γ-nitrobutyrate	$(i\text{-}C_3H_7)_2NH$	$O_2NCH(A)CH_2CH_2CO_2CH_3$ (32)	116
Ethyl Sorbate and			
Diethyl malonate	Na	$HO_2CCH_2CH{=}CHCH(CH_3)CO_2H$*	928
Ethyl cyanoacetate	$NaOC_2H_5$	$CH_3CHCH{=}CHCH_2CO_2C_2H_5$ | (77) $CH(CN)(CO_2C_2H_5)$ and $CH_3CH{=}CHCHCH_2CO_2C_2H_5$ | (9) $CH(CN)CO_2C_2H_5$	397

Ethyl acetoacetate	KOC_4H_9-*t*	$CH_3CH[CH(COCH_3)CO_2C_2H_5]CH{=}CHCH_2CO_2C_2H_5$ (75)	488
Ethyl α-Methylsorbate and			
Ethyl cyanoacetate	$NaOC_2H_5$	$CH_3CH[CH(CN)CO_2C_2H_5]CH{=}CHCH(CH_3)CO_2C_2H_5$ (67)	397
Ethyl β-Methylsorbate and			
Diethyl malonate	$NaOC_2H_5$	$CH_3CH[CH(CO_2C_2H_5)_2]CH{=}C(CH_3)CH_2CO_2C_2H_5$ and $CH_3CH{=}CHC[CH(CO_2C_2H_5)_2](CH_3)CH_2CO_2C_2H_5$ (Mixture 9 : 1; 39–42)	173
Ethyl cyanoacetate	$NaOC_2H_5$	$CH_3CH[CH(CN)CO_2C_2H_5]CH{=}C(CH_3)CH_2CO_2C_2H_5$ and $CH_3CH{=}CHC[CH(CN)CO_2C_2H_5](CH_3)CH_2CO_2C_2H_5$ (65)	397

Note: References 491–1045 are on pp. 545–555.

* This product was obtained after hydrolysis and partial decarboxylation.

TABLE XIV—*Continued*

MICHAEL CONDENSATIONS WITH ALIPHATIC DIENIC AND TRIENIC ESTERS

Reactants	Catalyst	Product (Yield, %)	References
Ethyl γ-Methylsorbate and			
Ethyl cyanoacetate	$NaOC_2H_5$	$CH_3CHC(CH_3)=CHCH_2CO_2C_2H_5$ | $CH(CN)CO_2C_2H_5$ and $CH_3CH=C(CH_3)CHCH_2CO_2C_2H_5$ | $CH(CN)CO_2C_2H_5$ (Mixture 1 : 3; 18–40)	173
Methyl Hexa-1,3,5-triene-1-carboxylate and			
Dimethyl malonate	$NaOC_2H_5$	Mixture of isomers of the formula $C_{13}H_{18}O_6$ (44)	929
Methyl Hepta-1,3,5-triene-1-carboxylate and			
Dimethyl malonate	$NaOCH_3$	$CH_3CHCH=CHCH=CHCH_2CO_2CH_3$ | $CH(CO_2CH_3)_2$ and $CH_3CH=CHCH=CHCHCH_2CO_2CH_3$ | $CH(CO_2CH_3)_2$ (Mixture 7 : 1; 74)	930

Dimethyl Penta-1,3-diene-1,1-dicarboxylate and			
Methyl cyanoacetate	$NaOCH_3$	$CH_3CHCH{=}CHCH(CO_2CH_3)_2$ | $CH(CN)CO_2CH_3$ and $CH_3CH{=}CHCHCH(CO_2CH_3)_2$ | $CH(CN)CO_2CH_3$	379
Methyl α-Carbomethoxy-δ-methylsorbate and			
Dimethyl malonate	$NaOCH_3$	$(CH_3)_2C{=}CHCH[CH(CO_2CH_3)_2]_2$ (83)	381
Diethyl Muconate and			
Diethyl malonate	Na	$C_2H_5O_2CCH_2CH_2C({=}CHCO_2C_2H_5)CH(CO_2C_2H_5)_2$ (32, 90)	931, 326
	$NaOC_2H_5$ (small quant.)	$C_2H_5O_2CCH_2CH{=}CCH_2CO_2C_2H_5$ | $CH(CO_2C_2H_5)_2$ (70)	932
Ethyl cyanoacetate	$NaOC_2H_5$	$C_2H_5O_2CCH_2CH_2C({=}CHCO_2C_2H_5)CH(CN)CO_2C_2H_5$ (90)	326

Note: References 491–1045 are on pp. 545–555.

TABLE XV

Michael Condensations with Alicyclic α,β-Ethylenic Esters

Reactants	Catalyst	Product (Yield, %)	References
Methyl 1-*Cyclobutene*-1-*carboxylate and*			
Diethyl malonate	KOC_4H_9-*t*	Diethyl (2-carbomethoxycyclobutyl)malonate (54)	933
Ethyl cyanoacetate	KOC_4H_9-*t*	Ethyl (2-carbomethoxycyclobutyl)cyanoacetate (52)	933
Methyl 3,3-*Dimethyl*-1-*cyclobutene*-1-*carboxylate and*			
Diethyl malonate	KOC_4H_9-*t*	Diethyl (4-carbomethoxy-2,2-dimethylcyclobutyl)malonate (57)	933
Ethyl cyanoacetate	KOC_4H_9-*t*	Ethyl (4-carbomethoxy-2,2-dimethylcyclobutyl)cyanoacetate (9)	933
Ethyl 1-*Cyclopentene*-1-*carboxylate and*		A = $CO_2C_2H_5$	
Diethyl malonate	$NaOC_2H_5$	$ACH(CO_2C_2H_5)_2$ (80–85)	92
Ethyl acetoacetate	$NaOC_2H_5$	$ACH_2CO_2C_2H_5$ (23), $CH_3COCH(A)CO_2C_2H_5$ (8)	93
Ethyl cyanoacetate	$NaOC_2H_5$	$ACH(CN)CO_2C_2H_5$ (30–35) $CO_2C_2H_5$ / $CH(CN)CO_2H$	92, 934, 935
Ethyl 2-*Hydroxy*-1-*cyclopentene*-1-*carboxylate and*			
Ethyl cyanoacetate	Piperidine; KOC_2H_5	$CH(CN)CO_2C_2H_5$ / $CO_2C_2H_5$ (50, 59)	936
Cyanoacetamide	Piperidine	NC, HO, N, OH (38)	937

Ethyl 1-Cyclohexene-1-carboxylate and		*A* 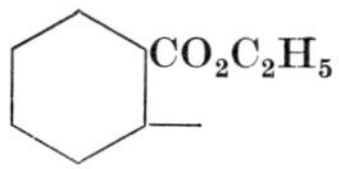 =	
Diethyl malonate	$NaOC_2H_5$	ACH($CO_2C_2H_5$)$_2$ (40)	59, 938
Diethyl methylmalonate	$NaOC_2H_5$	AC(CH_3)($CO_2C_2H_5$)$_2$ (6)	59
Ethyl cyanoacetate	$NaOC_2H_5$; KOC_2H_5; piperidine	ACH(CN)($CO_2C_2H_5$) (74, 35, 18)	939
	$NaOC_2H_5$	AC(CN)($CO_2C_2H_5$)$CH_2CO_2C_2H_5$*	940
Ethyl 2-Hydroxycyclohexene-1-carboxylate and			
Cyanoacetamide	Pyridine	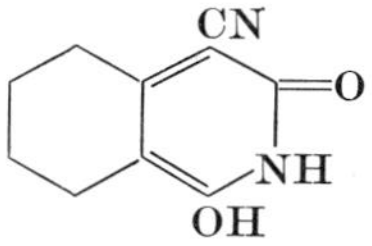	398
		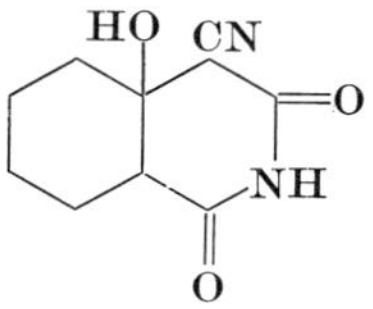	941
Ethyl 2-Aminocyclohexene-1-carboxylate and			
Cyanoacetamide	None	4-Cyano-1-hydroxy-3-oxo-2,3,5,6,7,8-hexahydroisoquinoline	398
Malonamide	Piperidine	1-Hydroxy-3-oxo-2,3,5,6,7,8-hexahydroisoquinoline-4-carboxamide	391

Note: References 491–1045 are on pp. 545–555.

* This compound was obtained by direct treatment of the condensation product with ethyl bromoacetate.

TABLE XV—*Continued*

MICHAEL CONDENSATIONS WITH ALICYCLIC α,β-ETHYLENIC ESTERS

Reactants	Catalyst	Product (Yield, %)	References
Ethyl 4-Methyl-1-cyclohexene-1-carboxylate and			
Ethyl cyanoacetate	$NaOC_2H_5$	Ethyl 1-carbethoxy-4-methylcyclohexane-2-cyanoacetate†	942
Ethyl (3-Methylcyclopentylidene)cyanoacetate‡ and			
Ethyl cyanoacetate	NH_3	H_3C; CH(CN)CO; NH; CH(CN)CO (50)	943
Ethyl Cyclohexylidenecyanoacetate‡ and			
Ethyl cyanoacetate	$NaOC_2H_5$	Cyclohexane-1,1-diacetic acid	221
Ethyl (3-Methyl-2-cyclohexenylidene)cyanoacetate‡ and			
Ethyl cyanoacetate	NH_3	$CH(CN)CONH_2$; NH; =O; CH_3; CN (44)	649
Ethyl (3-Ethyl-2-cyclohexenylidene)cyanoacetate‡ and			
Ethyl cyanoacetate	NH_3	$CH(CN)CONH_2$; NH; =O; C_2H_5; CN (25)	649

Reactants	Catalyst	Product (Yield, %)	Refs.
Ethyl (cis-2-Hydrindanylidene)cyanoacetate‡ *and* Ethyl cyanoacetate	NH_3	(37)	90
Ethyl (trans-2-Hydrindanylidene)cyanoacetate‡ *and* Ethyl cyanoacetate	NH_3	(60)	90
(cis-2-Hydrindanylidene)cyanoacetamide and Cyanoacetamide	Piperidine		90
(trans-2-Hydrindanylidene)cyanoacetamide§ *and* Cyanoacetamide	Piperidine	(15)	90

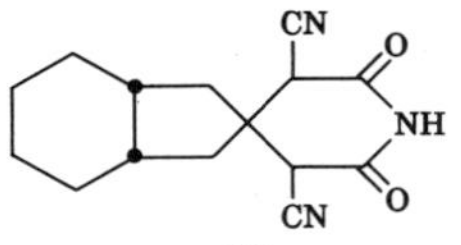

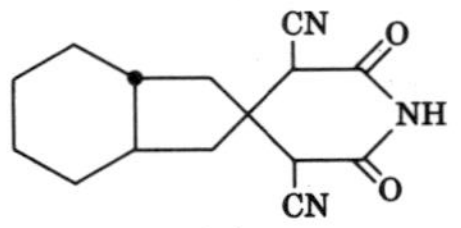

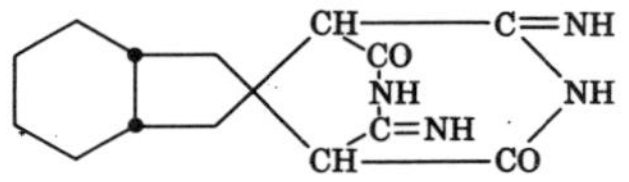

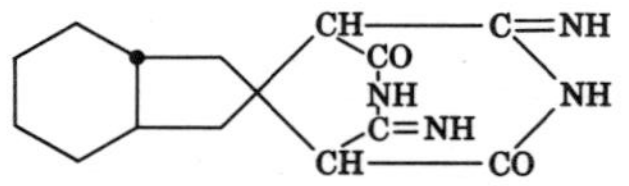

Note: References 491–1045 are on pp. 545–555.

† This product was directly condensed further with ethyl bromoacetate or ethyl β-chloropropionate.

‡ This compound was formed *in situ* from ethyl cyanoacetate and the corresponding ketone.

§ This compound was formed *in situ* from cyanoacetamide and the corresponding ketone.

TABLE XV—*Continued*

MICHAEL CONDENSATIONS WITH ALICYCLIC α,β-ETHYLENIC ESTERS

Reactants	Catalyst	Product (Yield, %)	References
Ethyl (cis-2-Decalylidene)cyanoacetate and			
Ethyl cyanoacetate	NH_3	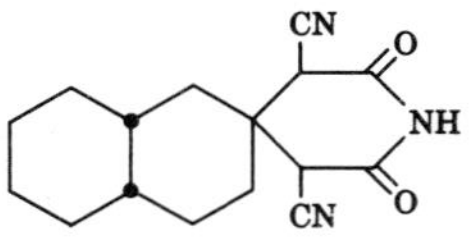 (70)	944
Ethyl (trans-2-Decalylidene)cyanoacetate ‖ *and*			
Ethyl cyanoacetate	NH_3	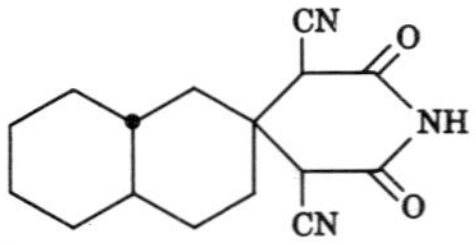	944

Note: References 491–1045 are on pp. 545–555.

‖ When this compound was formed *in situ* from ethyl cyanoacetate and *trans*-2-decalone, a 60% yield of the same condensation product was obtained.

TABLE XVI

MICHAEL CONDENSATIONS WITH AROMATIC α,β-ETHYLENIC ESTERS

Reactants	Catalyst	Product (Yield, %)	References
Ethyl (2-Furyl)acrylate and			
Diethyl malonate	$NaOC_2H_5$	2-C_4H_3O-$CH(CH_2CO_2C_2H_5)CH(CO_2C_2H_5)_2$ (49)	945
Ethyl (4-Pyridyl)acrylate and			
Diethyl malonate	$NaOC_2H_5$	4-C_5H_4N-$CH(CH_2CO_2C_2H_5)CH(CO_2C_2H_5)_2$ (94)	946
Methyl Cinnamate and			
Benzyl cyanide	$KOCH_3$	$C_6H_5CH(CH_2CO_2CH_3)CH(C_6H_5)CN$ (59)	83
	Dry $NaOC_2H_5$	$C_6H_5CH(CH_2CO_2CH_3)CH(C_6H_5)CN$	83
Acetophenone	$NaNH_2$	$C_6H_5CH(CH_2CO_2H)CH_2COC_6H_5$ (49)*	327

Note: References 491–1045 are on pp. 545–555.

* This product was isolated after hydrolysis.

TABLE XVI—*Continued*

MICHAEL CONDENSATIONS WITH AROMATIC α,β-ETHYLENIC ESTERS

Reactants	Catalyst	Product (Yield, %)	References
Ethyl Cinnamate and		$A = C_6H_5CH(—)CH_2CO_2C_2H_5$	
Diethyl malonate†	$NaOC_2H_5$	$ACH(CO_2C_2H_5)_2$ (quant.)	2, 24, 878, 947
Diethyl methylmalonate	$NaOC_2H_5$ (catalyt. amt.)	$AC(CH_3)(CO_2C_2H_5)_2$ (50)	50
	$NaOC_2H_5$ (1 equiv.)	$C_6H_5CH(CH(CO_2C_2H_5)_2)CH(CH_3)CO_2C_2H_5$ (Mixture of 2 isomers, 40)	50
Ethyl isobutyrate	$NaOC_2H_5$	$(CH_3)_2C(A)CO_2C_2H_5$ (50)	468
	$(C_6H_5)_3CNa$	$(CH_3)_2C(A)CO_2C_2H_5$ (20)	468
Diethyl succinate	$NaOC_2H_5$	2-Phenylbutane-1,3,4-tricarboxylic acid (24)*	948
Ethyl phenylacetate	$NaOC_2H_5$	$C_6H_5CH(A)CO_2C_2H_5$ (quant.)	81, 82
	$(C_6H_5)_3CNa$	$C_6H_5CH(A)CO_2C_2H_5$ (10)	468
Ethyl acetoacetate‡	$(C_6H_5)_3CNa$	$CH_3COCH(A)CO_2C_2H_5$ (60)	468
Ethyl cyanoacetate	$NaOC_2H_5$	$NCCH(A)CO_2C_2H_5$ (two isomers, 85)	290, 79, 80, 949
Cyanoacetamide	Na enolate	3-Cyano-2,6-dioxo-4-phenylpiperidine	843
Ethyl α-cyanobutyrate	$NaOC_2H_5$	$NCC(C_2H_5)(A)CO_2C_2H_5$	80
Ethyl α-cyanoisovalerate	$NaOC_2H_5$	$NCC(C_3H_7\text{-}i)(A)CO_2C_2H_5$	80
Ethyl α-cyanohydrocinnamate	$NaOC_2H_5$	$NCC(CH_2C_6H_5)(A)CO_2C_2H_5$	80

Reactant	Catalyst	Product (Yield %)	Refs.
Benzyl cyanide	$NaOC_2H_5$	$C_6H_5CH(A)CN$ (Two isomers: 27 total; 50 total; and 32 + 12 or 44 total)	27, 83, 952, 84
		$C_6H_5CH(A)CN$ (80); $C_6H_5CH(CN)CH(C_6H_5)CH_2CO_2H$ (Small);	950
		2-oxo-cyclohexane with $CO_2C_2H_5$, C_6H_5, H_5C_6, CN, C_6H_5 substituents (Small)	
	Dry $NaOC_2H_5$	2-oxo-cyclohexane with $CO_2C_2H_5$, C_6H_5, H_5C_6, CN, C_6H_5 substituents (43, 66)	83, 952, 951

Note: References 491–1095 are on pp. 545–555.

* This product was isolated after hydrolysis.

† According to ref. 80, amides of cinnamic acid and cinnamonitrile react analogously. Hydrolysis of the primary condensation product affords, with partial decarboxylation, β-phenylglutaric acid. The primary product from cinnamamide is

(piperidine-2,6-dione (N–H) bearing C_6H_5 and $CO_2C_2H_5$)

‡ Ethyl acetate was used; it was transformed into ethyl acetoacetate before the reaction with ethyl cinnamate.

TABLE XVI—*Continued*

Michael Condensations with Aromatic α,β-Ethylenic Esters

Reactants	Catalyst	Product (Yield, %)	References
		$A = C_6H_5CHCH_2CO_2C_2H_5$ (attached at the CH)	
Ethyl Cinnamate (Cont.) and			
Benzyl cyanide (*Cont.*)	$NaOCH_3$	$C_6H_5CH(CN)CH(C_6H_5)CH_2CO_2CH_3$	83
	Dry NaOH	$C_6H_5CH(A)CN$ (33); $C_6H_5CH(CN)CH(C_6H_5)CH_2CO_2H$ (35); $C_6H_5CH(A)CONH_2$ (12)	950
γ-Benzoyl-α,β-diphenyl-butyronitrile	$NaOC_2H_5$	Cyclohexanone ring (O at C-1) with substituents COC_6H_5, C_6H_5, CN and C_6H_5, H_5C_6 (4)	952
Pinacolone	$NaNH_2$	$ACH_2COC(CH_3)_3$ (64)	327
Acetophenone	$NaNH_2$	$ACH_2COC_6H_5$ (19) or $C_6H_5COCH_2CH(C_6H_5)CH_2CO_2H$ (37–66)	327, 953
Nitromethane	$[C_6H_5CH_2N(CH_3)_3]OC_4H_9$-*n*	ACH_2NO_2 (76)	40
Ethyl nitroacetate	$[C_6H_5CH_2N(CH_3)_3]OH$	$ACH(NO_2)CO_2C_2H_5$ (66)	154
2-Quinaldine	—	Quinoline ring (N) with $CH_2CH(C_6H_5)CH_2CO_2H$ at C-2 (10)*	374
Triethyl phosphonoacetate	$NaOC_2H_5$; K	$(C_2H_5O)_2P(O)CH(A)(CO_2C_2H_5)$ (24, 50)	124, 817
Ethyl 4-Nitrocinnamate and			
Cyanoacetamide	Na enolate	3-Cyano-2,6-dioxo-4-(*p*-nitrophenyl)piperidine	843

Ethyl β-Hydroxycinnamate and			
$CH_3C({=}NH)CH_2CO_2C_2H_5$	None	6-Hydroxy-2-methyl-4-phenylpyridine-3-carboxylic acid (25)*	954
Ethyl Atropate (α-Phenylacrylate) and			
Triethyl ethane-1,1,2-carboxylate	$NaOC_2H_5$	$C_2H_5O_2CCH(C_6H_5)CH_2C(CO_2C_2H_5)_2CH_2CO_2C_2H_5$	56
Ethyl β-Methoxy-α-phenylacrylate and			
Cyanoacetamide	$NaOC_2H_5$	2,6-Dihydroxy-3-phenylpyridine (28)	955
β-Methoxy-α-phenylacrylonitrile and			
Cyanoacetamide	$NaOC_2H_5$	NC, C_6H_5, HO, N, NH_2 (78)	955
Ethyl β-Ethoxy-α-(p-chlorophenyl)acrylate and			
Cyanoacetamide	$NaOC_2H_5$	C_6H_4Cl-*p*, HO, N, OH (33) or H_2NOC, C_6H_4Cl-*p*, HO, N, OH	955
Ethyl β-Isobutoxy-α-phenylacrylate and			
Cyanoacetamide	$NaOC_2H_5$	2,6-Dihydroxy-3-phenylpyridine (31)	955
β-Isobutoxy-α-phenylacrylonitrile and			
Cyanoacetamide	$NaOC_2H_5$	NC, C_6H_5, HO, N, NH_2 (81)	955

Note: References 491–1045 are on pp. 545–555.

* This product was isolated after hydrolysis.

TABLE XVI—*Continued*

MICHAEL CONDENSATIONS WITH AROMATIC α,β-ETHYLENIC ESTERS

Reactants	Catalyst	Product (Yield, %)	References
Ethyl p-Methylcinnamate and			
Ethyl α-cyanopropionate	$NaOC_2H_5$	$CH_3C(CN)(CO_2C_2H_5)CH(C_6H_4CH_3\text{-}p)CH_2CO_2C_2H_5$	80
Ethyl α-Methylcinnamate and			
Ethyl cyanoacetate	$NaOC_2H_5$	$NCCH(CO_2C_2H_5)CH(C_6H_5)CH(CH_3)CO_2C_2H_5$ (Two isomers, 58)	50, 80
Ethyl Hydroxymethylenephenylacetate and			
Malonic acid	None	α-Phenylglutaconic acid (75)*	366
Cyanoacetic acid	None	Ethyl 4-cyano-2-phenyl-2-butenoate (47)	366
Ethyl β-Benzylacrylate and		$A = C_6H_5CH_2\underset{\vert}{C}HCH_2CO_2C_2H_5$	
Diethyl malonate	Na enolate	$ACH(CO_2C_2H_5)_2$ (51)	956
Diethyl methylmalonate§	$NaOC_2H_5$	$AC(CH_3)(CO_2C_2H_5)_2$ (42)	77
Ethyl cyanoacetate§	$NaOC_2H_5$	$ACH(CN)CO_2C_2H_5$ (67)	77
β-Isobutoxy-α-phenylcrotononitrile and			
Cyanoacetamide	$NaOC_2H_5$	Pyrimidine ring: 4-CH_3, 5-NC, 6-HO, 2-NH_2... (ring bearing CH_3, NC, HO, N, NH_2, C_6H_5) (33)	955
Dimethyl Benzylidenemalonate and		$A = C_6H_5\underset{\vert}{C}HCH(CO_2CH_3)_2$	
Isobutyraldehyde	$NaOCH_3$	$(CH_3)_2C(A)CHO$ (80)	957
Deoxybenzoin	$NaOCH_3$	$C_6H_5COCH(A)C_6H_5$ (44)	163

Anthrone	$NaOCH_3$	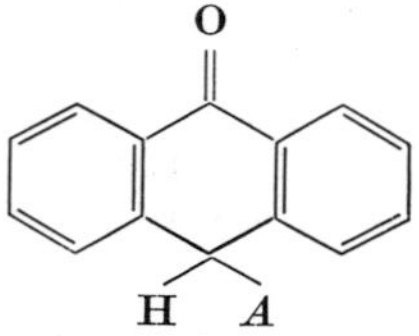 O H *A* (71)	163
Nitromethane	$NaOCH_3$	ACH_2NO_2 (95)	329
Dimethyl m-Nitrobenzylidenemalonate and			
Anthrone	Piperidine	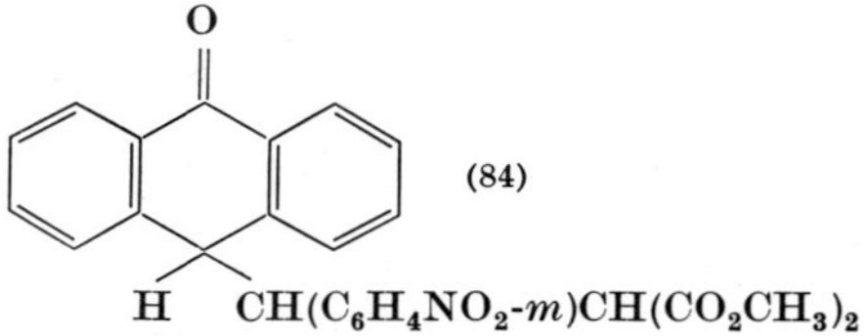 O H $CH(C_6H_4NO_2\text{-}m)CH(CO_2CH_3)_2$ (84)	958
Phenylnitromethane	$NaOCH_3$	$C_6H_5CH(NO_2)CH(C_6H_4NO_2\text{-}m)CH(CO_2CH_3)_2$ (78)	959
Dimethyl o-Chlorobenzylidenemalonate and			
Anthrone	Piperidine	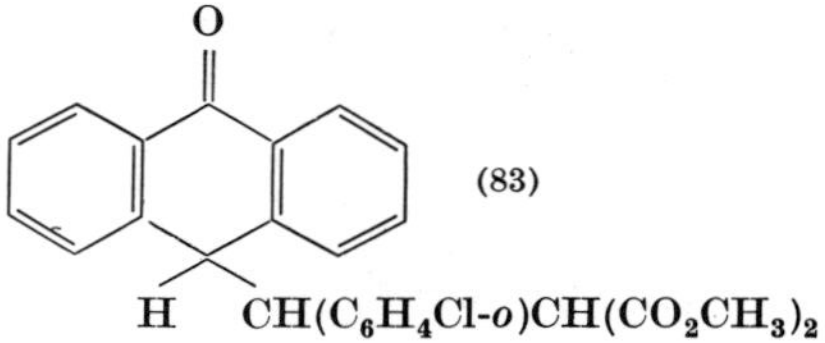 O H $CH(C_6H_4Cl\text{-}o)CH(CO_2CH_3)_2$ (83)	960

Note: References 491–1045 are on pp. 545–555.

* This product was isolated after hydrolysis.

§ Instead of ethyl β-benzylacrylate, ethyl styrylacetate was employed.

TABLE XVI—*Continued*

MICHAEL CONDENSATIONS WITH AROMATIC α,β-ETHYLENIC ESTERS

Reactants	Catalyst	Product (Yield, %)	References
Diethyl Benzylidenemalonate and		$A = C_6H_5\overset{\vert}{C}HCH(CO_2C_2H_5)_2$	
Diethyl malonate	Na enolate	$ACH(CO_2C_2H_5)_2$ (quant.)	901
Ethyl acetoacetate	$NaOC_2H_5$	$CH_3COCH(A)CO_2C_2H_5$ (81)	961
$CH_3C({=}NH)CH_2CO_2C_2H_5$	None	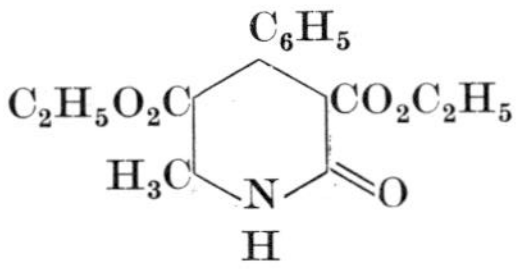 4-C_6H_5, 3,5-di-$CO_2C_2H_5$, 6-H_3C piperidin-2-one ring: C_6H_5; $C_2H_5O_2C$; $CO_2C_2H_5$; H_3C; N–H; =O (75)	962, 580, 963
Ethyl isobutyrylacetate	$NaOC_2H_5$	$(CH_3)_2CHCOCH(A)CO_2C_2H_5$ (65)	964
Anthrone	Piperidine; $(C_2H_5)_2NH$	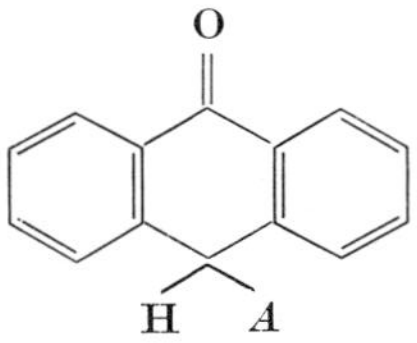 10-A-anthrone (O; H, A) (71, 91)	46, 960
Deoxybenzoin	$NaOC_2H_5$	$C_6H_5COCH(A)C_6H_5$	416
Phenylnitromethane	$(C_2H_5)_2NH$; $NaOC_2H_5$	$C_6H_5CH(A)NO_2$ (86, 52)	29, 965
Ethyl nitroacetate	$(C_2H_5)_2NH$	$ACH(NO_2)CO_2C_2H_5$ (99)	29

Substituted Diethyl Benzylidenemalonates

Substituent(s) in $C_6H_5CH{=}C(CO_2C_2H_5)_2$	Addend	Catalyst	Product (Yield, %)	References
2-Chloro	Anthrone	Piperidine	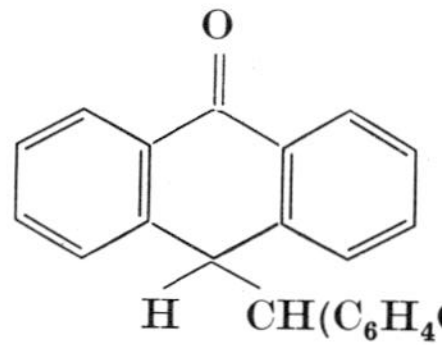 O; H $CH(C_6H_4Cl\text{-}2)CH(CO_2C_2H_5)_2$ (73)	960
3-Nitro	Diethyl malonate	Na enolate	$(C_2H_5O_2C)_2CHCH(C_6H_4NO_2\text{-}3)CH(CO_2C_2H_5)_2$	901
	Anthrone	Piperidine	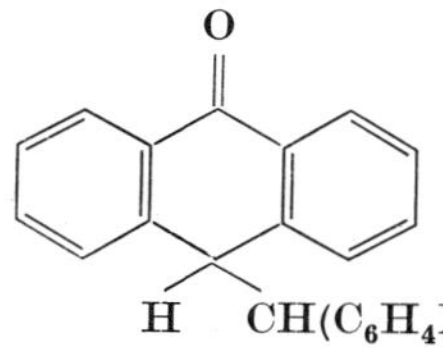 O; H $CH(C_6H_4NO_2\text{-}3)CH(CO_2C_2H_5)_2$	958
4-Nitro	Nitromethane	$NaOC_2H_5$	$O_2NCH_2CH(C_6H_4NO_2\text{-}3)CH(CO_2C_2H_5)_2$	966
	Diethyl malonate	Na enolate	$(C_2H_5O_2C)_2CHCH(C_6H_4NO_2\text{-}4)CH(CO_2C_2H_5)_2$	901
	Nitromethane	$NaOC_2H_5$	$O_2NCH_2CH(C_6H_4NO_2\text{-}4)CH(CO_2C_2H_5)_2$	966
4-Methoxy	Deoxybenzoin	$NaOC_2H_5$	$C_6H_5COCH(C_6H_5)CH(C_6H_4OCH_3\text{-}4)CH(CO_2C_2H_5)_2$	416
4-Dimethylamino	Deoxybenzoin	$NaOC_2H_5$	$C_6H_5COCH(C_6H_5)CH[C_6H_4N(CH_3)_2\text{-}4]CH(CO_2C_2H_5)_2$	416
3,4-Methylenedioxy	Deoxybenzoin	$NaOC_2H_5$	$C_6H_5COCH(C_6H_5)CH[C_6H_3(O_2CH_2)\text{-}3,4]CH(CO_2C_2H_5)_2$	416

Note: References 491–1045 are on pp. 545–555.

TABLE XVI—*Continued*

MICHAEL CONDENSATIONS WITH AROMATIC α,β-ETHYLENIC ESTERS

Substituted Diethyl Benzylidenemalonates—Continued

Substituent(s) in $C_6H_5CH{=}C(CO_2C_2H_5)_2$	Addend	Catalyst	Product (Yield, %)	References
4-Acetoxy	Ethyl acetoacetate	$NaOC_2H_5$	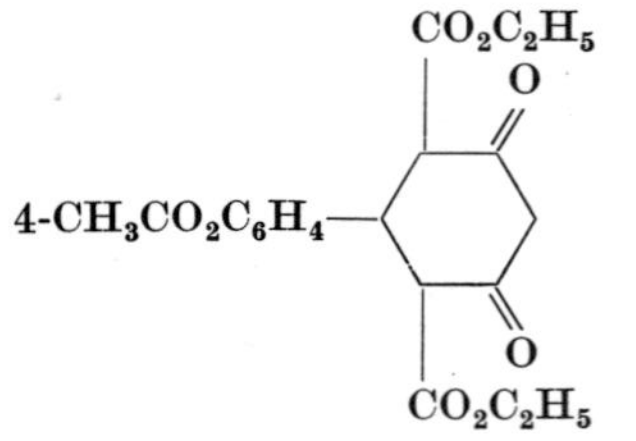 $CO_2C_2H_5$, O, 4-$CH_3CO_2C_6H_4$—, O, $CO_2C_2H_5$	967
	Ethyl propionyl-acetate	$NaOC_2H_5$	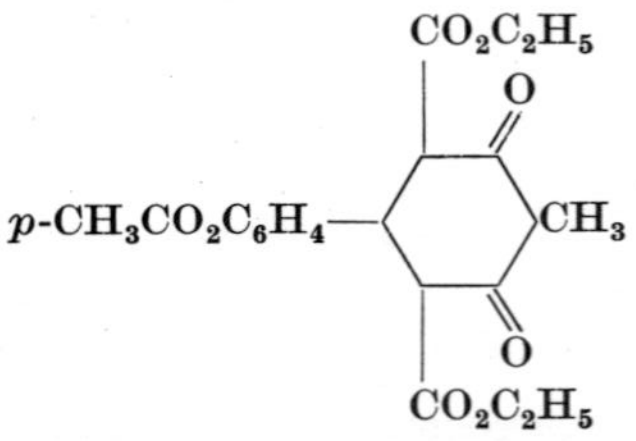 $CO_2C_2H_5$, O, p-$CH_3CO_2C_6H_4$—, CH_3, O, $CO_2C_2H_5$	426

3-Methoxy-4-acetoxy	Ethyl acetoacetate	$NaOC_2H_5$	CH_3CO_2, OCH_3, $CO_2C_2H_5$, O, O, $CO_2C_2H_5$	968

Reactants	Catalyst	Product (Yield, %)	References
Ethyl Benzylidenecyanoacetate and			
Ethyl cyanoacetate	$(C_2H_5)_2NH$	C_6H_5, NC, CN, O, N, O, H (Diethylammonium salt, 60)	969
$C_6H_5C({=}NH)CH_2CN$	$(C_2H_5)_2NH$	3,5 Dicyano-4,6-diphenyl-2-piperidone (5)	331
Ethyl (α-Phenylethylidene)cyanoacetate and			
Ethyl acetoacetate	$NaOC_2H_5$	O, O, NC, $CO_2C_2H_5$, CH_3 C_6H_5	415

Note: References 491–1045 are on pp. 545–555.

TABLE XVI—*Continued*

MICHAEL CONDENSATIONS WITH AROMATIC α,β-ETHYLENIC ESTERS

Reactants	Catalyst	Product (Yield, %)	References
Benzylidenecyanoacetamide and			
Cyanoacetamide	KOH	$C_6H_5CH_2CH(CN)CONH_2$ or $C_6H_5CH{=}C(CN)CONH_2$	896
		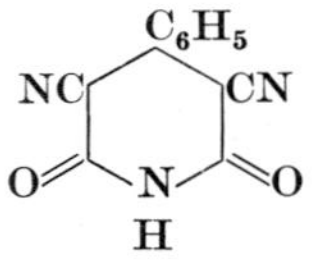 C_6H_5 NC CN O N O H	
Ethyl Cinnamylideneacetate and			
Diethyl malonate	$NaOC_2H_5$	β-Styrylglutaric acid (38)*	194, 195
Ethyl 3,4-Dihydronaphthoate and			
Ethyl acetoacetate	—	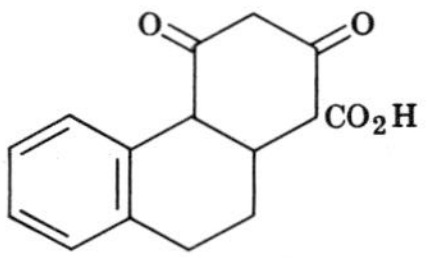 O O CO_2H (20)*	970
Ethyl 4-Phenyl-2-pentenoate and			
Ethyl cyanoacetate	—	$C_6H_5CH(CH_3)CH(CH_2CO_2C_2H_5)CH(CN)CO_2C_2H_5$ (56)	77

Reactant	Catalyst	Product (Yield, %)	Refs.
Diethyl 3-Pyridylmethylenemalonate and			
Phenylnitromethane	$(C_2H_5)_2NH$	3-pyridyl-$CH[CH(CO_2C_2H_5)_2]CH(C_6H_5)NO_2$ (84)	29
Ethyl nitroacetate	$(C_2H_5)_2NH$	3-pyridyl-$CH[CH(CO_2C_2H_5)_2]CH(NO_2)CO_2C_2H_5$ (91)	29
Dimethyl Cinnamylidenemalonate and			
Dimethyl malonate	$NaOCH_3$	$C_6H_5CH[CH(CO_2CH_3)_2]CH_2CH[CH(CO_2CH_3)_2]_2$ ‖	56, 971
Nitromethane	$NaOCH_3$	$C_6H_5CH{=}CHCH(CH_2NO_2)CH(CO_2CH_3)_2$ (87)	329
Diethyl Benzylidenesuccinate and			
Diethyl malonate	KOC_2H_5	2-Phenylbutane-1,1,3,4-tetracarboxylic acid,* 2-phenylbutane-1,3,4-tricarboxylic acid*	948
Ethyl α-Cyano-γ,γ-diphenylcrotonate and			
Ethyl cyanoacetate¶	$(C_2H_5)_2NH$	β-Benzhydrylglutaric acid* (12–21)	972

Note: References 491–1045 are on pp. 545–555.

* This product was isolated after hydrolysis.

‖ This is the formula of the expected condensation product; in fact, a pentamethyl ester was isolated. This same product is obtained in 97% yield when cinnamaldehyde and dimethyl malonate are condensed in the presence of sodium methoxide.

¶ The unsaturated ester was formed *in situ* from diphenylacetaldehyde and ethyl cyanoacetate.

TABLE XVIA

INTRAMOLECULAR MICHAEL CONDENSATIONS OF AROMATIC α,β-ETHYLENIC ESTERS

Reactant	Catalyst	Product (Yield, %)	References
C_6H_4: $CH{=}CHCO_2C_2H_5$, $OCH_2CO_2C_2H_5$	$NaOC_2H_5$	benzofuran ring: $CH_2CO_2C_2H_5$, $CO_2C_2H_5$, O (77)	974, 973
C_6H_3: $CH{=}CHCO_2C_2H_5$, $OCH_2CO_2C_2H_5$, OCH_3	$NaOC_2H_5$	benzofuran ring: $CH_2CO_2C_2H_5$, $CO_2C_2H_5$, O, OCH_3 (65)	973
C_6H_4: $CH{=}CHCO_2CH_3$, $SCH_2CO_2CH_3$	$NaOCH_3$	benzothiophene ring: $CH_2CO_2CH_3$, CO_2CH_3, S (75)	332
C_6H_2: O_2N, $CH{=}CHCO_2CH_3$, $NHCH_2CO_2CH_3$, CH_3	$NaOCH_3$	indoline ring: $CH_2CO_2CH_3$, CO_2CH_3, NH, CH_3 (60)	332
H_3C–C_6H_3: $C(CH_3){=}CHCO_2C_2H_5$, $OCH_2CO_2C_2H_5$	$NaOC_2H_5$	H_3C–benzofuran ring: CH_3, $CH_2CO_2C_2H_5$, $CO_2C_2H_5$, O (90)	973, 974

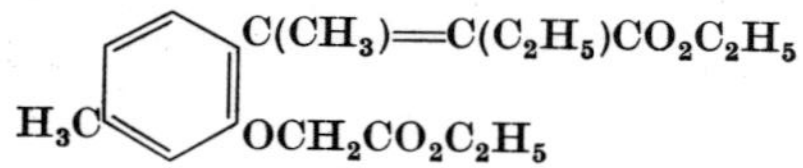	$NaOC_2H_5$	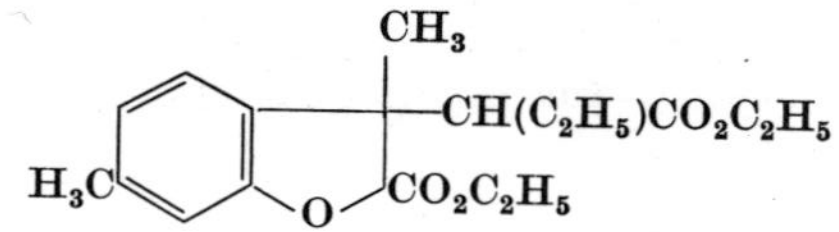 (88)	974
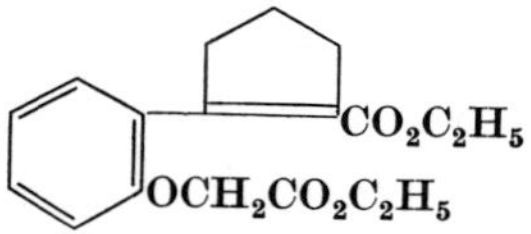	$NaOC_2H_5$	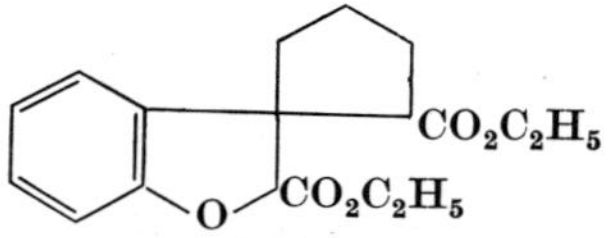 (85)	974, 973
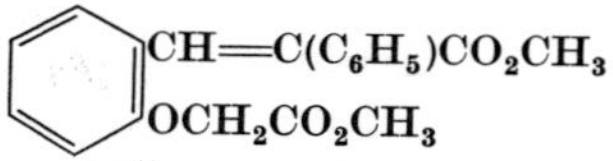	$NaOCH_3$	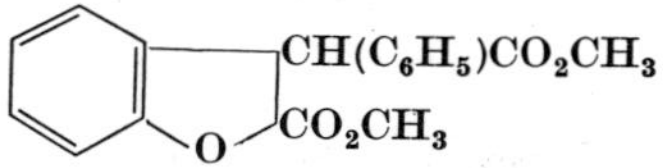 (43)	332
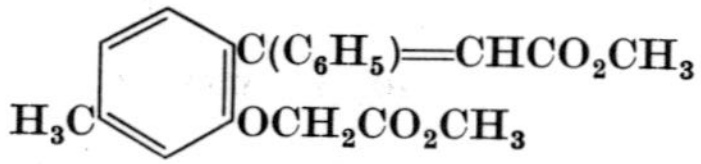	$NaOCH_3$	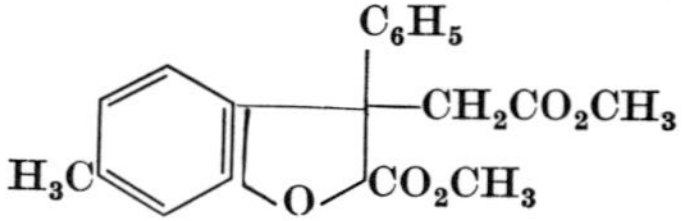 (80)	332
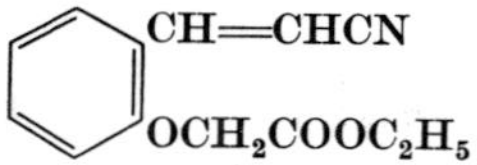	$NaOC_2H_5$	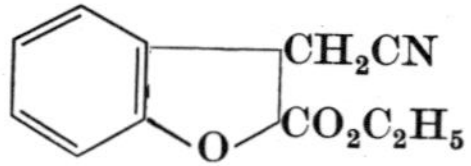	974
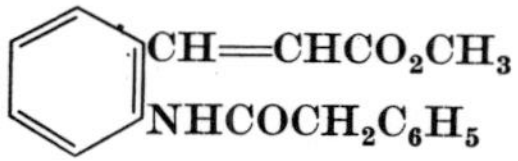	$NaOCH_3$	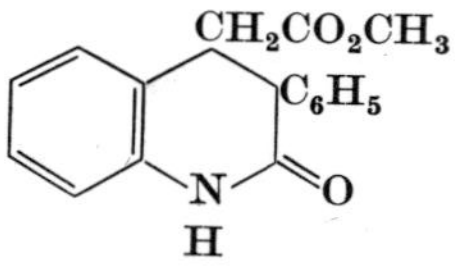 (71)	332

Note: References 491–1045 are on pp. 545–555.

TABLE XVII

MICHAEL REACTIONS WITH α,β-ETHYLENIC KETO ESTERS

Reactants	Catalyst	Product (Yield, %)	References
Sodium Methyleneacetoacetate and*			
2-Carboxycyclohexanone	NaOH	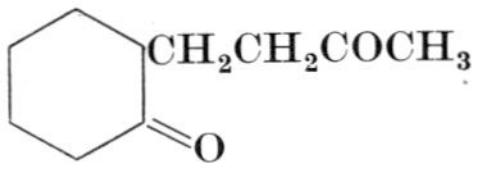 [structure: 2-($CH_2CH_2COCH_3$)cyclohexanone] and [structure: octalone] 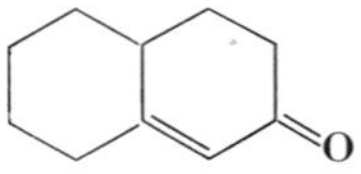	528
2-Carbethoxycyclohexanone	NaOH	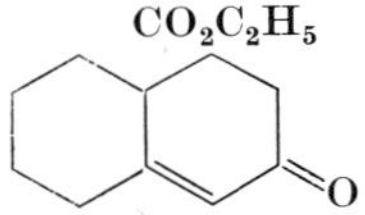 [structure: $CO_2C_2H_5$-substituted octalone] and [structure: octalone] 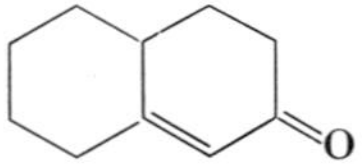	528
2-Methylcyclopentane-1,3-dione	NaOH, piperidine	8-Hydroxy-9-methylhydrindane-3,6-dione	528
2-Methylcyclohexane-1,3-dione	NaOH	2-(β-Acetylethyl)-2-methylcyclohexane-1,3-dione	528
Ethyl Methyleneacetoacetate† and			
Ethyl acetoacetate	NaOH, *sec*-amine	4-Carbethoxy-3-methyl-2-cyclohexen-1-one	528
2-Carbethoxycyclohexanone	NaOH	10-Carbethoxy-2-oxo-2,3,4,5,6,7,8,10-octahydronaphthalene	528
2-Carbethoxy-1-tetralone	NaOH	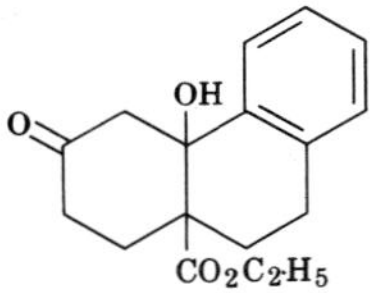 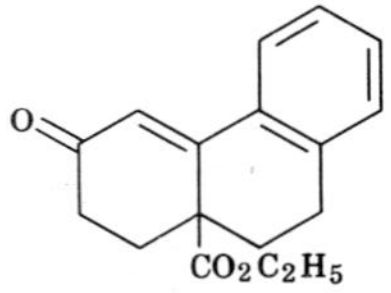 [structure: OH, O, $CO_2C_2H_5$] [structure: O, $CO_2C_2H_5$]	528
2-Formyl-1-cyclohexanone	NaOH	2-(β-Acetyl-β-carbethoxyethyl)-2-formylcyclohexanone (37)	528

Sodium Methyleneacetonedicarboxylate‡ and			
2-Methylcyclopentane-1,3-dione	NaOH	[structure: bicyclic dione with CH_3 at ring junction, =O on five-membered ring, O= on six-membered ring]	528
2-Methylcyclohexane-1,3-dione	NaOH	[structure: bicyclic dione with CH_3 at ring junction, O on six-membered ring, O= on enone ring]	528
Ethyl α-(Aminomethylene)acetoacetate and			
Ethyl acetoacetate	None	Diethyl 2,6-dimethylpyridine-3,5-dicarboxylate (30)	120
Acetone	None	Ethyl 2,5,6-trimethylpyridine-3-carboxylate (8)	120
Cyclohexanone	None	Ethyl 2-methyl-5,6,7,8-tetrahydroquinoline-3-carboxylate (20–30)	120
Ethyl β-Acetylacrylate and			
Diethyl malonate	$NaOC_2H_5$	$CH_3COCH_2CH(CO_2C_2H_5)CH(CO_2C_2H_5)_2$	975
Ethyl β-Acetyl-α-hydroxyacrylate (Acetylpyruvate) and			
Cyanoacetamide	NH_3; $(C_2H_5)_2NH$	4-Carbethoxy-3-cyano-6-methyl-2-pyridone	371
	Piperidine	4-Carbethoxy-3-cyano-6-methyl-2-pyridone (15)	976
	$NaOCH_3$	4-Carbethoxy-3-cyano-6-methyl-2-pyridone (65)	976
	K_2CO_3	4-Carbethoxy-3-cyano-6-methyl-2-pyridone (82)	976, 977
$CH_3C(=NH)CH_2CO_2C_2H_5$	None	Diethyl 2,6-dimethylpyridine-3,4-dicarboxylate (90)	978, 979

Note: References 491–1045 are on pp. 545–555.

* A mixture of sodium acetoacetate and formaldehyde was employed.

† A mixture of ethyl acetoacetate and formaldehyde was employed.

‡ A mixture of sodium acetonedicarboxylate and formaldehyde was employed.

TABLE XVII—*Continued*

Michael Reactions with α,β-Ethylenic Keto Esters

Reactants	Catalyst	Product (Yield, %)	References
Ethyl β-Acetyl-α-ethoxyacrylate and			
Cyanoacetamide	K_2CO_3	2-Carbethoxy-5-cyano-4-methyl-6-pyridone (73)	99
Ethyl 3-Oxo-4-pentenoate and			
2-Methylcyclohexane-1,3-dione	$NaOCH_3$	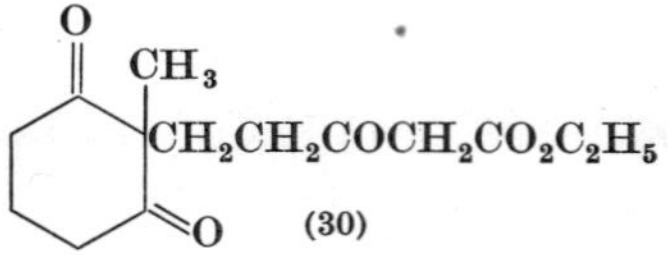 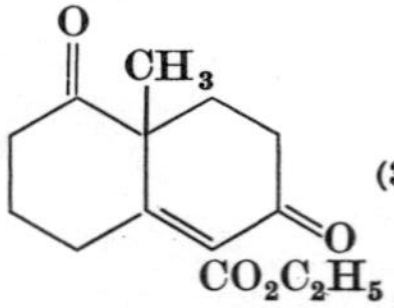 O, CH_3, $CH_2CH_2COCH_2CO_2C_2H_5$, O (30); O, CH_3, O, $CO_2C_2H_5$ (30)	538
Ethyl α-Acetyl-β-hydroxycrotonate (Diacetylacetate) and			
Cyanoacetamide	Pyridine	3-Cyano-4-methyl-6-hydroxy-2-pyridone §	398
Methyl 5-Oxo-6-heptenoate and			
2-Methylcyclohexane-1,3-dione	$NaOCH_3$	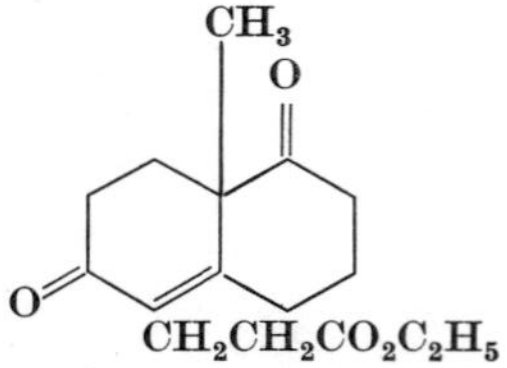 CH_3, O, O, $CH_2CH_2CO_2C_2H_5$	538
Ethyl β-Propionyl-α-hydroxyacrylate (Propionylpyruvate) and			
Cyanoacetamide	Piperidine	Ethyl 3-cyano-6-ethyl-2-hydroxypyridine-4-carboxylate (58)	980

Ethyl α-Ethylideneacetoacetate and			
Ethyl acetoacetate‖	$NaOC_2H_5$; piperidine	Diethyl α,α′-diacetyl-β-methylglutarate (93)	981, 982, 983
1-Tetralone	$NaNH_2$	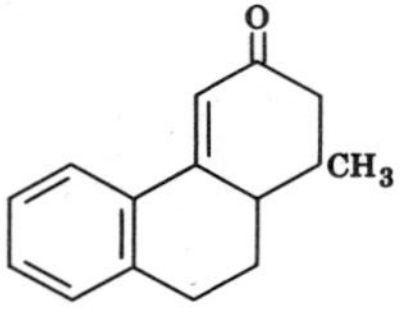 O, CH_3 (35)	206
Ethylideneacetoacetanilide and			
Acetoacetanilide	Pyridine	$CH_3CH[CH(COCH_3)CONHC_6H_5]_2$ (50)	984
	None	$CH_3CH[CH(COCH_3)CONHC_6H_5]_2$ (60)	984
	Pyridine	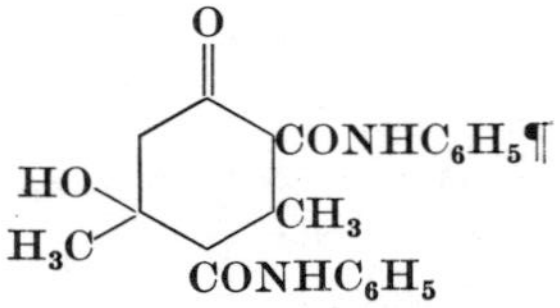 O, HO, H_3C, $CONHC_6H_5$¶, CH_3, $CONHC_6H_5$	984
Ethylideneacetoacet-o-toluide and			
Acetoacet-*o*-toluide	Pyridine	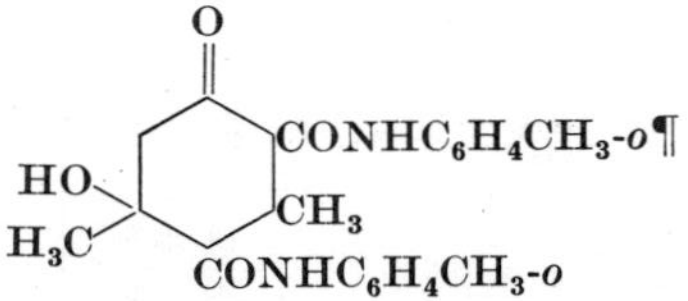 O, HO, H_3C, $CONHC_6H_4CH_3$-*o*¶, CH_3, $CONHC_6H_4CH_3$-*o*	984

Note: References 491–1045 are on pp. 545–555.

§ Ethyl acetate is eliminated in this reaction.

‖ The ethylenic compound was formed *in situ* from the corresponding aldehyde and the keto acid derivative.

¶ This product is formed when the reaction is carried out in *boiling* pyridine.

TABLE XVII—*Continued*

MICHAEL REACTIONS WITH α,β-ETHYLENIC KETO ESTERS

Reactants	Catalyst	Product (Yield, %)	References
Ethylideneacetoacet-p-toluide and			
Acetoacet-*p*-toluide	None	$CH_3CH[CH(COCH_3)CONHC_6H_4CH_3\text{-}p]_2$	984
	Pyridine	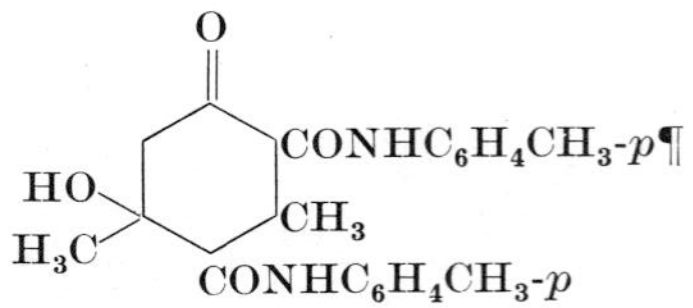 O; HO, H_3C; $CONHC_6H_4CH_3\text{-}p$¶; CH_3; $CONHC_6H_4CH_3\text{-}p$	984
Ethyl α-Methoxymethyleneacetoacetate and			
Cyanoacetamide	$NaOC_2H_5$	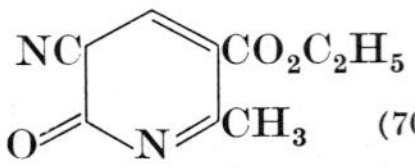 NC, $CO_2C_2H_5$, O, N, CH_3 (70)	330
Ethyl α-Ethoxymethyleneacetoacetate and			
Diethyl malonate	$NaOC_2H_5$	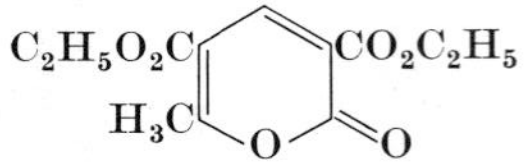 $C_2H_5O_2C$, $CO_2C_2H_5$, H_3C, O, O	310
Ethyl cyanoacetate	$NaOC_2H_5$	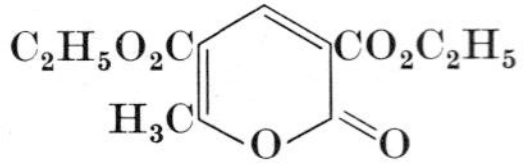 $C_2H_5O_2C$, $CO_2C_2H_5$, H_3C, O, O	310
Ethyl β-n-Butyryl-α-hydroxyacrylate (n-Butyrylpyruvate) and			
Cyanoacetamide	Piperidine	Ethyl 3-cyano-2-hydroxy-6-propylpyridine-4-carboxylate (51)	985

Ethyl β-Isobutyryl-α-hydroxyacrylate (Isobutyrylpyruvate) and			
Cyanoacetamide	K_2CO_3	Ethyl 3-cyano-2-hydroxy-6-isopropylpyridine-4-carboxylate (70)	977
4-Carbomethoxy-3-methyl-2-cyclohexen-1-one and			
Diethyl malonate	Na enolate	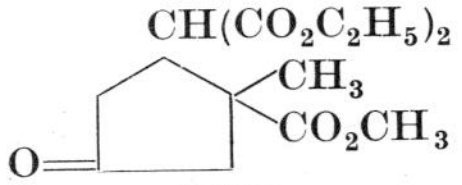 O= ; $CH(CO_2C_2H_5)_2$; CH_3 ; CO_2CH_3 (27)**	986
Ethyl α-Propylideneacetoacetate and			
Ethyl acetoacetate	$NaOC_2H_5$; $(C_2H_5)_2NH$	Diethyl α,α′-diacetyl-β-ethylglutarate	982, 983, 986*a*
	Piperidine	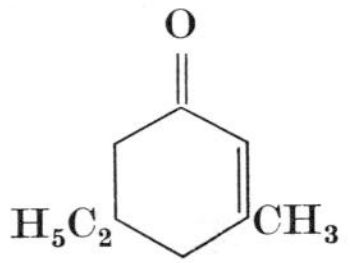 O ; H_5C_2 ; CH_3 (66)	982
α-Propylideneacetoacetanilide‖ and			
Acetoacetanilide	None	$C_2H_5CH[CH(COCH_3)CONHC_6H_5]_2$	984
	Pyridine	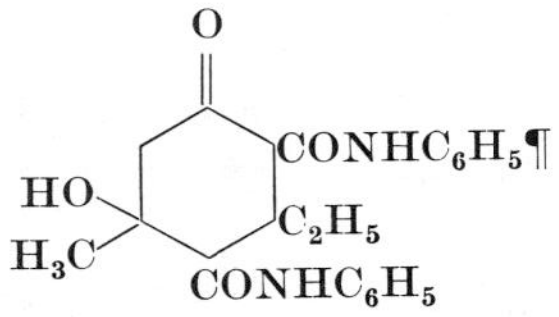 O ; HO ; H_3C ; $CONHC_6H_5$¶ ; C_2H_5 ; $CONHC_6H_5$	984

Note: References 491–1045 are on pp. 545–555.

‖ The ethylenic compound was formed *in situ* from the corresponding aldehyde and the keto acid derivative.

¶ This product is formed when the reaction is carried out in *boiling* pyridine.

** This is the structure assumed by the authors.

TABLE XVII—*Continued*

MICHAEL REACTIONS WITH α,β-ETHYLENIC KETO ESTERS

Reactants	Catalyst	Product (Yield, %)	References
Ethyl α-Isopropylideneacetoacetate‖ and			
Ethyl acetoacetate	$NaOC_2H_5$; $KOC(CH_3)_3$	4-Carbethoxy-3,5,5-trimethyl-2-cyclohexen-1-one (80–94, 76)	988, 989, 987
Ethyl β-Isovaleryl-α-hydroxyacrylate (Isovalerylpyruvate) and			
Cyanoacetamide	K_2CO_3	Ethyl 3-cyano-2-hydroxy-6-isobutylpyridine-4-carboxylate (65)	977
Ethyl β-Pivaloyl-α-hydroxyacrylate (Pivaloylpyruvate) and			
Cyanoacetamide	K_2CO_3	Ethyl 3-cyano-2-hydroxy-6-*t*-butylpyridine-4-carboxylate (70)	977
Ethyl α-n-Butylideneacetoacetate‖ and			
Ethyl acetoacetate	Piperidine	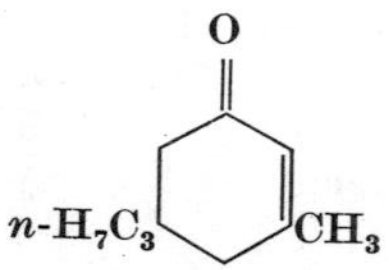 O; *n*-H_7C_3; CH_3	981
Ethyl α-Isobutylideneacetoacetate‖ and			
Ethyl acetoacetate	$NaOC_2H_5$; $(C_2H_5)_2NH$	Diethyl α,α′-diacetyl-β-isopropylglutarate	981, 990
	Piperidine	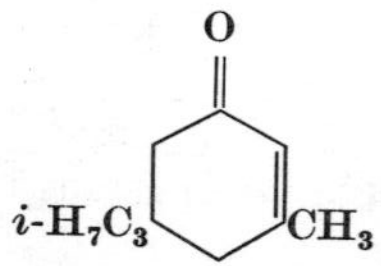 O; *i*-H_7C_3; CH_3 (71)	981

Ethyl 6-Carbethoxy-6-methyl-2-cyclohexen-1-one and			
Diethyl malonate	$NaOC_2H_5$	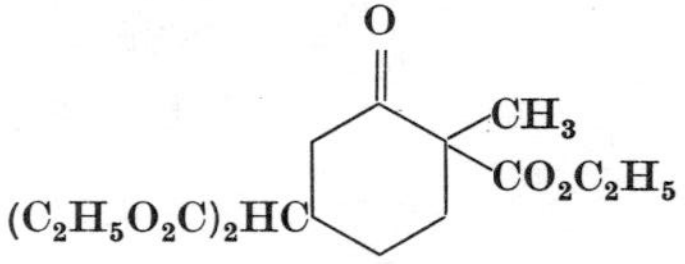 O; CH_3; $CO_2C_2H_5$; $(C_2H_5O_2C)_2HC$	991
Ethyl (2-Ketocyclohexyl)glyoxalate Enol and			
$CH_3C({=}NH)CH_2CO_2C_2H_5$	None	Diethyl 2-methyl-9-hydroxy-5,6,7,8,9,10-hexahydroquinoline-3,4-dicarboxylate (36)	652
Cyanoacetamide	Piperidine; $NaOC_2H_5$	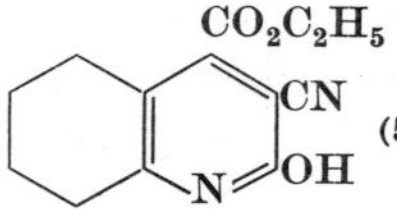 $CO_2C_2H_5$; CN; N; OH (50)	977, 592
Diethyl acetone-1,3-dicarboxylate	Na enolate	Triethyl 6-hydroxytetralin-5,7,8-tricarboxylate (72)	427
Methyl β-Benzoylacrylate and			
Nitromethane	$NaOCH_3$	$C_6H_5COCH_2CH(CO_2C_2H_5)CH_2NO_2$ (92)	329
Ethyl α-Hydroxy-β-benzoylacrylate and			
Cyanoacetamide	$(C_2H_5)_2NH$	4-Carbethoxy-3-cyano-6-phenyl-2-pyridone	594
Ethyl α-Isopentylideneacetoacetate and			
Ethyl acetoacetate	$(C_2H_5)_2NH$; piperidine	Diethyl α,α′-diacetyl-β-isobutylglutarate	990

Note: References 491–1045 are on pp. 545–555.

‖ The ethylenic compound was formed *in situ* from the corresponding aldehyde and the keto acid derivative.

TABLE XVII—*Continued*

MICHAEL REACTIONS WITH α,β-ETHYLENIC KETO ESTERS

Reactants	Catalyst	Product (Yield, %)	References
Ethyl (2-Keto-3-methylcyclohexyl)glyoxalate and			
$CH_3C({=}NH)CH_2CO_2C_2H_5$	None	Diethyl 2,8-dimethyl-9-hydroxy-5,6,7,8,9,10-hexahydroquinoline-3,4-dicarboxylate	652
Ethyl (2-Keto-4-methylcyclohexyl)glyoxalate and			
$CH_3C({=}NH)CH_2CO_2C_2H_5$	None	Diethyl 2,7-dimethyl-9-hydroxy-5,6,7,8,9,10-hexahydroquinoline-3,4-dicarboxylate	652
Ethyl (2-Keto-5-methylcyclohexyl)glyoxalate and			
$CH_3C({=}NH)CH_2CO_2C_2H_5$	None	Diethyl 2,6-dimethyl-9-hydroxy-5,6,7,8,9,10-hexahydroquinoline-3,4-dicarboxylate	652
Ethyl Methylenebenzoylacetate‖ *and*			
Ethyl benzoylacetate	$(C_2H_5)_2NH$	$CH_2[CH(COC_6H_5)CO_2C_2H_5]_2$	992
Ethyl β-Benzoyl-α-hydroxyacrylate (Benzoylpyruvate) and			
Cyanoacetamide	Piperidine	Ethyl 3-cyano-2-hydroxy-6-phenylpyridine-4-carboxylate (30)	977
Ethyl γ-Benzylideneacetoacetate and			
Deoxybenzoin	$NaOC_2H_5$	3,4,5-Triphenyl-2-cyclohexen-1-one	993
Ethyl α-Benzylideneacetoacetate and			
Ethyl acetoacetate‖	Piperidine	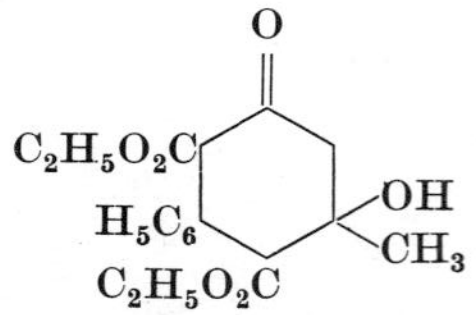 O; $C_2H_5O_2C$; H_5C_6; OH; CH_3; $C_2H_5O_2C$ (Three stereoisomers)	982

Ethyl cyanoacetate	$(C_2H_5)_2NH$	[ring structure: C_6H_5; NC; $CO_2C_2H_5$; O=; CH_3; OH; N; H] (68)	969
	Aq. $(C_2H_5)_2NH$	$C_2H_5O_2CCH(COCH_3)CH(C_6H_5)CH(CN)CONH_2$;‖	969
		[ring structure: C_6H_5; NC; $CO_2C_2H_5$; O=; CH_3; OH; N; H]	
$CH_3C({=}NH)CH_2CN$	$(C_2H_5)_2NH$	[ring structure: C_6H_5; NC; $CO_2C_2H_5$; H_3C; CH_3; OH; N; H] or [ring structure: C_6H_5; NC; $CO_2C_2H_5$; H_3C; N; CH_3]	440
$C_6H_5C({=}NH)CH_2CN$	$NaOCH_3$	Ethyl 5-cyano-4,6-diphenyl-2-methylpyridine-3-carboxylate††	331
p-$CH_3C_6H_4C({=}NH)CH_2CN$	$NaOCH_3$	Ethyl 5-cyano-2-methyl-4-phenyl-6-p-tolylpyridine-3-carboxylate	331
p-$CH_3OC_6H_4C({=}NH)CH_2CN$	$NaOCH_3$	Ethyl 5-cyano-6-p-methoxyphenyl-2-methyl-4-phenyl-pyridine-3-carboxylate	331
Phenylacetaldehyde	$NaOC_2H_5$	$C_6H_5CH[CH(C_6H_5)CHO]CH(COCH_3)CO_2C_2H_5$ (36)	163

Note: References 491–1045 are on pp. 545–555.

‖ The ethylenic compound was formed *in situ* from the corresponding aldehyde and the keto acid derivative.

†† By self-condensation, part of the $C_6H_5C({=}NH)CH_2CN$ is converted into 3,5-dicyano-2,4,6-triphenyldihydropyridine.

TABLE XVII—*Continued*

Michael Reactions with α,β-Ethylenic Keto Esters

Reactants	Catalyst	Product (Yield, %)	References
Ethyl α-Benzylideneacetoacetate (Cont.) and			
Anthrone	$NaOC_2H_5$	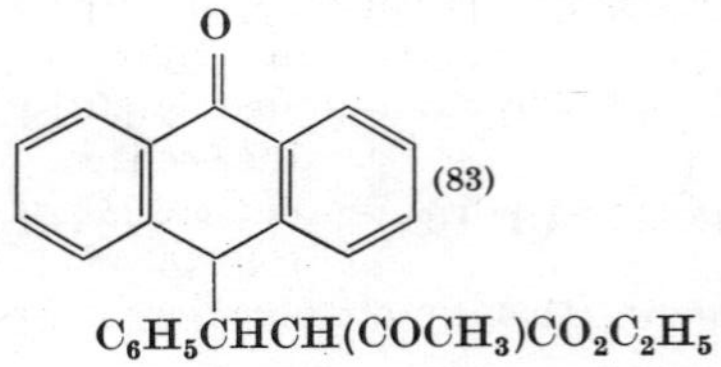 10-substituted anthrone: $C_6H_5CHCH(COCH_3)CO_2C_2H_5$ (83)	163
Phenylnitromethane	$(C_2H_5)_2NH$	3-Carbethoxy-5-nitro-4,5-diphenyl-2-pentanone (78)	29

Substituted Ethyl α-Benzylideneacetoacetates

Substituent(s) in $CH_3COC(=CH\text{-}C_6H_5)CO_2C_2H_5$ 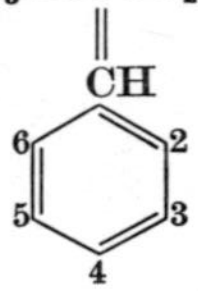 (ring positions 2–6)	Addend	Catalyst	Product (Yield, %)	References
3-Nitro	Ethyl acetoacetate ‖	Piperidine	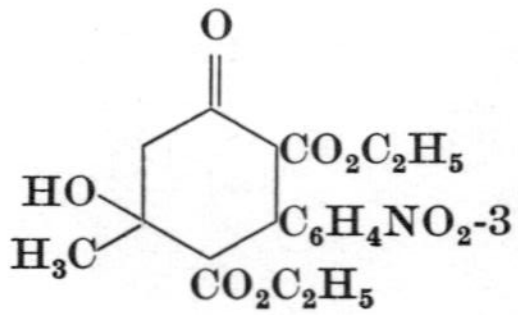 Cyclohexanone ring: O, $CO_2C_2H_5$, $C_6H_4NO_2$-3, $CO_2C_2H_5$, HO, H_3C	982, 994

Substituent	Reactant	Catalyst	Product (Yield, %)	Refs.
	Deoxybenzoin	$NaOC_2H_5$	$3\text{-}O_2NC_6H_4CHCH(COCH_3)CO_2C_2H_5$ | $C_6H_5CHCOC_6H_5$	416
4-Nitro	Ethyl acetoacetate ‖	Piperidine	O; HO, H_3C; $CO_2C_2H_5$; $C_6H_4NO_2\text{-}4$; $CO_2C_2H_5$	982, 994
2-Methoxy	Ethyl acetoacetate ‖	$NaOC_2H_5$	O; HO, H_3C; $CO_2C_2H_5$; $C_6H_4OCH_3\text{-}2$; $CO_2C_2H_5$	982; cf. 995
3-Cyano	Ethyl acetoacetate ‖	Pyridine	$3\text{-}NCC_6H_4CH[CH(COCH_3)CO_2C_2H_5]_2$ (77)	996
4-Cyano	Ethyl acetoacetate ‖	Pyridine	$4\text{-}NCC_6H_4CH[CH(COCH_3)CO_2C_2H_5]_2$ (77)	996
3,4-Methylenedioxy	Ethyl acetoacetate ‖	$[C_6H_5CH_2N(CH_3)_3]OH$	O; HO, H_3C; $CO_2C_2H_5$; $C_6H_3(O_2CH_2)\text{-}3,4$; $CO_2C_2H_5$ (21)	536

Note: References 491–1045 are on pp. 545–555.

‖ The ethylenic compound was formed *in situ* from the corresponding aldehyde and the keto acid derivative.

TABLE XVII—*Continued*

MICHAEL REACTIONS WITH α,β-ETHYLENIC KETO ESTERS

Substituted Ethyl α-Benzylidenacetoacetates—Continued

Substituent(s) in $CH_3COCCO_2C_2H_5$ 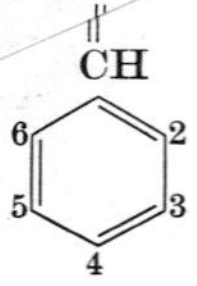 (=CH–C$_6$H$_5$, ring positions 2–6)	Addend	Catalyst	Product (Yield, %)	References
3,4-Dimethoxy	Ethyl acetoacetate‖	$[C_6H_5CH_2N(CH_3)_3]OH$	Cyclohexanone: O; HO, H_3C; $CO_2C_2H_5$; $C_6H_3(OCH_3)_2$-3,4; $CO_2C_2H_5$ (14)	536
			Cyclohexenone: O; H_3C; $CO_2C_2H_5$; $C_6H_3(OCH_3)_2$-3,4; $CO_2C_2H_5$ (Mixtures of stereoisomers, 34)	

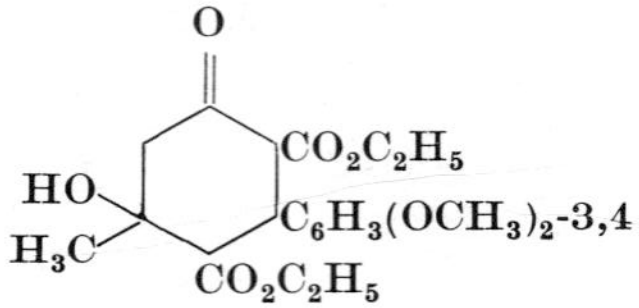

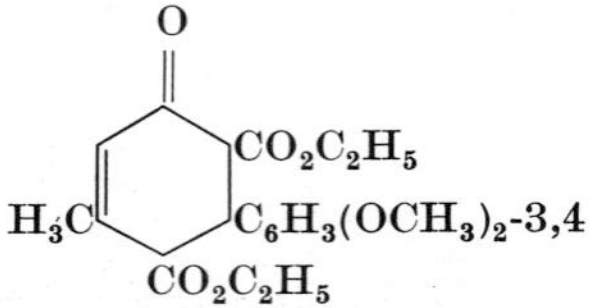

Reactants	Catalyst	Product (Yield, %)	References
Ethyl α-n-Heptylideneacetoacetate and			
Ethyl acetoacetate‖	$NaOC_2H_5$; $(C_2H_5)_2NH$	Diethyl α,α′-diacetyl-β-*n*-hexylglutarate	990
	Piperidine	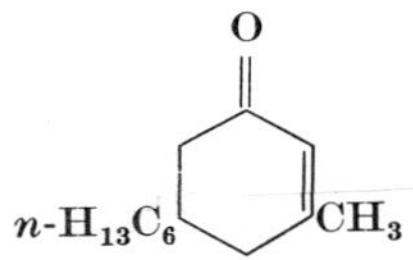 O n-$H_{13}C_6$ CH_3	981
α-n-Heptylideneacetoacetanilide‖ and			
Acetoacetanilide	None	n-$C_6H_{13}CH[CH(COCH_3)CONHC_6H_5]_2$	984
	Pyridine	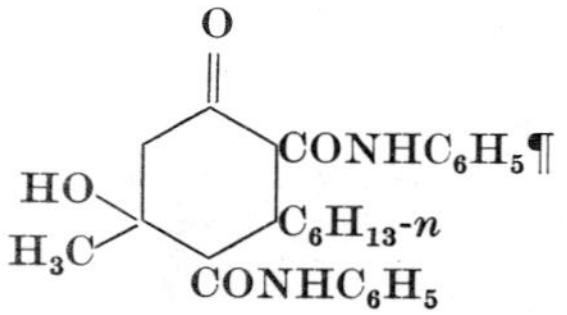 O HO $CONHC_6H_5$¶ H_3C C_6H_{13}-n $CONHC_6H_5$	984
α-n-Heptylideneacetoacet-o-toluide‖ and			
Acetoacet-*o*-toluide	Pyridine	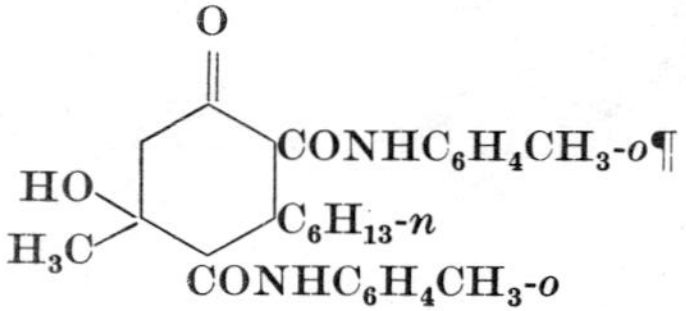 O HO $CONHC_6H_4CH_3$-*o*¶ H_3C C_6H_{13}-n $CONHC_6H_4CH_3$-*o*	984

Note: References 491–1045 are on pp. 545–555.

‖ The ethylenic compound was formed *in situ* from the corresponding aldehyde and the keto acid derivative.

¶ This product is formed when the reaction is carried out in *boiling* pyridine.

TABLE XVII—*Continued*

MICHAEL REACTIONS WITH α,β-ETHYLENIC KETO ESTERS

Reactants	Catalyst	Product (Yield, %)	References
α-n-Heptylideneacetoacet-p-toluide ‖ *and*			
Acetoacet-*p*-toluide	Pyridine	1-Hydroxy-1-methyl-3-oxo-cyclohexane ring bearing $CONHC_6H_4CH_3$-*p*, C_6H_{13}-*n*, $CONHC_6H_4CH_3$-*p* (HO, H_3C on one carbon; C=O) ¶	984
Ethyl β-Cinnamoyl-α-hydroxyacrylate (Cinnamoylpyruvate) and			
$CH_3C(=NH)CH_2CO_2C_2H_5$	None	Diethyl 2-methyl-6-styrylpyridine-3,4-dicarboxylate (48)	954
Ethyl α-Benzylideneisobutyrylacetate and			
Diethyl malonate	$NaOC_2H_5$	$C_6H_5CHCH(CO_2C_2H_5)COCH(CH_3)_2$ with $CH(CO_2C_2H_5)_2$ on the benzylic carbon (72)	964
Ethyl Citrylideneacetoacetate ‖ *and*			
Ethyl acetoacetate	Piperidine	Diethyl citrylidene-bis-acetoacetate (61)	997
Ethyl Benzylidenebenzoylacetate and			
Phenylnitromethane	$(C_2H_5)_2NH$	Ethyl α-benzoyl-γ-nitro-β,γ-diphenylbutyrate (71)	29

Note: References 491–1045 are on pp. 545–555.

‖ The ethylenic compound was formed *in situ* from the corresponding aldehyde and the keto acid derivative.

¶ This product is formed when the reaction is carried out in *boiling* pyridine.

TABLE XVIII

MICHAEL CONDENSATIONS WITH α,β-ACETYLENIC ESTERS

Reactants	Catalyst	Product (Yield, %)	References
Methyl Propiolate and			
1-Tetralone	$NaNH_2$, liq. NH_3	Methyl 1-tetralone-2-acrylate*	998
Ethyl Propiolate and		$A = —CH{=}CHCO_2C_2H_5$	
Diethyl methylmalonate	Na	$CH_3C(A)(CO_2C_2H_5)_2$ (14)	333
Ethyl acetoacetate	$NaOC_2H_5$	$CH_3COCH(A)CO_2C_2H_5$	999
6-Methoxy-1-tetralone	$NaNH_2$, liq. NH_3	[structure: 6-methoxy-1-tetralone with A at C-2; labels CH_3O, O, A]	998
1-Keto-1,2,3,4-tetrahydrophenanthrene	$NaNH_2$, liq. NH_3	[structure: 1-keto-1,2,3,4-tetrahydrophenanthrene with A at C-2; labels O, A] (83)	998
α-Phenylbutyronitrile	$[C_6H_5CH_2N(CH_3)_3]OH$	$CH_3CH_2C(C_6H_5)(A)CN$ (35)	1000

Note: References 491–1045 are on pp. 545–555.

* The product was directly reduced to methyl 1-tetralone-2-propionate.

TABLE XVIII—*Continued*

MICHAEL CONDENSATIONS WITH α,β-ACETYLENIC ESTERS

Reactants	Catalyst	Product (Yield, %)	References
Ethyl Propiolate (Cont.) and		$A = —CH{=}CHCO_2C_2H_5$	
γ-Diethylamino-α-phenylbutyronitrile	$[C_6H_5CH_2N(CH_3)_3]OH$	$(C_2H_5)_2NCH_2CH_2C(C_6H_5)(A)CN$ (59)	1000
Diphenylacetonitrile	$[C_6H_5CH_2N(CH_3)_3]OH$	$(C_6H_5)_2C(A)CN$ (92)	1000
Ethyl Tetrolate and		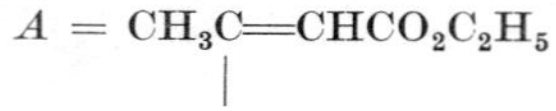 $A = CH_3C{=}CHCO_2C_2H_5$ (with a free bond at the C)	
Diethyl malonate	$NaOC_2H_5$	$ACH(CO_2C_2H_5)_2$	109, 1001, 1002
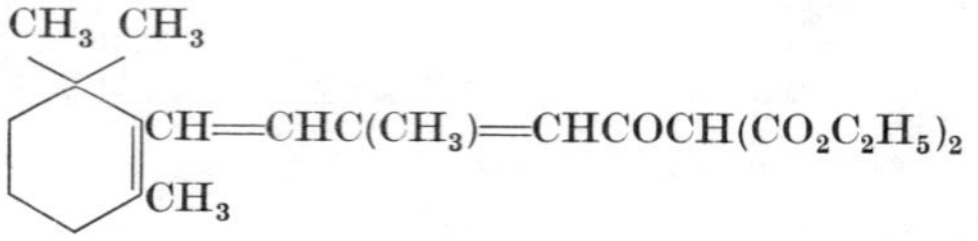 CH_3 CH_3 [cyclohexene ring] $CH{=}CHC(CH_3){=}CHCOCH(CO_2C_2H_5)_2$ CH_3	$NaOC_2H_5$	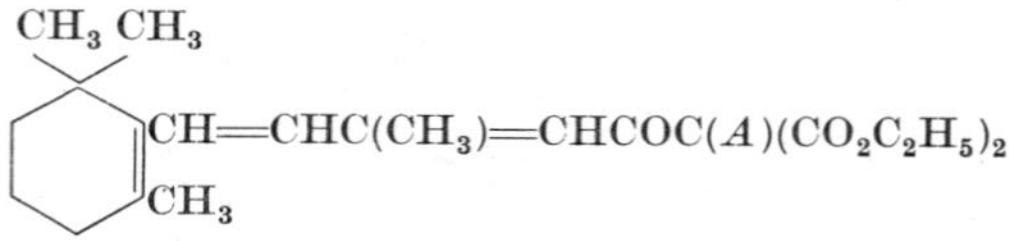 CH_3 CH_3 [cyclohexene ring] $CH{=}CHC(CH_3){=}CHCOC(A)(CO_2C_2H_5)_2$ CH_3	1003, 1004
Tetrolonitrile and			
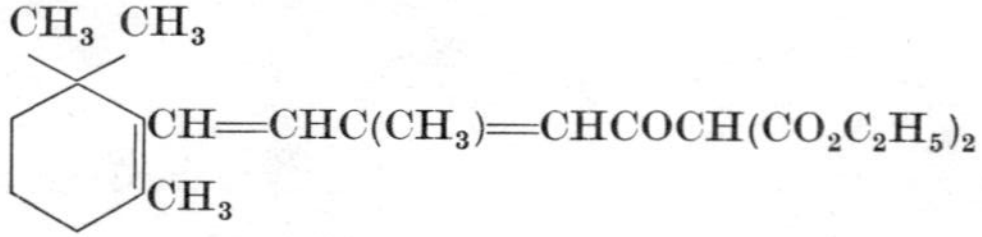 CH_3 CH_3 [cyclohexene ring] $CH{=}CHC(CH_3){=}CHCOCH(CO_2C_2H_5)_2$ CH_3	$NaOC_2H_5$	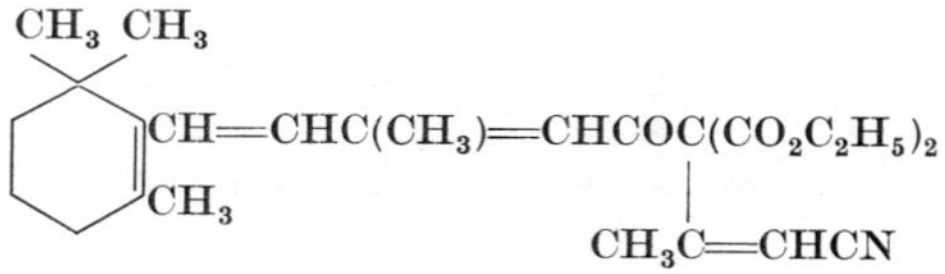 CH_3 CH_3 [cyclohexene ring] $CH{=}CHC(CH_3){=}CHCOC(CO_2C_2H_5)_2$ CH_3 (on the C: $CH_3C{=}CHCN$)	1003
Ethyl Phenylpropiolate and		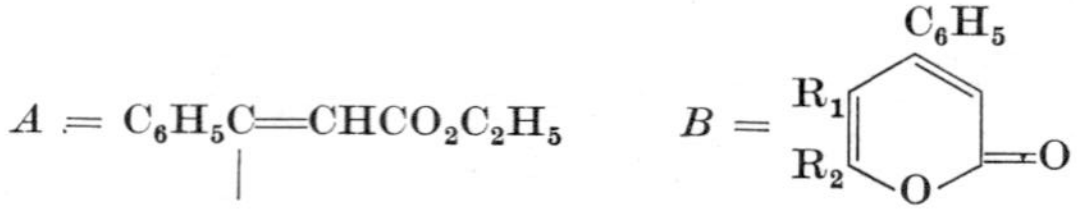 $A = C_6H_5C{=}CHCO_2C_2H_5$ (with a free bond at the C) $B =$ [2-pyrone ring: R_1, R_2, C_6H_5, O, =O]	
Diethyl malonate	Na; $NaOC_2H_5$	$ACH(CO_2C_2H_5)_2$	25, 26, 878, 1005

Reactant	Catalyst	Product	Refs.
		β-Phenylglutaconic acid†	1006, 1007, 1008,
Diethyl methylmalonate	Na; $NaOC_2H_5$	$CH_3C(A)(CO_2C_2H_5)_2$ (14)	333, 25, 26, cf. 334
Diethyl benzylmalonate	$NaOC_2H_5$	$C_6H_5CH_2C(A)(CO_2C_2H_5)_2$	431
Ethyl acetoacetate	$NaOC_2H_5$	B, $R_1 = CO_2C_2H_5$, $R_2 = CH_3$ (14)	430, 431
Ethyl *n*-propylacetoacetate	$NaOC_2H_5$	$CH_3COC(A)(C_3H_7\text{-}n)CO_2C_2H_5$	433
Ethyl oxaloacetate	$NaOC_2H_5$	B, $R_1 = R_2 = CO_2C_2H_5$	433
Ethyl benzoylacetate	$NaOC_2H_5$	B, $R_1 = CO_2C_2H_5$, $R_2 = C_6H_5$	431
Ethyl cyanoacetate	Na	$NCCH(A)CO_2C_2H_5$	25
Acetylacetone	$NaOC_2H_5$	$CH_3COCH(A)COCH_3$; B, $R_1 = COCH_3$, $R_2 = CH_3$	432
		B, $R_1 = H$, $R_2 = CH_3$	433
Benzoylacetone	$NaOC_2H_5$	B, $R_1 = COCH_3$, $R_2 = C_6H_5$	432, 433
Deoxybenzoin	$NaOC_2H_5$	B, $R_1 = R_2 = C_6H_5$	1009
Ethyl fluorene-9-carboxylate	Na enolate	Ethyl β-(9-fluorenyl)cinnamate (28)	1010
Ethyl p-Nitrophenylpropiolate and			
Ethyl acetoacetate	$NaOC_2H_5$	2-pyrone ring bearing $C_6H_4NO_2\text{-}p$, $C_2H_5O_2C$, H_3C, =O	433
Ethyl benzoylacetate	$NaOC_2H_5$	dihydro-2-pyrone ring bearing $C_6H_4NO_2\text{-}p$, $C_2H_5O_2C$, H_5C_6, =O	433

Note: References 491–1045 are on pp. 545–555.

† This product results from hydrolysis and partial decarboxylation.

TABLE XVIII—*Continued*

MICHAEL CONDENSATIONS WITH α,β-ACETYLENIC ESTERS

Reactants	Catalyst	Product (Yield, %)	References
Ethyl 2,3-Dimethoxyphenylpropiolate and			
Ethyl acetoacetate	$NaOC_2H_5$	5-Carbethoxy-4-(2′,3′-dimethoxyphenyl)-6-methyl-α-pyrone (71)	1011
Acetylacetone	$NaOC_2H_5$	$2,3\text{-}(CH_3O)_2C_6H_3C{=}CHCO_2C_2H_5$, with $CH_3COC{=}C(OH)CH_3$ on the ring-bearing C (33)‡	1011
2,3-Dimethoxyphenylpropiolonitrile and			
Acetylacetone	$NaOC_2H_5$	$2,3\text{-}(CH_3O)_2C_6H_3C{=}CHCN$, with $CH_3COC{=}C(OH)CH_3$ on the ring-bearing C (43)‡	1011
Diethyl Acetylenedicarboxylate and		$A = C_2H_5O_2CCH{=}CCO_2C_2H_5$ (attached through the second C)	
Diethyl malonate	Na	$ACH(CO_2C_2H_5)_2$ (30)	333
Diethyl methylmalonate	Na; $NaOC_2H_5$	$CH_3C(A)(CO_2C_2H_5)_2$	333
Triethyl ethane-1,1,2-tricarboxylate	$NaOC_2H_5$	Pentaethyl 1-butene-1,2,3,3,4-pentacarboxylate	325
Tetraethyl ethane-1,1,2,2-tetracarboxylate	$NaOC_2H_5$	Hexaethyl 1-butene-1,2,3,3,4,4-hexacarboxylate (16)§	325, 489
Ethyl acetoacetate	$NaOC_2H_5$	$CH_3COCH(A)CO_2C_2H_5$	433, 1012
Ethyl benzoylacetate	$NaOC_2H_5$	$C_6H_5COCH(A)CO_2C_2H_5$	433, 1012

Note: References 491–1045 are on pp. 545–555.

‡ The free acid corresponding to this product was actually isolated.

§ Originally (ref. 489), this product was assumed to be a cyclobutane derivative, formed by a second, intramolecular, Michael reaction. The cyclobutane structure has now been disproved (ref. 325).

TABLE XIX

Michael Condensations with α,β-Ethylenic Nitro Compounds

Reactants	Catalyst	Product (Yield, %)	References
1-*Nitro*-1-*propene and*			
Ethyl acetoacetate	$NaOC_2H_5$	$O_2NCH_2CH(CH_3)CH(COCH_3)CO_2C_2H_5$ (31)	1013
$CH_3C({=}NCH_3)CH_2CO_2C_2H_5$	None	Pyrrole ring: H_3C, $CO_2C_2H_5$, CH_3, N–CH_3 (70)	1013
$CH_3C[{=}NCH(CH_3)_2]CH_2CO_2C_2H_5$	None	Pyrrole ring: H_3C, $CO_2C_2H_5$, CH_3, N–$CH(CH_3)_2$ (54)	1013
$CH_3C[{=}NCH(CH_3)CH_2NO_2]$-$CH_2CO_2C_2H_5$	None	Pyrrole ring: H_3C, $CO_2C_2H_5$, CH_3, N–$CH(CH_3)CH_2NO_2$ (55)	1013
2-*Nitro*-1-*propene and*		$A = CH_3CH(NO_2)CH_2$—	
2-Nitropropane	$NaOC_2H_5$	$AC(CH_3)_2NO_2$ (20)	1014
Methyl 2-nitropropyl ether	$NaOC_2H_5$	$AC(NO_2)(CH_3)CH_2OCH_3$ (50)	1014
Methyl 2-nitropropyl sulfide	$NaOCH_3$	$AC(NO_2)(CH_3)CH_2SCH_3$ (30)	1014

Note: References 491–1045 are on pp. 545–555.

TABLE XIX—*Continued*

MICHAEL CONDENSATIONS WITH α,β-ETHYLENIC NITRO COMPOUNDS

Reactants	Catalyst	Product (Yield, %)	References
Nitromalonaldehyde (Hydroxymethylenenitroacetaldehyde) and			
Ethyl acetoacetate	Alkali	5-Nitrosalicylic acid	111
Cyanoacetamide	$[C_6H_5CH_2N(CH_3)_3]OH$	3-Cyano-5-nitro-2-pyridone (93)	111
Levulinic acid	Alkali	2-Hydroxy-5-nitrophenylacetic acid (82)	111
Acetonedicarboxylic acid	Alkali	2-Hydroxy-5-nitrobenzene-1,3-dicarboxylic acid	111
Acetone	Alkali	*p*-Nitrophenol	339
Methyl ethyl ketone	Alkali	2-Methyl-4-nitrophenol (90)	111
Acetonylacetone	Alkali	Methyl 2-hydroxy-5-nitrobenzyl ketone, 2,2′-dihydroxy-5,5′-dinitrobiphenyl	1015, 1016
Methyl benzyl ketone	Alkali	2-Hydroxy-5-nitrobiphenyl	111, 340, 341
Dibenzyl ketone	Alkali	2,6-Diphenyl-4-nitrophenol (94)	111, 340, 341
Cycloöctanone	Na enolate	2,6-Pentamethylene-4-nitrophenol* (10)	342, 343
Cyclononanone	Na enolate	2,6-Hexamethylene-4-nitrophenol (62)	342
Cyclodecanone	Na enolate	2,6-Heptamethylene-4-nitrophenol (6)	342
Cycloundecanone	Na enolate	2,6-Octamethylene-4-nitrophenol (2)	343
Cyclododecanone	Na enolate	2,6-Nonamethylene-4-nitrophenol (28)	342
Cyclotridecanone	Na enolate	2,6-Decamethylene-4-nitrophenol (70)	342
Cyclotetradecanone	Na enolate	2,6-Undecamethylene-4-nitrophenol (64)	342
Cyclopentadecanone	Na enolate	2,6-Dodecamethylene-4-nitrophenol (74)	342
Cyclohexadecanone	Na enolate	2,6-Tridecamethylene-4-nitrophenol (63)	342
Cycloheptadecanone	Na enolate	2,6-Tetradecamethylene-4-nitrophenol (57)	342
Cycloöctadecanone	Na enolate	2,6-Pentadecamethylene-4-nitrophenol (40)	342
Cyclononadecanone	Na enolate	2,6-Hexadecamethylene-4-nitrophenol (43)	343

Cycloeicosanone	Na enolate	2,6-Heptadecamethylene-4-nitrophenol (47)	342
Cycloheneicosanone	Na enolate	2,6-Octadecamethylene-4-nitrophenol (16)	342
Cyclotriacontanone	Na enolate	2,6-Heptacosamethylene-4-nitrophenol	342
1-*Nitro*-1-*butene and*		$A = CH_3CH_2CHCH_2NO_2$ (with a bond downward from CH)	
Ethyl *n*-propylacetoacetate	Na	$CH_3COC(A)(C_3H_7\text{-}n)CO_2C_2H_5$	1017
Ethyl α-cyanobutyrate	$NaOC_2H_5$	$CH_3CH_2C(CN)(A)CO_2C_2H_5$	1018
Benzyl cyanide†	$KOC_5H_{11}\text{-}t$	$C_6H_5CH(A)CN$	1018
Acetylacetone	Na	$CH_3COCH(A)COCH_3$ (30)	1019
2-*Nitro*-1-*butene and*		$A = CH_3CH_2CH(NO_2)CH_2—$	
Diethyl malonate	$NaOC_2H_5$	$ACH(CO_2C_2H_5)_2$	1020‡
Diethyl phenylmalonate	$NaOC_2H_5$	$C_6H_5C(A)(CO_2C_2H_5)_2$ (13)	1020
Ethyl acetoacetate	Na	$CH_3COCH(A)CO_2C_2H_5$ (25)	1017
Methyl cyanoacetate§	None	$ACH(CN)CO_2CH_3$ (23)	1021
Ethyl cyanoacetate‖	$NaOC_2H_5$	$ACH(CN)CO_2C_2H_5$ (16 crude)	1018, 1021
1-Nitropropane‖	NaOH	$CH_3CH_2CH(A)NO_2$ (18)	1021
2-Nitropropane¶	NaOH	$(CH_3)_2C(A)NO_2$ (55)	1021
Acetylacetone	Na	$CH_3COCH(A)COCH_3$	1019

Note: References 491–1045 are on pp. 545–555.

* *Chemical Abstracts* name: 9-Nitrobicyclo[5.3.1]hendeca-1(11),4,9-triene-11-ol.

† Instead of 1-nitro-1-butene, β-nitroisopropyl acetate was employed.

‡ In this patent, a number of similar products of Michael condensations are mentioned.

§ 1-Dimethylamino-2-nitrobutane was employed instead of 2-nitro-1-butene.

‖ Instead of 2-nitro-1-butene, 1-diethylamino-2-nitrobutane was used. When the corresponding 1-dimethylamino compound was employed, the yield was somewhat higher.

¶ Instead of 2-nitro-1-butene, 1-dimethylamino-2-nitrobutane was employed.

TABLE XIX—*Continued*

Michael Condensations with α,β-Ethylenic Nitro Compounds

Reactants	Catalyst	Product (Yield, %)	References
2-*Nitro*-2-*butene and*		$A = CH_3CHCH(NO_2)CH_3$ (attached at the central CH)	
Benzyl cyanide	$NaOCH_3$	$C_6H_5CH(A)CN$	85
Nitroethane	$[C_6H_5CH_2N(CH_3)_3]OH$; $NaOC_2H_5$; piperidine	$CH_3CH(A)NO_2$ (28)	1014
2-Nitropropane	$NaOC_2H_5$	$(CH_3)_2C(A)NO_2$ (47)	1014
2-*Methyl*-1-*nitro*-1-*propene and*		$A = (CH_3)_2CCH_2NO_2$ (attached at the C)	
Diethyl malonate	$NaOC_2H_5$	$ACH(CO_2C_2H_5)_2$ (72)	1020
Ethyl acetoacetate	Na	$CH_3COCH(A)CO_2C_2H_5$	1017
Ethyl cyanoacetate	$(C_2H_5)_3N$	$ACH(CN)CO_2C_2H_5$	1018
Benzyl cyanide	KOC_5H_{11}-*t*	$C_6H_5CH(A)CN$ (60)	85
p-Bromobenzyl cyanide	KOC_5H_{11}-*t*	*p*-$BrC_6H_4CH(A)CN$ (70)	85
Acetone	Na	ACH_2COCH_3	1022
1-*Chloro*-3-*nitro*-2-*butene and*			
2-Nitropropane	$NaOC_2H_5$	Ring: O←N(–O–CH₂)=C(CH₃)–CH–, i.e. $H_3C\overset{}{C}=N(\rightarrow O)-O-CH_2-CHC(CH_3)_2NO_2$ (35–40)	1023
		$(CH_3)_2C(NO_2)C(CH_3)_2NO_2$ (10–12)	
		$CH_3C(NO_2){=}CHCH{=}C(CH_3)_2$ (3)	

1-*Nitro*-1-*pentene and*			
Diethyl malonate	Na	$CH_3CH_2CH_2CH(CH_2NO_2)CH(CO_2C_2H_5)_2$ (95)	1020
3,3,4,4,5,5,5-*Heptafluoro*-1-*nitro*-1-*pentene and*		$A = CF_3CF_2CF_2CHCH_2NO_2$	
Nitromethane	$NaOCH_3$	ACH_2NO_2 (68)	863
Diethyl malonate	$NaOC_2H_5$	$ACH(CO_2C_2H_5)_2$ (54)	863
3-*Nitro*-3-*hexene and*			
Diethyl malonate	$NaOC_2H_5$	$CH_3CH_2CH(NO_2)CH(C_2H_5)CH(CO_2C_2H_5)_2$	1020
Ethyl α-Nitro-γ,γ,γ-trichlorocrotonate and			
Ethyl nitroacetate	$(C_2H_5)_2NH$	$Cl_3CCH[CH(NO_2)CO_2C_2H_5]_2$ (34)	1024
1-*Nitrocyclohexene and*			
p-Bromobenzyl cyanide	KOC_5H_{11}-*t*	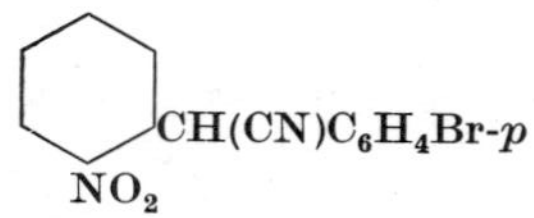 (Mixture of isomers, 8)	85
2-Nitropropane	$NaOC_2H_5$	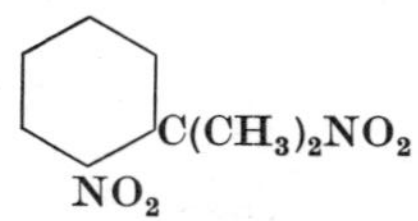 (16)	1014

Note: References 491–1045 are on pp. 545–555.

TABLE XIX—*Continued*

MICHAEL CONDENSATIONS WITH α,β-ETHYLENIC NITRO COMPOUNDS

Reactants	Catalyst	Product (Yield, %)	References
Methyl 2-Nitro-2-pentenoate and		$A = CH_3CH_2CHCH(NO_2)CO_2CH_3$ (attached at the $CHCH_2$ carbon)	
1,1-Dinitroethane	NaOH, aq. CH_3OH	$AC(NO_2)_2CH_3$ (61)	813
Methyl 2,2-dinitrobutyrate	Na derivative, water	$(NO_2)_2C(A)CH_2CH_2CO_2CH_3$	813
1-(α-Furyl)-2-nitroethylene and			
Ethyl nitroacetate	$(C_2H_5)_2NH$	Ethyl 3-(α-furyl)-2,4-dinitrobutanoate (95)	622
ω-Nitrostyrene and		$A = C_6H_5CHCH_2NO_2$ (attached at the CH carbon)	
Dimethyl malonate	Na	$ACH(CO_2CH_3)_2$	329
Diethyl malonate	$NaOC_2H_5$	$ACH(CO_2C_2H_5)_2$ (51)	1025
Ethyl acetoacetate	Na; $(C_2H_5)_3N$	$CH_3COCH(A)CO_2C_2H_5$ (98)	1017, 1025
Ethyl benzoylacetate	Na	$C_6H_5COCH(A)CO_2C_2H_5$	1017
Acetylacetone	Na, $(C_2H_5)_3N$	$CH_3COCH(A)COCH_3$ (78)	1019, 1025
Benzoylacetone	$(C_2H_5)_3N$	$C_6H_5COCH(A)COCH_3$ (86)	1025
Ethyl nitroacetate	$(C_2H_5)_2NH$	$ACH(NO_2)CO_2C_2H_5$ (97)**	154
Phenylnitromethane	$(C_2H_5)_2NH$	$C_6H_5CH(A)NO_2$ (94)	622
o-Nitrostyrene and		$A = o\text{-}O_2NC_6H_4CH_2CH_2$—	
Dimethyl malonate	$NaOCH_3$	$ACH(CO_2CH_3)_2$ (49); $(A)_2C(CO_2CH_3)_2$ (2)	344
Diethyl malonate	$NaOC_2H_5$	$ACH(CO_2C_2H_5)_2$ (72)	344
Diethyl ethylmalonate	$NaOC_2H_5$	$C_2H_5C(A)(CO_2C_2H_5)_2$ (44)	344
Methyl acetoacetate	$NaOCH_3$	$CH_3COCH(A)CO_2CH_3$ (32)	344

Ethyl acetoacetate	$NaOC_2H_5$	$CH_3COCH(A)CO_2C_2H_5$ (42)	344
Ethyl *n*-butylacetoacetate	$NaOC_2H_5$	$CH_3COC(C_4H_9\text{-}n)(A)CO_2C_2H_5$ (61)	344
Methyl cyanoacetate	$NaOCH_3$	$A CH(CN)CO_2CH_3$ (69)	344
Ethyl cyanoacetate	$NaOC_2H_5$	$A CH(CN)CO_2C_2H_5$ (78)	344
Cyanoacetamide	$NaOC_2H_5$	$(A)_2C(CN)CONH_2$ (42)	344
p-Nitrostyrene and		$A = p\text{-}O_2NC_6H_4CH_2CH_2$—	
Dimethyl malonate	$NaOCH_3$	$A CH(CO_2CH_3)_2$ (43), $(A)_2C(CO_2CH_3)_2$ (32)	344
Diethyl malonate	$NaOC_2H_5$	$A CH(CO_2C_2H_5)_2$ (45), $(A)_2C(CO_2C_2H_5)_2$ (34)	344
Diethyl ethylmalonate	$NaOC_2H_5$	$A C(C_2H_5)(CO_2C_2H_5)_2$ (56)	344
Methyl acetoacetate	$NaOCH_3$	$CH_3COCH(A)CO_2CH_3$ (38), $CH_3COC(A)_2CO_2CH_3$ (24)	344
Ethyl acetoacetate	$NaOC_2H_5$	$CH_3COCH(A)CO_2C_2H_5$ (47), $CH_3COC(A)_2CO_2C_2H_5$ (19)	344
Ethyl *n*-butylacetoacetate	$NaOC_2H_5$	$CH_3COC(C_4H_9\text{-}n)(A)CO_2C_2H_5$ (57)	344
Methyl cyanoacetate	$NaOCH_3$	$(A)_2C(CN)CO_2CH_3$ (79)	344
Ethyl cyanoacetate	$NaOC_2H_5$	$(A)_2C(CN)CO_2C_2H_5$ (80)	344
Cyanoacetamide	$NaOC_2H_5$	$(A)_2C(CN)CONH_2$ (73)	344
Malononitrile	$NaOC_2H_5$	$(A)_2C(CN)_2$ (36)	344
β-Methyl-β-nitrostyrene and			
Diethyl malonate	Na enolate	Diethyl 3-nitro-2-phenylbutane-1,1-dicarboxylate (79)††‡‡	86

Note: References 491–1045 are on pp. 545–555.

** The product was isolated as the *aci*-diethylammonium salt.

†† In ether as solvent, only one of the two diastereomerides is formed; in alcohol a mixture of the two is obtained.

‡‡ When the reaction product is worked up with acid, this compound is transformed into 1,1-dicarbethoxy-2-phenylbutan-3-one.

TABLE XIX—*Continued*

Michael Condensations with α,β-Ethylenic Nitro Compounds

Reactants	Catalyst	Product (Yield, %)	References
Ethyl β-(2-Furyl)-α-nitroacrylate§§ and			
Ethyl nitroacetate	$(C_2H_5)_2NH$	2-Furyl-$CH[CH(NO_2)CO_2C_2H_5]_2$ (83, 88)**	154, 1024
Ethyl α-Nitro-β-(2-pyridyl)acrylate§§ and			
Ethyl nitroacetate	$(C_2H_5)_2NH$	2-Pyridyl-$CH[CH(NO_2)CO_2C_2H_5]_2$ (82, 84)**	154, 1024
Ethyl α-Nitro-β-(3-pyridyl)acrylate§§ and			
Ethyl nitroacetate	$(C_2H_5)_2NH$	3-Pyridyl-$CH[CH(NO_2)CO_2C_2H_5]_2$ (55)**	154
Methyl α-Nitrocinnamate§§ and			
Methyl nitroacetate	CH_3NH_2; $(C_2H_5)_2NH$	$C_6H_5CH[CH(NO_2)CO_2CH_3]_2$ (76)	1024
Ethyl α-Nitrocinnamate and		$A = C_6H_5CHCH(NO_2)CO_2C_2H_5$ (attachment at the C_6H_5CH carbon)	
Diethyl malonate	$(C_2H_5)_2NH$	3,3-Dicarbethoxy-1-nitro-2-phenylbutyric acid diethylamide (82)	1026
Ethyl acetoacetate	$(C_2H_5)_2NH$	$CH_3COCH(A)CO_2C_2H_5$ (85)	1026
Benzyl cyanide	$(C_2H_5)_2NH$	$C_6H_5CH(A)CN$ (83)	1026
Ethyl nitroacetate§§	$(C_2H_5)_2NH$	$ACH(NO_2)CO_2C_2H_5$ (80, 84–98, 74)**	154, 1024, 1026
Phenylnitromethane	$(C_2H_5)_2NH$	$C_6H_5CH(A)NO_2$ (82)	1026

Reactants	Catalyst	Product (Yield, %)	Refs.
Ethyl α,2-Dinitrocinnamate§§ and			
Ethyl nitroacetate	$(C_2H_5)_2NH$	2-$O_2NC_6H_4CH[CH(NO_2)CO_2C_2H_5]_2$ (82, 68)**	154, 1024
Ethyl α,3-Dinitrocinnamate§§ and			
Ethyl nitroacetate	$(C_2H_5)_2NH$	3-$O_2NC_6H_4CH[CH(NO_2)CO_2C_2H_5]_2$ (90–95, 66)**	154, 1024
Ethyl α,4-Dinitrocinnamate and			
Ethyl acetoacetate	$(C_2H_5)_2NH$	$CH_3COCH(CO_2C_2H_5)CH(C_6H_4NO_2$-4)-$CH(NO_2)CO_2C_2H_5$ (65)	1026
Ethyl nitroacetate§§	$(C_2H_5)_2NH$	4-$O_2NC_6H_4CH[CH(NO_2)CO_2C_2H_5]_2$ (82, 60, 38)**	154, 1024, 1026
Ethyl 2-Hydroxy-α-nitrocinnamate§§ and			
Ethyl nitroacetate	$(C_2H_5)_2NH$	2-$HOC_6H_4CH[CH(NO_2)CO_2C_2H_5]_2$ (90, 98)**	154, 1024
Ethyl 4-Hydroxy-α-nitrocinnamate§§ and			
Ethyl nitroacetate	$(C_2H_5)_2NH$	4-$HOC_6H_4CH[CH(NO_2)CO_2C_2H_5]_2$ (64)**	154
Ethyl 2-Chloro-α-nitrocinnamate§§ and			
Ethyl nitroacetate	$(C_2H_5)_2NH$	2-$ClC_6H_4CH[CH(NO_2)CO_2C_2H_5]_2$ (97)**	154, 1024
Ethyl 4-Chloro-α-nitrocinnamate and			
Ethyl acetoacetate	$(C_2H_5)_2NH$	$CH_3COCH(CO_2C_2H_5)CH(C_6H_4Cl$-4)$CH(NO_2)CO_2C_2H_5$ (85)	1026
Ethyl cyanoacetate	$(C_2H_5)_2NH$	$NCCH(CO_2C_2H_5)CH(C_6H_4Cl$-4)$CH(NO_2)CO_2C_2H_5$ (85)	1026
Ethyl nitroacetate§§	$(C_2H_5)_2NH$	4-$ClC_6H_4CH[CH(NO_2)CO_2C_2H_5]_2$ (97)**	154, 1024

Note: References 491–1045 are on pp. 545–555.

** The product was isolated as the *aci*-diethylammonium salt.

§§ The unsaturated ester was formed *in situ* from the ester of nitroacetic acid and the appropriate aldehyde.

TABLE XIX—*Continued*

MICHAEL CONDENSATIONS WITH α,β-ETHYLENIC NITRO COMPOUNDS

Reactants	Catalyst	Product (Yield, %)	References
Ethyl 4-Methoxy-α-nitrocinnamate§§ *and*			
Ethyl nitroacetate	$(C_2H_5)_2NH$	$4\text{-}CH_3OC_6H_4CH[CH(NO_2)CO_2C_2H_5]_2$ (72)**	154
Ethyl β-Methyl-α-nitrocinnamate§§ *and*			
Ethyl nitroacetate	$[C_6H_5CH_2N(CH_3)_3]OC_4H_9\text{-}n$	Diethyl 1,3-dinitro-2-methyl-2-phenylglutarate (70)	154
Ethyl Cyclohexylidenenitroacetate‖‖ *and*			
Ethyl nitroacetate	$[C_6H_5CH_2N(CH_3)_3]OC_4H_9\text{-}n$	$(CH_2)_5C[CH(NO_2)CO_2C_2H_5]_2$ (61)	154
Ethyl α-Nitro-β-propylacrylate§§ *and*			
Ethyl nitroacetate	$(C_2H_5)_2NH$	Diethyl 1,3-dinitro-2-*n*-propylglutarate (95)**	622
Ethyl β-Isopropyl-α-nitroacrylate§§ *and*			
Ethyl nitroacetate	$(C_2H_5)_2NH$	Diethyl 1,3-dinitro-2-isopropylglutarate**	622
Ethyl β-Isobutyl-α-nitroacrylate§§ *and*			
Ethyl nitroacetate	$(C_2H_5)_2NH$	Diethyl 1,3-dinitro-2-isobutylglutarate (90)**	622
2-*Nitro*-2-*phenyl*-1-(3′-*pyridyl*)*ethylene*¶¶ *and*			
Phenylnitromethane	CH_3NH_2	1,3-Dinitro-1,3-diphenyl-2-(3′-pyridyl)propane (48)	29

Reactant	Catalyst	Product (Yield, %)	Refs.
α-Nitrostilbene and		$A = C_6H_5CHCH(NO_2)C_6H_5$ (with attachment bond at the first CH)	
Dimethyl malonate	$NaOCH_3$	$ACH(CO_2CH_3)_2$ (85)	965
Diethyl malonate	$NaOC_2H_5$	$ACH(CO_2C_2H_5)_2$ (29)	29, 965
		$ACH(CO_2C_2H_5)_2$ (two isomers, 87)***	86
Ethyl acetoacetate	$NaOC_2H_5$	$CH_3COCH(A)CO_2C_2H_5$ (42)	29
Ethyl cyanoacetate	$NaOC_2H_5$	$C_6H_5CH_2NO_2$ and $C_6H_5CH{=}C(CN)CO_2C_2H_5$ (60)	29
Acetylacetone	$NaOC_2H_5$	$CH_3COCH(A)COCH_3$ (11)	29
Phenylacetone	$NaOC_2H_5$	$C_6H_5CH(A)COCH_3$ (13); $C_6H_5CH_2NO_2$ and $C_6H_5CH{=}C(C_6H_5)COCH_3$	29
Benzoylacetone	$NaOC_2H_5$	$C_6H_5COCH(A)COCH_3$ (21)	29
Phenylnitromethane†††	CH_3NH_2	$C_6H_5CH(A)NO_2$; 1-nitro-1,2,3-triphenyl-1-propene; 3,4,5-triphenylisoxazole	1027
3-Nitro-1,4-diphenyl-3-buten-1-one and			
Dimethyl malonate	$NaOCH_3$	$C_6H_5COCH_2CH(NO_2)CH(C_6H_5)CH(CO_2CH_3)_2$ (65)‡‡‡	1028

Note: References 491–1045 are on pp. 545–555.

** The product was isolated as the *aci*-diethylammonium salt.

§§ The unsaturated ester was formed *in situ* from the ester of nitroacetic acid and the appropriate aldehyde.

‖‖ The unsaturated ester was formed *in situ* from ethyl nitroacetate and the appropriate ketone.

¶¶ This compound was formed *in situ* from pyridine-3-carboxaldehyde and phenylnitromethane.

*** Upon separation of the two isomers, yields of 47 and 17%, respectively, of the pure compounds were obtained.

††† This reaction takes place when benzaldehyde and phenylnitromethane are condensed in the presence of methylamine.

‡‡‡ This product is obtained at −20°; at −50°, a 30% yield of $C_6H_5CH[CH(CO_2CH_3)_2]CH{=}CHCOC_6H_5$ is obtained, and at −33° 10% of an unidentified product, $C_{20}H_{15}NO_4$, which gives the same 2,4-dinitrophenylhydrazone as the products obtained at the lower temperature.

TABLE XIX—*Continued*

MICHAEL CONDENSATIONS WITH α,β-ETHYLENIC NITRO COMPOUNDS

Reactant	Catalyst	Product (Yield, %)	References
β-Nitrobenzylideneacetophenone and			
Dimethyl malonate	$NaOCH_3$	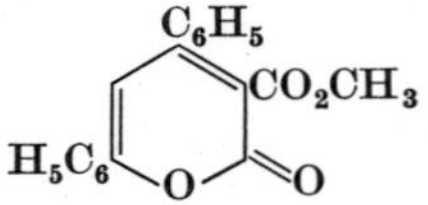 C_6H_5, CO_2CH_3, H_5C_6, O, O (pyranone structure) (5) or $C_6H_5CH{=}C[CH(CO_2CH_3)_2]COC_6H_5$ (20)	1029
$C_6H_5COCH{=}C(NO_2)CH_2C_6H_5$ *and*			
Diethyl malonate	$NaOCH_3$	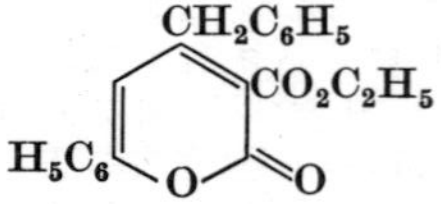 $CH_2C_6H_5$, $CO_2C_2H_5$, H_5C_6, O, O (pyranone structure) (Small)	1029

Note: References 491–1045 are on pp. 545–555.

TABLE XX

Michael Condensations with α,β-Ethylenic Sulfones

Reactants	Catalyst	Product (Yield, %)	References
Methyl Vinyl Sulfone and		$A = CH_3SO_2CH_2CH_2$—	
Diethyl malonate	$[C_6H_5CH_2N(CH_3)_3]OH$	$(A)_2C(CO_2C_2H_5)_2$ (61)	118
Diethyl phenylmalonate	$[C_6H_5CH_2N(CH_3)_3]OH$	$AC(C_6H_5)(CO_2C_2H_5)_2$ (58)	118
Ethyl acetoacetate	$[C_6H_5CH_2N(CH_3)_3]OH$	$CH_3COC(A)_2CO_2C_2H_5$ (70)	118
Ethyl cyanoacetate	$[C_6H_5CH_2N(CH_3)_3]OH$	$NCC(A)_2CO_2C_2H_5$ (81)	118
Benzyl cyanide	$[C_6H_5CH_2N(CH_3)_3]OH$	$NCC(A)_2C_6H_5$ (68)	118
Acetylacetone	$[C_6H_5CH_2N(CH_3)_3]OH$	$CH_3COC(A)_2COCH_3$ (36), $CH_3COCH(A)_2$ (24)	118
Phenylacetone	$[C_6H_5CH_2N(CH_3)_3]OH$	$C_6H_5CH(A)COCH_3$ (61)	118
Nitromethane	Aq. KOH	$(A)_3CNO_2$ (50)	1030
p-Bromophenylnitromethane	$[CH_3N(C_2H_5)_3]OH$	*p*-$BrC_6H_4CH(A)NO_2$ (50)	1030
Phenacyl *p*-tolyl sulfone	$[C_6H_5CH_2N(CH_3)_3]OH$	$C_6H_5COCH(A)SO_2C_6H_4CH_3$-*p* (61)	118
Bisbenzenesulfonylmethane	$[C_6H_5CH_2N(CH_3)_3]OH$	$(A)_2C(SO_2C_6H_5)_2$ (82)	118
Bismethanesulfonylmethane	$[C_6H_5CH_2N(CH_3)_3]OH$	$(A)_2C(SO_2CH_3)_2$ (84)	118
Vinyl n-Butyl Sulfone and		$A = n\text{-}C_4H_9SO_2CH_2CH_2$—	
Nitroethane	Aq. NaOH	$ACH(CH_3)NO_2$ (45), $(A)_2C(CH_3)NO_2$ (13)	1030
	Aq. KOH	$(A)_2C(CH_3)NO_2$ (75)	1030
1-Nitropropane	Aq. NaOH	$ACH(C_2H_5)NO_2$ and $A_2C(C_2H_5)NO_2$ (16)	1030
Vinyl Isobutyl Sulfone and			
p-Bromophenylnitromethane	NaOH	*i*-$C_4H_9SO_2CH_2CH_2CH(NO_2)C_6H_4Br$-*p* (30)	1030
Divinyl Sulfone and			
2-Nitropropane	Aq. KOH	$O_2S[CH_2CH_2C(CH_3)_2NO_2]_2$	1030

Note: References 491–1045 are on pp. 545–555.

TABLE XX—*Continued*

MICHAEL CONDENSATIONS WITH α,β-ETHYLENIC SULFONES

Reactants	Catalyst	Product (Yield, %)	References
Vinyl p-Tolyl Sulfone and		$A = p\text{-}CH_3C_6H_4SO_2CH_2CH_2$—	
Nitromethane	$NaOCH_3$	$(A)_2CHNO_2$ (91)	1031
1-Nitropropane	Aq. KOH	$(A)_2C(C_2H_5)NO_2$	1030
2-Nitropropane	Aq. KOH	$(CH_3)_2C(A)NO_2$	1030
Phenyl Styryl Sulfone and			
Diethyl malonate	Na	$C_6H_5SO_2CH_2CH(C_6H_5)CH(CO_2C_2H_5)_2$ (97)	1031
p-Tolyl Styryl Sulfone and			
Diethyl malonate	Na	$p\text{-}CH_3C_6H_4SO_2CH_2CH(C_6H_5)CH(CO_2C_2H_5)_2$ (quant.)	1032
Distyryl Sulfone and			
Diethyl malonate	Na	$O_2S[CH_2CH(C_6H_5)CH(CO_2C_2H_5)_2]_2$ (74)	1033
Vinylsulfonic Acid N-Ethylanilide and		$A = \underset{\mid}{C}H_2CH_2SO_2N(C_2H_5)C_6H_5$	
Nitromethane	KOH, CH_3OH	$(A)_3CNO_2$ (38–48)	358
	Excess KOH, CH_3OH	$(A)_2CHNO_2$ (18)	358
Nitroethane	KOH, CH_3OH	$(A)_2C(NO_2)CH_3$ (18–61), $ACH(NO_2)CH_3$ (31–44)	358
1-Nitropropane	KOH, CH_3OH	$(A)_2C(NO_2)CH_2CH_3$ (31), $ACH(NO_2)CH_2CH_3$ (35–40)	358
2-Nitropropane	KOH, CH_3OH	$(CH_3)_2C(A)NO_2$ (83)	358
Vinyldimethylsulfonium Bromide and			
Diethyl malonate	Aq. NaOH	3,3-Dicarbethoxypropyldimethylsulfonium salt (48)	22
Methyl acetoacetate	Aq. NaOH	(3-Acetyl-3-carbomethoxypropyl)dimethylsulfonium bromide (68)	22

Note: References 491–1045 are on pp. 545–555.

TABLE XXI

Michael Condensations with 2- and 4-Vinylpyridine, with Analogs of 2-Vinylpyridine, and with Diethyl Vinylphosphonate

A. 2-Vinylpyridine

A = 2-pyridyl-CH_2CH_2—

Donor	Catalyst	Product (Yield, %)	References
Diethyl malonate	Na	$ACH(CO_2C_2H_5)_2$ (53)	1034
	$NaOC_2H_5$	$ACH(CO_2C_2H_5)_2$ (84, 42–43, 62)	1035, 1036, 1037
		$(A)_2C(CO_2C_2H_5)_2$ (42–43)	1037, 1035
Diethyl ethylmalonate	Na	$AC(C_2H_5)(CO_2C_2H_5)_2$ (39)	1035
Ethyl isobutyrate	Na	$(CH_3)_2C(A)CO_2C_2H_5$ (48)	1038
Ethyl phenylacetate	$[C_6H_5CH_2N(CH_3)_3]OH$	$C_6H_5CH(A)CO_2C_2H_5$	1038
Ethyl 2-pyridylacetate	$NaOC_2H_5$	2-pyridyl-$CH(A)CO_2C_2H_5$ (41, 61)	1039, 1040
Ethyl acetoacetate	Na; $NaOC_2H_5$	$CH_3COCH(A)CO_2C_2H_5$ (58, 50)	1034, 1035
Ethyl *n*-butylacetoacetate	Na	$CH_3COC(C_4H_9\text{-}n)(A)CO_2C_2H_5$ (3)	1038
2-Carbethoxycyclopentanone	Na	2-A-2-$CO_2C_2H_5$-cyclopentanone (42)	1041

Note: References 491–1045 on are pp. 545–555.

TABLE XXI—*Continued*

A. 2-*Vinylpyridine*—*Continued*

A = 2-pyridyl-CH_2CH_2—

Donor	Catalyst	Product (Yield, %)	References
Ethyl benzoylacetate	Na	$C_6H_5COCH(A)CO_2C_2H_5$ (70)	490
	$[C_6H_5CH_2N(CH_3)_3]OH$	$C_6H_5COCH(A)CO_2C_2H_5$	1038
γ-Acetyl-γ-butyrolactone	Na	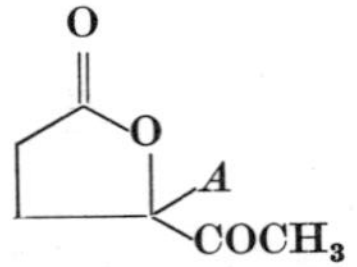 γ-butyrolactone bearing A and $COCH_3$ at the γ-carbon (40)	490
Ethyl cyanoacetate	Na	$ACH(CN)CO_2C_2H_5$ (48)	798
Propionitrile	Na	$CH_3CH(A)CN$ (19); $CH_3C(A)_2CN$ (39)	1038
Benzyl cyanide	Na	$C_6H_5CH(A)CN$ (77)	798
Methyl ethyl ketone	None	$CH_3CH(A)COCH_3$	1042
	$[C_6H_5CH_2N(CH_3)_3]OH$	$CH_3CH(A)COCH_3$ (53), $CH_3C(A)_2COCH_3$ (31)	1038
	Na	$CH_3COCH(A)CH_3$ (71), $CH_3COC(A)_2CH_3$ (31), $ACH_2COC(A)_2CH_3$ (16)	1038
Diethyl ketone	Na	$CH_3CH_2COCH(A)CH_3$ (53), $CH_3CH_2COC(A)_2CH_3$ (32)	1038
Acetylacetone	$NaOC_2H_5$	$CH_3COCH(A)COCH_3$ (16), $CH_3COC(A)_2COCH_3$ (7)	1035
Methyl isopropyl ketone	Na	$CH_3COC(A)(CH_3)_2$ (65), $ACH_2COC(A)(CH_3)_2$ (31), $(A)_2CHCOC(A)(CH_3)_2$ (39)	1038
Methyl isobutyl ketone	Na	$CH_3COCH(A)CH(CH_3)_2$ (20) $CH_3COC(A)_2CH(CH_3)_2$ (34), $ACH_2COC(A)_2CH(CH_3)_2$ (13)	1038

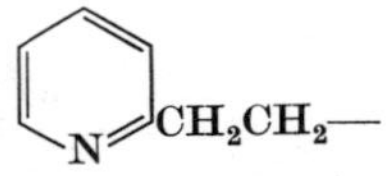

Diisopropyl ketone	Na	$(CH_3)_2CHCOC(A)(CH_3)_2$ (72), $(CH_3)_2C(A)COC(A)(CH_3)_2$ (5)	1038
Methyl *n*-amyl ketone	Na	$CH_3COCH(A)C_4H_9$-*n* (39), $CH_3COC(A)_2C_4H_9$-*n* (19)	1038
	$[C_6H_5CH_2N(CH_3)_3]OH$	$CH_3COCH(A)C_4H_9$-*n* (3)	1038
Diisobutyl ketone	Na	$(CH_3)_2CHCH_2COCH(A)CH(CH_3)_2$ (63), $(CH_3)_2CHCH_2COC(A)_2CH(CH_3)_2$ (14)	1038
2,5,6-Trimethyl-4-hepten-3-one*	Na	$(CH_3)_2C(A)COCH{=}C(CH_3)CH(CH_3)_2$ (29)	1038
Acetophenone	Na	$C_6H_5COCH_2A$ (8), $C_6H_5COCH(A)_2$ (53)	1038
	$[C_6H_5CH_2N(CH_3)_3]OH$	$C_6H_5COCH_2A$ (11)	1038
Phenylacetone	$NaOC_2H_5$	$CH_3COCH(A)C_6H_5$ (32)	1041
	Na	$CH_3COCH(A)C_6H_5$ (44)	1038
Propiophenone	Na	$C_6H_5COCH(A)CH_3$ (43), $C_6H_5COC(A)_2CH_3$ (45)	1038
	$[C_6H_5CH_2N(CH_3)_3]OH$	$C_6H_5COCH(A)CH_3$ (59)	1038
Deoxybenzoin	$NaOC_2H_5$	$C_6H_5COCH(A)C_6H_5$ (46)	1041
2-Acetylfuran	$[C_6H_5CH_2N(CH_3)_3]OH$	2-Furyl-$COCH_2A$ (5)	1038
2-Picoline	Na	1,3-Di-(α-pyridyl)propane (33)	454
4-Hydroxycoumarin	Na	3-A-4-hydroxycoumarin (44)	490

Note: References 491–1045 are on pp. 545–555.

* This ketone was formed and reacted when methyl isopropyl ketone was brought together with sodium metal and 2-vinylpyridine.

TABLE XXI—*Continued*

A. 2-Vinylpyridine—Continued

Donor	Catalyst	Product (Yield, %)	References
3-Methyl-4-hydroxycoumarin	Na	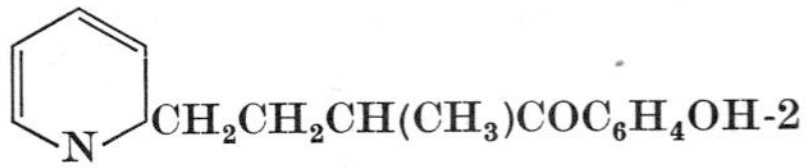 N $CH_2CH_2CH(CH_3)COC_6H_4OH$-2 (90)	490
1-Cyano-2-benzoyl-1,2-dihydro-isoquinoline	Li salt	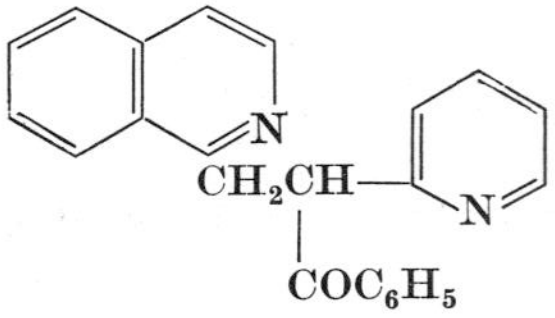 N CH_2CH— N, COC_6H_5 (50)	805*a*

B. 4-Vinylpyridine

Donor	Catalyst	Product (Yield, %)	References
Ethyl benzoylacetate	Na	1-Benzoyl-3-(γ-pyridyl)propane (51)†	1041
γ-Picoline	K	1,3-Di-(γ-pyridyl)propane (44)	484

C. Analogs of 2-Vinylpyridine

Reactants	Catalyst	Product (Yield, %)	References
2-*Vinylquinoline*‡ *and*		A 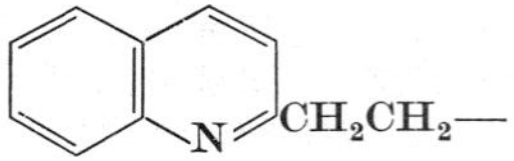 = N CH_2CH_2—	
Diethyl malonate	$NaOC_2H_5$	$A CH(CO_2C_2H_5)_2$ (43)	1043
Ethyl acetoacetate	$NaOC_2H_5$	$CH_3COCH(A)CO_2C_2H_5$ (44)	1043
Ethyl benzoylacetate	$NaOC_2H_5$	$C_6H_5COCH(A)CO_2C_2H_5$ (33)	1043

1-*Vinylisoquinoline*§ *and*			
Diethyl malonate	$NaOC_2H_5$	1-isoquinolyl-$CH_2CH_2CH(CO_2C_2H_5)_2$ (40)	1044

D. Diethyl Vinylphosphonate[1045]

Catalyst $NaOC_2H_5$

$A = (C_2H_5O)_2P(O)CH_2CH_2$—

Donor	Product (Yield, %)
Diethyl malonate	$ACH(CO_2C_2H_5)_2$ (80)
Diethyl methylmalonate	$CH_3C(A)(CO_2C_2H_5)_2$ (79)
Diethyl ethylmalonate	$C_2H_5C(A)(CO_2C_2H_5)_2$ (59)
Diethyl *n*-propylmalonate	n-$C_3H_7C(A)(CO_2C_2H_5)_2$ (78)
Diethyl *n*-butylmalonate	n-$C_4H_9C(A)(CO_2C_2H_5)_2$ (86)
Ethyl acetoacetate	$CH_3COCH(A)CO_2C_2H_5$ (15)
Ethyl *n*-propylacetoacetate	$CH_3COC(A)(C_3H_7\text{-}n)CO_2C_2H_5$ (16)
Ethyl cyanoacetate	$NCCH(A)CO_2C_2H_5$ (16); $NCC(A)_2CO_2C_2H_5$ (18)
Ethyl methylcyanoacetate	$NCC(A)(CH_3)CO_2C_2H_5$ (89)
Ethyl ethylcyanoacetate	$NCC(A)(C_2H_5)CO_2C_2H_5$ (66)
Ethyl isopropylcyanoacetate	$NCC(A)(C_3H_7\text{-}i)CO_2C_2H_5$ (84)
Ethyl *n*-butylcyanoacetate	$NCC(A)(C_4H_9\text{-}n)CO_2C_2H_5$ (78)
Benzyl cyanide	$C_6H_5C(A)_2CN$ (8)

Note: References 491–1045 are on pp. 545–555.

† This product is obtained after hydrolysis and decarboxylation.

‡ This compound was formed *in situ* from 2-(β-diethylaminoethyl)quinoline methosulfate.

§ When this compound was formed *in situ* from 1-(β-dimethylaminoethyl)isoquinoline methiodide, a more complex reaction product was obtained.

TABLE XXII

Donors Used in Michael Condensations

Malonates, $RCH(CO_2C_2H_5)_2$: R = H, Cl, Br, NO_2, methyl, ethyl, *n*-propyl, *n*-butyl, *n*-hexyl, *n*-octyl, *n*-decyl, *n*-dodecyl, *n*-tetradecyl, *n*-hexadecyl, β-methoxyethyl, β-ethoxyethyl, phenyl, benzyl, phenethyl, 1-naphthyl, 1-naphthylmethyl, β-(1-naphthylethyl), 2-naphthyl, 2-naphthylmethyl, β-(2-naphthylethyl); β-aldehydoethyl, β-aldehydopropyl, acetoxy, formamido, acetamido, phthalimido, $R'O_2CCH_2$—, $(R'O_2C)_2CH$—, $R'O_2CCH(CH_3)$-$CH(CO_2R')$—, CH_2=$C(CO_2C_2H_5)$—, β-ionylideneacetyl, isobutyryl.

Dibenzyl malonate, malonamide, ethyl malonamate, ethyl malonamidinate, diethyl α-cyano-β-methylsuccinate, diethyl α-cyano-β,β-dimethylglutarate.

Cyanoacetates, $RCH(CN)CO_2C_2H_5$: R = H, methyl, ethyl, isopropyl, *n*-butyl, phenyl, phenethyl, β-aldehydoethyl, acetamido, $R'O_2C(CH_2)_3$-$C(CH_3)(CN)$—.

Acetoacetates, $CH_3COCHRCO_2C_2H_5$: R = H, methyl, ethyl, *n*-propyl, isopropyl, *n*-butyl, isoamyl, hexyl, phenyl, benzyl, allyl; acetoacetanilide. Ethyl iminoacetoacetate, $CH_3C(=NH)CH_2CO_2C_2H_5$, and its N-methyl derivative; ethyl iminomethylacetoacetate, $CH_3C(=NH)CH(CH_3)CO_2C_2H_5$.

Other ketonic esters: ethyl propionylacetate, butyrylacetate, isobutyrylacetate, hexanoylacetate, γ-ethoxyacetoacetate, palmitoylacetate, stearoylacetate; diethyl acetone-1,3-dicarboxylate, ethyl isobutyrylisobutyrate, ethyl α-acetylsuccinate, ethyl α-acetyladipate, $C_2H_5O_2CCH_2CH_2COCH(CH_3)$-$CO_2C_2H_5$, ethyl benzoylacetate, ethyl 2-oxocyclohexane-1-carboxylate and its 3-methyl derivative, ethyl 2-oxocyclopentane-1-carboxylate and its 5-methyl derivative, higher cycloalkanone-2-carboxylates, 2-carbomethoxy-1-tetralone, methyl 1-keto-1,2,3,4-tetrahydrophenanthrene-2-carboxylate, ethyl camphor-3-carboxylate, 3-ethoxy-5,5-dimethyl-6-carbethoxy-2-cyclohexen-1-one, ethyl phenylpyruvate (α-keto ester).

Monocarboxylic acid esters: ethyl acetate, ethyl isobutyrate, diethyl glutaconate, diethyl itaconate, ethyl phenylacetate (also *m*-NO_2, *p*-NO_2, Cl, Br, and C_2H_5 analogs) and its α-ethyl, *n*-propyl, *n*-butyl, isobutyl derivatives, ethyl furan-2-acetate, ethyl thiophene-2-acetate, ethyl α-naphthylacetate, methyl diphenylacetate, ethyl α-pyridylacetate, triethyl phosphonoacetate, triethyl α-phosphonohexanoate.

Ketones: acetone, methyl ethyl ketone, methyl *n*-propyl ketone,* methyl isopropyl ketone,* methyl isobutyl ketone,* pinacolone, methyl *n*-butyl ketone,* methyl *n*-amyl ketone,* diisopropyl ketone,* diisobutyl ketone, isopropyl *n*-amyl ketone,* isopropyl *n*-nonyl ketone,* methyl β-cyanoethyl ketone, β,β-diethoxyethyl alkyl ketones, acetylacetone, acetonylacetone,* heptadecane-2,4-dione, octadecane-2,4-dione, isobutyrylacetone, diisobutyrylmethane, cyclopentanone, 2-methylcyclopentane-1,3-dione, cyclohexanone,

* Condensed only with acrylonitrile as acceptor.

2-, 3-, and 4-methylcyclohexanone, carvenone, dihydro- and tetrahydrocarvone, carvotanacetone, cyclohexane-1,2-dione, 2-hydroxy- and 2-acetoxycyclohexanone, cyclohexane-1,3-dione and its 2-alkyl derivatives, 5,5-dimethyl-1,3-cyclohexanedione, cyclohexenylcyclohexanone, 2-methyl-6-isopropenylcyclohexanone, 2-aldehydocyclohexanone, 2-aldehydo-4-(*p*-carboxy- and *p*-carbomethoxy-cyclohexyl)cyclohexanone, higher cycloalkanones, 1-tetralone, 2-methyl-1-tetralone, 6-methoxy-1-tetralone, 2-(β-diethylaminoethyl)-1-tetralone, 2-hydroxymethylene-6-methoxy-1-tetralone, *trans*-2-decalone, 1-methyl-2-decalone (*cis* and *trans*) and its 5-methoxy, 6-methoxy, 5,6-dimethoxy, and 6-carbethoxy derivatives, 10-methyl-2-decalone, 9-methyl-8-hydrindanone, anthrone, 4-keto-1,2,3,4-tetrahydrophenanthrene, 4-keto-1,2,3,4,9,10,11,12-octahydrophenanthrene,* 4,9-diketo-1,2,3,4,9,10,11,12-octahydrophenanthrene,*

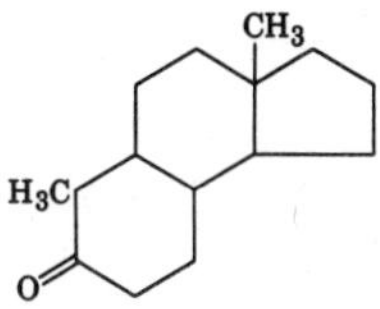

CH_3 ... H_3C ... O and H_3C ... O ... H_3C ... O

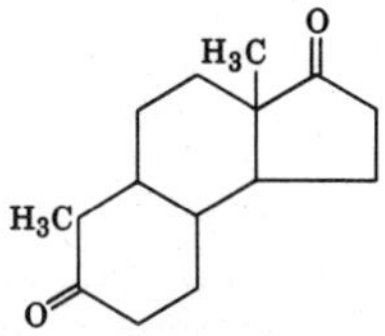

Acetophenone, phenylacetone, propiophenone, isobutyrophenone, benzoylacetone, dibenzyl ketone, deoxybenzoin, *p*-phenylacetylbiphenyl, dibenzoylmethane, 1,2-dibenzoylethane, α-methyl-α-*n*-butylacetophenone,* α-methyl-α-*n*-octylacetophenone,* α-ethyl-α-*n*-propylacetophenone,* isopropyl benzyl ketone,* α-phenyl-α-*n*-octylacetone,* 2-phenylcyclohexanone and its 6-benzylidene derivative,* 2-aldehydo-4-(*p*-carboxy- and *p*-carbomethoxyphenyl)-cyclohexanone, 2-phenylcycloheptanone.

2-Acetylfuran,* 5-methyl-2-acetylfuran,* 2-propionylfuran,* 5-methyl-2-propionylfuran,* 2,5-dimethyl-3-acetylfuran,* 2,5-dimethyl-3-propionylfuran,* 2-butyrylfuran,* 2,5-dimethyl-3-butyrylfuran,* 2-acetyl-, 2-propionyl-, and 2-butyryl-thiophene and their 5-methyl derivatives,* 2-acetoacetylthiophene.*

Acetylacetone imine, benzoylacetone imine, (*p*-methylbenzoyl)acetone imine.

Aldehydes: acetaldehyde,* propionaldehyde,* butyraldehyde, isobutyraldehyde, diethylacetaldehyde,* heptaldehyde, 2-ethylhexanal, diethylacetaldehyde, phenylacetaldehyde, α-phenylpropionaldehyde.*

Nitriles: malononitrile, acetonitrile, propionitrile, cyanoacetamide and its N-alkyl derivatives, benzyl cyanide and its derivatives nuclearly substituted by *o*-Cl, *m*-Cl, Br, CH_3, NH_2, *p*-Br, CH_3, OCH_3, NO_2; benzyl cyanide α-substituted by methyl, ethyl, isopropyl, *n*-butyl, *n*-pentyl, 3-methylbutyl, (1-cyclohexenyl), cyclohexyl, (*p*-chlorophenyl), (2-thienyl), (2-pyridyl) and β-diethylaminoethyl; diphenylacetonitrile; diethyl cyanomethanephosphonate, 2-cyanocycloheptanone, $CH_3C(=NH)CH_2CN$, $C_6H_5C(=NH)CH_2CN$.

* Condensed only with acrylonitrile as acceptor.

TABLE XXII—*Continued*

DONORS USED IN MICHAEL CONDENSATIONS

Nitro compounds: nitromethane, nitroethane, 1-nitropropane, 2-nitropropane, 1-nitrobutane, 1-nitroisobutane, β,β-dinitroethanol, methyl 2-nitropropyl ether, methyl 2-nitropropyl sulfide, butyl 3-nitrobutyl sulfone, nitrocyclohexane, dinitromethane, phenylnitromethane and its *p*-bromo derivative, methyl 2-nitro-1-phenylpropyl ether, methyl and ethyl nitroacetates, methyl γ,γ-dinitrobutyrate, diethyl nitromalonate, 1,1-dinitroethane.

Sulfones: phenyl benzyl sulfone, *p*-tolyl benzyl sulfone, allyl *p*-tolyl sulfone, ethyl *p*-toluenesulfoacetate, phenacyl *p*-tolyl sulfone, bis(benzenesulfonyl)methane, bis(methanesulfonyl)methane.

Hydrocarbons and derivatives: cyclopentadiene, divinylmethane, indene, 1-isopropylideneindene, fluorene, 2-nitrofluorene,* 2,7-dibromofluorene, 1-methylfluorene, 9-phenylfluorene, 9-hydroxyfluorene, fluorene-9-carboxylates, ethyl 1-methylfluorene-9-carboxylate, 1,2,3,4-tetrahydrofluoranthene, 2,3,4-trimethyl-1,2-dihydrofluoranthene, 4,5-methylenephenanthrene, methyl 4-cyclopenta[*def*]phenanthrene-4-carboxylate.

Miscellaneous donors (of occasional use): α-aceto-γ-butyrolactone, ethyl oxaloacetate and its α-methyl derivative, ethyl β-methyl-γ-nitrobutyrate, diethyl succinate, isophorone, 1-formyl-2-keto-10-methyl-$\Delta^{3,6}$-hexahydronaphthalene, α-naphthol (keto form), ethyl 4-hydroxy-2,3-benzofuran-5-carboxylate (keto form), 4-hydroxycoumarin (keto form), 2-hydroxy-1,4-naphthoquinone (keto form), 2-acetyl-5-cyclohexan-1-one, ethyl (3,4-dihydro-1-naphthyl)cyanoacetate, ethyl (1-methyl-1,2,5,6-tetrahydro-4-pyridyl)acetate, α- and γ-picoline, α- and γ-quinaldine, rhodanine, Inhoffen ketone, kojic acid, 1-methyloxindole, 1,3-dimethyloxindole, methyl oxindole-3-propionate, 2,3-dihydro-2-phenylbenzo-γ-pyrone.

* Condensed only with acrylonitrile as acceptor.

REFERENCES FOR TABLES I-XXII

[491] Warner and Moe, U.S. pat. 2,520,666 [*C.A.*, **45,** 643 (1951)].
[492] Warner and Moe, U.S. pat. 2,575,375 [*C.A.*, **46,** 5081 (1952)].
[493] Moe and Warner, U.S. pat. 2,540,053 [*C.A.*, **45,** 5720 (1951)].
[494] Warner and Moe, U.S. pat. 2,523,746 [*C.A.*, **45,** 5719 (1951)].
[495] Warner and Moe, U.S. pat. 2,523,743 [*C.A.*, **45,** 5718 (1951)].
[496] Yamada, Chibata, and Tsurui, *J. Pharm. Soc. Japan,* **73,** 123 (1953) [*C.A* , **47,** 11132 (1953)].
[497] Warner and Moe, U.S. pat. 2,546,958 [*C.A.*, **45,** 8035 (1951)].
[498] Jacquier, Zagdoun, and Fontaine, *Bull. soc. chim. France,* **1953,** 25.
[499] Mousseron, Jacquier, Fontaine, and Zagdoun, *Bull. soc. chim. France,* **1954,** 1246.
[500] Moe and Warner, U.S. pat. 2,610,204 [*C.A.*, **47,** 5961 (1953)].
[501] Jacquier and Fontaine, *Bull. soc. chim. France,* **1952,** 248.
[502] Warner and Moe, U.S. pat. 2,532,047 [*C.A.*, **45,** 2971 (1951)].
[503] Warner and Moe, U.S. pat. 2,532,048 [*C.A.*, **45,** 2971 (1951)].
[504] Moe and Warner, U.S. pat. 2,551,566 [*C.A.*, **46,** 133 (1952)].
[505] Smith, U.S. pat. 2,516,729 [*C.A.*, **45,** 6217 (1951)].
[506] Shechter, Ley, and Zeldin, *J. Am. Chem. Soc.*, **74,** 3664 (1952).
[507] Warner and Moe, *J. Am. Chem. Soc.*, **74,** 1064 (1952).
[508] N.V. de Bataafsche Petroleum Maatschappij, Brit. pat. 666,623 [*C.A.*, **46,** 11230 (1952)].
[509] Moe and Warner, U.S. pat. 2,599,653 [*C.A.*, **47,** 3339 (1953)].
[510] Moe and Warner, U.S. pat. 2,546,960 [*C.A.*, **45,** 8036 (1951)].
[511] Moe and Warner, U.S. pat. 2,540,054 [*C.A.*, **45,** 5720 (1951)].
[512] Mukherjee and Bhattacharyya, *J. Indian Chem. Soc.*, **23,** 451 (1946) [*C.A.*, **42,** 128 (1948)].
[513] Distillers Company Ltd., British pat. 706,176 [*C.A.*, **49,** 9030 (1955)].
[514] Dornow and Karlson, *Ber.*, **73,** 542 (1940).
[515] Baumgarten and Dornow, *Ber.*, **72,** 563 (1939).
[516] Fischer and Hultzsch, *Ber.*, **68,** 1726 (1935).
[517] Weizmann, Brit. pat. 594,182 [*C.A.*, **42,** 2986 (1948)].
[518] Weizmann, U.S. pat. 2,472,135 [*C.A.*, **43,** 6664 (1949)].
[519] Moe and Warner, U.S. pat. 2,523,710 [*C.A.*, **45,** 5717 (1951)].
[520] Moe and Warner, U.S. pat. 2,628,980 [*C.A.*, **48,** 724 (1954)].
[521] Dornow and Hargesheimer, *Chem. Ber.*, **86,** 461 (1953).
[522] Kress, U.S. pat. 2,540,267 [*C.A.*, **45,** 5720 (1951)].
[523] Tsuruta, *Bull. Inst. Chem. Research, Kyoto Univ.*, **31,** 190 (1953) [*C.A.*, **49,** 6183 (1955)].
[524] Rhinesmith, *J. Am. Chem. Soc.*, **58,** 596 (1936).
[525] Nazarov and Zav'yalov, *Izvest. Akad. Nauk S.S.S.R. Otdel. Khim. Nauk,* **1952,** 300 [*C.A.*, **47,** 5364 (1953)].
[526] Boehme and Mundlos, *Chem. Ber.*, **86,** 1414 (1953).
[527] Walker, *J. Chem. Soc.*, **1935,** 1585.
[528] Wieland and Miescher, *Helv. Chim. Acta,* **33,** 2215 (1950); cf. Miescher and Wieland *ibid.*, **33,** 1847 (1950).
[529] Dauben, Tweit, and MacLean, *J. Am. Chem. Soc.*, **77,** 48 (1955).
[530] Dreiding and Tomasewski, *J. Am. Chem. Soc.*, **77,** 411 (1955).
[531] Stork, *Bull. soc. chim. France,* **1955,** 256.
[532] Wilds and Werth, *J. Org. Chem.*, **17,** 1149 (1952).
[533] Wilds and Werth, *J. Org. Chem.*, **17,** 1154 (1952).
[534] Chem. Werke Huels, Ger. pat. 833,645 [*C.A.*, **47,** 2205 (1953)].
[535] Stork, Terrell, and Szmuszkovicz, *J. Am. Chem. Soc.*, **76,** 2029 (1954).
[536] Walker, *J. Am. Chem. Soc.*, **77,** 3664 (1955).
[537] Ralls, Wildman, McCaleb, and Wilds, U.S. pat. 2,674,627 [*C.A.*, **49,** 1813 (1955)].
[538] Nazarov and Zav'yalov, *Zhur. Obshcheĭ Khim.*, **23,** 1703 (1953) [*C.A.*, **48,** 13667 (1954)]

[539] Wendler and Slates, U.S. pat. 2,542,223 [*C.A.*, **45,** 7599 (1951)].
[540] Poos, Arth, Beyler, and Sarett, *J. Am. Chem. Soc.*, **75,** 422 (1953).
[541] Sarett and Beyler, U.S. pat. 2,617,828 [*C.A.*, **47,** 9365 (1953)].
[542] Wieland, Ueberwasser, Anner, and Miescher, *Helv. Chim. Acta*, **36,** 1231 (1953).
[543] British Celanese Ltd., Brit. pat. 671,412 [*C.A.*, **47,** 2198 (1953)].
[544] Stubbs and Tucker, *J. Chem. Soc.*, **1950,** 3288.
[545] Dannenberg and Dannenberg-von Dresler, *Ann.*, **593,** 232 (1955).
[546] Leonard and Simon, *J. Org. Chem.*, **17,** 1262 (1952).
[547] Mariella, *Org. Syntheses*, **32,** 32 (1952).
[548] Wilds and Djerassi, *J. Am. Chem. Soc.*, **68,** 1715 (1946).
[549] Blaise and Maire, *Bull. soc. chim. France*, [4], **3,** 421 (1908).
[550] Blaise and Maire, *Bull. soc. chim. France*, [4], **3,** 413 (1908).
[551] Woodward, Sondheimer, Taub, Heusler, and McLamore, *J. Am. Chem. Soc.*, **74,** 4223 (1952).
[552] Dreux, *Bull. soc. chim. France*, **1954,** 1443.
[553] van Wagtendonk and Wibaut, *Rec. trav. chim.*, **61,** 728 (1942).
[554] Mariella and Leech, *J. Am. Chem. Soc.*, **71,** 331 (1949).
[555] Guareschi, *Chem. Zentr.*, **1899, I,** 289.
[556] Moir, *J. Chem. Soc.*, **81,** 113 (1902).
[557] Basu, *J. Indian Chem. Soc.*, **12,** 289 (1935) [*C.A.*, **29,** 6891 (1935)].
[558] Steiner and Willhalm, *Helv. Chim. Acta*, **35,** 1752 (1952).
[558a] Stobbe, *Ber.*, **34,** 1955 (1901).
[559] Qudrat-I-Khuda, *J. Chem. Soc.*, **1929,** 201.
[560] Smith and Engelhardt, *J. Am. Chem. Soc.*, **71,** 2671, 2676 (1949).
[561] France, Maitland, and Tucker, *J. Chem. Soc.*, **1937,** 1739.
[562] Prelog, Komzak, and Moor, *Helv. Chim. Acta*, **25,** 1654 (1942).
[563] Oparina, *Ber.*, **64,** 569 (1931).
[564] Kochetkov, *Doklady Akad. Nauk S.S.S.R.*, **84,** 289 (1952) [*C.A.*, **47,** 3309 (1953)].
[565] Eccott and Linstead, *J. Chem. Soc.*, **1930,** 905.
[566] Qudrat-I-Khuda, *J. Chem. Soc.*, **1929,** 1913.
[567] Frank and Hall, Jr., *J. Am. Chem. Soc.*, **72,** 1645 (1950).
[568] Crossley, *Proc. Chem. Soc.*, **17,** 172 (1901).
[569] Bardhan, *J. Chem. Soc.*, **1928,** 2604.
[570] Kon and Linstead, *J. Chem. Soc.*, **127,** 815 (1925).
[571] Kon and Leton, *J. Chem. Soc.*, **1931,** 2496.
[572] Birch and Robinson, *J. Chem. Soc.*, **1942,** 488.
[573] Allen and Cressman, *J. Am. Chem. Soc.*, **55,** 2953 (1933).
[574] Abdullah, *J. Indian Chem. Soc.*, **12,** 62 (1935) [*C.A.*, **29,** 3995 (1935)].
[575] Allen and Barker, *J. Am. Chem. Soc.*, **54,** 736 (1932).
[576] Allen and Bridgess, *J. Am. Chem. Soc.*, **51,** 2151 (1929).
[577] Walker, *J. Chem. Soc.*, **1939,** 120.
[578] Rosenmund, Herzberg, and Schütt, *Chem. Ber.*, **87,** 1258 (1954).
[579] Vorlaender, *Ber.*, **27,** 2053 (1894).
[580] Gohdes, *J. prakt. Chem.*, [2], **123,** 169 (1929).
[581] Albertson, *J. Am. Chem. Soc.*, **72,** 2594 (1950).
[582] Baddar and Warren, *J. Chem. Soc.*, **1939,** 944.
[583] Zaugg, *J. Am. Chem. Soc.*, **71,** 1890 (1949).
[584] Seidman, Robertson, and Link, *J. Am. Chem. Soc.*, **72,** 5193 (1950).
[585] Starr and Haber, U.S. pat. 2,666,064 [*C.A.*, **49,** 380 (1955)].
[586] Kuhn and Weiser, *Chem. Ber.*, **88,** 1601 (1955).
[587] Hinkel, Ayling, and Dippy, *J. Chem. Soc.*, **1935,** 539.
[588] Horning and Field, *J. Am. Chem. Soc.*, **68,** 387 (1946).
[589] Friedmann, *J. prakt. Chem.*, [2], **146,** 71 (1936).
[590] Hinkel and Dippy, *J. Chem. Soc.*, **1930,** 1387.
[591] Barat, *J. Indian Chem. Soc.*, **8,** 699 (1931) [*C.A.*, **26,** 1608 (1932)].
[592] Basu, *J. Indian Chem. Soc.*, **7,** 481 (1930) [*C.A.*, **24,** 5752 (1930)].

[593] Linstead and Williams, *J. Chem. Soc.*, **1926**, 2735.
[594] Basu, *J. Indian Chem. Soc.*, **8**, 119 (1931) [*C.A.*, **25**, 4881 (1931)].
[595] Friedmann, *J. prakt. Chem.*, [2], **146**, 65 (1936).
[596] Mukherji, *Science and Culture India*, **13**, 39 (1947) [*C.A.*, **42**, 2957 (1948)].
[597] Profft, Runge, and Jumar, *J. prakt. Chem.*, [4], **1**, 57 (1954).
[598] Hill, *J. Am. Chem. Soc.*, **49**, 566 (1927).
[599] Vorlaender and Kalkow, *Ber.*, **30**, 2268 (1897).
[600] Avery, Biswell, and Liston, *J. Am. Chem. Soc.*, **54**, 229 (1932).
[601] Kohler and Rao, *J. Am. Chem. Soc.*, **41**, 1697 (1919).
[602] Badger, Cook, and Walker, *J. Chem. Soc.*, **1948**, 2011.
[603] Vorlaender and Kunze, *Ber.*, **59**, 2078 (1926).
[604] Mehr, Becker, and Spoerri, *J. Am. Chem. Soc.*, **77**, 984 (1955).
[605] Wislicenus and Carpenter, *Ann.*, **302**, 223 (1898).
[606] Ziegler and Schnell, *Ann.*, **445**, 266 (1925).
[607] Michael and Ross, *J. Am. Chem. Soc.*, **54**, 407 (1932); see Michael and Ross, *ibid.*, **52**, 4598 (1930).
[608] Allen, Massey, and Nicholls, *J. Am. Chem. Soc.*, **59**, 679 (1937).
[609] Kohler, Graustein, and Merrill, *J. Am. Chem. Soc.*, **44**, 2536 (1922).
[610] Kohler and Souther, *J. Am. Chem. Soc.*, **44**, 2903 (1922).
[611] Rupe and Stern, *Helv. Chim. Acta*, **10**, 859 (1927).
[612] Upson, Maxwell, and Parmelee, *J. Am. Chem. Soc.*, **52**, 1971 (1930).
[613] Allen and Sallans, *Can. J. Research*, **9**, 574 (1933) [*C.A.*, **28**, 2006 (1934)].
[614] Kaplash, Shah, and Wheeler, *J. Indian Chem. Soc.*, **19**, 117 (1942) [*C.A.*, **37**, 375 (1943)].
[615] Kaplash, Shah, and Wheeler, *Current Sci. India*, **8**, 512 (1939) [*C.A.*, **34**, 5830 (1940)].
[616] Stobbe, *J. prakt. Chem.*, [2], **86**, 209 (1912).
[617] Cope, Fawcett, and Munn, *J. Am. Chem. Soc.*, **72**, 3399 (1950).
[618] Mikhaĭlov, *J. Gen. Chem. U.S.S.R.*, **7**, 2950 (1937) [*C.A.*, **32**, 5402 (1938)].
[619] Kohler, *J. Am. Chem. Soc.*, **46**, 503 (1924).
[620] Kohler, *J. Am. Chem. Soc.*, **38**, 889 (1916).
[621] Worrall and Bradway, *J. Am. Chem. Soc.*, **58**, 1607 (1936).
[622] Dornow and Frese, *Ann.*, **581**, 211 (1953).
[623] Tucker and Whalley, *J. Chem. Soc.*, **1949**, 50.
[624] Kohler, Hill, and Bigelow, *J. Am. Chem. Soc.*, **39**, 2405 (1917).
[625] Kohler and Williams, *J. Am. Chem. Soc.*, **41**, 1644 (1919).
[626] Hill, *J. Chem. Soc.*, **1935**, 1115.
[627] Kohler and Conant, *J. Am. Chem. Soc.*, **39**, 1699 (1917).
[628] Petrow, *Ber.*, **63**, 898 (1930).
[629] Dilthey, Trösken, Plum, and Schommer, *J. prakt. Chem.*, [2], **141**, 331 (1934).
[630] Petrow and Anzus, *Ber.*, **66**, 420 (1933).
[631] Allen and Scarrow, *Can. J. Research*, **11**, 395 (1934) [*C.A.*, **29**, 121 (1935)].
[632] Hedenburg and Wachs, *J. Am. Chem. Soc.*, **70**, 2216 (1948).
[633] Hedenburg, U.S. pat. 2,524,107 [*C.A.*, **45**, 811 (1951)].
[634] Lutz and Palmer, *J. Am. Chem. Soc.*, **57**, 1947 (1935).
[635] Garden and Gunstone, *J. Chem. Soc.*, **1952**, 2650.
[636] Fuson and Mange, *J. Org. Chem.*, **19**, 806 (1954).
[637] Polonovski, Pesson, and Polmanss, *Bull. soc. chim. France*, **1953**, 200.
[638] Kwartler and Lindwall, *J. Am. Chem. Soc.*, **59**, 524 (1937).
[639] Seshadri and Venkateswarlu, *Proc. Indian Acad. Sci.*, **15A**, 424 (1942) [*C.A.*, **36**, 7015 (1942)].
[640] Lo and Croxall, *J. Am. Chem. Soc.*, **76**, 4166 (1954).
[641] Westöö, *Acta Chem. Scand.*, **7**, 355 (1953) [*C.A.*, **48**, 3349 (1954)].
[642] Bartlett and Woods, *J. Am. Chem. Soc.*, **62**, 2933 (1940).
[643] McCoubrey, *J. Chem. Soc.*, **1951**, 2931.
[644] Rosenfelder and Ginsburg, *J. Chem. Soc.*, **1954**, 2955.
[645] Colonge, Dreux, and Delplace, *Compt. rend.*, **238**, 1237 (1954).

[646] Colonge, *Bull. soc. chim. France*, **1955**, 250.
[647] Shafer, Loeb, and Johnson, *J. Am. Chem. Soc.*, **75**, 5963 (1953).
[648] Rabe, *Ber.*, **37**, 1671 (1904).
[649] Cronyn and Riesser, *J. Am. Chem. Soc.*, **75**, 1664 (1953).
[650] Nightingale, Erickson, and Shackelford, *J. Org. Chem.*, **17**, 1005 (1952).
[651] Robinson and Saxton, *J. Chem. Soc.*, **1953**, 2596.
[652] Basu, *Ann.*, **530**, 131 (1937).
[653] Basu, *Ann.*, **514**, 292 (1934).
[654] Eistert and Reiss, *Chem. Ber.*, **87**, 92 (1954).
[655] Nazarov and Zav'yalov, *Izvest. Akad. Nauk S.S.S.R. Otdel. Khim. Nauk*, **1952**, 437 *C.A.*, **47**, 5365 (1953)].
[656] Robinson and Walker, *J. Chem. Soc.*, **1935**, 1530.
[657] Rabe and Appuhn, *Ber.*, **76**, 982 (1943). Cf. Rabe, *Ann.*, **360**, 1005 (1952).
[658] Desai, *J. Indian Chem. Soc.*, **10**, 257 (1933) [*C.A.*, **27**, 5310 (1933)].
[659] Stauffacher and Schinz, *Helv. Chim. Acta*, **37**, 1207 (1954).
[660] Rosenmund and Herzberg, *Chem. Ber.*, **87**, 1575 (1954).
[661] Eschenmoser, Schreiber, and Julia, *Helv. Chim. Acta*, **36**, 482 (1953).
[662] Qudrat-I-Khuda and Mukherji, *J. Chem. Soc.*, **1936**, 570.
[663] Friedmann and Robinson, *Chemistry & Industry*, **1951**, 777.
[664] Gunstone and Tulloch, *J. Chem. Soc.*, **1955**, 1130.
[665] Winternitz, Mousseron, and Rouzier, *Bull. soc. chim. France*, **1954**, 316.
[666] Amiel, Loeffler, and Ginsburg, *J. Am. Chem. Soc.*, **76**, 3625 (1954).
[667] Ginsburg, *J. Chem. Soc.*, **1954**, 2361.
[668] Pappo and Ginsburg, *Bull. Research Council Israel*, **1**, Pt. 1–2, 145 (1951) [*C.A.*, **46**, 7064 (1952)].
[669] Pappo and Ginsburg, *Bull. Research Council Israel*, **1**, Pt. 3, 121 (1951) [*C.A.*, **47**, 2161 (1953)].
[670] Sen and Neogi, *J. Indian Chem. Soc.*, **7**, 305 (1930) [*C.A.*, **24**, 4767 (1930)].
[671] McQuillin, *Chemistry & Industry*, **1954**, 311.
[672] Dutta, Chakravarti, and Dutta, *Chemistry & Industry*, **1955**, 170.
[673] Mukharji and Raha, *Science and Culture India*, **19**, 569 (1954) [*C.A.*, **49**, 5414 (1955)].
[674] Birch and Quartey, *Chemistry & Industry*, **1953**, 489.
[675] Ott and Tarbell, *J. Am. Chem. Soc.*, **74**, 6266 (1952).
[676] Ginsburg, *J. Am. Chem. Soc.*, **76**, 3628 (1954).
[677] Parihar and Dutt, *Indian Soap J.*, **16**, 154 (1950) [*C.A.*, **46**, 8066 (1952)].
[678] Ralls, *J. Am. Chem. Soc.*, **75**, 2123 (1953).
[679] Mannich and Fourneau, *Ber.*, **71**, 2090 (1938).
[680] Bardhan, *Chemistry & Industry*, **1940**, 369.
[681] Cardwell and McQuillin, *J. Chem. Soc.*, **1949**, 708.
[682] Jacquier and Boyer, *Bull. soc. chim. France*, **1955**, 8.
[683] Jacquier and Boyer, *Bull. soc. chim. France*, **1954**, 717.
[684] Roy, *Science and Culture India*, **19**, 156 (1953) [*C.A.*, **48**, 13660 (1954)].
[685] Martin and Robinson, *J. Chem. Soc.*, **1949**, 1866.
[686] Robinson and Seijo, *J. Chem. Soc.*, **1941**, 582.
[687] Hussey, Liao, and Baker, *J. Am. Chem. Soc.*, **75**, 4727 (1953).
[688] Prelog, Wirth, and Ruzicka, *Helv. Chim. Acta*, **29**, 1425 (1946).
[689] Prelog, Barman, and Zimmermann, *Helv. Chim. Acta*, **32**, 1284 (1949).
[690] Prelog, Ruzicka, Barman, and Frenkiel, *Helv. Chim. Acta*, **31**, 92 (1948).
[691] Gill, James, Lions, and Potts, *J. Am. Chem. Soc.*, **74**, 4923 (1952).
[692] Wilds, Hoffman, and Pearson, *J. Am. Chem. Soc.*, **77**, 647 (1955).
[693] Johnston and Holly, U.S. pat. 2,671,808 [*C.A.*, **49**, 3264 (1955)].
[694] Banerjee, Chatterjee, and Bhattacharya, *J. Am. Chem. Soc.*, **77**, 408 (1955).
[695] Buechi, Jeger, and Ruzicka, *Helv. Chim. Acta*, **31**, 241 (1948).
[696] Robinson and Weygand, *J. Chem. Soc.*, **1941**, 386.
[697] Cook and Robinson, *J. Chem. Soc.*, **1941**, 391.
[698] Cornforth and Robinson, *J. Chem. Soc.*, **1946**, 676.

[699] Grob and Jundt, *Helv. Chim. Acta,* **31,** 1691 (1948).
[700] Shunk and Wilds, *J. Am. Chem. Soc.,* **71,** 3946 (1949).
[701] Ghosh and Robinson, *J. Chem. Soc.,* **1944,** 506.
[702] Wilds and Shunk, *J. Am. Chem. Soc.,* **72,** 2388 (1950).
[703] Martin and Robinson, *J. Chem. Soc.,* **1943,** 491.
[704] Mukharji, *J. Indian Chem. Soc.,* **24,** 91 (1947) [*C.A.,* **42,** 1312 (1948)].
[705] Huang, *J. Chem. Soc.,* **1954,** 3655.
[706] Wieland and Miescher, *Helv. Chim. Acta,* **33,** 2215 (1950).
[707] CIBA, Swiss pat. 293,104 [*C.A.,* **49,** 3263 (1955)].
[708] Chaudhuari and Mukharji, *Science and Culture India,* **18,** 602 (1953) [*C.A.,* **48,** 7592 (1954)].
[709] Wendler, Slates, and Tishler, *J. Am. Chem. Soc.,* **73,** 3816 (1951).
[710] Reichert and Posemann, *Arch. Pharm.,* **275,** 67 (1937) [*C.A.,* **31,** 3984 (1937)].
[711] Barltrop, *J. Chem. Soc.,* **1946,** 958.
[712] Cardwell, *J. Chem. Soc.,* **1949,** 715.
[713] Szmuszkovicz and Born, *J. Am. Chem. Soc.,* **75,** 3350 (1953).
[714] McQuillin, *J. Chem. Soc.,* **1955,** 528.
[715] Roy, *Chemistry & Industry,* **1954,** 1393.
[716] Howe and McQuillin, *J. Chem. Soc.,* **1955,** 2423.
[717] Adamson, McQuillin, Robinson, and Simonsen, *J. Chem. Soc.,* **1937,** 1576.
[718] Abe, Harukawa, Ishikawa, Miki, Sumi, and Toga, *J. Am. Chem. Soc.,* **75,** 2567 (1953).
[719] Abe, Harukawa, Ishikawa, Miki, Sumi, and Toga, *Proc. Japan Acad.,* **29,** 113 (1953) [*C.A.,* **48,** 10706 (1954)].
[720] Roy, *Science and Culture India,* **19,** 266 (1953) [*C.A.,* **49,** 1676 (1955)].
[721] Szmuszkowicz, *J. Org. Chem.,* **19,** 1424 (1954).
[722] Jacquier and Boyer, *Bull. soc. chim. France,* **1954,** 442.
[723] Mannich and Koch, *Ber.,* **75,** 803 (1942).
[724] Mannich, Koch, and Borkowsky, *Ber.,* **70,** 355 (1937).
[725] Logan, Marvell, La Pore, and D. C. Bush, *J. Am. Chem. Soc.,* **76,** 4127 (1954).
[726] Jacquier and Lanet, *Bull. soc. chim. France,* **1953,** 795.
[727] Treibs and Muehlstaedt, *Chem. Ber.,* **87,** 407 (1954).
[728] Jacquier and Christol, *Bull. soc. chim. France,* **1954,** 556.
[729] Novello, Christy, and Sprague, *J. Am. Chem. Soc.,* **75,** 1330 (1953).
[730] F. C. Novello, private communication.
[731] Cope and Hermann, *J. Am. Chem. Soc.,* **72,** 3405 (1950).
[732] Harradence and Lions, *J. Proc. Roy. Soc. N.S. Wales,* **72,** 284 (1939) [*C.A.,* **33,** 6825 (1939)].
[733] Gill and Lions, *J. Am. Chem. Soc.,* **72,** 3468 (1950).
[734] Juday, *J. Am. Chem. Soc.,* **75,** 4071 (1953).
[735] Novello and Christy, *J. Am. Chem. Soc.,* **75,** 5431 (1953).
[736] Lieberman and Wagner, *J. Org. Chem.,* **14,** 1001 (1949).
[737] Dalgliesh, *J. Am. Chem. Soc.,* **71,** 1697 (1949).
[738] Eliel, *J. Am. Chem. Soc.,* **73,** 43 (1951).
[739] Snyder and Hamlin, *J. Am. Chem. Soc.,* **72,** 5082 (1950).
[740] Bernatek, *Acta Chem. Scand.,* **7,** 677 (1953) [*C.A.,* **48,** 4501 (1954)].
[741] Ionescu, *Bull. soc. chim. France,* [4], **41,** 1094 (1927).
[742] Smith and Nichols, *J. Am. Chem. Soc.,* **65,** 1739 (1943).
[743] Smith and Wiley, *J. Am. Chem. Soc.,* **68,** 894 (1946).
[744] Smith and Byers, *J. Am. Chem. Soc.,* **63,** 612 (1941).
[745] Smith and MacMullen, *J. Am. Chem. Soc.,* **58,** 629 (1936).
[746] Bergel, Jacob, Todd, and Work, *J. Chem. Soc.,* **1938,** 1375.
[747] Smith and Johnson, *J. Am. Chem. Soc.,* **59,** 673 (1937).
[747a] Smith, *J. Am. Chem. Soc.,* **56,** 472 (1934).
[747b] Smith and Denyes, *J. Am. Chem. Soc.,* **58,** 304 (1936).
[748] Smith and Opie, *J. Am. Chem. Soc.,* **63,** 932 (1941).
[749] Smith and Webster, *J. Am. Chem. Soc.,* **59,** 662 (1937).

[749a] Adams and Acker, *J. Am. Chem. Soc.* **74,** 5872 (1952).
[750] Adams and Blomstrom, *J. Am. Chem. Soc.,* **75,** 3404 (1953).
[751] Adams and Moje, *J. Am. Chem. Soc.,* **74,** 5557 (1952).
[752] Adams and Way, *J. Am. Chem. Soc.,* **76,** 2763 (1954).
[753] CIBA, Swiss pat. 276,141 [*C.A.,* **47,** 7546 (1953)].
[754] CIBA, British pat. 666,713 [*C.A.,* **47,** 7546 (1953)].
[755] Hoffmann and Tagmann, *Helv. Chim. Acta,* **32,** 1470 (1949).
[756] E. I. du Pont de Nemours and Co., Brit. pat. 576,427 [*C.A.,* **42,** 2269 (1948)].
[757] Hoch and Karrer, *Helv. Chim. Acta,* **37,** 397 (1954).
[758] Fuson and Miller, *J. Org. Chem.,* **17,** 886 (1952).
[759] Terent'ev and Gurvich, *Vestnik Moskov. Univ.,* **5,** No. 5 (1950) [*C.A.,* **45,** 7005 (1951)].
[760] Bruson, U.S. pat. 2,383,444 [*C.A.,* **40,** 351 (1946)].
[761] Bruson and Riener, *J. Am. Chem. Soc.,* **64,** 2850 (1942).
[762] Baumgarten and Eifert, *J. Am. Chem. Soc.,* **75,** 3015 (1953).
[763] Wiest and Glaser, U.S. pat. 2,403,570 [*C.A.,* **40,** 6498 (1946)].
[764] Frank and McPherson, Jr., *J. Am. Chem. Soc.,* **71,** 1387 (1949).
[765] Bruson, U.S. pat. 2,386,736 [*C.A.,* **40,** 7234 (1946)].
[766] Terent'ev and Gurvich, *Sbornik Stateĭ Obshcheĭ Khim. Akad. Nauk S.S.S.R.,* **1,** 404 (1953) [*C.A.,* **49,** 1047 (1955)].
[767] Terent'ev, Kost, and Gurvich, *Zhur. Obshcheĭ Khim.,* **22,** 1977 (1952) [*C.A.,* **47,** 8663 (1953)].
[768] Levina, Shusherina, and Kaminskaya, *Doklady Akad. Nauk S.S.S.R.,* **86,** 79 (1952) [*C.A.,* **47,** 4849 (1953)].
[769] Nazarov, Shvekgheĭmer, and Rudenko, *Zhur. Obshcheĭ Khim.,* **24,** 319 (1954) [*C.A.,* **49,** 4651 (1955)].
[770] Nazarov and Zav'yalov, *Zhur. Obshcheĭ Khim.,* **24,** 469 (1954) [*C.A.,* **49,** 6142 (1955)].
[771] Stetter and Coenen, *Chem. Ber.,* **87,** 990 (1954).
[772] Iwanoff, *Chem. Ber.,* **87,** 1600 (1954).
[773] Boekelheide, *J. Am. Chem. Soc.,* **69,** 790 (1947).
[774] Barkley, Farrar, Knowles, Raffelson, and Thompson, *J. Am. Chem. Soc.,* **76,** 5014 (1954).
[775] Pinder and Robinson, *Nature,* **167,** 484 (1951).
[776] Chem. Werke Huels, Ger. pat. 811,350 [*C.A.,* **47,** 3337 (1953)].
[777] Daub and Doyle, *J. Am. Chem. Soc.,* **74,** 4449 (1952).
[778] Acara and Levine, *J. Am. Chem. Soc.,* **72,** 2864 (1950).
[779] Horning and Rutenberg, *J. Am. Chem. Soc.,* **72,** 3534 (1950).
[780] Albertson and Fillman, *J. Am. Chem. Soc.,* **71,** 2818 (1949).
[781] Mikeska, U.S. pat. 2,461,336 [*C.A.,* **43,** 4689 (1949)].
[781a] Hesse and Buecking, *Ann.,* **563,** 31 (1949).
[782] Smrt and Šorm, *Collections Czechoslov. Chem. Communs.,* **18,** 131 (1953) [*C.A.,* **48,** 3903 (1954)].
[783] Ansell and Hey, *J. Chem. Soc.,* **1950,** 1683.
[784] Floyd, *J. Am. Chem. Soc.,* **71,** 1746 (1949).
[785] Wideqvist, *Arkiv Kemi,* **3,** 59 (1951) [*C.A.,* **45,** 10217 (1951)].
[786] Green and Hey, *J. Chem. Soc.,* **1954,** 4306.
[787] Newman and McPherson, *J. Org. Chem.,* **19,** 1717 (1954).
[788] Talukdar and Bagchi, *Science and Culture India,* **19,** 201 (1953) [*C.A.,* **49,** 1656 (1955)].
[789] Talukdar and Bagchi, *J. Org. Chem.,* **20,** 21 (1955).
[790] Talukdar and Bagchi, *Science and Culture India,* **18,** 503 (1953) [*C.A.,* **48,** 8180 (1954)].
[791] Raha and Mukharji, *J. Org. Chem.,* **19,** 1376 (1954).
[792] Horning and Finelli, *J. Am. Chem. Soc.,* **71,** 3204 (1949); *Org. Syntheses,* **30,** 80 (1950).
[793] Banerjee and Shafer, *J. Am. Chem. Soc.,* **72,** 1931 (1950).
[794] Walter and Barry, U.S. pat. 2,524,643 [*C.A.,* **45,** 7154 (1951)].
[795] Campbell and Tucker, *J. Chem. Soc.,* **1949,** 2623.
[796] Holbro and Tagmann, *Helv. Chim. Acta,* **33,** 2178 (1950).
[797] Campbell and Reid, *J. Chem. Soc.,* **1952,** 3281.

[798] Boekelheide, Linn, O'Grady, and Lamborg, *J. Am. Chem. Soc.*, **75**, 3243 (1953).
[799] Yoho and Levine, *J. Am. Chem. Soc.*, **74**, 5597 (1952).
[800] Misra and Shukla, *J. Indian Chem. Soc.*, **29**, 455 (1952).
[801] Misra and Shukla, *J. Indian Chem. Soc.*, **30**, 37 (1953).
[802] Koelsch and Walker, *J. Am. Chem. Soc.*, **72**, 346 (1950).
[803] Nakazawa and Matsuura, *J. Pharm. Soc. Japan*, **72**, 51 (1952) [*C.A.*, **46**, 11142 (1952)].
[804] Bachmann and Johnson, *J. Am. Chem. Soc.*, **71**, 3463 (1949).
[805] Kost and Terent'ev, *J. Gen. Chem. U.S.S.R.*, **22**, 655 (1952) [*C.A.*, **47**, 2759 (1953)].
[805a] Boekelheide and Godfrey, *J. Am. Chem. Soc.*, **75**, 3679 (1953).
[806] Misra and Shukla, *J. Indian Chem. Soc.*, **29**, 201 (1952).
[807] Rubin and Wishinsky, *J. Am. Chem. Soc.*, **68**, 828 (1946).
[808] Tagmann, Sury, and Hoffmann, *Helv. Chim. Acta*, **35**, 1541 (1952).
[809] Herzog, Gold, and Geckler, *J. Am. Chem. Soc.*, **73**, 749 (1951).
[810] Klager, *J. Org. Chem.*, **16**, 161 (1951).
[811] Boyd and Leshin, *J. Am. Chem. Soc.*, **74**, 2675 (1952).
[812] Rodionov and Belikov, *Doklady Akad. Nauk S.S.S.R.*, **93**, 827 (1953) [*C.A.*, **49**, 1550 (1955)].
[813] Klager, *J. Org. Chem.*, **20**, 650 (1955).
[814] Bruson, U.S. pat. 2,435,552 [*C.A.*, **42**, 3778 (1948)].
[815] Asthana and Misra, *J. Indian Chem. Soc.*, **31**, 459 (1954).
[816] Ladd, U.S. pat. 2,632,019 [*C.A.*, **48**, 1418 (1954)].
[817] Fiszer and Michalski, *Roczniki Chem.*, **28**, 185 (1954) [*C.A.*, **49**, 9493 (1955)].
[818] Koelsch, *J. Am. Chem. Soc.*, **65**, 2460 (1943).
[819] Koelsch, *J. Am. Chem. Soc.*, **68**, 146 (1946).
[820] Koelsch and Rolfson, *J. Am. Chem. Soc.*, **72**, 1871 (1950).
[821] Birch and Kon, *J. Chem. Soc.*, **123**, 2440 (1923).
[822] Linstead and Millidge, *J. Chem. Soc.*, **1936**, 478.
[823] Oesterr. Stickstoffwerke A.G., Austrian pat. 176,845 [*C.A.*, **48**, 10772 (1954)].
[824] Albertson, *J. Am. Chem. Soc.*, **70**, 669 (1948).
[825] Koelsch, *J. Am. Chem. Soc.*, **65**, 2458 (1943).
[826] Sury and Hoffmann, *Helv. Chim. Acta*, **36**, 1815 (1953); cf. Tagmann, Sury, and Hoffmann, *Helv. Chim. Acta*, **35**, 1235, 1541 (1952).
[827] Johnson, Johnson, and Petersen, *J. Am. Chem. Soc.*, **68**, 1926 (1946).
[828] Schneider, Riener, and Bruson, *J. Am. Chem. Soc.*, **72**, 1486 (1950).
[829] Lloyd and Horning, *J. Am. Chem. Soc.*, **76**, 3651 (1954).
[830] Bruson, U.S. pat. 2,390,918 [*C.A.*, **40**, 2456 (1946)].
[831] Micheel and Albers, *Ann.*, **581**, 225 (1953).
[832] Kloetzel, *J. Am. Chem. Soc.*, **70**, 3571 (1948).
[833] Theilacker and Wendtland, *Ann.*, **570**, 33 (1950).
[834] Moffett, *Org. Syntheses*, **32**, 86 (1952).
[835] Brown and van Gulick, *J. Am. Chem. Soc.*, **77**, 1079 (1955).
[836] Klager, U.S. pat. 2,640,072 [*C.A.*, **48**, 7626 (1954)].
[837] Klager, U.S. pat. 2,668,176 [*C.A.*, **49**, 4013 (1955)].
[838] Floyd and Miller, *J. Org. Chem.*, **16**, 882 (1951).
[839] Kappeler, Stauffacher, Eschenmoser, and Schinz, *Helv. Chim. Acta*, **37**, 957 (1954).
[840] Stauffacher and Schinz, *Helv. Chim. Acta*, **37**, 1223 (1954).
[841] Perkin, Jr., and Thorpe, *J. Chem. Soc.*, **85**, 128 (1904).
[842] Plattner, Fuerst, Meyer, and Keller, *Helv. Chim. Acta*, **37**, 266 (1954).
[843] Barat, *J. Indian Chem. Soc.*, **8**, 37 (1931).
[844] Stetter, Buentgen, and Coenen, *Chem. Ber.*, **88**, 77 (1955).
[845] Horner, *Ann.*, **548**, 117 (1941).
[846] Palazzo and Rosnati, *Gazz. chim. ital.*, **82**, 584 (1952).
[847] Weisblat and Lyttle, U.S. pat. 2,606,921 [*C.A.*, **47**, 4903 (1953)].
[848] Dryamova, Zav'yalov, and Preobrazhenskii, *J. Gen. Chem. U.S.S.R.*, **18**, 1733 (1948) [*C.A.*, **43**, 2625 (1949)].
[849] Woods, *J. Am. Chem. Soc.*, **75**, 1510 (1953).

[850] Hunsdiecker, *Ber.*, **75,** 1197 (1942).
[851] Komppa and Rohrmann, *Ann. Acad. Sci. Fennicae,* **A44, No. 3** (1935) [*C.A.*, **30,** 2949 (1936)].
[852] Scheibler, Emden, and Neubner, *Ber.*, **63,** 1557 (1930).
[853] Edwards, Jr., and Cashaw, *J. Am. Chem. Soc.*, **76,** 6188 (1954).
[854] Schilling and Vorlaender, *Ann.*, **308,** 184 (1899).
[855] Blanchard and Goering, *J. Am. Chem. Soc.*, **73,** 5863 (1951).
[856] Bhattacharyya, *J. Indian Chem. Soc.*, **22,** 214 (1945).
[857] Bhattacharyya, *Science and Culture India,* **8,** 426 (1943) [*C.A.*, **37,** 5031 (1943)].
[858] Herz, *J. Org. Chem.*, **20,** 1062 (1955).
[859] Chakravarti, *J. Indian Chem. Soc.*, **21,** 319 (1944).
[860] Hope and Perkin, Jr., *J. Chem. Soc.*, **99,** 762 (1911).
[861] Barltrop, *J. Chem. Soc.*, **1947,** 399.
[862] Ruhemann and Wolf, *J. Chem. Soc.*, **69,** 1383 (1896).
[863] Cook, Pierce, and McBee, *J. Am. Chem. Soc.*, **76,** 83 (1954).
[864] Noller and Pannell, *J. Am. Chem. Soc.*, **77,** 1862 (1955).
[865] Talukdar and Bagchi, *J. Org. Chem.*, **20,** 25 (1955).
[866] von Auwers and Koebner, *Ber.*, **24,** 1935 (1891).
[867] Ruzicka, *Helv. Chim. Acta,* **2,** 144 (1919).
[868] Phalnikar and Nargund, *J. Univ. Bombay,* **4,** 106 (1935) [*C.A.*, **30,** 5186 (1936)].
[869] Miwa, Ohsuka, and Sakan, *J. Chem. Soc. Japan Pure Chem. Sect.*, **74,** 113 (1953) [*C.A.*, **48,** 9962 (1954)].
[870] Welch, *J. Chem. Soc.*, **1930,** 257.
[871] Kotake, Sakan, and Miwa, *J. Am. Chem. Soc.*, **72,** 5085 (1950).
[872] Romeo, Corrodi, and Hardegger, *Helv. Chim. Acta,* **38,** 463 (1955).
[873] Phalnikar, *J. Univ. Bombay,* **19,** Sect. A, Pt. 3, Sci. No. 28, 62 (1950) [*C.A.*, **47,** 1606 (1953)].
[874] Aoki, *J. Pharm. Soc. Japan,* **66,** 51 (1946) [*C.A.*, **45,** 6173 (1951)].
[875] Ruhemann and Browning, *J. Chem. Soc.*, **73,** 727 (1898).
[876] Ghosh, *J. Indian Chem. Soc.*, **24,** 45 (1947).
[877] Staudinger, *Ann.*, **341,** 99 (1905).
[878] Ruhemann and Cunnington, *J. Chem. Soc.*, **73,** 1006 (1898).
[879] Challenger and Fishwick, *J. Inst. Petroleum,* **39,** 220 (1953) [*C.A.*, **48,** 9355 (1954)].
[880] Malachowski, Bilbel, and Biliński-Tarasowicz, *Ber.*, **69,** 1295 (1936).
[881] Henze, *Ber.*, **33,** 966 (1900).
[882] Ruhemann, *J. Chem. Soc.*, **71,** 325 (1897).
[883] Ruhemann and Stapleton, *J. Chem. Soc.*, **77,** 804 (1900).
[884] Ruhemann and Tyler, *J. Chem. Soc.*, **69,** 530 (1896).
[885] Woodward and Reed, *J. Am. Chem. Soc.*, **65,** 1569 (1943).
[886] Perkin, Jr., *J. Chem. Soc.*, **69,** 1472 (1896).
[887] Ray, *J. Am. Chem. Soc.*, **50,** 558 (1928).
[888] Blaise, *Compt. rend.*, **136,** 243 (1903).
[889] Blaise and Luttringer, *Bull. soc. chim. France,* [3], **33,** 760 (1905).
[890] Kohler and Reid, *J. Am. Chem. Soc.*, **47,** 2803 (1925).
[891] Leonard and Shoemaker, *J. Am. Chem. Soc.*, **71,** 1876 (1949).
[892] Komnenos, *Ann.*, **218,** 145 (1883).
[893] Koetz and Stalmann, *J. prakt. Chem.*, [2], **68,** 156 (1903).
[894] Knoevenagel, *Ber.*, **31,** 2585 (1898).
[895] Gupta, *J. Chem. Soc.*, **119,** 298 (1921).
[896] Day and Thorpe, *J. Chem. Soc.*, **117,** 1469 (1920).
[897] Diels, Gaertner, and Kaack, *Ber.*, **55,** 3439 (1922).
[898] Sonn, *Ber.*, **61,** 2479 (1928).
[899] Robinson and Thompson, *J. Chem. Soc.*, **1938,** 2009.
[900] Farmer, *J. Chem. Soc.*, **123,** 3324 (1923).
[901] Koetz, *J. prakt. Chem.*, [2], **75,** 433 (1907).
[902] Gaind and Guha, *J. Indian Chem. Soc.*, **11,** 421 (1934).

[903] Clemo and Welch, *J. Chem. Soc.*, **1928,** 2621.
[904] Kerr, *J. Am. Chem. Soc.*, **51,** 614 (1929).
[905] Mayuranathan and Guha, *J. Indian Inst. Sci.*, **15A,** 131 (1932) [*C.A.*, **27,** 3211 (1933)].
[906] Komppa, *Ber.*, **33,** 3530 (1900).
[907] Brown and van Gulick, *J. Am. Chem. Soc.*, **77,** 1083 (1955).
[908] Zakharkin and Preobrazhenskiĭ, *Zhur. Obshcheĭ Khim.*, **22,** 1890 (1952) [*C.A.*, **47,** 7507 (1953)].
[909] Baĭnova, Evstigneeva, Livshits, Kuz'mina, and Preobrazhenskiĭ, *Zhur. Obshcheĭ Khim.*, **23,** 149 (1953) [*C.A.*, **48,** 1360 (1954)].
[910] Curtis, Day, and Kimmins, *J. Chem. Soc.*, **123,** 3131 (1923).
[911] Ingold and Shoppee, *J. Chem. Soc.*, **1926,** 1912.
[912] Ingold, Shoppee, and Thorpe, *J. Chem. Soc.*, **1926,** 1477.
[913] Arnold, Amidon, and Dodson, *J. Am. Chem. Soc.*, **72,** 2871 (1950).
[914] Bertram, *Ber.*, **36,** 3291 (1903).
[915] Ranganathan, *Current Sci. India*, **9,** 276 (1940) [*C.A.*, **34,** 7861 (1940)].
[916] Ingold and Perren, *J. Chem. Soc.*, **119,** 1582 (1921).
[916a] Henrich, *Ber.*, **35,** 1663 (1902).
[917] Knoevenagel, Ger. pat. 156,560 [*Chem. Zentr.*, **1905, I,** 56].
[918] Ruhemann and Cunnington, *J. Chem. Soc.*, **75,** 778 (1899).
[919] Traube, *Ber.*, **40,** 4942 (1907).
[920] Malachowski and Czornodola, *Ber.*, **68,** 363 (1935).
[921] Ingold and Perren, *J. Chem. Soc.*, **121,** 1414 (1922).
[922] Claisen, *Ann.*, **297,** 1 (1897), especially p. 88.
[923] Boekelheide and Lodge, Jr., *J. Am. Chem. Soc.*, **73,** 3681 (1951).
[924] Boekelheide and Gall, *J. Org. Chem.*, **19,** 499 (1954).
[925] Kohler and Butler, *J. Am. Chem. Soc.*, **48,** 1036 (1926).
[926] Farmer and Healey, *J. Chem. Soc.*, **1927,** 1065.
[927] Farmer and Mehta, *J. Chem. Soc.*, **1930,** 1610.
[928] Vorlaender, Weissheimer, and Sponnagel, *Ann.*, **345,** 227 (1906).
[929] Cairns, Engelhardt, Jackson, Kalb, and Sauer, *J. Am. Chem. Soc.*, **74,** 5636 (1952).
[930] Farmer and Martin, *J. Chem. Soc.*, **1933,** 960.
[931] Blood, Cartwright, and Linstead, *J. Chem. Soc.*, **1952,** 2268.
[932] Farmer and Mehta, *J. Chem. Soc.*, **1931,** 1762.
[933] Campbell and Rydon, *J. Chem. Soc.*, **1953,** 3002.
[934] Bardhan and Banerji, *J. Chem. Soc.*, **1935,** 474.
[935] Sircar, *J. Chem. Soc.*, **1927,** 1252.
[936] Kon and Nanji, *J. Chem. Soc.*, **1932,** 2426.
[937] Prelog and Metzler, *Helv. Chim. Acta*, **29,** 1170 (1946).
[938] Helfer, *Helv. Chim. Acta*, **9,** 814 (1926).
[939] Bhattacharyya, *J. Indian Chem. Soc.*, **22,** 85 (1945).
[940] Chatterjee, *J. Indian Chem. Soc.*, **14,** 417 (1937).
[941] Sen and Bose, *J. Indian Chem. Soc.*, **4,** 51 (1927).
[942] Bardhan and Banerji, *J. Chem. Soc.*, **1935,** 476.
[943] Vogel, *J. Chem. Soc.*, **1931,** 907.
[944] Rao, *J. Chem. Soc.*, **1929,** 1954.
[945] Reichstein, Zschokke, Gehring, and Rona, *Helv. Chim. Acta*, **15,** 1118 (1932).
[946] Rubtsov and Mikhlina, *Doklady Akad. Nauk S.S.S.R.*, **88,** 1003 (1953) [*C.A.*, **48,** 8782 1954)].
[947] Herrmann and Vorlaender, *Abhandl. naturforsch. Ges. Halle*, **21,** 251 (1899).
[948] Stobbe, *Ann.*, **315,** 219 (1901).
[949] Desai, *J. Chem. Soc.*, **1932,** 1079.
[950] Barr and Cook, *J. Chem. Soc.*, **1945,** 438.
[951] Erlenmeyer, Jr., *Ber.*, **33,** 2006 (1900).
[952] Helmkamp, Tanghe, and Plati, *J. Am. Chem. Soc.*, **62,** 3215 (1940).
[953] Stobbe, *Ber.*, **34,** 653 (1901).
[954] Lawson, Perkin, Jr., and Robinson, *J. Chem. Soc.*, **125,** 626 (1924).

[955] Chase and Walker, *J. Chem. Soc.*, **1953,** 3548.
[956] Vorlaender and Strunck, *Ann.*, **345,** 233 (1906).
[957] Meerwein and co-workers, *J. prakt. Chem.*, [2], **116,** 229 (1927).
[958] Vachon, Gagnon, and Kane, *Can. J. Research,* **11,** 644 (1934) [*C.A.*, **29,** 1087 (1935)].
[959] Kohler and Darling, *J. Am. Chem. Soc.*, **52,** 1174 (1930).
[960] Gravel, *Naturaliste can.*, **57,** 181 (1931) [*C.A.*, **28,** 169 (1934)].
[961] Bredt, *Ber.*, **24,** 603 (1891).
[962] Knoevenagel and Fries, *Ber.*, **31,** 761 (1898).
[963] Knoevenagel and Brunswig, *Ber.*, **35,** 2177 (1902).
[964] Kroeker and McElvain, *J. Am. Chem. Soc.*, **56,** 1171 (1934).
[965] Kohler and Barrett, *J. Am. Chem. Soc.*, **48,** 1773 (1926).
[966] Kohler and Darling, *J. Am. Chem. Soc.*, **52,** 424 (1930).
[967] Papadakis, *J. Am. Chem. Soc.*, **67,** 1799 (1945).
[968] Papadakis, Scigliano, Chin, and Adrian, *J. Am. Chem. Soc.*, **72,** 4256 (1950).
[969] Palit, *J. Indian Chem. Soc.*, **14,** 219 (1937).
[970] Rabe, *Ber.*, **31,** 1896 (1898).
[971] Meerwein, *Ann.*, **360,** 323 (1908).
[972] Newman and Joshel, *J. Am. Chem. Soc.*, **60,** 485 (1938).
[973] Koelsch, U.S. pat. 2,507,473 [*C.A.*, **44,** 7883 (1950)].
[974] Koelsch, *J. Am. Chem. Soc.*, **67,** 569 (1945).
[975] Emery, *J. prakt. Chem.*, [2], **53,** 308 (1896).
[976] Henecka, *Chem. Ber.*, **82,** 36 (1949).
[977] Isler, Gutmann, Straub, Fust, Böhni, and Stüder, *Helv. Chim. Acta,* **38,** 1033 (1955).
[978] Mumm and Hueneke, *Ber.*, **50,** 1568 (1917).
[979] Mumm and Hueneke, *Ber.*, **51,** 150 (1918).
[980] Tracy and Elderfield, *J. Org. Chem.*, **6,** 70 (1941).
[981] Horning, Denekas, and Field, *J. Org. Chem.*, **9,** 547 (1944).
[982] Rabe and Elze, *Ann.*, **323,** 83 (1902).
[983] West, *J. Biol. Chem.*, **66,** 63 (1925).
[984] Pastour, *Compt. rend.*, **237,** 1094 (1953).
[985] Gruber and Schloegl, *Monatsh.*, **81,** 83 (1950).
[986] Nazarov and Zav'yalov, *Izvest. Akad. Nauk S.S.S.R. Otdel. Khim. Nauk,* **1952,** 703 [*C.A.*, **47,** 10515 (1953)].
[986a] Wallach, *Ann.*, **323,** 135 (1902).
[987] Merling, *Ber.*, **38,** 979 (1905).
[988] Merling and Welde, *Ann.*, **366,** 119 (1909).
[989] Jeger and Buechi, *Helv. Chim. Acta,* **31,** 134 (1948).
[990] Knoevenagel, *Ann.*, **288,** 323 (1895).
[991] Mukherji, *Science and Culture India,* **8,** 190 (1942) [*C.A.*, **37,** 1994 (1943)].
[992] Knoevenagel, *Ann.*, **281,** 25 (1894).
[993] Cornubert, Borrel, de Demo, Garnier, Humeau, Le Bihan, and Sarkis, *Bull. soc. chim. France*, [5], **2,** 195 (1935).
[994] Knoevenagel, *Ann.*, **303,** 223 (1898).
[995] Schilling and Vorlaender, *Ann.*, **308,** 184 (1899).
[996] Dyer, Kidd, and Walker, *J. Chem. Soc.*, **1952,** 4778.
[997] Knoevenagel, *J. prakt. Chem.*, [2], **97,** 288 (1918).
[998] Bachmann, Fujimoto, and Raunio, *J. Am. Chem. Soc.*, **72,** 2533 (1950).
[999] Simonsen, *J. Chem. Soc.*, **97,** 1910 (1910).
[1000] Urech, Tagmann, Sury, and Hoffmann, *Helv. Chim. Acta,* **36,** 1809 (1953).
[1001] Feist, *Ann.*, **345,** 100 (1906).
[1002] Feist, *Ann.*, **345,** 60 (1906).
[1003] Milas, U.S. pat. 2,369,158 [*C.A.*, **39,** 5044 (1945)].
[1004] Milas, U.S. pat. 2,432,921 [*C.A.*, **42,** 2278 (1948)].
[1005] Thorpe and Wood, *J. Chem. Soc.*, **103,** 1569 (1913).
[1006] Feist, *Ann.*, **428,** 25 (1922).
[1007] Feist, *Ann.*, **428,** 40 (1922).

[1008] Haerdi and Thorpe, *J. Chem. Soc.*, **127,** 1237 (1925).
[1009] Ruhemann, *J. Chem. Soc.*, **97,** 457 (1910).
[1010] Ruhemann, *Ber.*, **53,** 287 (1920).
[1011] Walker, *J. Am. Chem. Soc.*, **76,** 309 (1954).
[1012] Ruhemann and Stapleton, *J. Chem. Soc.*, **77,** 239 (1900).
[1013] Grob and Camenisch, *Helv. Chim. Acta*, **36,** 49 (1953).
[1014] Lambert and Piggott, *J. Chem. Soc.*, **1947,** 1489.
[1015] Hale and Robertson, *Am. Chem. J.*, **39,** 685 (1908); cf. Hale, *Ber.*, **45,** 1600 (1912).
[1016] Fanta and Stein, *J. Am. Chem. Soc.*, **77,** 1045 (1955).
[1017] Bahner, U.S. pat. 2,425,276 [*C.A.*, **41,** 7410 (1947)].
[1018] Bahner, U.S. pat. 2,426,158 [*C.A.*, **41,** 7410 (1947)].
[1019] Bahner, U.S. pat. 2,447,626 [*C.A.*, **42,** 8819 (1948)].
[1020] Bahner, U.S. pat. 2,431,451 [*C.A.*, **42,** 2615 (1948)].
[1021] Snyder and Hamlin, *J. Am. Chem. Soc.*, **72,** 5082 (1950).
[1022] J. F. Bourland, Thesis, Purdue University, 1941, quoted by Hass and Riley in *Chem. Revs.*, **32,** 414 (1943).
[1023] Shechter and Conrad, *J. Am. Chem. Soc.*, **76,** 2716 (1954).
[1024] Dornow and Wiehler, *Ann.*, **578,** 113 (1952).
[1025] Perekalin and Sopova, *Zhur. Obshcheĭ Khim.*, **24,** 513 (1954); *Doklady Akad. Nauk S.S.S.R.*, **95,** 993 (1954) [*C.A.*, **49,** 6180–6181 (1955)].
[1026] Dornow and Menzel, *Ann.*, **588,** 40 (1954).
[1027] Heim, *Ber.*, **44,** 2016 (1911).
[1028] Smith and Kelly, *J. Am. Chem. Soc.*, **74,** 3300 (1952).
[1029] Smith and Davis, *J. Am. Chem. Soc.*, **76,** 5376 (1954).
[1030] Buckley, Charlish, and Rose, *J. Chem. Soc.*, **1947,** 1514.
[1031] Smith and Davis, *J. Org. Chem.*, **15,** 824 (1950).
[1032] Kohler and Potter, *J. Am. Chem. Soc.*, **57,** 1316 (1935).
[1033] Backer, *Rec. trav. chim.*, **72,** 119 (1953).
[1034] Doering and Weil, *J. Am. Chem. Soc.*, **69,** 2461 (1947).
[1035] Boekelheide and Rothchild, *J. Am. Chem. Soc.*, **71,** 879 (1949).
[1036] Winterfeld and Heinen, *Ann.*, **573,** 85 (1951); **578,** 171 (1952).
[1037] Boekelheide and Rothchild, *J. Am. Chem. Soc.*, **69,** 3149 (1947).
[1038] Wilt and Levine, *J. Am. Chem. Soc.*, **75,** 1368 (1953).
[1039] Winterfeld, Wald, and Rink, *Ann.*, **588,** 125 (1954).
[1040] Winterfeld, Wald, and Rink, *Naturwiss.*, **41,** 230 (1954) [*C.A.*, **49,** 14759 (1955)].
[1041] Boekelheide and Mason, *J. Am. Chem. Soc.*, **73,** 2356 (1951).
[1042] Clifford, U.S. pat. 2,579,419 [*C.A.*, **46,** 7593 (1952)].
[1043] Boekelheide and Marinetti, *J. Am. Chem. Soc.*, **73,** 4015 (1951).
[1044] Boekelheide and Sieg, *J. Org. Chem.*, **19,** 587 (1954).
[1045] Pudovik and Grishina, *Zhur. Obshcheĭ Khim.*, **23,** 267 (1953) [*C.A.*, **48,** 2573 (1954)].

AUTHOR INDEX, VOLUMES 1–10

CHAPTER INDEX, VOLUMES 1–10

SUBJECT INDEX, VOLUME 10

Since the tables of contents of the individual chapters provide a quite complete index, only those items which are not readily found on the contents pages are indexed here.

Numbers in **boldface** type refer to experimental procedures.